OPERATIONS RESEARCH FOR MANAGEMENT DECISIONS

SAMUEL B. RICHMOND
GRADUATE SCHOOL OF BUSINESS
COLUMBIA UNIVERSITY

THE RONALD PRESS COMPANY • NEW YORK

Library of Congress Catalog Card Number: 68-20552

PRINTED IN THE UNITED STATES OF AMERICA

To

Phyllis

Douglas

Clifford

Preface

This book is designed to provide an introduction to the study of operations research, a scientific methodology for examining, defining, analyzing, and solving complex problems. When applied to the solution of management problems, operations research is often called *management science.*

Operations research is the approach to decision making which asks specific questions about objectives and about controllable and uncontrollable input variables, and seeks to build mathematical models to describe the systems in which these input variables and output objectives interact. Its purpose is to help management make rational decisions. It should be kept in mind that operations research neither eliminates nor diminishes the importance of the experience of individual managers and the intuitions and instincts born of that experience. Rather, operations research encourages managers to use these often immensely valuable assets in a rational way at the appropriate points in the decision-making process as, for example, in delineating objectives, defining an appropriate value system, identifying possible courses of action, and assigning subjective probabilities to events or situations where available information is incomplete.

Since operations research is decision oriented, it is closely related to the area of study known as *decision theory,* and in this book aspects of decision theory are interwoven with operations research techniques throughout. Indeed the book begins and ends with decision theory, and in addition several other chapters deal with the subject in varying degrees.

Over the years, operations researchers have developed and accumulated mathematical techniques which they have found to be useful in decision making. A list of these techniques may be seen in the table of contents of this book. However, these techniques themselves do not constitute operations research. Rather, operations research is the approach which seeks to build mathematical models to help solve problems.

This is an introductory book, and its mathematical requirements are minimal. The mathematical techniques used—set theory, differential and integral calculus, matrix algebra, series, Lagrange multipliers, Newton's method of approximation, and other topics—are introduced and developed as, where, and to the extent needed. The reader is not required to have prior familiarity with these subjects. A background of high school algebra will adequately prepare him to study the full content. Also, it is not necessary for the reader to have studied probability theory, since this subject is treated from first principles. Much of the material in this subject area, as well as that in decision theory, is closely related to the probability and decision theory portions of *Statistical Analysis,** and passages from that book have been reproduced here, usually extended and interwoven with more advanced materials.

Reading references are given at the end of each chapter. There has been no attempt to present there an extensive bibliography, but rather the few references cited have been carefully selected to serve the purpose of guiding the reader who wishes to study further in the specific area of each chapter. Also at the end of chapters, exercise material is presented with the intention of illustrating various ideas developed in the respective chapters. Chapters 1 and 17 have no exercises, and others have varying numbers of exercises, the number usually related to the number of concepts requiring or deserving the kind of educational reinforcement that exercises provide.

I should like to express my indebtedness to Professor Russell L. Ackoff of the University of Pennsylvania who, ten years ago, invited me to spend a sabbatical year as visiting professor in the operations research group which he headed at the then Case Institute of Technology. He thereby led my career into a new direction, one fruit of which is this book.

I am grateful to Professor Wayne S. Marshall and Mr. Richard C. Applegate, each of whom read the entire manuscript, made valuable suggestions, and pointed out various weaknesses and errors which I have sought to correct. Mr. Eric Kisch was extremely helpful in preparing and organizing the end-of-chapter exercises, and Miss Anastasia Papalitskas and Mrs. Judith Dumas typed much of the manuscript. Evelyn Richmond, my wife, helped directly by reading and criticizing much of the manuscript and indirectly in a multitude of ways by making

* Richmond, S. B., *Statistical Analysis,* 2d ed., New York, The Ronald Press Company, 1964.

it possible for me to devote to the book the incredible amount of time which its writing required. The responsibility for any errors or shortcomings, however, is solely mine.

SAMUEL B. RICHMOND

Englewood, New Jersey
January, 1968

Contents

Part I
OPTIMIZATION PROBLEMS

Part III
ALLOCATION PROBLEMS

Part VI
DECISION THEORY

APPENDIXES

Part I

OPTIMIZATION PROBLEMS

1

Models and Decisions

1–1. The Nature of Operations Research. The primary purpose of this book is to introduce to its readers a rational and methodical approach to problem solving. It is not a new method, but rather it has been used by investigators in the sciences since the dawn of science, and it has been used by operations researchers and management scientists since the early 1940's, when operations research was created to solve military problems in the great war of that period. In this book we shall consider applications of this methodology to problems of management in business, government, universities, and similar organizations.

To be sure, there is a group or set of mathematical techniques which have become associated with and identified with operations research. Many of these are discussed in this book, and most of them have been either developed by operations researchers or used by operations researchers. But these techniques do not constitute operations research. *Operations research is an approach to problem solving* that makes it possible to use these techniques in the social sciences, in military operations and—most important for us—in management. We shall use the term *management science* to refer to applications of the operations research approach in the general area of management. Therefore, we may use the terms *operations research* and *management science* almost interchangeably.

This book deals both with the approach to problem solving which is operations research and with many of the techniques and methods which have been found to be useful in the practice of operations research.

Operations research is the approach to problem solving that examines the system (set of interacting entities) in which the decision problem is contained and asks—and tries to answer—the following questions (not necessarily in this order).

1. What are the *controllable variables?* Every decision problem involves one or more variables or *inputs* which are subject to the control of the decision maker. Indeed, the very essence of decision making is the selection of the appropriate values or settings for these controllable inputs. The inputs over which the decision maker has control may be: price, quantity ordered, number of salesmen, advertising budget, transportation routings, cities for plant location, or any of a myriad such controllable variables.

We may imagine the decision maker as sitting at a control console with a series of one or more dials, each labeled: price, quantity ordered, etc.; and his problem is to set these dials to the values or settings which he finds best for his purposes. Any distinct identifiable configuration of these controllable variables is called a *course of action*, and any change in any one of these controllable variables produces a different course of action.

2. What is the *objective* of the decision? What is it that should be measured and considered to be the index of performance, or the *objective function* of the system? It might be sales, costs, profits, market share, or any of several others. The objective of the decision maker is to choose a course of action that leads to the optimum value of the objective function. He might seek to maximize sales, minimize costs, or maximize profits. The word *optimize* is often used to mean: maximize that which we wish to maximize, or minimize that which we wish to minimize. *The objective function is the output of the system.* We shall see that the correct identification of the objective function is one of the most difficult aspects of decision making.

3. What are the *uncontrollable variables* and what are their values? There are in the system one or more input variables—perhaps very many—that are not subject to the control of the decision maker, but which affect the output, the measure of performance, and therefore require identification and, if possible, measurement. These might be: competitor's price, supplier's price, customer income, level of demand, competitive advertising, meteorological variables, government actions, and many more. Any distinct identifiable configuration of the values of these uncontrollable variables may be referred to as a *state of nature*, or a *background*.

4. What is the *relationship* between the inputs and the output? The various possible configurations and combinations of the controllable and uncontrollable input variables interact within the system and produce some value of the output, the objective function. It is this functional relationship which the operations researcher attempts to discover and to describe in mathematical terms. In the simplest case, with one controllable input and one uncontrollable input, the mathematical equation or *model* takes the following general form:

$$E = f(x,y) \tag{1–1.1}$$

where: x is the controllable input
y is the uncontrollable input
E is the output or objective function (the measure of "effectiveness")
f represents the appropriate functional relationship; i.e., it expresses the relationship between the variables

A specific example might be:

C is the cost of servicing a car with gasoline (the output or objective)
g is the number of gallons of gasoline purchased (controllable)
p is the price per gallon of gasoline (not controllable)

and then

$$C = f(g,p) \tag{1–1.2}$$

This equation says that the cost is a function of the number of gallons purchased and the price per gallon. This is in general form. More specifically, for this fuel–automobile system:

$$C = gp \tag{1–1.3}$$

and, if it is ascertained that the price is 33 cents per gallon, the equation is completely specified.

$$C = 33g \text{ cents}$$

Once the equation or model is completely specified, the decision maker can select any value of the controllable input, and compute the associated value of the objective function. In this case, if he buys, for example, 10 gallons of gasoline, the cost is \$3.30. However, he might wish to minimize his cost subject to the condition that he have enough fuel to travel, say, 100 miles. Then he needs the value of an additional uncontrollable input variable; namely, the fuel consumption rate. To make a general model of this system,

$$C = gp \tag{1–1.3}$$

$$g = \frac{D}{r} \tag{1–1.4}$$

where: D is the distance to be traveled
r is the fuel consumption rate (miles per gallon)

Then

$$C = \frac{Dp}{r} \tag{1–1.5}$$

In this example, if the trip to be made is 100 miles, and if the fuel consumption rate, r, is 12.5 miles per gallon, and the price is 33 cents ($0.33), per gallon, then the fuel cost is $2.64.

$$C = \frac{Dp}{r} = \frac{(100)(0.33)}{12.5} = \$2.64 \tag{1–1.6}$$

However, it is also easy to see that the problem could become vastly more complicated if we take into account that the fuel consumption rate depends upon the time of day (both traffic and atmospheric conditions might have some effect), the kind of terrain covered, and the rate of speed. Since we cannot predict all of these factors with absolute certainty, we shall need some reserve supply to assure, with some degree of confidence, arrival at the desired destination. If all of these factors are taken into account, the computation of the true optimal number of gallons for minimum cost might be complex indeed.

Before we leave this example, let us express Equation (1–1.5) in its more general form, using again the designation, x, for controllable inputs and y for uncontrollable inputs. Since there are two uncontrollable inputs, we shall assign subscripts to indicate this.

$$E = f(x,y_1,y_2) \tag{1–1.7}$$

Clearly, if there had been, say, three controllable variables and five uncontrollable variables, we would be required to write

$$E = f(x_1,x_2,x_3,y_1,y_2,y_3,y_4,y_5) \tag{1–1.8}$$

Mathematicians have developed systems of notations to avoid such cumbersome and repetitious statements. The customary notation for this general model is

$$E = f(x_i,y_j) \tag{1–1.9}$$

The subscripts i and j indicate that there is some number of both controllable and uncontrollable variables in the problem.

1–2. The Model of the System. The purpose of the model is to predict. It is used because it, the model, is easier and less costly to manipulate than the real system in the real world, or because it is not possible to manipulate or experiment with the real-world system at all. If it is a good model, it provides useful information as to what would result from corresponding manipulations or experiments in the real world and thereby permits decisions to be made about the configuration of the controllable inputs.

Let us illustrate the operations research approach by building a model to solve a problem which involves manufacturing scheduling and inventory control.

The Courbro Company, an electronics manufacturer, is producing components as a subcontractor on a large project and is required to make daily deliveries, seven days a week, to the prime contractor, who keeps no inventories but puts these components into his process each day as they are received from the subcontractor.

The Courbro Company is thus faced with a constant demand for these components. This contract is only a small part of its total business, and since it must deliver each day, it must either produce a small lot each day or produce in larger lots and keep an inventory of finished goods. The problem is to determine the optimal lot size for cost minimization. Whatever inventories Courbro carries incur capital costs and storage costs for space, watchman, spoilage, and insurance. The total of all these *holding costs* is 4 cents per unit per month. If the lot size is too large, Courbro will be burdened with high holding costs. On the other hand, if the lots are too small, there are lower holding costs, but the setup expense becomes high, because the plant must go through the setup and make-ready procedure for each lot, and this costs $100 each time. These may be spoken of as "opposing costs." What is the lot size that balances these costs and minimizes the total cost?

The relevant facts are these:

1. Courbro must deliver 5,000 components per month in approximately equal daily shipments.
2. The *storage* or *holding costs* are 4 cents per unit per month.
3. The setup cost is $100 per run.
4. Production costs are independent of lot size; therefore costs of materials, labor, etc., do not enter into this problem.

The model, in general conceptual form, is:

$$\begin{aligned} \text{Total Cost} &= \text{Holding Cost} + \text{Setup Cost} \\ TC &= HC + SC \end{aligned} \tag{1–2.1}$$

The holding cost is $.04 per month multiplied by the average number of units in inventory. However, if we represent the lot size by x, the average number of units in inventory is $\frac{x}{2}$. This can be seen in Figure 1–2.1. If

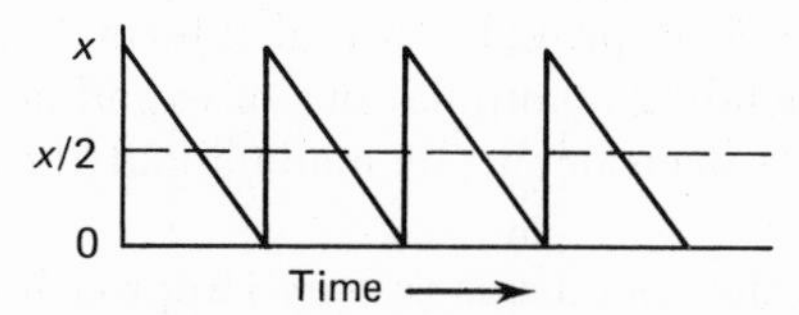

Fig. 1–2.1. Inventory levels of finished goods under fixed demand, with lot size, x, and daily deliveries.

they make x items each run and make daily deliveries until the inventory is reduced to zero, make x items again, etc., the inventory level follows the saw-tooth shape depicted in the figure, and its average level over a single production cycle or over a number of production cycles is $\frac{x}{2}$.

The monthly holding cost is thus

$$HC = .04\left(\frac{x}{2}\right) \text{ dollars per month} \tag{1-2.2}$$

We can derive the expression for the setup cost by noting that, if the lot size is x, the total number of setups per month is 5,000 divided by x, and the monthly total setup cost, in dollars, is

$$SC = 100\left(\frac{5{,}000}{x}\right)$$

$$= \frac{500{,}000}{x} \tag{1-2.3}$$

Then, the model of the system becomes

$$TC = 0.02x + \frac{500{,}000}{x} \tag{1-2.4}$$

It is in the form $E = f(x_i, y_j)$, where the controllable variable is x, the manufacturing lot size, and the objective function is the total cost. Since the values of the y_j are fixed, we may write

$$TC = f(x) \tag{1-2.5}$$

and the solution requires that we find that value of x which minimizes the total cost. For arithmetic simplicity let us assume that production can

TABLE 1–2.1

Courbro Company: Evaluation of Alternative Lot Sizes

x (units)	$HC = .02x$	$SC = \frac{500{,}000}{x}$	TC
1,000	20	500.0	520.0
2,000	40	250.0	290.0
3,000	60	166.7	226.7
4,000	80	125.0	205.0
5,000	100	100.0	200.0
6,000	120	83.3	203.3
7,000	140	71.4	211.4
8,000	160	62.5	222.5
9,000	180	55.6	235.6
10,000	200	50.0	250.0

take place only in lot sizes that are integral multiples of 1,000 units. Then the various possible values of x, i.e., the various possible courses of action, are evaluated in Table 1–2.1, which is based on Equation (1–2.4).

Clearly the optimal lot size is 5,000 units. Figure 1–2.2, which is a graphic representation of Table 1–2.1, indicates the behavior of costs as

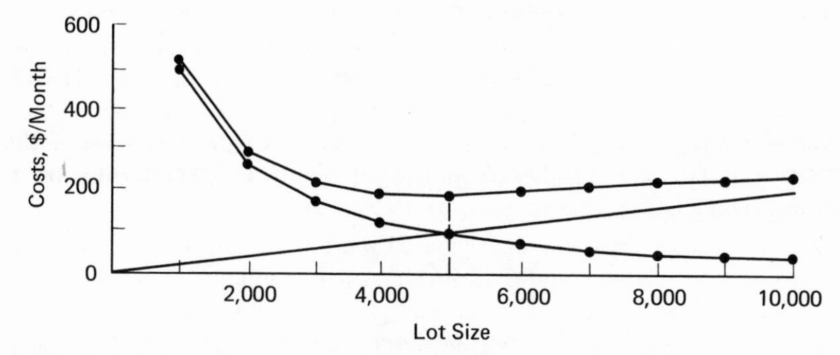

Fig. 1–2.2. Courbro Company. The behavior of holding costs and setup costs with lot sizes in integral multiples of 1,000 units.

lot size is varied. The holding cost is represented by a straight line—a *linear* function—and the setup cost is represented by a descending curved line—a *rectangular hyperbola*—in this case. (The name *rectangular hyperbola* is given to the curve whose general equation is xy = a constant). The sum of these two costs, the total cost, decreases as the lot size increases to 5,000 units, and it increases thereafter. The points are connected as a visual aid; but, with the simplifying restriction requiring discrete lot sizes, intermediate values cannot be realized. If production had not been constrained to integral multiples of 1,000 units, the lines of Figure 1–2.2 would be curved as in Figure 1–2.3, and the optimal

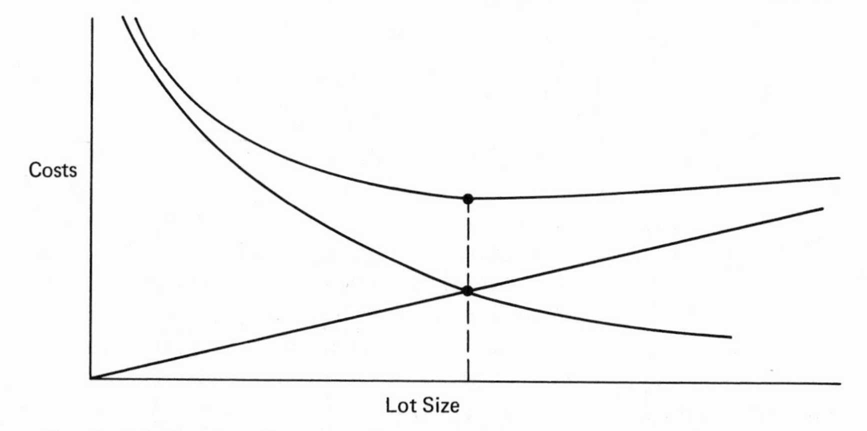

Fig. 1–2.3. Courbro Company. The behavior of holding costs and setup costs with continuously variable lot size.

solution could be found directly by calculus as we shall see in the next chapter. However, in this problem, the answer is the same.

1–3. The Requirements for the System Model. Equation (1–2.4) is a mathematical model of the system. A model is a representation of certain aspects of reality. Its purpose is to tell us all that we need to know—no more and no less—to make the decision. In the case of Equation (1–2.4), it does not describe the electronic components or even indicate that the problem deals with electronic components. The structure of the problem would be the same if the company manufactured a different product. The model includes only those facts and relationships which are relevant to the decision to be made.

The purpose of a model is to predict. It predicts the outcome—the value of the output variable—under various possible configurations of the input variable. This is true whether the model is a scale model of an airplane for use in a wind tunnel, a wiring diagram of an electrical circuit, or a mathematical equation. In all of these cases, the builder of the model intends and hopes that the model has taken into account those characteristics of the real-world system which are important for the decisions to be made on the basis of the model. If this is the case and the relationships in the model do indeed resemble adequately the real-world-system relationships, then the model can be used to experiment with various configurations of the inputs and *predict* the corresponding values of the output. Thus, it can be used to determine the configuration of the inputs necessary to achieve the optimum value of the output.

The models used in operations research are symbolic, or mathematical. For example, the familiar gravitational formula of physics can tell how much a man will weigh on Jupiter. As of this writing, no man has been weighed on Jupiter to verify this formula, and it may even be wrong. However, this mathematical equation has been used to make many useful predictions about the real world.

This kind of abstract reasoning is one of the unique capabilities of the human intellect. We can, with pencil and paper, create a mathematical model of some aspect of the real world. This model is based on information derived from past observations, and it is used to make predictions about future events in the real world. Think for a moment about the astonishing intellectual accomplishment represented by this process in the design and construction of, say, a new aircraft type. Teams of designers create and solve many kinds of complex mathematical equations, transform the results from numbers on paper into specifications for real materials, physical shapes, sizes, components, and operating procedures; and then, some years later, when the actual airplane is built, it really flies, thus verifying the predictions made by the models!

Management scientists try to apply mathematical models to problems in management, and they take the position that the test and the proof of true understanding of a problem is the ability to formulate that problem or the relevant system in mathematical or other symbolic terms. Management science holds that a wide range of real world phenomena can and should be so formulated and that our inability to construct any specific desired mathematical model is merely a manifestation of our ignorance and an indication of the kinds of information and knowledge we must seek.

1–4. The Generality of Models. One of the important reasons for the success of operations research is that most of the mathematical models that have been devised have been found to be useful also in areas of application other than those in which they were first used. Many of the models have been found to be useful in a wide range of areas of application. That is, the model is a mathematical structure, which describes an operation or process that, in its essential form, is found to occur in different areas, which at first glance may seem dissimilar. It is often found that the specific industry, location, profession, craft, materials, machines, etc., may be stripped away, to leave a system which can be described by a symbolic model that is similar to the basic model which has arisen in a seemingly completely different kind of situation. For example, the notion of centrifugal force and the equations describing it are the same for racing-car driving, water skiing, designing a centrifuge, orbiting a satellite, manufacturing a tire, dancing a waltz, or computing the mass of the moon.

The mathematical model thus is often *general* and independent of many of its peripheral aspects and of the specific nature of the inputs and outputs involved. Of course, each system must at first be analyzed in terms of its own specific characteristics, and no detail may be safely omitted until its irrelevance to the problem at hand is assured, but these analyses show, as we shall find, that many such general mathematical structures do emerge, and it is these which have accounted for much of the success of operations research. We shall study several of these in the chapters which follow.

We shall find that, although many mathematical structures are essentially the same in a wide variety of problems, it is seldom possible to use a previously developed mathematical model in a new real problem without *some* modification to take account of specific important differences. However, often these modifications may be minor and, in any event, the basic structure is the same.

For example, consider the training of employees who are trained in groups as, for example, in training courses such as are often used for new junior executives, airline stewardesses, computer programmers, sales trainees, and repair mechanics and engineers. If the training group is too large, the salaries of at least some of the new graduates must be paid for unproductive, or less than fully productive, work for some period until they are needed. This is a *holding cost.* Conversely, if the class size is too small, the course must be repeated too often with consequent high training costs. This last is a *setup cost.* The economic-lot size problem, which was discussed above in Section 1–2 in connection with a manufacturing problem, can be seen to be strictly applicable in this situation dealing with the training of personnel; and, clearly, this same model can also be applied equally well to determine the size of purchases for inventory for resale or for use. All of these applications (and many more) may thus be viewed and treated as occurrences of the mathematical structure known as the *inventory problem.*

Another well known model with very wide applicability is the *waiting line,* or *queueing* model. A representation of the system is shown in Figure 1–4.1. Elements arrive for service, wait their turn, are serviced,

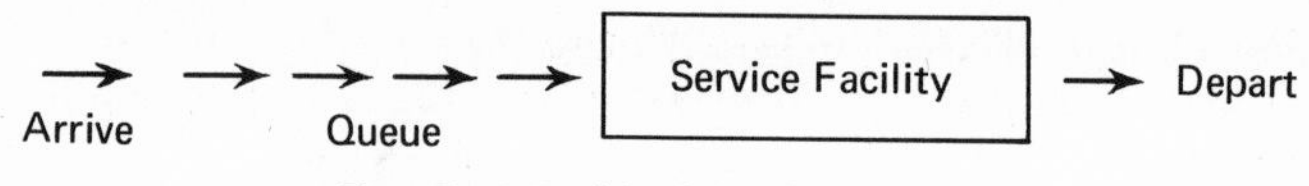

Fig. 1–4.1. Model of a queue.

and leave. Systems of equations have been formulated which enable us to compute queue length, average waiting time, and service-facility utilization, and even to estimate the amount of business lost because of unwillingness or inability of arrivals to wait in line. This, in turn, makes it possible to design service-facility capacity to achieve desired levels of average queue length and waiting time. This queueing model has been applied in a very wide range of situations, among which are: landing facilities for aircraft, tellers in banks, gasoline stations, toll booths in tunnels, turnpikes, and bridges, repair and maintenance facilities of all kinds, check-out counters in supermarkets, and clerks in retail stores, ticket booths, and tool cribs. In all of these seemingly different situations and in many more, essentially the same equations can be used.

An indication of the generality of mathematical models is seen in the fact that many of the mathematical models used in business are taken directly from the physical sciences. For example, in chemistry, there is a model for saturation of a chemical reaction which indicates how much excess of a particular chemical reagent must be used to achieve various amounts of output yield. This is shown in Figure 1–4.2. As the amount of reagent is increased, the yield of the reaction increases at a decreasing rate and approaches the theoretical maximum. This model clearly exemplifies the familiar concept of decreasing returns with some fixed factors, which has long been a part of economic theory. An interesting modern application of this concept of approaching a maximum or saturation level

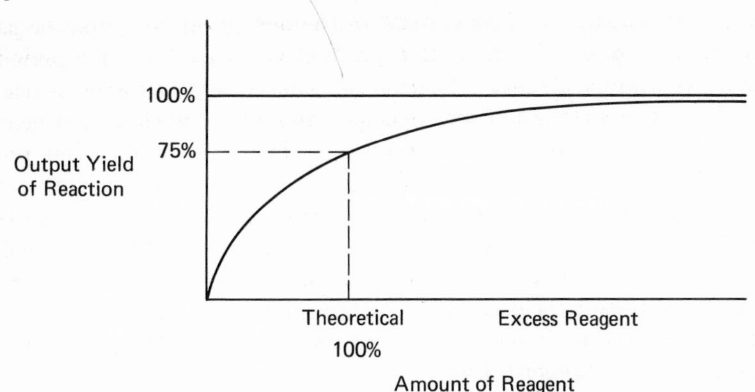

Fig. 1–4.2. Saturation model in chemistry.

has been in advertising, as indicated in Figure 1–4.3. There the theoretical maximum sales is some level based on population, incomes, family size, consumer characteristics, competitor behavior, etc.

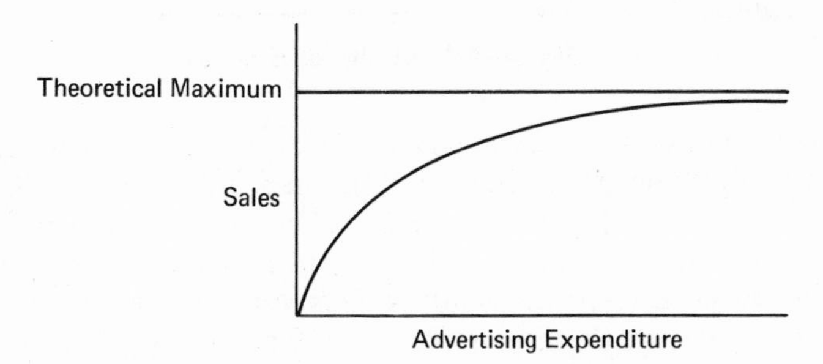

Fig. 1–4.3. Saturation model in advertising.

Another model from the physical sciences which has been applied in advertising and marketing is the radioactive-decay model seen in Figure 1–4.4. In physics, the weight of radioactive material has been found to decrease over time, as shown. During the time interval shown, known as

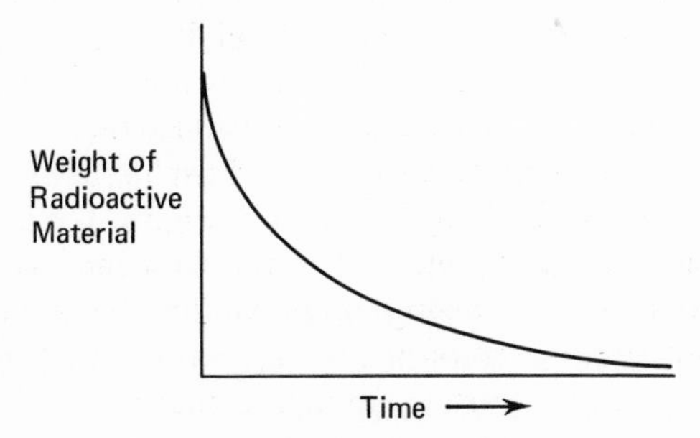

Fig. 1–4.4. Radioactive decay.

the *half-life* for that material, the weight of the remaining material is decreased by one-half. The same model has been used to represent the decay of the effect of advertising on consumer knowledge or behavior. This is shown in Figure 1–4.5. The length of the half-life interval may be

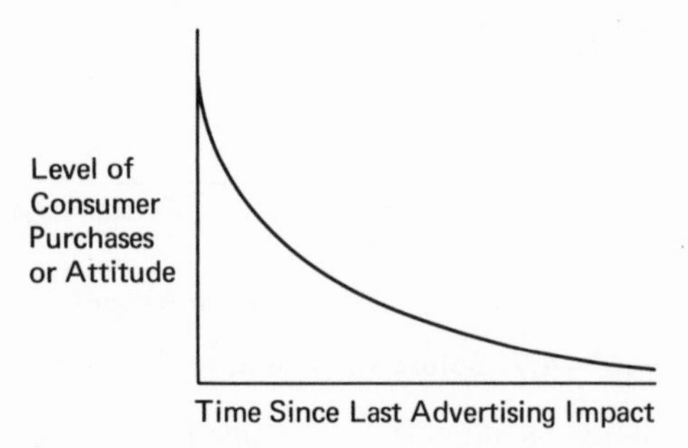

Fig. 1–4.5. Decay of advertising effect.

quite different for different products, and this can constitute evidence leading to the adoption of divergent policies with respect to frequency of advertising. If the slope is steep, as in Figure 1–4.6(a), frequent repetition of the message may be required in order to retain some desired level of consumer attitude, awareness, or behavior. This might be an argument for the very frequent repetition characteristic of advertising campaigns

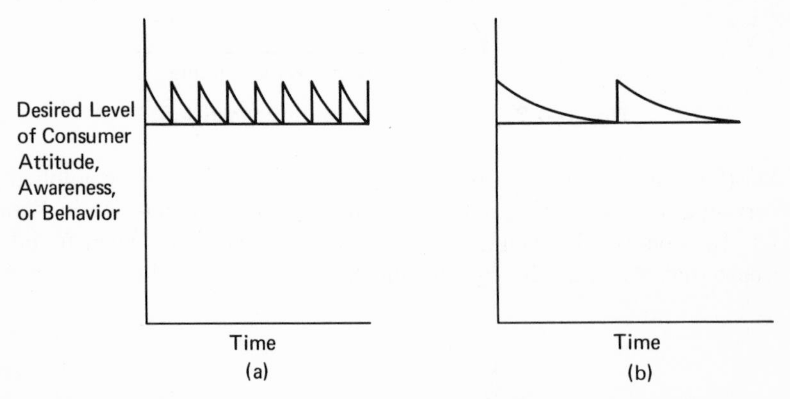

Fig. 1–4.6. Different rates of decay related to frequency of advertising.

for cigarettes, beer, and certain soap products. On the other hand, if the slope of the decay curve is as shown in Figure 1–4.6(b), a sequence of relatively infrequent advertising messages can maintain the desired level of advertising effect. On the graphs of Figure 1–4.6, of course, each vertical line represents the impact of another advertising exposure intended to keep the residual advertising effect from sinking below the desired level.

Finally, many of these types of model can be incorporated into optimization models, in which the output has an optimum value somewhere within a range of possible levels of input. This is characteristic of the inventory model which we have seen, but there are many other applications of this kind of model. Figures 1–4.7 and 1–4.8 each indicate

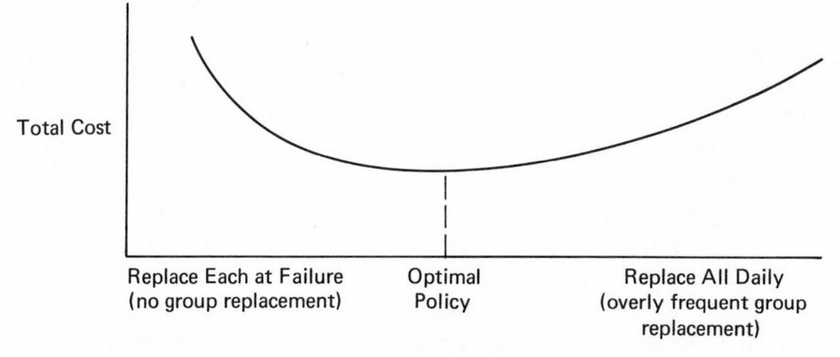

Fig. 1–4.7. Replacement problem.

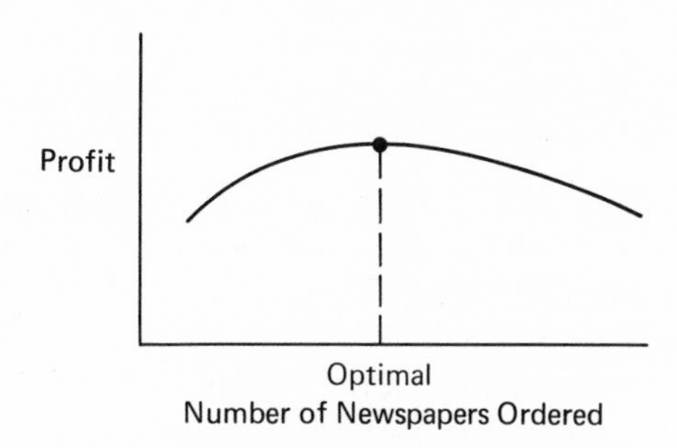

Fig. 1–4.8. The newsboy problem.

one of the many possibilities for a minimization and a maximization, respectively.

Figure 1–4.7 represents a *replacement* situation. Consider a large illuminated sign with hundreds of individual light bulbs (or a large chemical plant with many valves, etc.). One replacement policy might be to replace each bulb as it burns out. This might involve great personnel expense to bring a man out with scaffold and other equipment to replace each bulb as it expires. (In the chemical plant example, the cost of failure might be very great if it resulted in shutdown of all or part of the plant.) At the other extreme, one could replace all of the bulbs (or valves), say, once a week. This might be unduly expensive in that many good bulbs would thus be discarded. Usually there is an optimal intermediate position which involves some form of group replacement after some specific time interval. The usual optimal solution specifies that items are replaced as they fail and that, after some specified interval, all (or all older than some specified age) are replaced.

Figure 1–4.8 represents a problem, often referred to as the *newsboy problem.* A newsboy may err by ordering and stocking too few newspapers, thus losing potential profit; or he may err by stocking too many, losing profit because of unsold stock. This problem is the same as that of the dealer in Christmas trees or the merchant ordering style goods or any product for which there is a single selling period during which additional stock is available only at a premium cost, if at all, and after which unsold items are worth less, if anything. The same mathematical structure describes the problem faced by any equipment purchaser who must decide how much to invest in spare parts. In that case, the cost of shortage is in premium cost for parts or in idle time for the equipment, when there is a delay in purchasing spare parts that are not on hand when failure occurs. Thus, if too many are on hand, costs are too high, and if too few are on hand, costs are again too high. There is some intermediate optimum decision. Clearly, this situation, and many others which can easily be imagined, all have exactly the same mathematical structure as the newsboy problem.

1–5. The Objectives of Decision. Typically in a management science model, the output of the model is some measure of effectiveness somehow selected and defined. We shall see that the specification of this objective function is one of the most difficult problems in the construction of these models in the real world.

We have seen that it is possible to construct a symbolic model to describe an inventory system or a replacement system and many others. It is also possible to construct a symbolic model of a decision itself; we shall see this below in Sections 1–7 through 1–10. First, let us look at the problem and process of decision making. Our view of decision making is that it is a rational information-using process—not an emotional process. Thus, whenever anyone makes a wrong decision or has difficulty in making a decision, these difficulties can be attributable to either:

1. *Inadequate information;* incorrect or incomplete information about the various possible alternative courses of action and about their implications with respect to the ultimate outcome; or
2. *Inadequately specified objectives;* failure to specify which outcomes are more desirable than others.

Often there are conflicting objectives, and the decision maker must resolve the conflict. He must, as we shall see below, emerge with a single objective function. For example, if the problem is one of deciding on the proper level of customer service, and if superior service costs more money, and if the objective is only to save money, then, unless there is some measure of the value of customer service, the obvious (and ridiculous) solution is to minimize or eliminate customer service. The rational approach to this problem requires the objective measurement of quality of service and the transformation of the measure of the quality of the service into some concept of *value* to the decision maker or his organization; and this should ideally be expressed in money units, so that the effectiveness function to be maximized is this value minus the cost of the service. In this way, a set of conflicting objectives, cost vs. service quality, can be changed into a single objective function,

$$\text{Effectiveness} = \text{Service value} - \text{Cost of service}$$

and various possible configurations of customer service quality can be evaluated and compared.

Value measurement is one of the most vexing problems facing the social scientist today. The current attempts to peer into the human mind and to analyze and quantify subjective value systems, and to describe and explore valuation systems which may be generally applicable to a range of individuals will receive only brief treatment here. This is due not to the lack of importance of the problem, but rather to the complexity of the subject matter, and the inadequacy of the present state of knowledge. In this volume, we shall be dealing primarily with business problems, where, hopefully, the various conflicting objectives can be expressed in comparable, usually monetary, terms.

For example, a drug manufacturing firm, which has been exclusively in the prescription drug market, might discover that it has a new product which shows great promise for the patent medicine market; yet the company might hesitate before attempting to realize this promising source of revenue because it fears that such action might alienate the medical profession and endanger its corporate image, and hence its entire product line. Another illustration of an *external conflict* situation occurs in decisions about forward vertical integration, in which a company must decide whether or not to compete with its customers. In both of these cases, rational decision making requires objective estimation of the costs and benefits of all of the various alternative courses of action, and the decision should not be based on hunch or emotion.

The typical manufacturing company provides an excellent illustration of *internal conflict,* i.e. of conflicting goals among its various functions. The sales manager typically wants a wide product line with large inventories so that all customers may be served, and served rapidly. The production manager wants a restricted product line and long production runs to minimize production costs. The finance manager wants small inventories and short production runs to minimize financing costs. The company president, who must make company-wide decisions about the product line and inventory levels must look beyond the individual departmental preferences, because what is best for the company as a whole is probably not the best for any individual department as considered alone. The company-wide optimal course of action is probably some kind of a middle course between the preferences of the individual departments.

Optimizing on individual departments or on individual phases of a sytem is referred to as *suboptimization,* and it typically does not yield the best system-wide policy. It is the function of each higher level executive to consider a larger system and broader horizons than his subordinates. It is almost a truism that every decision involves suboptimization, when it is regarded from the vantage point of a larger system. The sales department suboptimizes with respect to the firm, the firm suboptimizes with respect to the industry, the industry suboptimizes with respect to the national economy, and the nation suboptimizes with respect to the world.

Nevertheless, it is not yet feasible to optimize on the universe, and, for any real decision, the decision maker must identify the scope of his real-world system, determine his objectives and how to measure them, and then choose his optimal course of action within that framework. The identification and measurement of the true objective function is often the most difficult aspect of a decision problem.

In addition to the determination of the true objective function, there are other aspects of decision making which involve complex processes in the human brain. Among these are the interpretation and utilization of probabilities and, indeed, the very concept of rationality itself. Scientific study and knowledge about human reasoning and evaluation processes are still in their infancy. Much research is currently being conducted, but many questions remain unanswered.

Here, however, we shall at the outset make the assumption that decision makers act rationally according to our definition, and we define a *rational decision* as the selection of that course of action which, in the light of the available information, yields the optimal expected value of the objective function. (We shall later, in Chapters 4 and 19, define and discuss the concept of expected value at some length.)

Thus, the result that emerges from our analysis is the course of action that the decision maker *should* accept, not necessarily the one he *does* accept. "Should" here refers to what he would do if he knew all of the implications of his action, and if he behaved *rationally.* It is possible, of course, as we have seen, that at some higher level of analysis there may be counterindications that render our solution wrong and impossible to implement; in which case, the problem to which we are addressing ourselves is the wrong problem, or our information is inadequate. It is futile and absurd to bother with seeking information and performing analyses toward the choice of a course of action unless the selected course of action can and will be implemented.

Returning to our previous example of the conflict of interest among departments of a firm, it can be expected that analyses of production methods and costs may lead to a cost-minimizing optimal solution for the production department that prescribes a small product line, while market analyses indicate that a broader product line is essential for maximizing sales, the optimal solution for the sales department. The rational decision for the production manager does not coincide with the rational decision for the marketing manager, and neither of their decisions may coincide with the rational decision for their superior, who must resolve both the production and marketing objectives. He must know the "cost" in sales and profits of a smaller than optimal product line, and he must set this off against the potential production-cost savings. One of the most important aspects of a management hierarchy is that, as we have seen, at each level the executive must work with larger systems and encompass broader horizons than those of his subordinates.

As we shall view it, the decision-making process consists of:

1. *Consideration of a set of alternatives,* which may be either qualitative or quantitative. The latter in turn may be either discrete or continuous.
2. *Selection of the best alternative in order to achieve a goal or objective,* which may be viewed as optimizing (minimizing or maximizing, as the case may be) some objective function such as profits, sales, costs, or any of many other possibilities.

What is involved in this simple phrase "best alternative"? First, we *must have access to* this best alternative. That is, it must be included among those being considered. This may involve what is often called *creativity.* That is, someone must conceive of a possible course of action before it can be eligible or available for consideration.

Second, the selected alternative must be "best" according to the appropriate *value system,* taking into account the possibility of conflicting goals and suboptimization.

After the problem of assessment of the objective of the decision has been satisfactorily met, in spite of our attempts to approach the decision-making process in this rational orderly way, we may still fail to select what may seem to be the best alternative because we are unwilling to seek the best alternative; and this may well be a conscious policy; that is, the decision may not be sufficiently important to warrant costly analysis or delay. What this really means is that, at a higher level, optimization dictates the acceptance of a less-than-optimal solution here, because the cost of seeking the optimal exceeds its potential value.

In this connection, the term *satisficing,* originally introduced by

Herbert Simon, has been used to describe the process whereby a decision maker does not seek an optimal course of action so much as one which *satisfies* him, i.e., one which *suffices*. This has been referred to as a characterization of the decision-making process which is basically different from the optimization concept. For example, under the optimization concept, an executive with a sum of money to invest would be pictured as seeking out all the available alternative investment possibilities, evaluating them, and then choosing the one which gives the highest return—if that is his objective. On the other hand, the "satisficing" concept suggests that men do not act in this way, and that the executive is more likely to have some concept of the minimum rate that is considered an acceptable return. He then systematically considers alternatives until he finds one that gives him this minimum, or better, and the search stops at this point, whether or not the chosen investment is in fact the best of all possible courses of action. While "satisficing" may seem to characterize much of decision making in the real world, it is doubtless that in many situations, the policy of "satisficing," so-called at a lower level, is actually the optimum as determined by a higher-level optimization decision encompassing a larger system. That is, the investor described above may invest when he finds an opportunity which meets only his minimum requirements, if this procedure is optimal in terms of the cost of further search, the cost of delay, and the anticipated possible improvement in the return. The decision maker is, in fact, optimizing in selecting, at the margin, the optimal of the two courses of action available to him; i.e., he may "accept," or he may "search further."

Thus, it may be argued that the difference between "satisficing" and optimizing is not so great as it may seem at first, that "satisficing" at one level is really optimizing at a higher level, and that the difference between optimization and "satisficing" is merely another manifestation of the problem of selection of the size of system to be considered in decision making. Every system is a subsystem within some larger system; and the selection of the size of the system to be enclosed is often a choice between small, relatively unimportant, easy problems and large, important problems that possibly cannot be solved at all. Also, the size of the system is often rigidly specified by the status, position, and authority of the decision maker and the existing restrictions on space, time, equipment, and personnel. Then, the decision maker has really no alternative but to proceed to optimize on his system, realizing that his result may well be nonoptimal for the larger system of which his system is a subsystem. This is the typical situation.

1–6. Reason and Reality. Decision making, like any other intellectual process, takes place in the mind. Such intellectual processes exist and are performed in terms of language and symbols which are models of the real world but do not affect the real world. In general we try to make our language, symbols, and models represent the real world closely enough to be useful, and we proceed to use them, hoping that we have succeeded.

For example, if we were asked to estimate how long it will take Donald Rooney to drive from New York to Cleveland, we must call upon several models. First, we might spread a road map before us. The map is a model of the real world. We hope and expect that the road map, with the appropriate highways shown, is an accurate representation of the real world. What we mean by this is that we expect the map to be drawn to scale, so that the distances on the map are related to those in the real world. Also, the quality of the various highways and road surfaces is shown on the map by a system of colors and types of lines. Our study of the map might suggest, first, that the fastest route is via the New Jersey, Pennsylvania, and Ohio Turnpikes, and we may decide to assume that he will use that route.

Now, for the detailed analysis, we examine the terminal points as given. "New York" and "Cleveland" as models of points in the real world or as points on the map are inadequate models. More specific information is needed. The designations "5th Avenue and 26th Street in New York" and "Public Square in Cleveland" are combinations of words which form expressions which unambiguously represent specific places in the real world or points on maps of those two cities.

Now that the distances are well defined, we must introduce mathematical models relating these distances to time, via some assumed rate or rates of speed (based on our knowledge of speed limits, weather, traffic conditions, his car, and certain aspects of his personality) and some estimated number of stops for fuel, food, rest, etc., some of which, e.g. fuel, may be computed via another mathematical model, and others of which must be estimated again by our model of his personality.

In any event, the final answer is a single number, e.g. 14 hours, which represents the use of many different kinds of model, such as words, symbols, maps, mathematical models, and psychological behavioral models. The final result refers to a real person with a real automobile in the real world, yet it was arrived at via this complex interaction of several different kinds of models. Our performance in this kind of estimation is probably quite good. That is, the models do resemble the real world sufficiently closely to be useful for prediction. Note that the map model did not tell us about the scenery en route or about the sounds and smells; and the mathematical model of time, rate, and distance did not consider the color of the car or any of innumerable other irrelevant characteristics of the real world—that is, *irrelevant for the purpose of this analysis*. Also, we made broad assumptions about the weather, surface, and traffic conditions, Donald's health and frame of mind, and the general reliability of his car.

In operations research, we try to use models that represent those aspects of the real world which are important for the problem at hand and to ignore those elements of the system which do not bear on that problem. Our models may be successful and resemble the appropriate aspects of the real world, or they may fail. There is no necessary relationship. Our reasoning and our conclusions, based on our models, are derived via criteria of *consistency* not of *truth*, and we may reason brilliantly to the wrong conclusion if one or more of the assumptions in our model are wrong.

An excellent example of a useful theoretical model is the "fair coin" of probability theory. We speak of and think about the probability of a "fair coin" coming up heads when it is tossed. The theory, or model, is consistent, regardless of whether a "fair coin" exists in the real world. Our experience tells us that the results of the theory have been very close to what happens in the real world, and that, therefore, the concept of a "fair coin" is a useful model.

It is the technique for proceeding from observations in the real world to useful statements about the real world via reasoning in terms of models which is the essence of the scientific method.

Let us now look at a model of a decision. We shall construct a model which treats a decision as involving two kinds of inputs, *courses of action* and *states of nature*, one output, the *effectiveness*, and a *system* model, within which these three elements interact. That is, the system model produces the output value associated with each of the possible configurations of the two inputs. The decision model then helps identify the optimal course of action.

1–7. The Courses of Action, A_i. We have referred to the x_i, the controllable variables, as those input variables which are subject to the control of the decision maker, and we have agreed that any configuration of the controllable variables constitutes a *course of action*. Indeed, the decision-making process consists of selecting the optimal configuration of the controllable variables, the optimal *action* or *course of action*. We shall designate these courses of action: $A_1, A_2, A_3, \ldots, A_m$ for m possible courses of action. The general designation will be A_i.

For example, in the New York–Cleveland trip, Donald had two courses of action available.

A_1 Use turnpikes (save time).

A_2 Use other roads (save tolls).

In describing the available courses of action, it must be remembered that any change in *any* of the controllable variables creates a new course of action. For example, Donald might have wished also to decide whether to stop in restaurants for meals or to bring his lunch and save time by eating while driving. Now he has four courses of action.

A_1 Use turnpikes and eat in restaurants.
A_2 Use other roads and eat in restaurants.
A_3 Use turnpikes and eat while driving.
A_4 Use other roads and eat while driving.

Also, he could have considered the possibility of an intermediate course of action whereby he did not stop to eat, but did stop to purchase sandwiches and snacks which he could then eat while driving. This adds two more A_i. In addition, he might have considered intermediate road-selection possibilities which involved some turnpikes and some use of other roads where, for example, the alternatives to the turnpikes met certain criteria. Now, the number of possible courses of action can become very large, and, by considering various possible configurations of still other controllable variables, the number of A_i can grow almost without limit.

If one controllable variable whose value is to be determined in advance is his speed for straight turnpike stretches, he could consider, for example, 55, 56, 57, 58, 59, 60, etc., miles per hour. But could he not consider 56.3 or 57.75 or 59.375 or any of a very large number of possibilities? Since speed is a *continuous* variable, the number of its possible values is infinite. We shall see that in problems involving the selection of the optimal value of a continuous variable, we are often able to construct a mathematical model which permits us to compute the optimal value of the continuous variable, without resorting to the simplification of selecting various discrete values for comparison.

The various courses of action may be *qualitative* or *quantitative*, and the quantitative courses of action may be *discrete* or *continuous*. The turnpike vs. nonturnpike alternative is qualitative. The number of stops and the speed are quantitative variables, the former being discrete and the latter continuous.

In addition, the courses of action must be mutually exclusive. One could not, for example, consider the following alternatives for a decision about his vacation.

A_1 Vacation in the Mediterranean.
A_2 Vacation in winter.
A_3 Vacation with wife.
A_4 Vacation by boat.

Since these are not necessarily mutually exclusive alternatives, a decision to select one of them would not ordinarily involve giving up all of the others. In our decision problems, the courses of action must be mutually exclusive.

In addition, as we have noted above, the list of A_i should be all-inclusive. That is, it should include all of the relevant courses of action which may be of interest. If the optimal course of action is not considered for selection, it obviously cannot be selected. It is in the discovery, identification, and inclusion of various unexpected possible courses of action that that elusive personal characteristic, known as "creativity," is of critical importance. In this volume, we shall be concerned primarily with the analysis and evaluation of sets or ranges of given courses of action, rather than the subtle problems of exploration and search for new and imaginative courses of action.

1–8. The Objective Function (Effectiveness), *E*. The purpose of the decision maker is to select that course of action (A_i) which will maximize some measure of gain or minimize some measure of loss or cost, i.e. which will *optimize* some function, E, which measures the *effectiveness* of the various courses of action.

$$E_i = f(A_i) \qquad (1\text{–}8.1)$$

Equation (1–8.1) says that effectiveness is a function of (i.e., depends upon) the course of action. That is, for each course of action, there is a value of the effectiveness function. That is, in the New York to Cleveland automobile trip, if time were the only criterion of effectivenss, and if the driver had decided to bring his lunch, the decision might be represented as the following.

A_1 = Turnpikes, E_1 = 14 hours.
A_2 = Other roads, E_2 = 19 hours.

Then, of the two possible courses of action, A_1 yields the optimum value of the *effectiveness function*, time. However, our traveler may wish to consider the cost in tolls of the two alternatives. Suppose, then, he finds that A_1, the turnpike route, costs $10 in tolls, while the other route costs $1 in tolls. Let us use the word *outcome* to represent the description of the result of each course of action.

A_i	Course of Action	Outcome
A_1	Turnpikes	14 hours, $10
A_2	Other roads	19 hours, $1

Now, although the outcomes are completely specified in terms of time and toll cost, it is not clear which is preferable, because there are conflicting objectives. One course of action is better with respect to time, and the other is better wth respect to money.

Whenever there are conflicting objectives, the rational approach to decision making requires that the conflict be resolved by expressing all of the dimensions of the outcomes in terms of one of them or perhaps in terms of some other common dimension. In this case, we might *transform* the time dimension into money. Suppose that Donald has a personal transformation function for the cost of driving time such that: Cost = \$5 per hour. Then, the "cost" of the 14 hours of driving would be \$70 and the 19 hours would cost \$95. From this, the evaluation of the effectiveness of the two courses of action would be the following.

A_i	Course of Action	Outcome	E_i	Effectiveness
A_1	Turnpikes	14 hr., \$10	$E_1 =$	\$80
A_2	Other roads	19 hr., \$1	$E_2 =$	\$96

Clearly now, the cost-minimizing course of action is A_1, the turnpikes. Note that we have not considered other possible dimensions of the outcome, such as the boredom of turnpike driving, the value of the scenery and sights *en route*, the differential wear and tear on the car, the differential cost of fuel, etc. In order to include any or all of these in the model, it would be essential to transform them into the same units of measurement, presumably, in this case, money.

The problem of conflicting objectives is very serious in attempts to apply the techniques of rational decision making to many business decisions. It is often necessary to construct transformation functions for such items as customer waiting time and customer displeasure into dollars. Obviously, without some such concept, it may be impossible to make a rational decision about various aspects of the quality of customer service.

The determination of the definition and method of measurement of the objective function is probably the most difficult and elusive aspect of rational decision making in the real world. Even the use of dollars does not always yield a true measure of the effectiveness. It is well known that the utility of money is not linear. That is, \$2 may be worth twice as much as \$1 to a decision maker, but is \$100 worth a hundred times as much? Is \$1,000,000 worth a million times as much? At some point, for all people and all business firms, the answer is negative. Normally, we expect the *marginal* utility for money to diminish somewhat as shown in Figure 1–8.1. This says that the thousandth dollar does not add to utility as much as did the first or second or tenth or hundredth, and the millionth dollar adds still less, etc. In the light of this, it is clear that effectiveness should be measured in terms of some general measure of utility, i.e., "utiles" instead of dollars. Unfortunately, we do not know enough about people's value systems to do this, and, in most cases, we are forced to use money or time or sales, etc., as the objective function and to treat that measure as the true measure of effectiveness. This, of course, makes the tacit assumption that twice as much is twice as good and a thousand times

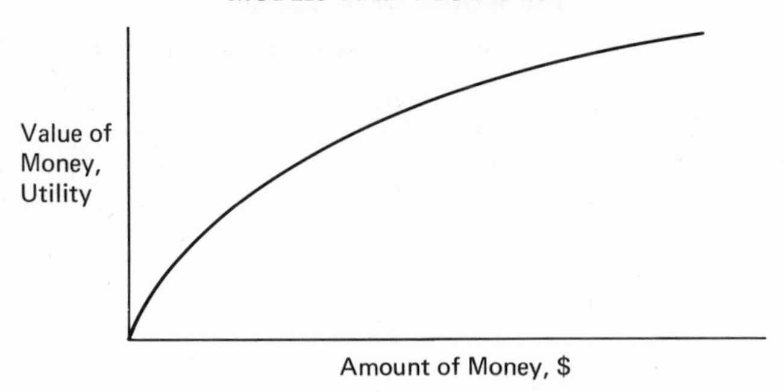

Fig. 1–8.1. A nonlinear utility function for money.

as much is a thousand times as good. This is the assumption of *linearity* of utility. It is no doubt wrong, but, if we are careful, we can avoid permitting it to lead us astray. We shall say more about this in Chapter 19.

1–9. The States of Nature, B_j. Thus far, we have ignored the effect on the outcome of the uncontrollable variables. Clearly when there are uncontrollable variables (y_j) which affect the outcome, they must be taken into account.

We shall introduce the uncontrollable variables into the model in much the same way as the controllable variables. Just as each different configuration of the controllable variables (x_i) constitutes a course of action (A_i), we shall define each configuration of the uncontrollable variables (y_j) as constituting a *state of nature* or *background* (B_j).

Let us suppose that in the case of Donald's trip from New York to Cleveland, there are two possible states of nature:

B_1 Roads clear.
B_2 Roads slippery.

Then, the outcome may depend on the B_j as well as on the A_i. We shall examine this problem in the next section.

In defining the states of nature, it is important, as in the other phases of model building, to include that which is relevant and to exclude that which is irrelevant. This requires, as we have seen, and as we shall see again and again, adequate familiarity with the system.

1–10. The Model of a Decision. The outcome associated with each course of action is determined not only by the course of action but also by the state of nature. For each course of action, A_i, and each state of nature, B_j, there is a unique outcome, O_{ij}. This entire decision model may be displayed in a simple and convenient matrix form, such as is shown in Figure 1–10.1, for a situation in which there are three courses of action and two states of nature.

	States of Nature ("Backgrounds"), B_j	
Courses of Action, A_i	B_1	B_2
A_1	O_{11}	O_{12}
A_2	O_{21}	O_{22}
A_3	O_{31}	O_{32}

Fig. 1–10.1. A model of a decision. A decision matrix.

The symbols and notation should be observed carefully. We have used the subscript i in connection with the courses of action and j in connection with the states of nature. That is because the A_i are arranged vertically and the B_j are arranged horizontally. Then, the i designates the row, and the j designates the column. The outcome, O_{ij}, is the outcome in the ith row and the jth column. We always write the dual subscript in this way, row designation followed by column designation. For example, O_{31} is the outcome in the third row and the first column. This system of notation can be remembered quite easily if we remember the order: row, then column. The designations i and j are then in alphabetical order, and the number of rows is called m and the number of columns, n. This also is in alphabetical order; row, then column. A matrix is described as an *m-by-n matrix*, meaning that there are m rows and n columns. The matrix of Figure 1–10.1 is a 3-by-2 matrix. The row designation always precedes the column designation.

In the case of Donald's drive from New York to Cleveland, let us suppose that slippery road conditions add 6 hours to the turnpike time but only 2 hours to the relatively slow other road time. The decision matrix then is as shown in Figure 1–10.2. Using the same transformation function as before; i.e., one hour equals \$5, the effectiveness matrix is as

	B_1 Roads Clear	B_2 Roads Slippery
A_1 Turnpikes	14 hr \$10	20 hr \$10
A_2 Other Roads	19 hr \$1	21 hr \$1

Fig. 1–10.2. The outcome matrix.

	B_1 Roads Clear	B_2 Roads Slippery
A_1 Turnpikes	\$80	\$110
A_2 Other Roads	\$96	\$106

Fig. 1–10.3. Effectiveness matrix.

shown in Figure 1–10.3. Clearly, now, the optimum decision is not independent of the state of nature. Donald must try to ascertain the condition of the roads before he leaves; or, if he cannot, he may be able to start his trip and shift to the optimum route as he observes road conditions en route.

This problem of decision making, when more than one state of nature is possible and one is not certain which is the true state of nature, is the heart of decision theory, and we shall say much more about it.

The effectiveness matrix, also often called the "payoff" matrix, as shown in Figure 1–10.3, uses the output given by Equation (1–10.1), the *system model:*

$$E_{ij} = f(A_i, B_j) \tag{1–10.1}$$

It is shown in general form in Figure 1–10.4. That is the model of a decision. Note that there are m rows and n columns and, of course, $m \times n$

	B_1	B_2	B_3	•	•	•	B_n
A_1	E_{11}	E_{12}	E_{13}	•	•	•	E_{1n}
A_2	E_{21}	E_{22}	E_{23}	•	•	•	•
A_3	E_{31}	E_{32}	E_{33}	•	•	•	•
•	•	•	•	•	•	•	•
•	•	•	•	•	•	•	•
A_m	E_{m1}	•	•	•	•	•	E_{mn}

Fig. 1–10.4. The general form of the effectiveness, or "payoff," matrix. The model of a decision.

payoffs. The matrix form used in Figures 1–10.3 and 1–10.4 is the usual form. The intermediate form, the outcome matrix, of Figure 1–10.2 is not widely used or useful since the analysis and decision must be made in terms of the total objective function.

The entire process involved in the system model is represented in equation form in Equation (1–10.2)

$$E_{ij} = f_v(O_{ij}) = f_m(A_i, B_j) = f_d(x_i, y_j) \qquad (1\text{–}10.2)$$

The subscripts attached to the f's in Equation (1–10.2) are temporary and are used *only in this equation,* where their purpose is to identify and emphasize the specific type of function involved at each *stage.* Reading the terms from right to left in Equation (1–10.2), the x_i and y_j are the controllable and uncontrollable variables, respectively. Some functional relationship, f_d, based on analysis of the system and involving recognition and *diagnosis* of the *decision problem* and its setting, identifies each of the possible relevant configurations of the controllable variables as a course of action, A_i, and each of the possible relevant configurations of the uncontrollable variables as a state of nature, B_j.

The functional relationship, f_m, which is the basic *model* of the system, combines the inputs A_i and B_j; and their interaction leads to the output, O_{ij}.

Finally, the relevant value system of the decision maker or his organization converts the output into the true measure of effectiveness, the objective function, E_{ij}, via the *value system* function, f_v. In representing the decision process, the form

$$E_{ij} = f(A_i, B_j) \qquad (1\text{–}10.1)$$

is sufficient for most purposes. That is because that equation represents the model of the system, and because we generally do not know enough about the relevant value systems to make it useful to consider the value function separately. Thus, Equation (1–10.1) represents that stage which is of main interest to us; namely, the interaction of the states of nature and courses of action to yield values of the objective function. It is, of course, the equation counterpart of the payoff matrix of Figure 1–10.4, and this is what we shall deal with primarily throughout this volume. We should recognize, however, that, while Equation (1–10.1) may refer to either discrete or continuous values of the A_i and the B_j, the matrix, as such, can represent real problems only if they involve a finite number of discrete A_i and B_j. However, conceptually, the idea of the matrix can help us to visualize a decision problem in terms of the interaction of the A_i and B_j.

We should note that the process of designing and constructing the matrix isolates and identifies the four tasks involved in the solution of a decision problem. First, f_d, there is the task of the *diagnosis* and analysis of the *decision problem;* the identification of all of the relevant inputs—both controllable and uncontrollable—and outputs; the measurement of these inputs and outputs; and the determination of the scope of the problem, i.e., the size of the system involved.

Second, f_v, there is the task of the analysis of the *value systems,* and the determination of the appropriate single measure of effectiveness and the technique for computing its value. (In many real-world problems, this may well be the first task to be performed.)

Third, f_m, there is the task of the construction of the *model of the system*, so that the decision maker will be able to relate each combination of some course of action and some state of nature to some value of the objective function.

The construction of the model of the system is, in a sense, the heart of the scientific method. The model must be built on the basis of such information and observations as may be available to the analyst, and it must be tested against the real world. This process may be represented by the triangular diagram of Figure 1–10.5. The model, once built, generates predictions. These predictions may then be compared with new

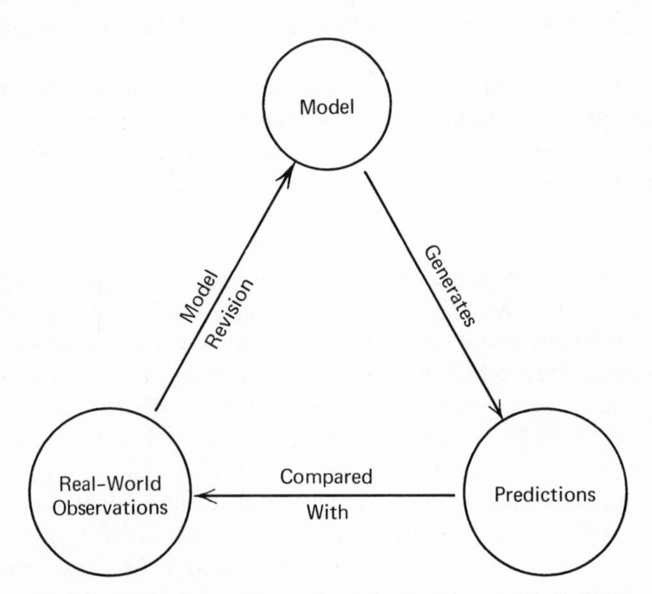

Fig. 1–10.5. Scientific methodology in model building.

observations from the real world, and, on the basis of this comparison, the model may be revised. Then the predictions of the modified model may be compared with additional real-world observations, etc., until the model meets some criterion of accuracy of prediction.

Fourth and finally, there is the task of the *selection* of the optimal course of action. In some cases, especially when the true state of nature is known to the decision maker, this may be a relatively simple matter involving merely the examination of the various possible values of the objective function and the identification of the course of act on associated with it.

In other cases, this fourth task may be extremely difficult and elusive even when there is only one possible state of nature; and it is typically more difficult when there are two or more possible states of nature, and the decision maker is uncertain which is the true state of nature.

In the many problems which will be investigated in this volume, some will have as their main task the construction of the model. These may be thought of as primarily *operations research* problems. Others will have as their main task the selection of the optimal course of action, given the complete decision matrix. These may be thought of as primarily problems in *decision theory*. Some problems will involve both tasks. The first problems which we shall examine are primarily problems in decision theory.

1–11. Types of Decision Situations. The matrix formulation of decision problems permits recognition of four distinct types of decision problems. In all four of these cases we can assume that we have access to the information represented in the matrix shown in Figure 1–10.4. That is, we know or can ascertain all of the relevant A_i and B_j, and we have a mathematical model of the system which enables us to compute the E_{ij} from each of the combinations of an A_i and a B_j. This would of course be in the form of Equation (1–10.1).

The four types of decision problem differ from one another in the extent and kind of information available about the B_j, the states of nature.

Decision making under certainty. If the decision maker has complete information about the state of nature and therefore knows which B_j is indeed the true state of nature, the decision matrix has only one column, as is shown in Figure 1–11.1. Then the solution to the decision problem

A_1	E_1
A_2	E_2
A_3	E_3
•	•
•	•
•	•
A_m	E_m

Fig. 1–11.1. Payoff matrix for decision making under certainty. The true state of nature is known.

requires only the computation of the payoff (the value of the objective function) associated with each course of action and the identification of the optimal. This is not always easy, but it comes as no shock to us to see that when information is most complete, decision making is easiest and most successful in achieving its objectives.

The other three types of decision problems are characterized by uncertainty about the true state of nature and each represents a different kind of partial information about the B_j. Obviously, when the decision is made and the action taken, some one of the B_j will turn out to be real. Under certainty, the decision maker knows the state of nature exactly before he makes the decision.

Decision making under conflict. When the states of nature are subject to the control of an adverse intellect, as when they are in reality the courses of action of an opponent, then each of the opposing decision makers will try to optimize at the other's expense. Thus, neither of them knows exactly which B_j will eventually materialize, but he has a basis for analysis. Situations such as this may arise in business competition, in bargaining, and in war. The body of techniques used for analysis of this kind of situation is known as *game theory,* and it is the subject of Chapter 18.

Decision making under risk. If the decision maker does not know the true state of nature, but rather has partial information which can be expressed in terms of probabilities applicable to all of the possible states of nature, then there is also a basis for analysis. In such cases, the optimal course of action is that which maximizes the *expectation* or *expected value,* as we shall define that term in Chapter 4.

Decision making under complete ignorance. It must be emphasized that the expression "complete ignorance" here does not mean complete ignorance in any general sense. Here, as before, we assume complete knowledge as to the identification of all of the elements shown in the payoff matrix; namely, the A_i, the B_j, and the E_{ij}. Thus, the expression "complete ignorance" refers specifically and solely to *complete ignorance as to the likelihood of occurrence of the various possible states of nature.* Each course of action will lead to one of a series of possible specified outcomes; but which it will be is unknown, and, indeed, even the probability of each of these various outcomes is completely unknown and possibly not even meaningful.

1–12. Decision Criteria Under Complete Ignorance. When there is such complete ignorance of the likelihood of the occurrence of the various possible states of nature, then the decision problem becomes essentially philosophical and psychological. For example, one decision maker might be extremely cautious or pessimistic and treat nature as if it were a rational opponent. In that case, the techniques of game theory might be used. On the other hand, another decision maker might be optimistic and a plunger and decide to try for the best payoff in the matrix, even if that course of action entails the possibility of great loss also. Alternatively, the decision maker may decide on some intermediate position on the optimism–pessimism scale, or he may decide to apply some other criterion for decision. Let us examine some of the criteria for decision that have been suggested for this kind of situation. We shall refer to the payoff matrix shown in Figure 1–12.1.

	B_1	B_2	B_3	B_4
A_1	25	20	90	20
A_2	27	26	30	25
A_3	0	45	68	100
A_4	75	60	17	50

Fig. 1–12.1. Payoff matrix.

Maximin. The pessimistic decision maker might seek the best payoff which he can be sure of, regardless of the state of nature. He might reason as follows:

If I select A_1, the worst that can happen is 20.
If I select A_2, the worst that can happen is 25.
If I select A_3, the worst that can happen is 0.
If I select A_4, the worst that can happen is 17.
Therefore, I shall select A_2, assuring me a payoff of at least 25.

This solution, the *maximin*, i.e., the maximum of the row minima, does indeed protect against any payoff lower than 25. But it also precludes any payoff higher than 30. This maximin criterion, which has been associated with the name of Abraham Wald, finds the maximum payoff which can be *assured.*

Maximax. The decision maker who is the true plunger and who is willing to speculate bravely if not wisely, might choose A_3, since that course of action makes it possible to enjoy the largest payoff in the matrix. In this case, it also permits the decision maker to suffer the worst payoff. Here, the criterion is the maximum possible payoff, and nothing else matters. The name of no scholar has been associated with this somewhat foolhardy criterion.

Optimism–pessimism coefficient. This criterion, which has been associated with the name of Leonid Hurwicz, suggests that there is an intermediate position between that of the utter pessimist and that of the complete optimist. If we define the value of the optimism–pessimism coefficient as 0 for the utter pessimist and 1 for the complete optimist, then to use this criterion, we must somehow assign a value to the coefficient, for the decision and decision maker at hand, which measures how he feels about his luck today or about his willingness to be exposed to dismal results in exchange for exposure to possible good results. Then, for each A_i, a weighted average is computed of the best and worst outcomes, with the weights being the optimism–pessimism coefficient for the best outcome, and 1 minus that coefficient for the worst. Suppose that, in this case, the decision maker feels quite buoyant and assigns a slightly optimistic value of 0.6 to the coefficient. Then, the following computation indicates that the optimal course of action is A_1. He does

Course of Action	Maximum	Weight	Minimum	Weight	Weighted Average
A_1	90	.6	20	.4	$54 + 8 = 62$
A_2	30	.6	25	.4	$18 + 10 = 28$
A_3	100	.6	0	.4	$60 + 0 = 60$
A_4	75	.6	17	.4	$45 + 6.8 = 51.8$

not feel quite optimistic enough to chance the zero payoff possible with A_3 in exchange for the higher maximum of that course of action. Presumably one should be able to estimate the value of his personal optimism–pessimism coefficient by exposing himself to a matrix such as, for example, the following abbreviation of Figure 1–12.1.

	Maximum	Minimum
A_1	90	20
A_3	100	0

Then, if he prefers A_1, he might ask which he would prefer if, instead of 100, the maximum payoff for A_3 were 105, or 110, or 115, etc. If he found that, at, say, 120, i.e., with the following matrix,

	Maximum	Minimum
A_1	90	20
A_3	120	0

he was indifferent between A_1 and A_3, then his optimism–pessimism coefficient could be computed as follows, letting c be the value of the coefficient:

$$\begin{aligned} \text{Desirability of } A_1 &= \text{Desirability of } A_3 \\ 90c + 20(1 - c) &= 120c + 0 \\ 20 - 20c &= 30c \\ 50c &= 20 \\ c &= 0.4 \end{aligned}$$

His optimism–pessimism index would then be 0.4. He does not feel very lucky.

Minimax regret. Another criterion suggests that what we might really worry about is how bad we might feel afterwards when we see what we might have done if we had only known enough to do the right thing. To use this criterion, which has been associated with the name of L. J. Savage, a *"regret"* matrix is computed from the original matrix by examining each *column* in turn. Starting with the first column, B_1, we ask, what is the best possible outcome if B_1 occurs? That is 75 in cell 41. If B_1 occurs, we will be most satisfied (least regretful) if we have chosen A_4. Thus, the amount of regret associated with cell 41 is zero. However, if B_1 should occur, and A_4 has not been chosen, there will be regret, and this regret may be measured by the difference between the actual payoff and the optimum payoff in that column. Similarly, each column is examined in turn, and, in each, zero is entered in the cell where the maximum payoff for that column occurs. Then the difference between that maximum value and the actual cell payoffs is entered in the other cells. The resulting regret matrix, derived from the payoff matrix of Figure 1–12.1, is shown in Figure 1–12.2.

	B_1	B_2	B_3	B_4
A_1	50	40	0	80
A_2	48	34	60	75
A_3	75	15	22	0
A_4	0	0	73	50

Fig. 1–12.2. Regret matrix. Derived from payoff matrix of Figure 1–12.1.

Each course of action, A_i, is now examined to find the maximum regret associated with that A_i. These maxima are:

A_i	Maximum Regret
A_1	80
A_2	75
A_3	75
A_4	73

Use of this criterion would lead to the selection of A_4, since that course of action exposes the decision maker to the least possible regret, i.e., the minimum of the maximum regret values, the minimax regret.

We shall have occasion later, in Section 7–12, to return to the concept of the regret matrix and derive very useful results.

Equal likelihood. Another solution which might be applied when there is complete ignorance about the likelihood of the various states of nature is to assume that the various states of nature are all equally likely. Then the choice would fall to that course of action whose simple arithmetic average (or sum) is greatest. In this case, A_3 would be selected. This criterion, based on the so-called "principle of insufficient reason," i.e., that there is no reason to believe that one event is more likely than another, has been associated with the name of Laplace.

It is possible to raise serious questions about each of these criteria for decision making under complete ignorance.[1] For example in the payoff matrix of Figure 1–12.1, if the payoffs in cells 13, 34, and 41, which are now 90, 100, and 75, respectively, were increased to very large numbers (thousands or millions), A_2 would still be selected under the maximin criterion, since its minimum is still largest. Luce and Raiffa point out that, even with the following matrix,

	B_1	B_2
A_1	.000001	.000001
A_2	0	1,000,000

the maximin criterion would lead to selection of A_1. This may seem unreasonable in the eyes of some.

The equal-likelihood criterion may be attacked and, in the eyes of some, demolished, by a simple *reductio ad absurdum* example such as the following involving rain or shine on the day of the departmental picnic. If we have absolutely no prior knowledge about the weather, and if we consider just two states of nature: rain and no rain, as shown in the upper diagram of Figure 1–12.3, then the equal-likelihood criterion says that the probability of each is 0.5. However, we might have described the problem by saying that there might be: no rain, light rain, moderate rain, or heavy rain, as shown in the lower diagram of Figure 1–12.3. Now, the equal-likelihood criterion says that the probability of no rain is 0.25, and the optimal course of action is A_2, *no picnic.* Obviously, we can further subdivide the possible rain types and thereby reduce to a very small number the probability of no rain, according to the equal-likelihood criterion. Thus, we can reduce the probability of one of the states of nature and make it as small as we wish merely by redefining the other states of nature. Clearly, the probabilities of the individual states of nature under the equal-likelihood criterion depend upon how the other states of nature are defined, and they are therefore not a valid basis for decision. Consequently, this equal-likelihood criterion is valueless in decision making.

[1] See, for example, the excellent treatment in R. D. Luce and H. Raiffa, *Games and Decisions* (New York: John Wiley & Sons, Inc., 1957), pp. 278–86.

Under complete ignorance of the likelihood of the states of nature, the two matrices of Figure 1–12.3 *are identical, and can be treated so;* and if

	Shine	Rain
A_1 Picnic	100	−200
A_2 No Picnic	−120	−5

	Shine	Heavy Rain	Mod. Rain	Light Rain
A_1 Picnic	100	−200	−200	−200
A_2 No Picnic	−120	−5	−5	−5

Fig. 1–12.3. Two decision matrices, which, under complete ignorance, are equivalent.

the reader refuses to accept this statement, that is evidence that he has some idea of the likelihood or relative likelihood of the various states of nature, and that he is not really faced with a decision problem under complete ignorance. If he does have such information, then he can use that information in ways we shall describe later.

Mixed strategies. In some complete ignorance situations the decision maker may find that, under certain assumptions about probabilities and about his preference patterns, he may prefer to select his course of action by tossing a coin or by using some other chance process. In that case he may be said to be following a *mixed strategy,* in that he is accepting a probabilistic mixture of two or more courses of action in which the final selection of the actual course of action to be adopted is subject to chance and therefore beyond his control.

We shall see that this concept of a *mixed strategy* arises is game theory. We shall defer discussion of this until we have discussed probabilities, and we shall consider it at length in later chapters on game theory and decision theory (Chapters 18 and 19).

Each of these criteria for decision making under complete ignorance is open to some attack; and, in the somewhat contrived example of Figure 1–12.1, each of the possible courses of action is selected by at least one of the criteria. Clearly, the solution to a problem of decision making under complete ignorance may be different for different decision makers, since it is deeply influenced by personal psychological attitudes or by policy considerations for decision makers within business, governmental, or other organizations.

Obviously, if ever faced with a decision problem under complete ignorance, the decision maker should, if the time and cost involved is not prohibitive, try to escape from this unfortunate position by acquiring information which will transform the problem into one of decision making under certainty. If he cannot obtain such *certain* information, he can try, by the use of statistical methods we shall examine later, to obtain whatever partial information he can and use that information to transform the problem into a problem of decision making under risk. Of course, he must balance the cost of acquiring the information against its expected value.

1–13. Models and Forecasting. We have noted above that *the purpose of the model is to predict.* That is, the model enables the investigator to predict the outcome, the value of the objective function, for various configurations of the controllable and uncontrollable inputs. We cannot leave this subject without emphasizing the risks inherent in any predictions over time.

Any prediction over time, or *forecast,* assumes persistence or stability of some one or more relationships. That is, an unsophisticated manager may forecast that tomorrow's or next year's sales will be the same as today's or this year's. A more sophisticated analyst may measure the change from year to year for the past several years, average these in some way, and forecast by assuming that this *average annual change* will persist. He might, alternatively, assume that the observed average *rate of change* will persist. He may be even more sophisticated and observe that the rate of change has been increasing at some observable rate, and then he might decide to forecast next year's or the next several years' sales on the basis of the assumption that the rate of change of the rate of change (the second derivative, as we shall see in Chapter 2) will persist.

If he is forecasting by the use of some mathematical model, such as those which we shall study in this book, or a statistical regression model, then, in order for the forecast to make sense, two conditions must be met. First, he must be able to forecast the uncontrollable input variables satisfactorily, and second, the relationships described in the model of the system must persist. That is the system must be stable in the sense that the observed interrelationships among the variables will persist over the forecast period.

Thus, any time an analyst prepares a forecast, he must not only have built a proper model of the system, but he must also ask himself what persistence assumptions about values of variables and about interrelationships are intrinsic to his forecast. And then *he must assess the reasonableness of those persistence assumptions.*

This must be given serious thought. Unfortunately, none of us has a valid crystal ball. We can only analyze the past and the present. The future is never visible. We can forecast for the future *only by assuming that some observed relationships of the present and the past will persist into the future.* There is no sure, objective, scientific way to select from all of the infinite number of possible persistence hypotheses that hypothesis which correctly identifies what will truly persist into the future. This is an important area for the application of the experience and judgment of the analyst or decision maker.

We shall now leave for a while the problems of decision theory, and, in the next chapters, we shall discuss and apply various subjects in mathematics and probability theory.

SUGGESTIONS FOR FURTHER READING

Ackoff, R. L. "The Meaning, Scope, and Methods of Operations Research," Chapter 1 in *Progress in Operations Research,* Vol. 1 (R. L. Ackoff, ed.). New York: John Wiley & Sons, Inc., 1961.

Ackoff, R. L., and Rivett, P. *A Manager's Guide to Operations Research.* New York: John Wiley & Sons, Inc., 1963.

Boulding, K. E. "The Ethics of Rational Decision," *Management Science,* 12: 161–69. (February, 1966).

Bross, I. D. J. *Design for Decision.* New York: The Macmillan Co., Publishers, 1953.

Miller, D. W., and M. K. Starr. *Executive Decisions and Operations Research,* Parts 1 and 2. Englewood Cliffs, N.J.: Prentice-Hall, Inc., 1960.

Shuchman, A. (ed.). *Scientific Decision Making in Business,* Parts 1 and 2. New York: Holt, Rinehart & Winston, Inc., 1963.

2

Introduction to Differential Calculus

2–1. Introduction. In the last chapter it was pointed out that management science is concerned with analyzing decision problems within a system by the manipulation of symbolic models of the system. Therefore, the first problem of the researcher is to create a model which adequately represents reality. This model must relate the three major elements: (1) the objectives of the decision maker, (2) the variables subject to his control, and (3) the variables over which he has no control. We represented this in the symbolic form, $O = f(x_i,y_j)$ where O is the *outcome* determined by the interaction of the controllable variables (x_i) and uncontrollable variables (y_j). The solution to the decision problem is the best combination of controllable inputs to gain the "best" possible outcome. The problem statement must thus include an objective function which enables us to compare alternative outcomes and choose the most desirable effect. This is the value or "effectiveness" function, E, where E is some measure which describes the effectiveness of the outcomes in achieving the goal. We, therefore, attempt to optimize the value of E. Of course, E is some function of O; i.e. $E = g(O)$, where g represents some mathematical relationship. Once this relationship is established, it can be incorporated into the system model, and the general formulation can be restated in the form,

$$E = f(x_i,y_j). \tag{2–1.1}$$

In most situations in this book, we shall assume that the effectiveness measure is linear with respect to its utility. For example, in the case of profit in dollars, we shall assume that n dollars is exactly n times as desirable as one dollar.

2–2. Continuous and Discrete Models. Clearly, a model of a system in the form of Equation (2–1.1) enables us to predict the value of E for various values of the x_i. If, for example, E is profit, represented by the symbol P, and if the single controllable variable in the system under study is the advertising budget, x, then, if the values of all of the relevant uncontrollable variables are known, the model is in the form

$$P = f(x) \tag{2–2.1}$$

and if our purpose is to secure the maximum profit, then we must find the value of x which will maximize P. In such a situation, the input, x, and the output, P, may usually be regarded as *continuous*, that is, they may take any value. The contrary situation, i.e. *discrete*, would exist if advertising could be purchased only in discrete packages of, say, a million dollars, and then the possible courses of action would be: no advertising, $1,000,000, $2,000,000, $3,000,000, etc.

Discrete Courses of Action	
A_1	0
A_2	1,000,000
A_3	2,000,000
.	3,000,000
.	.
.	.
.	.

In a *continuous*-decision situation, there is a large number of courses of action, each of which is some numerical value of the controllable input variable, and, over some range of values, *any* specific value may be selected; i.e., the best advertising budget may be $3,456,822, and this would be an admissible result (although, for convenience, one would normally round such an answer to the nearest hundred or thousand dollars). Thus, in the familiar matrix representation of a decision problem, a continuous case may be regarded as corresponding to a matrix with a very large number of rows (possible courses of action).

In continuous models generally, both the input and the output variables are continuous, as in the advertising-vs.-profit model or the lot-size-vs.-total-cost model of Chapter 1. In such cases, there is often some minimum or maximum value of the output variable, and the analyst seeks to find the value of the input variable which is associated with that point. Figure 2–5.1 illustrates both of these types of situation.

In the case of a discrete-decision situation under certainty, i.e., when the state of nature is known, the optimal course of action is that which yields the best value of the objective function; and this may usually be found readily by evaluating the various courses of action. However, this is not possible in the continuous case. There, some mathematical or computational technique is necessary to select that value of the controllable input which corresponds to the optimum value of the objective function.

A mathematical technique for finding the optimal course of action in such continuous models is differential calculus. The next several sections of this chapter will present a brief discussion of the mathematics necessary to solve these problems. Readers who have studied differential calculus and feel no need for review may skip these sections, or may perhaps leaf rapidly through these sections to assure themselves that they have adequate command of these materials.

2–3. Review of Mathematics—Graphs, Functions, Slopes. We shall begin our brief treatment of differential calculus by considering *graphs of functions*. Using the familiar *cartesian coordinate axes*, in which the *x-axis* is the horizontal axis and the *y-axis* is the vertical axis, we may plot any point, if we know its x-coordinate, its *abscissa*, and its y-coordinate, its *ordinate*. In the graph of Figure 2–3.1, we have plotted the points

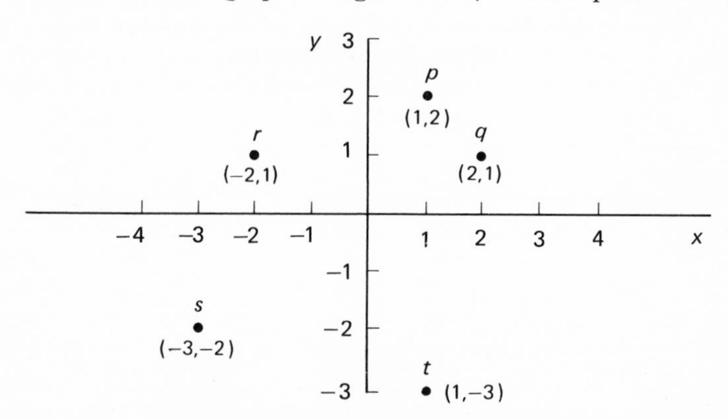

Fig. 2–3.1. Two-dimensional graph.

p: (1,2); q: (2,1); r: (−2,1); s: (−3,−2) and t: (1,−3). In examining the figure, several features should be noted.

1. On a graph, the scales are not necessarily the same on both axes. Here, they are. We shall find that, often, not only the scales, but also the *units* or *dimensions* are quite different, as, for example in Figure 1–2.3, where the vertical axis is cost, in dollars, and the horizontal axis is lot size, in number of items produced.
2. Each point may be identified by its coordinates, written as an

ordered pair, (x,y), with the x-coordinate (abscissa) always written first.

3. The point (0,0) at the intersection of the two axes is called the *origin*.
4. To the left of the y-axis, the x-value is negative, and below the x-axis, the y-value is negative.

A *function* may be defined as *a set or collection of ordered pairs* (x,y), *such that, for each x-value, there is one and only one y-value.* Alternatively, and, perhaps, more technically, a function may be defined as *a rule of correspondence from one set* (x) *to another set* (y). This second definition will be more meaningful later, after reading the introductory material on set notation in Section 4–3. A specific function may be represented by a complete list of the ordered pairs which it represents (of course, a *complete* list would not be feasible for a continuous function, since such a list would have to be infinitely long), or it is much more easily represented by an equation, such as, for example, $y = x$, or $y = 3 + 2x$, or $y = 3x^2$. Each of these three specific functions represents y as some function of x, and, as seen in Table 2–3.1, each function represents an infinitely large set of ordered pairs.

TABLE 2–3.1

Three Simple Functions and Some of the Ordered Pairs Which Each Represents

$y = x$	$y = 3 + 2x$	$y = 3x^2$
(0, 0)	(0, 3)	(0, 0)
(0.125, 0.125)	(0.125, 3.250)	(0.125, 0.046875)
(1, 1)	(1, 5)	(1, 3)
(2, 2)	(2, 7)	(2, 12)
(3, 3)	(3, 9)	(3, 27)
.	.	.
.	.	.
.	.	.
(10, 10)	(10, 23)	(10, 300)
(235, 235)	(235, 473)	(235, 165,675)
.	.	.
.	.	.
.	.	.
(−1, −1)	(−1, 1)	(−1, 3)
(−10, −10)	(−10, −17)	(−10, 300)
(−15.75, −15.75)	(−15.75, −28.50)	(−15.75, 744.1875)
.	.	.
.	.	.
.	.	.
(−350, −350)	(−350, −697)	(−350, 367,500)
.	.	.
.	.	.
.	.	.

The ordered pairs are computed by selecting any real number as the first number, i.e. x-value, and then computing the y-value from the selected x-value, using the equation for the function.

Obviously, it is not possible to list all of the ordered pairs which are represented by these continuous functions, nor is it even possible to list all of the ordered pairs within a small range of values, i.e., between $x = 1$ and $x = 2$.

We can represent these functions by graphs, as seen in Figure 2–3.2. In that figure, each curve, even within the relatively small segment

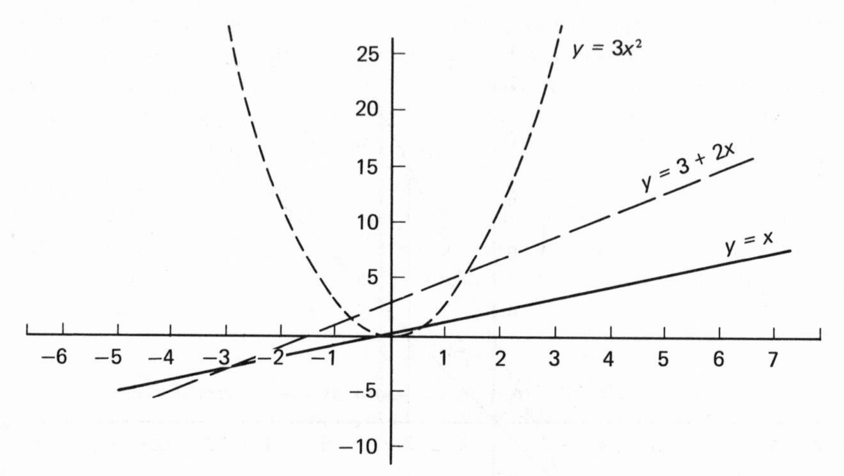

Fig. 2–3.2. Graphs of functions.

shown, represents an infinite number of points, or ordered pairs, each of which, of course, satisfies the equation describing the respective function.

It is convenient and customary to represent a function by a letter, most commonly the letter f. Then the statement "y is a function of x" may be written in general form

$$y = f(x) \tag{2–3.1}$$

and the function represented by Equation (2–3.1) may be any specific function, such as: $y = x$, $y = 3 + 2x$, $y = 3x^2$, or any of an infinite variety of functions of x.

The specific functions $y = x$ and $y = 3 + 2x$ are, as seen in Figure 2–3.2, *straight lines*. That is, the sets of points which represent the functions defined by those equations lie, respectively, on straight lines. The general formula for a straight line function is

$$y = a + bx \tag{2–3.2}$$

where a is the *y-intercept*, i.e., *the value of y when x is zero;* and b is the *slope* of the line, i.e., the *amount by which y changes as x increases by 1 unit.*

In the equation $y = x$, a, the y-intercept, is zero, and b, the slope, is 1. That is, this equation, expressed in the form of equation (2–3.2), is

$$y = 0 + 1x$$

This indicates that the line passes through the origin (0,0) and that, if x is increased by 1 unit, y is increased by 1 unit. This may be verified on Figure 2–3.3, which shows the same graphs as Figure 2–3.2, but on a

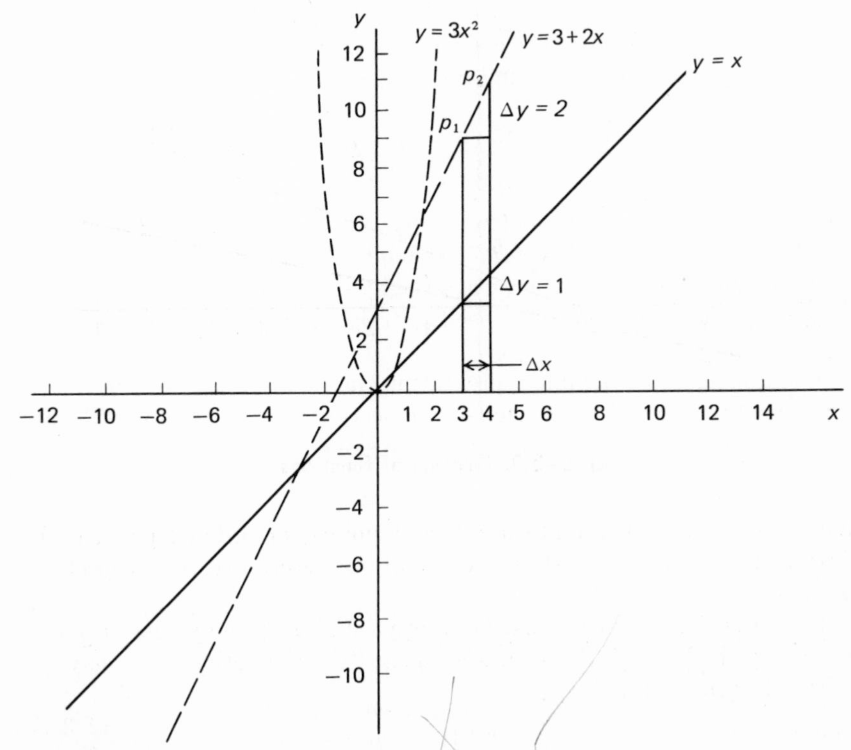

Fig. 2–3.3. Graphs of functions. The same functions as in Figure 2–3.2. Here the units are the same size on both axes.

different scale. In Figure 2–3.3 the units are represented by equal distances on both axes to facilitate visual verification of these comments.

In the equation, $y = 3 + 2x$, the y-intercept is 3, and the slope is 2, indicating that the line passes through the point (0,3), and, for each unit increase in x, y increases by 2. This also may be verified visually in Figure 2–3.3.

It is customary to represent a difference between two specific values by the capital Greek letter *delta*, Δ. That is, if, at one point, $y = 9$, and at another point, $y = 11$, we would say that, between these two points, the difference in the y-values is 2, or $\Delta y = 2$. On the graphs of Figure 2–3.3, vertical lines have been erected at $x = 3$ and $x = 4$. Obviously, in this interval, $\Delta x = 1$. For this same interval, $\Delta y = 1$ on the lower graph where $y = x$ and $\Delta y = 2$ on the upper graph where $y = 3 + 2x$. Let us define the *slope of the line segment between two points* as

$$\text{slope} = \frac{\Delta y}{\Delta x} = \frac{y_2 - y_1}{x_2 - x_1} \tag{2–3.3}$$

On the upper line, we may identify the point p_1 by its coordinates (x_1,y_1), which are (3,9) and p_2 by its coordinates (x_2,y_2), which are (4,11). Then $\Delta x = x_2 - x_1 = 4 - 3 = 1$ and $\Delta y = y_2 - y_1 = 11 - 9 = 2$. The slope of the line, then, is

$$b = \text{slope} = \frac{y_2 - y_1}{x_2 - x_1} = \frac{\Delta y}{\Delta x} = \frac{2}{1} = 2$$

and the slope of the straight line connecting these two points is 2. *For a straight line, the slope is constant throughout.* Indeed, this is the basic distinguishing characteristic of a straight line. That is, if we take any interval at any location on a specific straight line, the slope will always be the same.

Looking again at the line representing the function $y = 3 + 2x$, let us consider the interval between the intersection with the y-axis (0,3) and the point p_2 (4,11). In that interval, the slope is, of course, also 2.

$$\text{slope} = \frac{\Delta y}{\Delta x} = \frac{11 - 3}{4 - 0} = \frac{8}{4} = 2$$

In using Equation (2–3.3), it does not matter which of the two points is considered to be the first and which the second. However, it is extremely important that this choice be consistent; that is, the point which is considered first in the numerator, must be first in the denominator. If this is not done, the sign of the slope will be wrong. It is convenient to select the points so that Δx is positive, and then the sign of Δy gives the sign of b. That convention is followed throughout this volume.

The slope may be positive or negative or zero, depending on the signs of Δx and Δy. If y increases as x increases, then Δx and Δy are both positive and the slope is positive. If, however, y decreases as x increases, then Δy is negative when Δx is positive, and the slope is negative. This is the case in the curve for the function described by the equation, $y = 3x^2$, in the region to the left of the y-axis. A slope of zero means that Δy is zero, or the curve is horizontal. A vertical curve may be said to have a very steep (infinite) slope, but this is not important. We shall soon see that, for our purposes, zero slopes are of great interest and importance.

For example, in Figure 2–3.1, the slope of the line connecting points p and q is negative.

$$b = \text{slope} = \frac{\Delta y}{\Delta x} = \frac{y_q - y_p}{x_q - x_p} = \frac{1 - 2}{2 - 1} = \frac{-1}{1} = -1$$

This indicates that, as x increases, y decreases, or that the line slopes downward to the right. Of course, the slope of the line connecting points r and t is also negative. There the slope has the value

$$b = \frac{-3 - 1}{1 - (-2)} = \frac{-4}{3} = -\frac{4}{3}$$

It should be evident that, if we are given the coordinates of two points, it is a very simple matter to compute the equation for the straight line on which they lie. The slope, or b-value, may be found as demonstrated above, by use of Equation (2–3.3). Then the a-value may be found by the use of the same equation, with one of the points the intersection between the line and the y-axis. The coordinates of that point are, of course, $(0,a)$. Either of the other two points may be used.

$$\text{slope} = \frac{y - a}{x - 0} \qquad (2\text{–}3.4)$$

For example, we found that, for the line connecting the points p and q on Figure 2–3.1, the slope is -1. Then, using the y-intercept and point p and the fact that the slope is constant throughout, Equation (2–3.4) yields

$$-1 = \frac{2 - a}{1 - 0}$$

$$a = 3$$

and the equation for the line through points p and q is

$$y = 3 - x$$

Similarly, the line between points t and q in Figure 2–3.1 may be computed. From Equation (2–3.3),

$$b = \frac{y_q - y_t}{x_q - x_t} = \frac{1 - (-3)}{2 - 1} = 4$$

Then, from Equation (2–3.4), using point t,

$$4 = \frac{-3 - a}{1}$$

$$a = -7$$

and the equation for the line on which points t and q lie is

$$y = -7 + 4x$$

There is another, often simpler, method for finding the equation for a straight line, given two points which lie on that line. The procedure is to write two equations in the form of Equation (2–3.2), using the x-value and y-value for one of the given points in each equation. These two equations may then be solved simultaneously for a and b.

For example, to find the straight line on which lie the points t, $(1, -3)$ and q, $(2,1)$, the general equation is

$$y = a + bx \tag{2–3.2}$$

For Point t

$$-3 = a + 1b$$

and for Point q

$$1 = a + 2b$$

Solving these equations simultaneously by subtracting the first from the second:

$$\begin{array}{r} -3 = a + b \\ 1 = a + 2b \\ \hline 4 = 0 + b \end{array}$$

$$b = 4$$

Then substituting this value of b into the first equation (either equation could be used) yields

$$-3 = a + 4$$

$$a = -7$$

and the desired equation is again found to be

$$y = -7 + 4x$$

2–4. Slopes of Curves—Limits. On any straight line, the slope is constant throughout, but conversely, *if a line is not straight, it does not have the same slope throughout.* Visual examination of the graph for $y = 3x^2$ indicates that the curve becomes steeper as it moves farther away from the y-axis in either direction. The variation in the slope can be illustrated algebraically. Consider the points: $(1,3)$, $(2,12)$, $(3,27)$, and $(4,48)$, all of which lie on that curve as seen in Figure 2–4.1, which again shows the graph of the function $y = 3x^2$, but on a scale which is expanded horizontally.

These points have been labeled: p_1, p_2, p_3, and p_4, respectively. In the

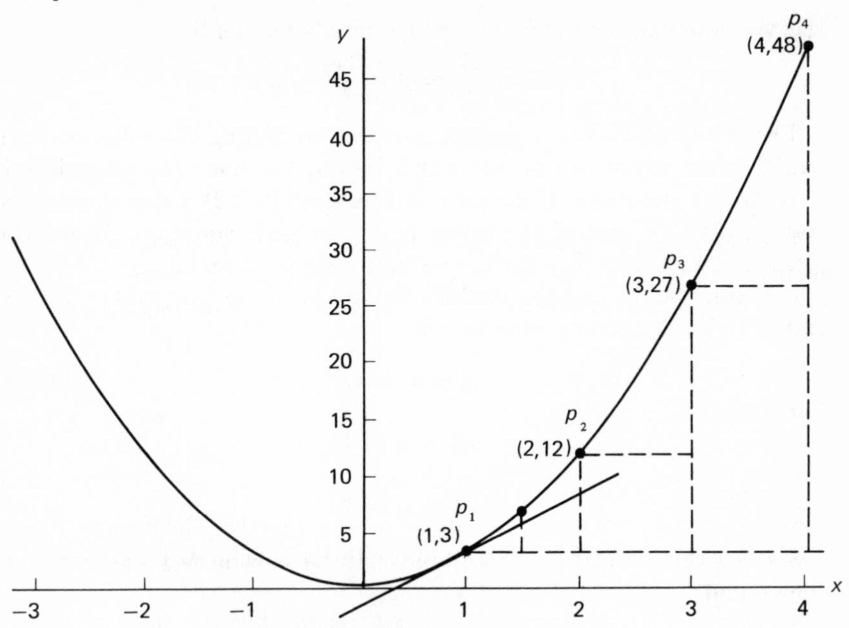

Fig. 2–4.1. Graph of function, $y = 3x^2$.

interval between p_1 and p_2 the *average* slope is

$$\text{slope} = \frac{\Delta y}{\Delta x} = \frac{12 - 3}{2 - 1} = \frac{9}{1} = 9$$

while between p_3 and p_4, the *average* slope is

$$\text{slope} = \frac{\Delta y}{\Delta x} = \frac{48 - 27}{4 - 3} = \frac{21}{1} = 21$$

The slope is changing at every point, and the formula of Equation (2–3.3) which is used here,

$$\text{slope} = \frac{\Delta y}{\Delta x} = \frac{y_2 - y_1}{x_2 - x_1} \tag{2–3.3}$$

can yield only the *average* slope between two points. We cannot use that formula, as it is given there, to compute the slope of the curve *at* some specified point, say p_1. We can only compute the average slope in some finite interval. If we want to compute the slope *at* p_1, we can *approach* that result by selecting smaller and smaller intervals and computing the slope of the straight lines over these respective intervals.

In the range p_1 to p_4

$$\text{slope} = \frac{\Delta y}{\Delta x} = \frac{48 - 3}{4 - 1} = \frac{45}{3} = 15$$

In the range p_1 to p_3

$$\text{slope} = \frac{27 - 3}{3 - 1} = \frac{24}{2} = 12$$

In the range p_1 to p_2

$$\text{slope} = \frac{12 - 3}{2 - 1} = 9$$

The average slope is smaller as the second point moves closer to p_1. In the interval from p_1 to the point on the curve half way between p_1 and p_2, horizontally, we should expect the average slope to be smaller than 9. Indeed it is. At that point,

$$y = 3x^2 = 3(1.5)^2 = 3(2.25) = 6.75$$

$$\text{slope} = \frac{\Delta y}{\Delta x} = \frac{6.75 - 3.0}{1.5 - 1.0} = \frac{3.75}{0.5} = 7.50$$

As we move the second point closer to p_1, we *approach* the desired value (the slope *at* p_1), but we can not compute the true value *at* p_1, because, at a single point, there is no Δx or Δy.

The slope of the curve at a point is therefore not the slope of a line connecting two points on the curve, rather, *the slope of the curve at a point is the slope of the straight line which is tangent to the curve at that point.* And the tangent at any point is, of course, the line which just touches the curve at that point.

That slope is the *limit* which the ratio $\frac{\Delta y}{\Delta x}$ *approaches as* Δx becomes infinitesimally small and *approaches* zero. We use the symbol $\frac{dy}{dx}$ to represent this limit.

$$\frac{dy}{dx} = \lim_{\Delta x \to 0} \frac{\Delta y}{\Delta x} \tag{2–4.1}$$

Equation (2–4.1) is to be read "The limit which the ratio $\frac{\Delta y}{\Delta x}$ approaches, as Δx approaches zero, is $\frac{dy}{dx}$." Further, $\frac{dy}{dx}$ is called "*the derivative of* y *with respect to* x."

The derivative $\frac{dy}{dx}$ is the slope of a curve at any specific point. It is the *rate of change of* y *with respect to* x. For example, if, for a moving body, y is the distance traveled, and x is the elapsed time, $\frac{dy}{dx}$ is the *speed.*

It is important to note that the limit, as Δx approaches zero, of the ratio $\frac{\Delta y}{\Delta x}$ can be a finite number. One might be tempted to conclude in haste that, as the denominator approaches zero, the ratio becomes infinitely large. This would, of course, be the case if the numerator were a constant, such as, say 5. Then, surely,

$$\lim_{\Delta x \to 0} \frac{5}{\Delta x} = \infty$$

However, in the ratio $\frac{\Delta y}{\Delta x}$, as Δx becomes very small, Δy also becomes very small, since y is a function of x, and the ratio can approach closer and closer to some finite number. Suppose the value of Δy is

$$\Delta y = 5\Delta x$$

then

$$\lim_{\Delta x \to 0} \frac{\Delta y}{\Delta x} = \lim_{\Delta x \to 0} \frac{5\Delta x}{\Delta x} \tag{2–4.2}$$

Let us think for a moment about this limit. Clearly the limit must be 5, since we can cancel Δx from numerator and denominator, and then

$$\lim_{\Delta x \to 0} \frac{\Delta y}{\Delta x} = \lim_{\Delta x \to 0} 5 = 5 \tag{2–4.3}$$

Clearly, since 5 is not a function of Δx, any change in the size of Δx does not affect it. It is still 5. Because of the identities in Equations (2–4.2) and (2–4.3), it is obvious that

$$\lim_{\Delta x \to 0} \frac{\Delta y}{\Delta x} = \lim_{\Delta x \to 0} \frac{5\Delta x}{\Delta x} = 5 \tag{2–4.4}$$

The ratio $\frac{5\Delta x}{\Delta x}$ is equal to 5 for any value of Δx except zero. Thus, it of course has this value, 5, as Δx approaches zero, no matter how small Δx becomes. That is, both the numerator and the denominator become extremely small, but the ratio remains equal to 5. Clearly, it is possible for the limit to be finite as the denominator becomes infinitesimally small.

Finally, let us consider an example in which the value of the ratio changes as the limit is approached.

Let

$$\Delta y = (5 + \Delta x)\,\Delta x$$

and let us seek the limit

$$\lim_{\Delta x \to 0} \frac{\Delta y}{\Delta x} = \lim_{\Delta x \to 0} \frac{(5 + \Delta x)\,\Delta x}{\Delta x} \tag{2–4.5}$$

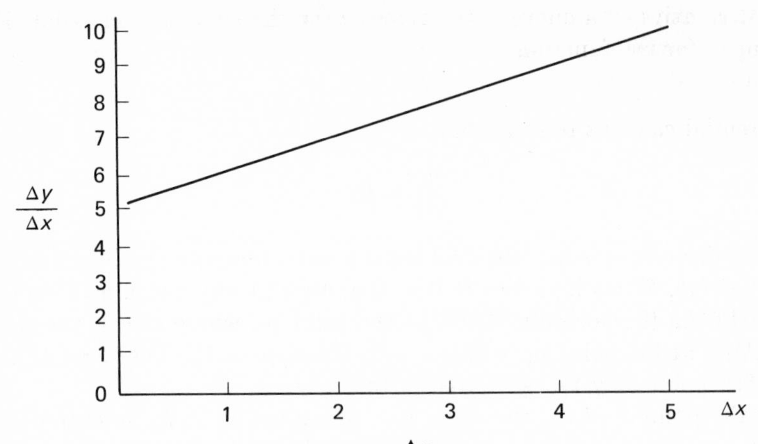

Fig. 2–4.2. Graph of the ratio $\frac{\Delta y}{\Delta x}$, for $\Delta y = (5 + \Delta x)\,\Delta x$.

As long as Δx is not equal to zero, we can cancel it from the numerator and denominator, and then

$$\lim_{\Delta x \to 0} \frac{\Delta y}{\Delta x} = \lim_{\Delta x \to 0} (5 + \Delta x) = 5 \tag{2–4.6}$$

Figure 2–4.2 shows the graph of the ratio $\frac{\Delta y}{\Delta x}$ for values of Δx between zero and 5. This graph may be plotted by solving the equation as given in Equation (2–4.8) for all values of Δx between zero and 5, inclusive.

$$\frac{\Delta y}{\Delta x} = \frac{(5 + \Delta x)\,\Delta x}{\Delta x} \tag{2–4.7}$$

$$\frac{\Delta y}{\Delta x} = 5 + \Delta x \tag{2–4.8}$$

However, if the form of Equation (2–4.7) is used we can solve the equation for all of those same points, *except zero.* Equation (2–4.7) is indeterminate when $\Delta x = 0$. However, we can choose numbers as small as we like and, the smaller the value of Δx, the closer does the ratio *approach* 5.

This concept of the limit is of critical importance in calculus. It enables us to compute the slope of a curve *at a point,* whereas, without this concept, we could speak only of the slope of a straight line segment *between two points.*

For our purposes, this is the essence of differential calculus; namely, that it enables us to compute the slope of a curve at any point. That is, by a process called *differentiation,* we compute the *derivative* of a curve.

The derivative of a curve is the formula for the slope at any point. For example, for the function

$$y = 3x^2$$

differential calculus tells us that

$$\frac{dy}{dx} = 6x$$

i.e., the derivative is $6x$. We shall learn how to compute this result in the next section. What it means is that the slope at any point may be calculated from this formula. Thus, at the point p_1, where $x = 1$, the slope is 6. Also, at the point p_2, where $x = 2$, the slope is 12. The slope at any specified point may be calculated in this way.

At the point $(-1,3)$, the slope is -6, indicating that, at that point, as x increases, y decreases, and the curve slopes downward to the right as the graph of Figure 2–4.1 shows.

The important fact to be noted here is that *the slope is a function of x*, and therefore the slope changes as x changes. *This is the basic characteristic of a curved line.*

In the next section we shall see how, in general, the formula for the slope of a curved line may be derived.

2–5. Differential Calculus. Before examining the procedure for finding the slope of a curve, let us take a moment to see how this procedure may be used in management science and why it is so very important. We saw in the first chapter that many systems may be described by mathematical models which have a maximum or a minimum value of the objective function at some value of a controllable input. For example, in Figure 2–5.1, there are two illustrations of such *optimization* models. In graph (a), the familiar inventory or economic lot size model is shown.

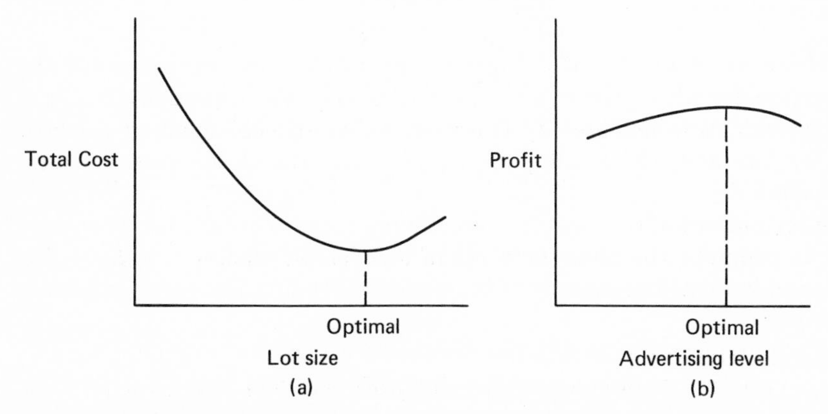

Fig. 2–5.1. Optimization models in management science.

If the lot size is smaller than the optimal, the setup costs are too high, and if the lot size is larger than the optimal, the holding costs are too high. At the optimal, these two costs are balanced. But how can we find the optimal lot size?

In graph (b), the model is the familiar diminishing returns model of economics. As one input factor—here, advertising level—is increased, it makes a positive contribution to overall profit, but, as the amount of this factor is increased, eventually its contribution decreases relative to its cost, and there is some optimal value, beyond which its contribution to profit is negative. But how do we find this optimal level?

Looking at Figure 2–5.1(a), we see that the slope of the curve is negative to the left of the optimal point and positive to the right. At the optimal point, the slope is zero, and a tangent line drawn at that point would be horizontal. Similarly, in graph (b), the slope of the curve is zero at the optimal point.

The importance of differential calculus is that it enables us to compute the formula for the slope of the curve and, from that formula, to compute the value of the input variable at which the slope (the derivative) is equal to zero. That value is, in models such as those shown in Figure 2–5.1, the optimal value of the input variable. It corresponds to the minimum or the maximum value—called the *extreme* value—of the dependent or output variable; the objective function.

Since there are many models in management science which are such optimization models, i.e., characterized by an extreme value of the output variable associated with some optimal value of the controllable input variable, differential calculus is of great importance in management science. It leads directly and simply to the optimal solution. Let us now investigate the process whereby the derivative—the formula for the slope of the curve—is obtained.

We recall from the previous section that the definition of the derivative is

$$\frac{dy}{dx} = \lim_{\Delta x \to 0} \frac{\Delta y}{\Delta x} \qquad (2\text{–}4.1)$$

This is to be interpreted to mean that the slope of a curve at any point is the limit which is approached by the ratio $\frac{\Delta y}{\Delta x}$ as Δx becomes infinitesimally small.

In order to illustrate the procedure which we shall apply, let us look at the familiar function

$$y = 3x^2$$

A part of this curve is plotted in Figure 2–5.2. The scales are not shown on the axes since this segment shown may be at any point on the entire

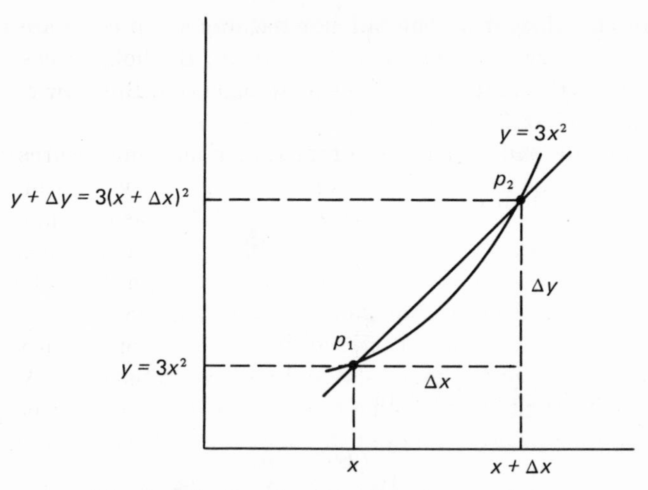

Fig. 2–5.2. Graph of the function $y = 3x^2$.

curve. The point p_1 has the coordinates (x,y) or $(x, 3x^2)$ as shown in the diagram. The point p_2 is very close to p_1. Its coordinates are $(x + \Delta x, y + \Delta y)$ or, as shown in the diagram, $(x + \Delta x, 3(x + \Delta x)^2)$.

The slope of the straight line segment between these two points is, as given by Equation (2–3.3),

$$\text{Slope} = \frac{\Delta y}{\Delta x} = \frac{y_2 - y_1}{x_2 - x_1} \tag{2–3.3}$$

$$\text{Slope} = \frac{\Delta y}{\Delta x} = \frac{3(x + \Delta x)^2 - 3x^2}{x + \Delta x - x}$$

$$= \frac{3(x^2 + 2x\,\Delta x + \Delta x^2) - 3x^2}{\Delta x}$$

$$= \frac{3x^2 + 6x\,\Delta x + 3\Delta x^2 - 3x^2}{\Delta x}$$

$$= \frac{6x\,\Delta x + 3\Delta x^2}{\Delta x}$$

Then, since $\Delta x \neq 0$, we can divide the numerator and denominator by Δx:

$$\text{Slope} = \frac{\Delta y}{\Delta x} = 6x + 3\Delta x \tag{2–5.1}$$

This last expression, Equation (2–5.1) is the slope of the straight line segment between the two points, p_1 and p_2. We are interested in the slope *at* point p_1, and that, clearly, is the limit which the slope of the straight line segment approaches as p_2 approaches p_1, or as Δx approaches zero.

This may be obtained by the familiar technique

$$\lim_{\Delta x \to 0} \frac{\Delta y}{\Delta x} = \lim_{\Delta x \to 0} (6x + 3\Delta x) = 6x \tag{2-5.2}$$

This is the desired derivative. From Equation (2-4.1), the derivative is defined as the limit of the ratio, $\frac{\Delta y}{\Delta x}$. Thus, if

$$y = 3x^2$$

then

$$\frac{dy}{dx} = 6x$$

or, it may be stated in the form

$$\frac{d}{dx}(3x^2) = 6x \tag{2-5.3}$$

and Equation (2-5.3) may be read "The derivative of $3x^2$ with respect to x is $6x$." The left side of Equation 2-5.3 may equally correctly be written as $\frac{d(3x^2)}{dx}$, which is an equivalent alternative form.

This result is an illustration of a general rule which itself may be derived by this same procedure, but we shall not derive it here. That rule, which is probably *the single most frequently used statement in calculus*, is

$$\frac{d}{dx}(ax^n) = nax^{n-1} \tag{2-5.4}$$

(See Exercise 2-1 at the end of this chapter.)

The following are some illustrations of applications of Equation (2-5.4)

1. $\frac{d}{dx}(5) = \frac{d}{dx}(5x^0) = (0)5x^{-1} = 0$

2. $\frac{d}{dx}(3x) = 3x^0 = 3$

3. $\frac{d}{dx}(x^2) = 2x$

4. $\frac{d}{dx}(5x^3) = 15x^2$

5. $\frac{d}{dx}(\sqrt{x}) = \frac{d}{dx}(x^{\frac{1}{2}}) = \frac{1}{2}x^{-\frac{1}{2}} = \frac{1}{2\sqrt{x}}$

6. $\frac{d}{dx}\left(\frac{1}{x}\right) = \frac{d}{dx}(x^{-1}) = (-1)x^{-2} = -\frac{1}{x^2}$

It may also be demonstrated by the same procedure that *the derivative of a sum is the sum of the derivatives.* This means that, if we are dealing with a polynomial, we may differentiate each term separately. A few examples follow. These should be verified by the reader.

1. $y = a + bx + cx^2$ $\qquad \dfrac{dy}{dx} = b + 2cx$

2. $y = 3 + 2x$ $\qquad \dfrac{dy}{dx} = 2$

3. $y = 5 + 3x + \dfrac{6}{x}$ $\qquad \dfrac{dy}{dx} = 3 - \dfrac{6}{x^2}$

4. $y = x + \sqrt{x}$ $\qquad \dfrac{dy}{dx} = 1 + \dfrac{1}{2\sqrt{x}}$

5. $y = 0.02x + \dfrac{500{,}000}{x}$ $\qquad \dfrac{dy}{dx} = 0.02 - \dfrac{500{,}000}{x^2}$

This last equation is the same as the equation which we obtained in Chapter 1 in the Courbro Company's economic lot size problem. The curve, as seen in Figure 1–2.3, had a minimum point at some value of x, the lot size. The dependent variable is the cost, and the minimum-cost point corresponds to the optimal lot size. Since the slope is, as seen above,

$$\frac{dy}{dx} = 0.02 - \frac{500{,}000}{x^2} \tag{2–5.5}$$

and since the minimum-cost point is the point at which the curve has a slope of zero, we need only set the derivative equal to zero, and solve for x, the optimal lot size:

$$0 = 0.02 - \frac{500{,}000}{x^2}$$

$$.02x^2 = 500{,}000$$

$$x^2 = 25{,}000{,}000$$

$$x = \pm 5{,}000$$

We discard the negative root, since $-5{,}000$ is not a feasible solution to the problem which we are solving. The positive root is the desired solution then, and the optimal lot size is 5,000 units. At that optimal lot size, the total cost is

$$\begin{aligned} TC &= 0.02x + \frac{500{,}000}{x} \\ &= 0.02(5{,}000) + \frac{500{,}000}{5{,}000} \\ &= 100 + 100 = \$200 \text{ per month} \end{aligned}$$

Note that, at this point, the holding cost and the setup cost are the same, indicating that the optimal point turns out to be at the intersection of the two curves. This is always true for models of this type, consisting of the sum of a straight line and a rectangular hyperbola.

Let us illustrate the general optimization procedure with a problem involving the relationship between advertising level and sales. The Do-Mor Frypan Company is planning its advertising budget for next year. The forecasted sales-to-advertising relationship for next year, at a selling price of \$10 per frypan, is

$$S = 1{,}000{,}000 - \frac{1{,}000{,}000}{x^2} \qquad \text{for } x \geq 1.5 \tag{2–5.6}$$

where: x is the advertising budget in millions of dollars
S is annual sales in units

The production cost in dollars is

$$C = 200{,}000 + 5S$$

indicating that there is a fixed cost of \$200,000 and a unit variable cost of \$5.

The sales-to-advertising relationship indicates, as can be seen in Figure 2–5.3, that there is a maximum possible sales potential of 1,000,000 units,

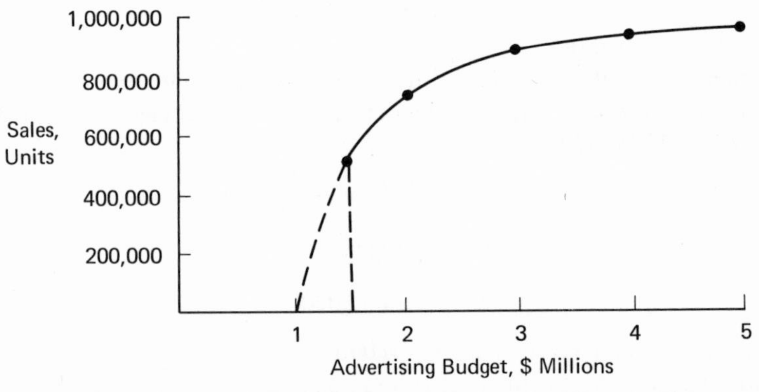

Fig. 2–5.3. Sales vs. advertising for Do-Mor Frypan Co.

but that the advertising cost of reaching this level is prohibitive. Table 2–5.1 indicates that the optimal advertising budget lies somewhere between \$1,500,000 and \$3,000,000. The exact value at the optimal is easily determined by the use of differential calculus:

$$\text{Profit } (P) = \text{Revenue} - \text{production cost} - \text{advertising cost} \tag{2–5.7}$$

$$P = 10S - (200{,}000 + 5S) - 1{,}000{,}000x$$

$$= 10S - 200{,}000 - 5S - 1{,}000{,}000x$$

$$P = -200{,}000 + 5S - 1{,}000{,}000x \tag{2–5.8}$$

TABLE 2–5.1

Do-Mor Frypan Co.
Planning Information

Advertising Budget (dollars) (1)	Sales (units) (2)	Production Costs (dollars) (3)	Revenue (dollars) (4)	Total Cost (1) + (3) (dollars) (5)	Profit (4) – (5) (dollars) (6)
1,500,000	555,556	2,977,780	5,555,560	4,477,780	1,077,780
2,000,000	750,000	3,950,000	7,500,000	5,950,000	1,550,000
3,000,000	888,889	4,644,445	8,888,890	7,644,445	1,244,444
4,000,000	937,500	4,887,500	9,375,000	8,887,500	487,500
5,000,000	960,000	5,000,000	9,600,000	10,000,000	–400,000

Then, using Equation (2–5.6),

$$P = -200{,}000 + 5\left(1{,}000{,}000 - \frac{1{,}000{,}000}{x^2}\right) - 1{,}000{,}000x$$

$$P = 4{,}800{,}000 - \frac{5{,}000{,}000}{x^2} - 1{,}000{,}000x \qquad (2\text{–}5.9)$$

$$\frac{dP}{dx} = \frac{10{,}000{,}000}{x^3} - 1{,}000{,}000 \qquad (2\text{–}5.10)$$

Setting the derivative, $\frac{dP}{dx}$, equal to zero.

$$1{,}000{,}000x^3 = 10{,}000{,}000$$

$$x^3 = 10$$

$$x = 2.1544$$

Thus, the optimal advertising level (to the nearest hundred dollars) is \$2,154,400, and the profit at this level of advertising is, from Equation (2–5.9),

$$P = 4{,}800{,}000 - \frac{5{,}000{,}000}{(2.1544)^2} - 1{,}000{,}000(2.1544)$$

$$= 4{,}800{,}000 - \frac{5{,}000{,}000}{4.6414} - 2{,}154{,}400$$

$$= 4{,}800{,}000 - 1{,}077{,}300 - 2{,}154{,}400$$

$$= \$1{,}568{,}300$$

Thus, the optimal advertising level of \$2,154,400 leads to a profit of \$1,568,300. Any other advertising level will result in a smaller profit.

The profit function, Equation (2–5.9), is plotted in the upper part of

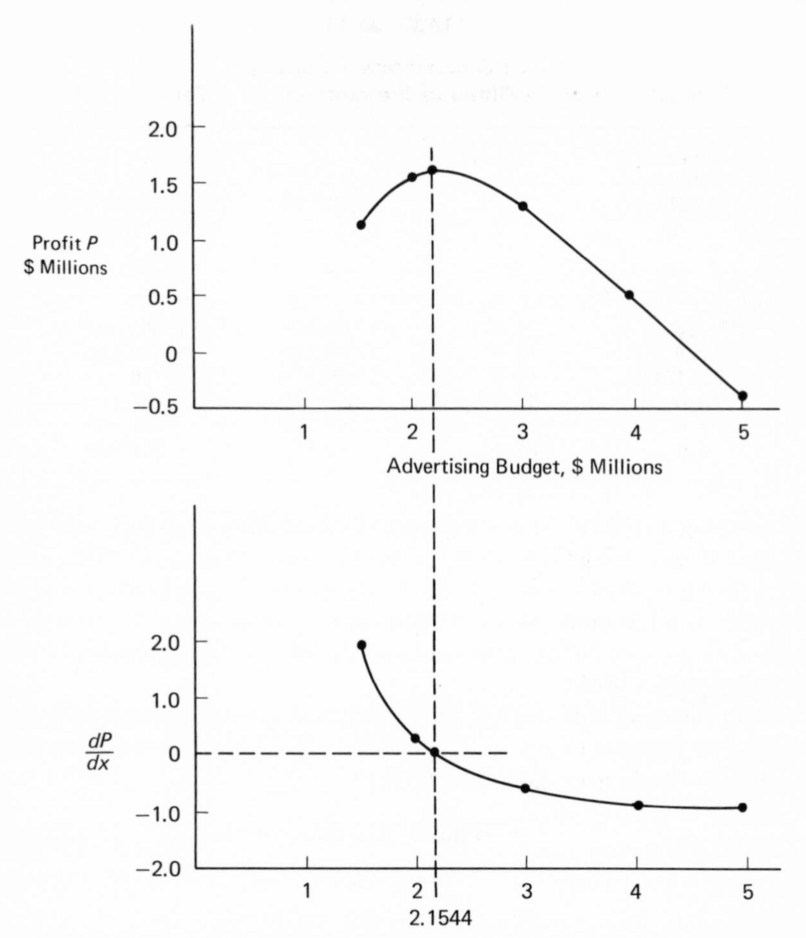

Fig. 2–5.4. Do-Mor Frypan Co. Upper graph: profit function; lower graph: slope of the profit function.

Figure 2–5.4. The data for this graph are seen in Table 2–5.1, Column (6). The lower part of this figure shows the slope of the profit function. At the optimal point, the slope is, of course, zero. The computations for this graph, using Equation (2–5.10), are shown in Table 2–5.2. The slope is decreasing throughout the curve, indicating that, as more advertising is applied, the rate of gain in profit per additional unit of advertising is decreasing, and, after the optimal point, $2,154,400, the "gain" in profit is negative. The numbers which appear in Column (4) of Table 2–5.2 and are plotted in the lower graph are to be interpreted as follows: "If the level of advertising expenditure is lower than the optimal value of $2,154,400, the rate of sales response to increases in advertising expenditure is such that profit (after advertising expenditures) rises as the

TABLE 2–5.2

Do-Mor Frypan Company
Computation of the Slope of the Profit Curve at Selected Points

Advertising Budget ($ millions) x (1)	x^3 (2)	$\frac{10,000,000}{x^3}$ (3)	Slope ((3) − 1,000,000) (4)
1.5	3.375	2,963,000	1,963,000
2.0	8.0	1,250,000	250,000
2.1544	10.0	1,000,000	0
3.0	27.0	370,400	−629,600
4.0	64.0	156,200	−843,800
5.0	125.0	80,000	−920,000

advertising expenditure is increased. This positive and desirable consequence of increasing advertising expenditure continues until that optimal advertising budget is reached. At the optimal point, the net gain is zero; beyond it, additional sales revenues do not compensate for increases in advertising expenditure, and increases in advertising expenditure result in decreases in profits."

Before leaving this section, we introduce a very important and useful variant of Equation (2–4.1). It is actually the form that was used in the derivation leading to Equation (2–5.1).

$$\frac{dy}{dx} = \lim_{\Delta x \to 0} \frac{\Delta y}{\Delta x} \tag{2–4.1}$$

But, if $y = f(x)$, then

$$\Delta y = f(x + \Delta x) - f(x)$$

and

$$\frac{dy}{dx} = \lim_{\Delta x \to 0} \frac{f(x + \Delta x) - f(x)}{\Delta x} \tag{2–5.11}$$

This form of the general definition of the derivative is the basis of the derivations presented below for the development of the derivatives of various functions.

2–6. The Second Derivative. The slope of a curve is zero at three kinds of points: maxima, minima, and points of inflection. (This, of course, does not apply to points of inflection that are *vertically* oriented.) It is often convenient to refer to maxima and minima as "extreme points." Then we can say that a slope of zero may identify either an extreme point or an inflection point. These are shown in Figure 2–6.1.

Sometimes it is necessary to establish that the point is, say, a maximum rather than a minimum. The profit function which we dealt with in the last section had, as is seen in Figure 2–5.4, a maximum and no minimum nor point of inflection, so that we knew that the point of zero slope was the maximum. However, without the graph, we cannot always be sure. When we determine a point of zero slope, we know that we have a point which is either a maximum, a minimum, or a point of inflection, but we do not always know which.

Actually, inflection points are extremely rare in management-science models, and we need not be concerned with them. We can almost always assume that a point of zero slope is an extreme point, but we cannot be sure whether it is a maximum or a minimum.

It is extremely simple mathematically to identify which of the three situations is the true one. Examination of Figure 2–6.1 indicates that, at

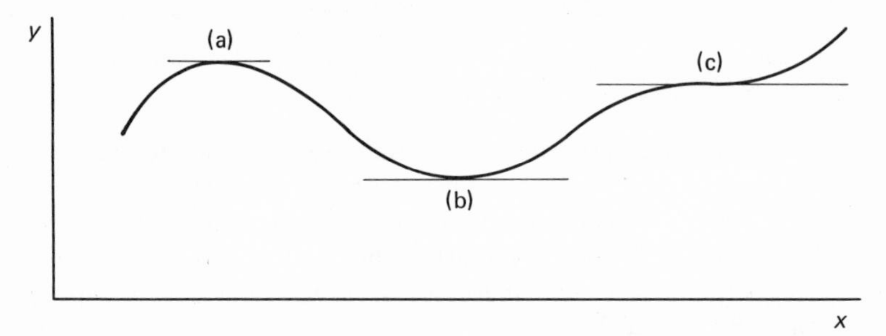

Fig. 2–6.1. Three kinds of situations in which the slope of a curve is zero: (a) maximum, (b) minimum, (c) inflection point.

point (a), the slope is zero and that, just to the left of point (a), a maximum, the slope is positive, but decreasing and, just to the right of point (a), the slope is negative and still decreasing (i.e., becoming more negative). Thus, at point (a), we can conclude that the slope is zero *and decreasing* as x increases. This may be seen in Figure 2–5.4, where the lower curve is the slope of the upper curve, and the upper curve has a maximum. Similarly, the slope at a minimum, such as point (b) of Figure 2–6.1, is *increasing*, and, at a point of inflection such as point (c), the slope itself has a minimum; i.e., it is decreasing as x increases toward point (c), zero at point (c), and increasing as x increases beyond point (c).

The mathematical procedure for distinguishing among these situations involves merely the examination of the slope of the slope. In the case of a maximum, as seen in Figure 2–5.4, the slope is decreasing, and we can say that the slope of the slope is negative. That is, if we compute the slope of the slope, by differentiating the expression for the slope, we should find that the derivative is negative, and indeed we do. This *second derivative* is generally expressed in the form

$$\frac{d}{dx}\left(\frac{dy}{dx}\right) = \frac{d^2y}{dx^2} \tag{2–6.1}$$

and, often, as a simplification, we write

$$\frac{dy}{dx} = y' \quad \text{and} \quad \frac{d^2y}{dx^2} = y'' \tag{2-6.2}$$

Another common and useful symbol form to represent differentiation and derivatives is the use of the *prime* sign to represent the derivative, but to retain the function expression as follows.

$$y = f(x) \tag{2-3.1}$$

$$\frac{dy}{dx} = \frac{d}{dx}(f(x)) = f'(x) \tag{2-6.3}$$

$$\frac{d^2y}{dx^2} = f''(x) \tag{2-6.4}$$

In the case of the profit function of the Do-Mor Company,

$$P = 4{,}800{,}000 - \frac{5{,}000{,}000}{x^2} - 1{,}000{,}000x \tag{2-5.9}$$

$$\frac{dP}{dx} = \frac{10{,}000{,}000}{x^3} - 1{,}000{,}000 \tag{2-5.10}$$

$$\frac{d^2P}{dx^2} = -\frac{30{,}000{,}000}{x^4} \tag{2-6.5}$$

Thus, the second derivative is negative (for any nonzero value of x) indicating that the extreme point (i.e., where $x = 2.1544$) is a maximum.

Conversely, if the second derivative of a function is positive at an extreme point, that point is a minimum. The second derivative is zero at an inflection point.

2-7. Derivatives of Other Algebraic Functions. Not all functions are found to be in the simple form, ax^n, or a polynomial all of whose terms are in that form. For example:

1. $y = \sqrt{1 - x^2}$
2. $y = (3 + x^2)\sqrt{1 - x^2}$
3. $y = \dfrac{x^2}{1 - x}$

The first is a function with a constant exponent; i.e., it is $(f(x))^{\frac{1}{2}}$, or, if we let $u = f(x)$, it is in the form u^n. This may be differentiated by the rule given below for a function of a function. The second is the product of two functions, and the third is the quotient of two functions. We shall see that there are simple rules for solving these forms and that, by using these rules, almost all algebraic functions can be differentiated.

The derivative of a function of a function is obtained by differentiating the expression as if the function were the independent variable and multiplying its derivative thus obtained by the derivative of the function. That is, if the expression to be differentiated, y, may be viewed as a function of a function of x, then $y = f(u)$, and u is some function of x, and

$$\frac{d}{dx}(f(u)) = \frac{d}{du}(f(u))\frac{du}{dx} \tag{2–7.1}$$

This expression is known as the *chain rule*, and it may be applied to all kinds of functions, i.e., to trigonometric, exponential, logarithmic, etc., as well as to algebraic functions. For example, if u is a function of x, the expression u^n may be differentiated as follows:

$$\frac{d}{dx}(u^n) = nu^{n-1}\frac{du}{dx} \tag{2–7.2}$$

Letting $u = (1 - x^2)$, we can now differentiate the first of the three expressions enumerated at the beginning of this section:

$$y = \sqrt{1 - x^2} = (1 - x^2)^{\frac{1}{2}} = u^{\frac{1}{2}}$$

$$\frac{dy}{du} = \frac{1}{2}u^{-\frac{1}{2}} \qquad \text{and} \qquad \frac{du}{dx} = -2x$$

Then, combining these two results,

$$\frac{dy}{dx} = \frac{dy}{du}\frac{du}{dx} = \frac{1}{2\sqrt{u}}(-2x) = -\frac{x}{\sqrt{1 - x^2}}$$

The derivative of the product of two functions is the *sum* of the first function times the derivative of the second, *plus* the second function times the derivative of the first. If the two functions are u and v,

$$\frac{d}{dx}(uv) = u\frac{dv}{dx} + v\frac{du}{dx} \tag{2–7.3}$$

Using this rule to differentiate the second expression

$$y = (3 + x^2)\sqrt{1 - x^2}$$

$$\frac{dy}{dx} = (3 + x^2)\frac{d}{dx}\sqrt{1 - x^2} + \sqrt{1 - x^2}\frac{d}{dx}(3 + x^2)$$

But we have just computed $\frac{d}{dx}\sqrt{1 - x^2}$. Therefore,

$$\frac{dy}{dx} = (3 + x^2)\left(-\frac{x}{\sqrt{1 - x^2}}\right) + 2x\sqrt{1 - x^2}$$

$$= 2x\sqrt{1 - x^2} - \frac{x(3 + x^2)}{\sqrt{1 - x^2}}$$

$$\frac{dy}{dx} = \frac{2x(1 - x^2) - x(3 + x^2)}{\sqrt{1 - x^2}} = \frac{2x - 2x^3 - 3x - x^3}{\sqrt{1 - x^2}}$$

$$= -\frac{x + 3x^3}{\sqrt{1 - x^2}}$$

The derivative of the quotient of two functions (i.e., a fraction) is the denominator times the derivative of the numerator, *minus* the numerator times the derivative of the denominator, all *divided* by the square of the denominator:

$$\frac{d}{dx}\left(\frac{u}{v}\right) = \frac{v\dfrac{du}{dx} - u\dfrac{dv}{dx}}{v^2} \tag{2–7.4}$$

This rule follows directly from the other two rules, and, indeed, often one can differentiate a quotient by treating it as a product, with the denominator given a negative exponent. However, it is frequently much easier to use the rule of Equation (2–7.4). We can, however, easily demonstrate that these two procedures are identical. Using the rule of Equation (2–7.3), we can derive Equation (2–7.4).

$$\frac{d}{dx}\left(\frac{u}{v}\right) = \frac{d}{dx}(uv^{-1}) = u\frac{d}{dx}(v^{-1}) + v^{-1}\frac{du}{dx}$$

$$= u\left(-\frac{1}{v^2}\right)\frac{dv}{dx} + \left(\frac{v^2}{v^2}\right)v^{-1}\frac{du}{dx}$$

$$\frac{d}{dx}\left(\frac{u}{v}\right) = \frac{v\dfrac{du}{dx} - u\dfrac{dv}{dx}}{v^2} \tag{2–7.4}$$

Using this quotient rule to differentiate the third expression

$$y = \frac{x^2}{1 - x}$$

$$\frac{dy}{dx} = \frac{(1 - x)\dfrac{d}{dx}(x^2) - x^2\dfrac{d}{dx}(1 - x)}{(1 - x)^2}$$

$$= \frac{2x - 2x^2 + x^2}{(1 - x)^2} = \frac{2x - x^2}{(1 - x)^2}$$

The student should verify this result as an exercise by differentiating it as a product: $y = x^2(1 - x)^{-1}$.

Finally, it has been noted above that the derivative of a constant is zero. That is, if $y = k$, $\dfrac{dy}{dx}(k) = 0$. This follows both from Equation

(2–5.4), in that a constant k may be viewed as kx^0, and also intuitively from the fact that $y = k$ represents a horizontal straight line with zero slope. Also, from Equation (2–7.3), it follows that the derivative of a constant multiplied by a function is equal to the constant multiplied by the derivative of the function:

$$\frac{d}{dx}(kf(x)) = k\frac{d}{dx}(f(x)) \tag{2–7.5}$$

A table of these and other derivatives may be found in Appendix D.

2–8. Derivatives of Trigonometric Functions. There are several kinds of function which are not the kind of algebraic function we have dealt with above but arise often in applications of mathematical analysis. These are called *transcendental functions*. They include trigonometric functions, exponentials, logarithms, and some others.

We shall not here examine all trigonometric functions, but we shall look at the derivatives of the simplest, the *sine* and the *cosine*. Any others which may be required can be found in Appendix D.

Some readers may wish to skip the derivations which follow. However, it is probably desirable for all students to spend at least some minimum amount of time skimming these pages to see whence came the very important results of Equations (2–8.26) and (2–8.27).

Figure 2–8.1 shows the first quadrant of a circle with unit radius. The sine of an angle of a right triangle, it will be recalled, is the ratio of the

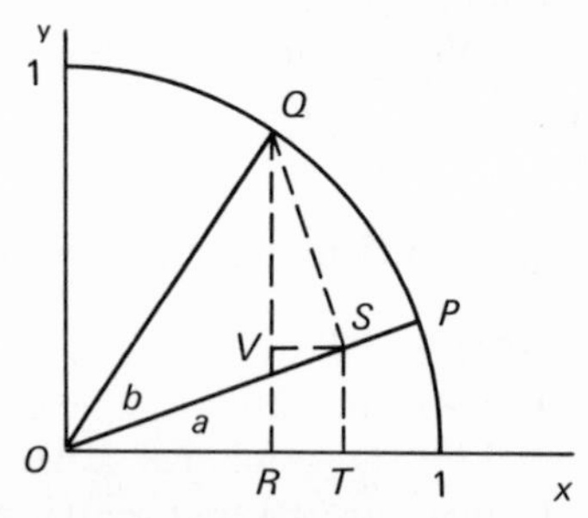

Fig. 2–8.1. Circle quadrant with unit radius. QS is constructed perpendicular to OP. QR and ST are perpendicular to the x-axis.

opposite side to the hypotenuse, and the cosine is the ratio of the adjacent side to the hypotenuse. In the diagram

$$\sin a = \frac{ST}{OS} \tag{2–8.1}$$

$$\sin b = \frac{QS}{OQ} = \frac{QS}{1} = QS \tag{2–8.2}$$

Similarly,

$$\cos b = OS \tag{2–8.3}$$

$$\sin (a + b) = QR = ST + QV \tag{2–8.4}$$

From the familiar rules of plane geometry

$$\text{angle } SQV = \text{angle } a$$

Thus,

$$\cos a = \frac{QV}{QS} \tag{2–8.5}$$

Then, from Equations (2–8.1), (2–8.4), and (2–8.5),

$$\sin (a + b) = OS \sin a + QS \cos a \tag{2–8.6}$$

Then, from Equations (2–8.2) and (2–8.3)

$$\sin (a + b) = \sin a \cos b + \cos a \sin b \tag{2–8.7}$$

Equation (2–8.7) is an important result which we shall use in a moment. Also, by similar reasoning, an equally important result for the $\cos (a + b)$ is obtained.

$$\cos (a + b) = OR = OT - RT \tag{2–8.8}$$

$$= OS \cos a - QS \sin a$$

$$\cos (a + b) = \cos a \cos b - \sin a \sin b \tag{2–8.9}$$

Before we proceed to the derivative of the trigonometric functions, we require two additional results. We shall need the limit, as a approaches zero, of two expressions:

$$\lim_{a \to 0} \frac{\sin a}{a} \qquad \text{and} \qquad \lim_{a \to 0} \frac{1 - \cos a}{a}$$

Let us solve for these, and then we can proceed.

At this point, we shall find it desirable to change our symbols, and to let the angle be represented by the symbol x in place of a. The symbol x is much more convenient for use in the material to follow. We have used a and b thus far to avoid confusion with the designations of the axes in the diagram, but that simplification is no longer necessary. Therefore, letting the angle be x, we shall seek:

$$\lim_{x \to 0} \frac{\sin x}{x} \qquad \text{and} \qquad \lim_{x \to 0} \frac{1 - \cos x}{x}$$

A circle of radius $r = 1$ has an area of π. In Figure 2–8.2, again, a sector of a unit-radius circle is shown. Let us measure the angle x in *radians*, the unit of *angular measure* such that there are 2π radians in a circle.

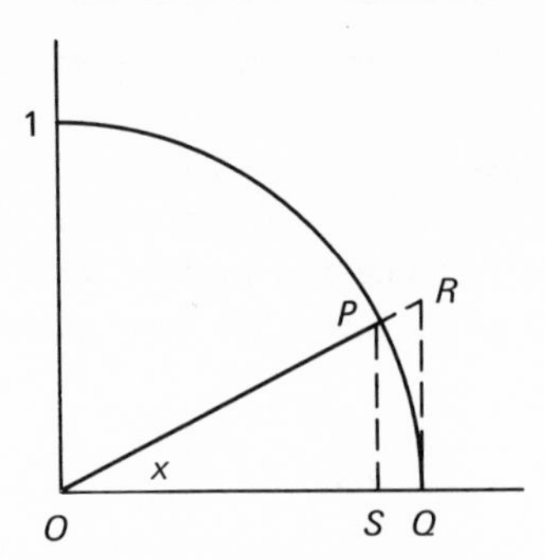

Fig. 2–8.2. Circle quadrant with unit radius.

Then, the area of the sector OPQ is

$$\text{Area } OPQ = \frac{x}{2\pi}(\pi) = \frac{x}{2} \tag{2–8.10}$$

Also, this sector's area lies between that of the two triangles, OPS and ORQ.

$$\text{Area } OPS < \text{Area } OPQ < \text{Area } ORQ \tag{2–8.11}$$

But

$$PS = \sin x \qquad \text{and} \qquad OS = \cos x$$

Therefore,

$$\text{Area of triangle } OPS = \tfrac{1}{2} \sin x \cos x \tag{2–8.12}$$

Also, by definition, the *tangent* of an angle is the ratio of the opposite side to the adjacent side:

$$\tan x = \frac{RQ}{OQ} = RQ \tag{2–8.13}$$

Therefore,

$$\text{Area of triangle } ORQ = \tfrac{1}{2} \tan x \tag{2–8.14}$$

Now, from Equations (2–8.10), (2–8.11), (2–8.12), and (2–8.14),

$$\tfrac{1}{2} \sin x \cos x < \frac{x}{2} < \tfrac{1}{2} \tan x \tag{2–8.15}$$

We multiply Equation (2–8.15) through by $\frac{2}{\sin x}$, yielding

$$\cos x < \frac{x}{\sin x} < \frac{1}{\cos x} \tag{2–8.16}$$

Now we take the reciprocal of all terms and reverse the direction of the inequality:

$$\frac{1}{\cos x} > \frac{\sin x}{x} > \cos x \tag{2–8.17}$$

This last is a trivial step, but now the middle term is in exactly the form which we require.

It is obvious that, since $\cos 0 = 1$, and since the cosine function is continuous, the limit of the first and last terms in Equation (2–8.17), as x approaches zero, is 1. Since the middle term is constrained to lie between these two terms at all times, its limit must also be 1. Therefore

$$\lim_{x \to 0} \frac{\sin x}{x} = 1 \tag{2–8.18}$$

This is the first of our two limits. For the second, $\lim_{x \to 0} \frac{1 - \cos x}{x}$, we recall that, for any angle, x, $\sin^2 x + \cos^2 x = 1$. Then,

$$\sin^2 x = 1 - \cos^2 x = (1 + \cos x)(1 - \cos x)$$

$$\frac{\sin^2 x}{1 + \cos x} = 1 - \cos x \tag{2–8.19}$$

but

$$\frac{\sin^2 x}{1 + \cos x} \leq \sin^2 x \qquad \text{for } \cos x \geq 0 \tag{2–8.20}$$

Thus, from Equations (2–8.19) and (2–8.20), dividing by x,

$$\frac{1 - \cos x}{x} \leq \frac{\sin^2 x}{x} \qquad \text{for } \cos x \geq 0 \qquad \text{and } x > 0 \tag{2–8.21}$$

Also, for any positive x,

$$\frac{1 - \cos x}{x} \geq 0 \tag{2–8.22}$$

Therefore, from Equations (2–8.21) and (2–8.22),

$$0 \leq \frac{1 - \cos x}{x} \leq \frac{\sin^2 x}{x} \tag{2–8.23}$$

but, from Equation (2–8.18)

$$\lim_{x \to 0} \frac{\sin^2 x}{x} = \left(\lim_{x \to 0} \frac{\sin x}{x}\right)(\lim_{x \to 0} \sin x) = (1)(0) = 0$$

Therefore, taking the limit as $x \to 0$ of Equation (2–8.23),

$$0 \leq \lim_{x \to 0} \frac{1 - \cos x}{x} \leq 0 \tag{2–8.24}$$

Clearly, then,

$$\lim_{x \to 0} \frac{1 - \cos x}{x} = 0 \tag{2–8.25}$$

This is the second result which we sought. Now we can proceed to find the derivative of the sine function. From Equation (2–5.11), this derivative is:

$$\frac{d}{dx}(\sin x) = \lim_{\Delta x \to 0} \frac{\sin (x + \Delta x) - \sin x}{\Delta x}$$

From Equation (2–8.7)

$$\frac{d}{dx}(\sin x) = \lim_{\Delta x \to 0} \frac{\sin x \cos \Delta x + \sin \Delta x \cos x - \sin x}{\Delta x}$$

$$= \lim_{\Delta x \to 0} \frac{\sin x \cos \Delta x - \sin x}{\Delta x} + \lim_{\Delta x \to 0} \frac{\sin \Delta x \cos x}{\Delta x}$$

$$= -\sin x \lim_{\Delta x \to 0} \frac{1 - \cos \Delta x}{\Delta x} + \cos x \lim_{\Delta x \to 0} \frac{\sin \Delta x}{\Delta x}$$

but, from Equations (2–8.25) and (2–8.18),

$$\frac{d}{dx}(\sin x) = (-\sin x)(0) + (\cos x)(1)$$

$$\frac{d}{dx}(\sin x) = \cos x \tag{2–8.26}$$

Similarly, again using Equation (2–5.11), the derivative of the cosine is:

$$\frac{d}{dx}(\cos x) = \lim_{\Delta x \to 0} \frac{\cos (x + \Delta x) - \cos x}{\Delta x}$$

Then, from Equation (2–8.9),

$$\frac{d}{dx}(\cos x) = \lim_{\Delta x \to 0} \frac{\cos x \cos \Delta x - \sin x \sin \Delta x - \cos x}{\Delta x}$$

$$= \lim_{\Delta x \to 0} \frac{\cos x \cos \Delta x - \cos x}{\Delta x} - \lim_{\Delta x \to 0} \frac{\sin x \sin \Delta x}{\Delta x}$$

$$= -\cos x \lim_{\Delta x \to 0} \frac{1 - \cos \Delta x}{\Delta x} - \sin x \lim_{\Delta x \to 0} \frac{\sin \Delta x}{\Delta x}$$

From Equations (2–8.25) and (2–8.18), the first limit is 0, and the second is 1:

$$\frac{d}{dx}(\cos x) = (-\cos x)(0) - (\sin x)(1)$$

$$\frac{d}{dx}(\cos x) = -\sin x \tag{2–8.27}$$

This completes the development of the derivatives of the sine and cosine functions. It will be recalled from Equation (2–8.21) that we have derived these results for the cases where the cosine of x is greater than or equal to zero, and x is greater than zero. However, it turns out that these same results hold for $\cos x < 0$. The student may wish to prove this at his leisure. Any other trigonometric functions may be differentiated by substitution of sines and cosines, or, of course, they may be found in tables of derivatives.

We shall illustrate the substitution technique for the tangent function. It will be remembered that the tangent of an angle is the ratio of the opposite side to the adjacent side.

$$\frac{d}{dx}(\tan x) = \frac{d}{dx}\left(\frac{\sin x}{\cos x}\right) = \frac{(\cos x)(\cos x) - (\sin x)(-\sin x)}{\cos^2 x} = \frac{1}{\cos^2 x}$$

and, since the *secant* is defined as the reciprocal of the cosine,

$$\frac{d}{dx}(\tan x) = \sec^2 x \tag{2–8.28}$$

Finally, the results of Equations (2–8.26) and (2–8.27) may be made clear in the graphic demonstration of Figure 2–8.3. Notice, in the top

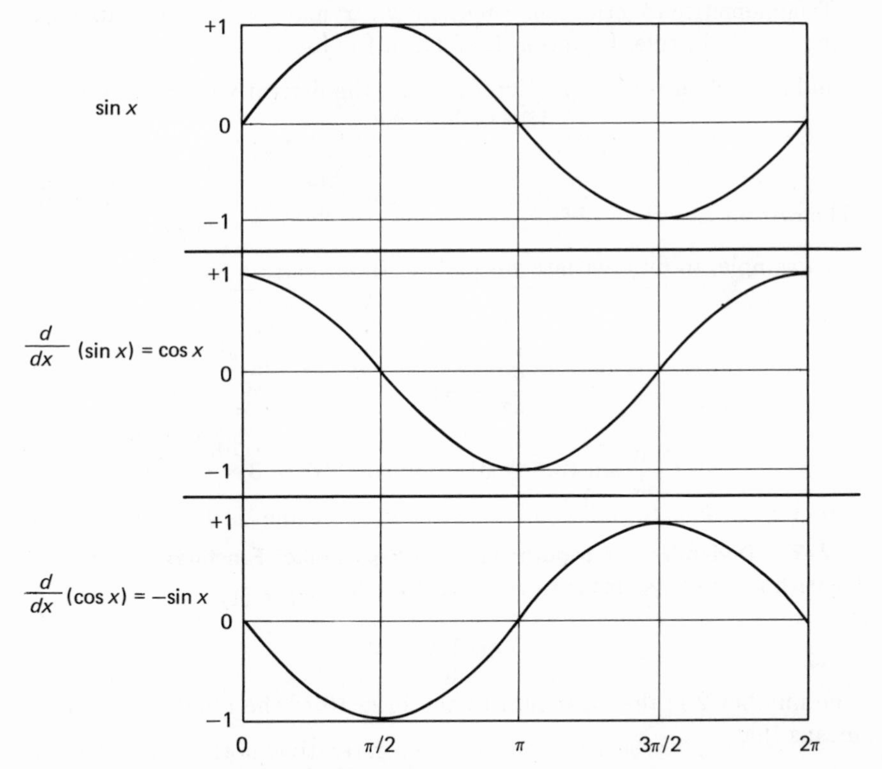

Fig. 2–8.3. Relationship between sin x, cos x, and $-$ sin x.

graph, that $\sin x$ starts at zero at its steepest slope (+1) at $x = 0$, and the slope gradually decreases to zero at $\frac{\pi}{2}$, where it becomes negative and is at its greatest negative value (−1) at $x = \pi$, after which the slope again levels off to zero at $\frac{3}{2}\pi$, and then increases again to its steepest at 2π, where $\sin x = 0$, but the slope has a value of 1. This pattern of the slope is exactly the pattern of $\cos x$ as shown in the middle graph, and the slope of the middle graph is similarly seen to be the function shown in the bottom graph, the function: $-\sin x$. Thus in the case of the sine and the cosine, the top two graphs, the graph directly beneath is the graph of the slope of that function, i.e., the first derivative.

It must be emphasized that the relationships derived here and shown in Figure 2–8.3 have their simple definitions only when the angle x is measured in *radians*. If the angle were to be measured in degrees, a constant factor $\left(\frac{\pi}{180}\right)$ would have to be introduced. In general, we avoid this complication and use the simple equations which we have derived above, thereby tacitly agreeing that the angles are measured in radians (2π radians = 360°).

Trigonometric functions of functions of x may be differentiated by using the chain rule, Equation (2–7.1), in the form

$$\frac{d}{dx}(\sin u) = \cos u \frac{du}{dx} \tag{2–8.29}$$

$$\frac{d}{dx}(\cos u) = -\sin u \frac{du}{dx} \tag{2–8.30}$$

For example, to differentiate $\sin(2x^2 + 3)$, let

$$u = 2x^2 + 3$$

$$\frac{du}{dx} = 4x$$

$$\frac{d}{dx}\sin(2x^2 + 3) = 4x \cos(2x^2 + 3)$$

2–9. Derivatives of Logarithmic and Exponential Functions. Common logarithms are logarithms to the *base* 10. That is

$$\log_{10} 100 = 2$$

The number 2 is the logarithm to the base 10 of the number 100. This means that

$$10^2 = 100$$

The *logarithm* is the *power* to which the *base* must be raised to reproduce the original number. In general, where a is the base,

$$\text{If } \log_a x = y, \qquad \text{then} \qquad a^y = x$$

In other words,

$$(\text{Base})^{\text{Logarithm of number}} = \text{Number}$$

Clearly, any number can be used as the base of logarithms. Often, we use the number 2 as a base, particularly for pedagogical demonstrations. In calculus, for reasons which we shall examine below, just as it was convenient to use radians to measure angles, it is convenient to use as the base for logarithms the number $e = 2.71828\ldots$. This number is an irrational number and like the constant π (3.14159 . . .), its value may be determined as precisely as one may wish, even to hundreds or even millions of decimal places.

We designate logarithms to the base e, also known as *natural* logarithms, by the symbol

$$\ln x = \log_e x$$

The numerical values of logarithms to the base e may be found directly in tables of natural logarithms; or they may be computed from values of common logarithms by the use of a simple conversion formula, which we shall now derive. Since the logarithm of a number is the power to which the base is raised to reproduce the number,

$$e^{\log_e x} = x$$

Taking the $\log_{10}$ of both sides

$$\log_{10} e^{\log_e x} = \log_{10} x$$

Since $\log x^a = a \log x$,

$$\log_e x \log_{10} e = \log_{10} x$$

$$\log_e x = \frac{\log_{10} x}{\log_{10} e}$$

From Appendix G,

$$\frac{1}{\log_{10} e} = \frac{1}{\log_{10} 2.7183} = \frac{1}{0.43428} = 2.303\ldots$$

Therefore, the conversion formula is

$$\log_e x = 2.303 \log_{10} x$$

The *derivative of a logarithm* is, again using Equation (2–5.11):

$$\frac{d}{dx}(\log x) = \lim_{\Delta x \to 0} \frac{\log(x + \Delta x) - \log x}{\Delta x}$$

but

$$\log(x + \Delta x) - \log x = \log\left(\frac{x + \Delta x}{x}\right)$$
$$= \log\left(1 + \frac{\Delta x}{x}\right)$$

Therefore

$$\frac{\log(x + \Delta x) - \log x}{\Delta x} = \frac{1}{\Delta x}\log\left(1 + \frac{\Delta x}{x}\right)$$
$$= \frac{1}{x}\frac{x}{\Delta x}\log\left(1 + \frac{\Delta x}{x}\right)$$
$$= \frac{1}{x}\log\left(1 + \frac{\Delta x}{x}\right)^{x/\Delta x}$$

Let $\frac{\Delta x}{x} = m$; then

$$\frac{d}{dx}(\log x) = \lim_{\Delta x \to 0}\frac{1}{x}\log(1 + m)^{1/m}$$
$$= \frac{1}{x}\log\left(\lim_{\Delta x \to 0}(1 + m)^{1/m}\right)$$

but

$$\lim_{\Delta x \to 0}\frac{\Delta x}{x} = 0$$

Thus, as $\Delta x \to 0$, $m \to 0$, and therefore

$$\frac{d}{dx}(\log x) = \frac{1}{x}\log\left(\lim_{m \to 0}(1 + m)^{1/m}\right) \tag{2-9.1}$$

Now, it is precisely this last term in parentheses which is defined to be e:

$$e = \lim_{m \to 0}(1 + m)^{1/m} \tag{2-9.2}$$

It may be evaluated quite easily. The term $(1 + m)^{1/m}$ may be expanded by the familiar procedure for expanding a binomial expression:

$$(q + p)^n = q^n + nq^{n-1}p + \frac{n(n-1)}{2!}q^{n-2}p^2 + \frac{n(n-1)(n-2)}{3!}q^{n-3}p^3 + \cdots$$

where the number $n!$, which is the product of successive positive integers from 1 to n inclusive, is called "*n-factorial.*" By definition, $0! = 1$. Then,

$$\text{1-factorial} = 1! = 1$$
$$\text{2-factorial} = 2! = 1 \cdot 2 = 2$$
$$\text{3-factorial} = 3! = 1 \cdot 2 \cdot 3 = 6$$
$$\text{4-factorial} = 4! = 1 \cdot 2 \cdot 3 \cdot 4 = 24$$

etc.

The result of this expansion is:

$$(1 + m)^{1/m} = 1^{\frac{1}{m}} + \frac{1}{m}(1)^{\frac{1}{m}-1}m^1 + \frac{\frac{1}{m} - 1}{m \cdot 2!}(1)^{\frac{1}{m}-2}m^2 + \cdots$$

$$= 1 + 1 + \frac{1 - m}{2!} + \frac{1 - 3m + 2m^2}{3!} + \cdots$$

and, taking the limit as m approaches zero, we have

$$\lim_{m \to 0} (1 + m)^{1/m} = 1 + 1 + \frac{1}{2!} + \frac{1}{3!} + \cdots$$

This infinite series may be evaluated directly on a digital computer to as many decimal places as may be desired. The sum is an irrational number, whose value is 2.71828 . . . :

$$e = 1 + 1 + \frac{1}{2!} + \frac{1}{3!} + \frac{1}{4!} + \cdots \tag{2–9.3}$$

Actually, Equation (2–9.3) is a special case of the more general formula:

$$e^x = 1 + x + \frac{x^2}{2!} + \frac{x^3}{3!} + \frac{x^4}{4!} + \cdots \tag{2–9.4}$$

which we shall derive below in Section 2–12, using infinite series. Equation (2–9.3) is the special case of e^x where $x = 1$. We shall have occasion to use these formulas below in Chapter 4. In any event, using Equation (2–9.3) we find that, to five decimal places, $e = 2.71828$, as seen in Table 2–12.1.

Returning to the development of the derivative of the logarithm, in Equation (2–9.1) the last term is now seen, from Equation (2–9.2), to be equal to ln e. From this we can see the importance of e, and we can see why we use e as the base of logarithms. The above development of the derivative of the logarithm did not, through Equation (2–9.1), specify the base of logarithms to be used. Now, Equation (2–9.1), which becomes

$$\frac{d}{dx}(\log x) = \frac{1}{x}\log\left(\lim_{m \to 0}(1 + m)^{1/m}\right) = \frac{1}{x}\log e$$

holds for any base of logarithms, be it e, 10, or any other. However *by introducing e as the base, we make the last term,* ln e, *equal to 1*. This yields the extremely useful result:

$$\frac{d}{dx}(\ln x) = \frac{1}{x}\ln e$$

$$\frac{d}{dx}(\ln x) = \frac{1}{x} \tag{2–9.5}$$

Thus, e is the *natural base* of logarithms in that the derivative of the logarithm of x is $\frac{1}{x}$ multiplied by a constant, the logarithm of e to the base used for the logarithm of x. That constant becomes 1 and disappears if the base of logarithms is selected to be e, because the logarithm of e to the base e is 1. For this reason, e is used as the base of logarithms in most mathematical applications, and logarithms to the base e are called *natural logarithms*.

This result can also be seen in a graphical representation. In Figure 2–9.1, the slope of the function, $y = \ln x$, is $\frac{1}{x}$ at every point.

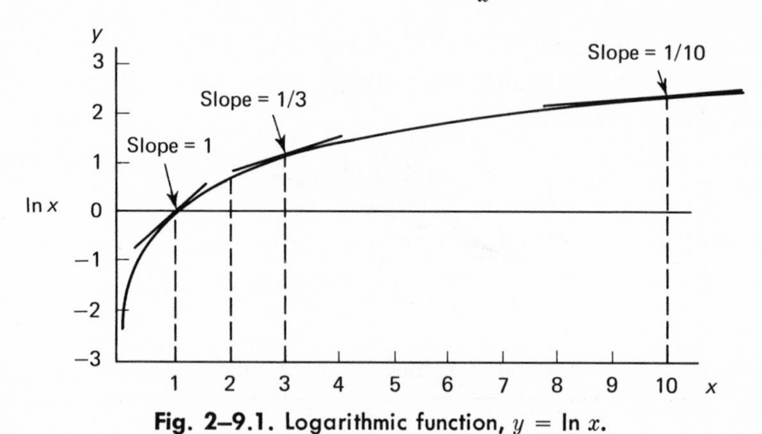

Fig. 2–9.1. Logarithmic function, $y = \ln x$.

We are now also able to differentiate the exponential function, e^x. By definition,

$$\ln e^x = x \ln e$$

but, since $\ln e = 1$,

$$\ln e^x = x$$

Using the chain rule of Equation (2–7.1), differentiate both sides of the equation with respect to x:

$$\frac{1}{e^x}\frac{d}{dx}(e^x) = 1$$

$$\frac{d}{dx}(e^x) = e^x \tag{2–9.6}$$

which is the desired result. The function, e^x, has the slope e^x at every point.

The chain rule, Equation (2–7.1), may be applied to differentiate exponentials and logarithms involving functions of x. For example,

$$\frac{d}{dx}(e^{ax}) = e^{ax}\frac{d}{dx}(ax) = ae^{ax} \tag{2–9.7}$$

2–10. Differentials. The expression for the derivative of y with respect to x, $\frac{dy}{dx}$, may be regarded as the ratio of two *differentials*, dy and dx. The *differential*, dx, is to be understood to be some very small increment in x, and in that case it is similar to Δx, but it is generally understood to be very small.

On the other hand, dy is quite different from Δy, as may be seen in Figure 2–10.1. In that figure, there are two points on a curve, P at (x_1,y_1)

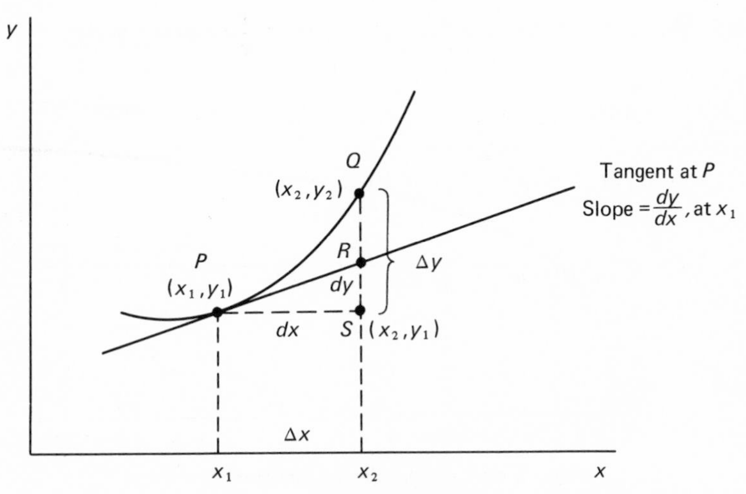

Fig. 2–10.1. The meaning of differentials; $dx = \Delta x$, but $dy \neq \Delta y$.

and Q at (x_2,y_2). The distance $x_2 - x_1 = \Delta x$, and also $y_2 - y_1 = \Delta y$. The distance Δx is very small, and we may call it dx. However, dy is not then equal to Δy. The definition of dy is

$$dy = \left(\frac{dy}{dx}\right) dx \tag{2–10.1}$$

This is not the trivial statement which it seems to be if one cancels dx in the numerator and denominator of the right side. Rather, it says that dy is obtained by applying to the increment dx the first derivative or slope, $\frac{dy}{dx}$. In the diagram dy is clearly smaller than Δy. Clearly, as dx becomes smaller and smaller, dy and Δy approach one another, and if dx is sufficiently small, dy and Δy may be treated as approximations of one another. Of course, at the limit, as dx approaches zero, dy approaches Δy.

$$\lim_{dx \to 0} \Delta y = dy \tag{2–10.2}$$

Now, it is possible to write the expressions for derivatives in differential form. Instead of

$$\frac{d(x^2)}{dx} = 2x \tag{2-10.3}$$

we may write

$$d(x^2) = 2x\,dx$$

also

$$d(\ln x) = \frac{1}{x}\,dx = \frac{dx}{x}$$

$$d(e^x) = e^x\,dx$$

$$d(\sin x) = \cos x\,dx$$

2–11. Partial Derivatives. Often, particularly in business applications, there are two or more independent controllable variables, and the object of the analysis is to find the best configuration of both variables. For example, one may wish to determine the optimal combination of product, price, and advertising budget, or the optimal prices of two products, whose demands overlap, i.e., the "standard" and "deluxe" models for mechanical equipment, permanent waves, or transportation service.

Suppose we have a function $E = f(x,y)$, where both x and y are independent variables, and we wish to find the combination of x and y which yields the optimum value of E. It is not possible to differentiate with respect to both independent variables at the same time, but rather, we hold one constant, i.e., treat it temporarily as if it were a constant, and differentiate with respect to the other. If necessary, we may then repeat the process with the roles of the two independent variables reversed. The symbol $\frac{\partial y}{\partial x}$ is used to designate a *partial derivative* (∂ is the lower case Greek letter "delta"). If $E = f(x,y)$, then, the partial derivative with respect to x is

$$\frac{\partial E}{\partial x} = \lim_{\Delta x \to 0} \frac{f(x + \Delta x,y) - f(x,y)}{\Delta x} \tag{2-11.1}$$

Thus, the partial derivative with respect to x is obtained by using the familiar rules for differentiation, treating all other variables as if they were constants. For example, given the polynomial

$$E = 10 + x^2 + 3y^3 - 5xy^2 \tag{2-11.2}$$

$$\frac{\partial E}{\partial x} = 2x - 5y^2 \tag{2-11.3}$$

$$\frac{\partial E}{\partial y} = 9y^2 - 10xy \tag{2-11.4}$$

We can take a *second partial derivative* with respect to the *same* variable according to the relationship

$$\frac{\partial^2 E}{\partial x^2} = \frac{\partial}{\partial x}\left(\frac{\partial E}{\partial x}\right) \quad \text{or} \quad \frac{\partial^2 E}{\partial y^2} = \frac{\partial}{\partial y}\left(\frac{\partial E}{\partial y}\right) \tag{2–11.5}$$

For the example of Equation (2–11.2),

$$\frac{\partial^2 E}{\partial x^2} = \frac{\partial}{\partial x}(2x - 5y^2) = 2$$

$$\frac{\partial^2 E}{\partial y^2} = \frac{\partial}{\partial y}(9y^2 - 10xy) = 18y - 10x$$

Also we can take a *second partial derivative* with respect to a *different* independent variable according to the relationship

$$\frac{\partial^2 E}{\partial x\, \partial y} = \frac{\partial}{\partial x}\left(\frac{\partial E}{\partial y}\right) \quad \text{or} \quad \frac{\partial^2 E}{\partial y\, \partial x} = \frac{\partial}{\partial y}\left(\frac{\partial E}{\partial x}\right) \tag{2–11.6}$$

For the example of Equation (2–11.2)

$$\frac{\partial^2 E}{\partial x\, \partial y} = \frac{\partial}{\partial x}(9y^2 - 10xy) = -10y \tag{2–11.7}$$

$$\frac{\partial^2 E}{\partial y\, \partial x} = \frac{\partial}{\partial y}(2x - 5y^2) = -10y \tag{2–11.8}$$

Note that the answer is the same in both Equation (2–11.7) and Equation (2–11.8). It is usually the case that the order of partial differentiation is of no consequence, and, if a second derivative with respect to both variables is desired, the differentiation may be performed in either order. However, when certain mathematical conditions regarding the continuity of the function are not met, this is not the case. A discussion of these conditions is beyond the scope of this introductory treatment; but fortunately, in most practical problems, the conditions are met.

2–12. Infinite Series. In subsequent chapters, we shall have need for the general expressions for the sum of the first n terms of an arithmetic progression (Section 3–4) and of a geometric progression (Section 14–5), and we shall there derive these general expressions.

It will be recalled that an *arithmetic progression* is a sequence of numbers such that each subsequent term is obtained by *adding* a constant to the previous term. Examples of arithmetic progressions are:

$$1, 2, 3, 4, 5, 6, \ldots$$

$$5, 10, 15, 20, 25, 30, \ldots$$

$$\tfrac{1}{2}, 1, 1\tfrac{1}{2}, 2, 2\tfrac{1}{2}, 3, 3\tfrac{1}{2}, \ldots$$

$$10, 6, 2, -2, -6, -10, -14, -18, \ldots$$

A *geometric progression* is a sequence of numbers such that each subsequent term is obtained by *multiplying* the previous term by a constant. Examples of geometric progressions are:

$$1, 2, 4, 8, 16, 32, \ldots$$

$$5, 25, 125, 625, 3125, \ldots$$

$$1, \tfrac{1}{2}, \tfrac{1}{4}, \tfrac{1}{8}, \tfrac{1}{16}, \tfrac{1}{32}, \ldots$$

The reader should note that all of the arithmetic progressions given above and all but the last of the geometric progressions are such that as n, the serial number of the term, becomes large, the terms become (absolutely) large. The *sums* of the first n terms of these progressions are given below. For the arithmetic progressions the sequences of sums are:

$$1, 3, 6, 10, 15, 21, \ldots$$

$$5, 15, 30, 50, 75, 105, \ldots$$

$$\tfrac{1}{2}, 1\tfrac{1}{2}, 3, 5, 7\tfrac{1}{2}, 10\tfrac{1}{2}, 14, \ldots$$

$$10, 16, 18, 16, 10, 0, -14, \ldots$$

and for the geometric progressions, the sequences of sums are:

$$1, 3, 7, 15, 31, 63, \ldots$$

$$5, 30, 155, 780, 3905, \ldots$$

$$1, 1\tfrac{1}{2}, 1\tfrac{3}{4}, 1\tfrac{7}{8}, 1\tfrac{15}{16}, 1\tfrac{31}{32}, \ldots$$

Clearly, in all cases but the last, the sum of the first n terms will become (absolutely) very large as n becomes very large. For the last sequence of sums above, this is not true. That sequence of sums tells, for example, the total distance walked (in miles) if we walk north to a point a mile away, turn and, retracing our steps, walk south to a point halfway back to the starting place, then, continuing south, walk halfway back from that point, then halfway back from there, etc. Obviously we will never return exactly to the starting place, but if the process is repeated a very large number of times, we can come as close as we wish. That is, we can *approach* a total distance walked of two miles. Therefore we can say that the last sequence of sums *approaches the number* 2 *as its limit.*

Let us define an *infinite series* as a sequence of numbers separated by plus signs indicating that the terms are to be added together. A series whose sum approaches a finite limit as n, the number of terms, increases to infinity is said to *converge,* and a series whose sum does not approach such a limit is said to *diverge.* Not all series whose terms decrease as n increases are convergent, nor is it true that only geometric progressions can converge. This will be illustrated below. The infinite series corresponding to the first of the arithmetic progressions given above is

$$1 + 2 + 3 + 4 + 5 + 6 + \cdots$$

This series, like all arithmetic series, is divergent. The infinite series corresponding to the last of the geometric progressions given above is the convergent series

$$1 + \frac{1}{2} + \frac{1}{4} + \frac{1}{8} + \frac{1}{16} + \frac{1}{32} + \cdots \qquad \text{(convergent)}$$

To illustrate that not all series whose terms decrease (absolutely) are convergent, the series $\frac{1}{n}$ surprisingly can be shown to be *not convergent.*

$$1 + \frac{1}{2} + \frac{1}{3} + \frac{1}{4} + \frac{1}{5} + \frac{1}{6} + \cdots \qquad \text{(divergent)}$$

and to illustrate that geometric series are not the only series which converge, the series $\frac{1}{n^2}$ is convergent.

$$1 + \frac{1}{4} + \frac{1}{9} + \frac{1}{16} + \frac{1}{25} + \frac{1}{36} + \cdots \qquad \text{(convergent)}$$

However, any geometric series, rn, where r is the constant of multiplication and *r is smaller (absolute value) than 1*, does converge.

Many expressions which have finite values may be expressed as convergent infinite series. Perhaps one of the most important of these is the constant e. It was noted above in Equation (2–9.3) that e can be expressed as the infinite series

$$e = 1 + 1 + \frac{1}{2!} + \frac{1}{3!} + \frac{1}{4!} + \cdots \qquad (2\text{–}9.3)$$

We shall now discuss *Taylor's series* and then, using that technique, derive this series formulation for the value of e.

Let us start with the assertion that any continuous function of a single variable $f(x)$ may be plotted as shown in Figure 2–12.1 and that any function may be approximated by a polynomial or *power function* of the form

$$f(x) = a + bx + cx^2 + dx^3 + ex^4 + \cdots \qquad (2\text{–}12.1)$$

in which the coefficients are selected to make it resemble the desired function. This polynomial may have as many terms as necessary to approximate the desired function as closely as desired.

In the following discussion we shall be more concerned with the pre-

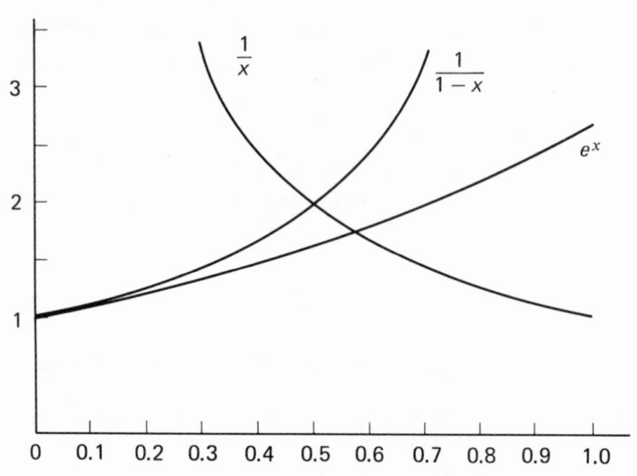

Fig. 2–12.1. Graphs of various functions of x.

sentation of the general reasoning leading to the result than with the strict requirements of mathematical rigor. The results which will emerge are correct, and readers wishing to see a completely rigorous presentation may consult a standard calculus text. We shall try to cover only the main points here.

Let us suppose that the power function given in Equation (2–12.1) does indeed closely resemble some desired function which we wish to represent as an infinite series. In order to describe completely the desired infinite series, we need only to find the values of the constants: a, b, c, d, e, etc. We can evaluate these constants by the following procedure.

If we set $x = 0$, we find that a, the first constant, is all that remains.

$$f(0) = a \tag{2–12.2}$$

Now, if we differentiate $f(x)$, we find that

$$f'(x) = b + 2cx + 3dx^2 + 4ex^3 + \cdots$$

Then, setting $x = 0$, all that remains is b:

$$f'(0) = b \tag{2–12.3}$$

Now, if we differentiate again and then set $x = 0$,

$$f''(x) = 2c + (2)(3)\ dx + (3)(4)ex^2 + \cdots$$

$$f''(0) = 2c \tag{2–12.4}$$

Repeating:

$$f'''(x) = (2)(3)d + (2)(3)(4)ex + \cdots$$

$$f'''(0) = (2)(3)d \tag{2–12.5}$$

Once more, adding another term at the end to emphasize the nature of the result,

$$\begin{aligned} f''''(x) &= (2)(3)(4)e + (2)(3)(4)(5)fx + \cdots \\ f''''(0) &= (2)(3)(4)e \end{aligned} \tag{2–12.6}$$

Now, using the results of Equations (2–12.2) through (2–12.6)

$$\begin{aligned} a &= f(0) \\ b &= f'(0) \\ c &= \frac{f''(0)}{2!} \\ d &= \frac{f'''(0)}{3!} \\ e &= \frac{f''''(0)}{4!} \\ &\vdots \end{aligned}$$

Then the original polynomial, Equation (2–12.1), may be rewritten

$$f(x) = f(0) + f'(0)x + \frac{f''(0)}{2!}x^2 + \frac{f'''(0)}{3!}x^3 + \cdots \tag{2–12.7}$$

If we let a (not to be confused with the a used above for the first term of the polynomial) be some fixed value of x, then Equation (2–12.7) can be rewritten

$$f(a + x) = f(a) + f'(a)x + \frac{f''(a)}{2!}x^2 + \frac{f'''(a)}{3!}x^3 + \cdots \tag{2–12.8}$$

With a moment's reflection, we can see that this step is equivalent to shifting the origin from $x = 0$ to $x = a$.

If the infinite series of Equation (2–12.8) is a convergent series, that is, if

$$\lim_{n\to\infty} \frac{f^{(n)}(a)}{n!}x^n = 0 \tag{2–12.9}$$

then the series shown in Equation (2–12.8), which is known as *Taylor's series*, can provide an approximate value of the function at any point in the vicinity of the point $x = a$, and we can make this approximation as close as we like by taking as many terms as we wish. Equation (2–12.7) is the special case where $a = 0$. Let us now apply this technique to the evaluation of e^x. We know that every derivative of e^x is e^x, and, of course, $e^0 = 1$. Therefore, from Equation (2–12.7),

$$e^x = 1 + x + \frac{x^2}{2!} + \frac{x^3}{3!} + \cdots \tag{2–9.4}$$

and

$$e = 1 + 1 + \frac{1}{2!} + \frac{1}{3!} + \cdots \tag{2–9.3}$$

The closeness of the approximation may be seen from the fact that, to five decimal places, the sum rapidly approaches the value $e = 2.71828$. This is shown in Table 2–12.1, where seven terms give the result correct to three decimal places, and nine terms yield the result correct to five decimal places. Since each entry in the middle column of Table 2–12.1 is

TABLE 2–12.1

Approximation of e with Taylor's Series

n	nth Term	Sum of n Terms
1	1	1
2	1	2
3	$\frac{1}{2!} = 0.500000$	2.500000
4	$\frac{1}{3!} = 0.166667$	2.666667
5	$\frac{1}{4!} = 0.041667$	2.708334
6	$\frac{1}{5!} = 0.008333$	2.716667
7	$\frac{1}{6!} = 0.001389$	2.718056
8	$\frac{1}{7!} = 0.000199$	2.718255
9	$\frac{1}{8!} = 0.000025$	2.718280

obtained from the next higher entry by dividing by $n - 1$, it is a very simple matter to compute e to be correct to any desired number of decimal places.

Let us further illustrate the use of Taylor's series by computing the value of ln 1.2. If

$$f(x) = \ln x, \qquad f(1) = \ln 1 = 0$$

then

$$f'(x) = \frac{1}{x}, \qquad f'(1) = 1$$

$$f''(x) = -\frac{1}{x^2}, \qquad f''(1) = -1$$

$$f'''(x) = \frac{2}{x^3}, \qquad f'''(1) = 2$$

Let

$$\ln 1.2 = \ln (1 + 0.2) = f(1) + f'(1)(0.2) + \frac{f''(1)(0.2)^2}{2!} + \frac{f'''(1)(0.2)^3}{3!} + \cdots$$

$$= 0 + 0.2 + (-1)\frac{0.04}{2} + \frac{(2)(0.008)}{6} + \cdots = 0.182 + \cdots$$

$$\simeq 0.18$$

which is already correct to two decimal places to the correct value 0.18.

In any practical use of Taylor's series, the closeness of the approximation after some fixed number of terms depends upon the smallness of x in the expression $f(a + x)$ in Equation (2–12.8). That is, a should be chosen to be as close as possible to the value of the independent variable for which the function is being evaluated.

SUGGESTIONS FOR FURTHER READING

Allen, R. G. D. *Mathematical Analysis for Economists.* London: Macmillan & Co., Ltd., 1942.

Dean, B. V., M. Sasieni, and S. Gupta. *Mathematics for Management.* New York: John Wiley & Co., Inc., 1963.

Fowler, F. P., Jr., and E. W. Sandberg. *Basic Mathematics for Administration.* New York: John Wiley & Co., 1962.

Kemeny, J. G., J. L. Snell, and G. L. Thompson. *Introduction to Finite Mathematics* (2d ed.). Englewood Cliffs, N.J.: Prentice-Hall, Inc., 1966.

Kleppner, D., and N. Ramsey. *Quick Calculus.* New York: John Wiley & Sons, Inc., 1965.

Meier, R. C., and S. H. Archer. *An Introduction to Mathematics for Business Analysis.* New York: McGraw-Hill Book Co., Inc., 1960.

Oakley, C. O. *The Calculus* (College Outline Series). New York: Barnes & Noble, Inc., 1965.

EXERCISES

2–1. Derive Equation (2–5.4). Hint: follow the procedure used in the derivation of Equation (2–5.3) with the modification that, in expanding the binomial raised to the nth power in the numerator, write the first few terms of the expansion of the general form of the binomial, i.e.,

$$(q + p)^n = q^n + nq^{n-1}p + \frac{n(n-1)}{2!} q^{n-2}p^2 + \frac{n(n-1)(n-2)}{3!} q^{n-3}p^3 + \cdots$$

2–2. Differentiate the following expressions with respect to x:

a) $3x \sin x$

b) $(x^2 + \sin x)^{\frac{1}{2}}$

c) $e^x(1 - x)^2$

d) $(5 + e^{3x})^{-1}$

e) $(\cos x)(3x + 4)$

f) $3x \ln (2x + 3x^2)$

g) $4x \cos 3x$

h) $\cos\left(2 + \frac{3}{x}\right)$

i) $\sin x^3$

j) $\frac{\cos x}{\cos 2x}$

k) $\frac{\ln 3x}{\sin x^2} + \frac{e^{2x}}{\cos x/2}$

l) $\frac{e^{bx} - e^{ax}}{x}$

The following six problems, while not related to management, require the building and solution of simple mathematical models.

2–3. The sum of two numbers is 25. What must these numbers be for their product to be maximized?

2–4. What is the shape of the rectangle with largest area for a given perimeter?

2–5. A 10-inch-square sheet of metal is to be formed into a topless box by cutting out an equal-sized square from each corner and folding up the sides. How large should the cut-out squares be for maximum volume of the box? What is the maximum capacity of the box?

2–6. What is the shape of the rectangle with shortest diagonal for a given area?

2–7. A 5-foot-tall boy walks directly away from a 15-foot-high lamppost at the rate of 3 miles per hour. How fast does the shadow of the tip of his head move?

2–8. A 10-foot-long ladder is leaning against a vertical wall. If the bottom of the ladder is moving away from the wall at the rate of 2 feet per minute, how fast is the top of the ladder moving down along the wall when the foot of the ladder is 6 feet from the wall?

2–9. Calculate the second derivative with respect to x of:

$$y = x^3e^{-3x}$$

2–10. Calculate the partial derivative of the following function with respect to y.

$$z = x^4 - 2x^2y - y^6 + e^{-x} - 10$$

2–11. Calculate

$$\frac{\partial^2 z}{\partial x^2} \quad \text{and} \quad \frac{\partial^2 z}{\partial y\, \partial x} \quad \text{for the function}$$

$$z = e^{x^2y} + \ln (4xy + 3x)$$

2–12. Derive Formula 14 of Appendix D. What is the result in the special case where $u = x$?

3

Deterministic Models

3–1. Optimization Models. In this chapter we shall construct and solve mathematical models in which the measure to be optimized is a function of one or two controllable input variables. Typically, the objective function has an extreme value, and we shall solve for this using the methods of calculus which were discussed in the last chapter.

We shall examine several different kinds of problems, each of which is intended to introduce some new mathematical concepts. We shall start with the general case of the familiar economic-lot-size problem.

3–2. The Economic-Lot-Size Problem—General Case. In Chapter 1 we introduced the Courbro problem in which we developed that company's inventory model to be, where TC = total cost, and x = lot size,

$$TC = 0.02x + \frac{500{,}000}{x} \qquad (1\text{–}2.4)$$

This equation was later solved in Chapter 2, where it was found that, letting $y = TC$,

$$\frac{dy}{dx} = 0.02 - \frac{500{,}000}{x^2} \qquad (2\text{–}5.5)$$

and that the optimal value of x, the lot size, was 5,000 units.

We shall now derive the simple *general* rule for this kind of problem. If we use the general symbols:

C_s is the setup or preparation cost per lot or per order
C_h is the inventory holding cost per unit for the planning period (in the Courbo case, we used one month)
D is the demand or requirement for the planning period, and
x is the lot size.

Then total cost of setup plus holding in the planning period is

$$TC = \left(\frac{x}{2}\right)(C_h) + \left(\frac{D}{x}\right)(C_s) \qquad (3\text{–}2.1)$$

Differentiating and setting the derivative equal to zero,

$$\frac{d}{dx}(TC) = \frac{C_h}{2} - \frac{DC_s}{x^2} = 0$$

$$x^* = \sqrt{\frac{2DC_s}{C_h}} \qquad (3\text{–}2.2)$$

where x^* is the *economic lot size.* (It is common practice in mathematics to add the asterisk (*) to the variable of differentiation after differentiating and setting the derivative equal to zero. This is done here, where x^* then represents the *optimal* value of x. It is not always convenient to do this, but, where convenient, it is a useful device. Here the asterisk identifies the fixed, optimal value of the controllable variable.)

Substituting the Courbro data into this equation

D = 5,000 units per month
C_s = \$100 per setup
C_h = \$0.04 per unit per month

$$x^* = \sqrt{\frac{(2)(5{,}000)(100)}{0.04}} = \sqrt{25{,}000{,}000} = 5{,}000$$

and the result is exactly the same as before:

$$TC = \left(\frac{5{,}000}{2}\right)0.04 + \left(\frac{5{,}000}{5{,}000}\right)100$$
$$= 100 + 100 = \$200$$

Most interesting inventory problems involve dealing with probabilistic demand, that is, where the exact demand for any fixed future time period is not known, but where there is information about the probability of various possible future levels of demand. We shall examine some problems of this sort later in Chapter 7, after we have discussed probability theory.

3–3. A Replacement Problem. In this section and those which follow, we shall examine a replacement problem in which the purpose is to ascertain the optimal time for replacement of a capital asset whose operating cost increases over time and whose salvage value decreases over time. The objective here is to minimize the *average annual cost* over the life of the asset

The Gethom Printing Company finds that a particular piece of capital equipment, whose initial purchase price is \$100, has operating costs which are a linear function of time according to the following formula, where V_i

is the *annual operating cost* in dollars in the ith year, and i is the age in years (at the end of the year):

$$V_i = 20 + 5i \tag{3–3.1}$$

In this equation, clearly, i is merely the ith positive integer, starting with 1.

The salvage value of the machine is its price on the used equipment market. This decreases by one-third of the residual value each year. The resale price, then, after n years, is

$$\text{Resale price} = 100\left(\frac{2}{3}\right)^n \tag{3–3.2}$$

and the *total* capital cost *over n years* is C_n, where

$$C_n = 100 - 100\left(\frac{2}{3}\right)^n \tag{3–3.3}$$

Thus, the average annual cost over n years is

$$AC = \frac{1}{n}\left[\sum_{i=1}^{n} V_i + C_n\right]$$

$$AC = \frac{1}{n}\left[\sum_{i=1}^{n} (20 + 5i) + 100 - 100\left(\frac{2}{3}\right)^n\right] \tag{3–3.4}$$

The minimum average cost may be found in two ways. First, it may be found by enumeration under the assumption that an integral number of years is either the desired answer or close enough for practical purposes. The solution under this assumption is shown in Table 3–3.1. Salvage value is entered to the nearest dollar to simplify the computations.

In the worksheet which is Table 3–3.1, Column (2) is computed from Equation (3–3.1), Column (3) is computed from Equation (3–3.2), Column (4) is computed from Equation (3–3.3), Column (5) is the cumulative sum of Column (2), Column (6) is the sum of Columns (4) and (5), and Column (7) is Column (6) divided by the years of operation, Column (1).

The age of replacement at which average cost is minimized is five years, as seen in Column (7). If the machine is retired and sold at the end of five years, its average cost over its life time will be $52.40 per year, and there is no *integral* number of years which yields equally low average costs.

However, it is possible to drop the integral-year assumption. The problem can also be solved on the assumption that the functions are continuous over time and that it is possible to retire the machine after a period of time which is not an integral number of years.

The average cost function, as given in Equation (3–3.4), can be differentiated and the derivative set equal to 0 in the usual way. We shall now proceed to do this. However, the solution of this problem will be a

TABLE 3–3.1

Gethom Printing Company
Solution by Enumeration

Age (Year of Operation) (1)	Annual Operating Cost ($) (2)	Salvage Value ($) (3)	Total Capital Cost ($) (4)	Total Operating Cost ($) (5)	Total Cost ($) (6)	Average Annual Cost ($) (7)
1	25	67	33	25	58	58.00
2	30	44	56	55	111	55.50
3	35	29	71	90	161	53.67
4	40	19	81	130	211	52.75
5	45	13	87	175	262	52.40*
6	50	9	91	225	316	52.67
7	55	6	94	280	374	53.43
8	60	4	96	340	436	54.50
9	65	3	97	405	502	55.78
10	70	2	98	475	573	57.30

somewhat drawn-out procedure since, to solve it, we shall require the introduction of two mathematical methods which have thus far not been introduced. These are, respectively, a technique for summing an arithmetic series and Newton's approximation method for solving equations. However, let us proceed with the analysis, and at the appropriate points we shall introduce these two new techniques.

The equation for the average annual cost over n years is

$$AC = \frac{1}{n}\left[\sum_{i=1}^{n}(20+5i) + 100 - 100\left(\frac{2}{3}\right)^n\right] \tag{3–3.4}$$

$$= \frac{1}{n}\left[20n + 5\sum_{i=1}^{n} i + 100 - 100\left(\frac{2}{3}\right)^n\right]$$

$$AC = 20 + \frac{5}{n}\sum_{i=1}^{n} i + \frac{100}{n} - \frac{100}{n}\left(\frac{2}{3}\right)^n \tag{3–3.5}$$

To find the minimum cost, we differentiate with respect to n:

$$\frac{d}{dn}(AC) = 5\frac{d}{dn}\left(\frac{1}{n}\sum_{i=1}^{n} i\right) - \frac{100}{n^2} - \frac{100}{n}\left(\frac{2}{3}\right)^n \ln\frac{2}{3} + \left(\frac{2}{3}\right)^n\left(\frac{100}{n^2}\right) \tag{3–3.6}$$

The solution to this equation requires the evaluation of the sum of the simple arithmetic series: $1 + 2 + 3 + 4 + \cdots + n$.

In the following section we shall develop the general expression for the sum of an arithmetic series, and we shall then proceed to use it in differentiating that part of Equation (3–3.6).

3–4. The Sum of an Arithmetic Series. Any arithmetic series may be put in the following form, the familiar form for a linear function, in which the ith term is

$$y_i = a + b(i - 1) \tag{3–4.1}$$

where: a is the first term
b is the constant increment
i is the number of the term in the series

The sum of the first n terms of the series is

$$S_n = \sum_{i=1}^{n} y_i = na + b \sum_{i=1}^{n} (i - 1) = na + b \sum_{i=1}^{n-1} i \tag{3–4.2}$$

This sum can be easily evaluated by means of a simple mathematical trick. The sum may be written

$$S_n = [a] + [a + b] + \cdots + [a + (n - 2)b] + [a + (n - 1)b]$$

but it may also be written in reverse order:

$$S_n = [a + (n - 1)b] + [a + (n - 2)b] + \cdots + [a + b] + [a]$$

Adding these two expressions together by adding the two first terms, the two second terms, etc., the sum of each pair of corresponding terms is seen to be equal to $2a + (n - 1)b$. Since there are n of these pairs of terms,

$$2S_n = n[2a + (n - 1)b] \tag{3–4.3}$$

$$S_n = \frac{n}{2}[2a + (n - 1)b] \tag{3–4.4}$$

This last equation is the general expression for the sum of the first n terms of an arithmetic progression.

In the Gethom Printing Company problem which we are solving, the arithmetic progression which occurs is the sum of the first n integers. This progression may be put into the form of Equation (3–4.1), and it becomes

$$y_i = 1 + 1(i - 1) = i \tag{3–4.5}$$

Thus $a = 1$ and $b = 1$, and Equation (3–4.4) becomes

$$S_n = \sum_{i=1}^{n} i = \frac{n(n + 1)}{2} \tag{3–4.6}$$

Equation (3–4.6) is the general form used to represent the sum of the first n positive integers. Such an interval $(1,2,3, \cdots, n)$, with fixed numbers at its two extremes, is called a *closed interval,* and expressions like this one for summations over closed intervals, are called *closed forms,* as distinct from expressions such as that for the sum of an infinite series over an *open interval* as given in Equation (2–9.3) above.

Substituting the result of Equation (3–4.6) into Equation (3–3.6) for $\sum_{i=1}^{n} i$ and substituting also for $\ln 0.6667 = -0.4055$,

$$\frac{d}{dn}(AC) = 5\frac{d}{dn}\left[\left(\frac{1}{n}\right)\left(\frac{n(n+1)}{2}\right)\right] - \frac{100}{n^2} - \frac{100}{n}(-0.4055)\left(\frac{2}{3}\right)^n + \frac{100}{n^2}\left(\frac{2}{3}\right)^n$$

The first term simplifies to $\frac{5}{2}$. Then, setting this derivative equal to zero yields (with asterisks omitted for simplicity)

$$0 = 2.5 - \frac{100}{n^2} + \frac{40.55}{n}\left(\frac{2}{3}\right)^n + \frac{100}{n^2}\left(\frac{2}{3}\right)^n \qquad (3\text{–}4.7)$$

in which n is the optimal replacement period.

This last equation is not easy to solve by the familiar analytical methods, but it can be approximated easily by iterative methods. We shall now introduce *Newton's approximation,* a convenient iterative method for solving difficult equations.

3–5. Newton's Method of Approximation. In many problems, we arrive at an equation of the form

$$f(x) = 0 \qquad (3\text{–}5.1)$$

and it is necessary to find the *root* or *roots* of the equation. A *root* of an equation is defined as a number such that, when it is substituted for the unknown in the equation, the equation *is satisfied;* i.e., it becomes an identity. For example, for Equation (3–5.1), the root is that number such that, when substituted for x in $f(x)$, the equation becomes $0 = 0$.

This situation often arises when a function is differentiated in order to set the derivative equal to 0 and find the root, i.e., the value of the unknown for which that derivative is equal to zero.

In Figure 3–5.1, the diagram on the left represents a function which increases as x increases. That is, if this function is a derivative (slope), the original equation had a minimum at the point where this function has a value of zero. In the right diagram, the function is decreasing, and, if it is a derivative (slope), the original equation has a maximum at the point where this function crosses the x-axis. In either event, our purpose is to find the value of x at which $f(x) = 0$.

The procedure is based on the following reasoning, which may be followed on the diagrams of Figure 3–5.1. First, one must make an estimate of the desired root. Call this x_0. Then, the iteration procedure, which is Newton's method, may be traced on either graph as follows. From the point $(x_0,0)$, go up to the graph of the function. At the point $(x_0,f(x_0))$, construct the tangent. Move along the tangent to the point where it intersects the x-axis. This is the point $(x_1,0)$, and x_1 is the second estimate. Clearly, in these graphs, x_1 is closer to the desired root x^* than is x_0, and repetition of the procedure will lead to successive values of x_i which converge to x^*. The reader may verify that, if x_0 had been selected on the other side of x^* in either of the graphs of Figure 3–5.1, this method would

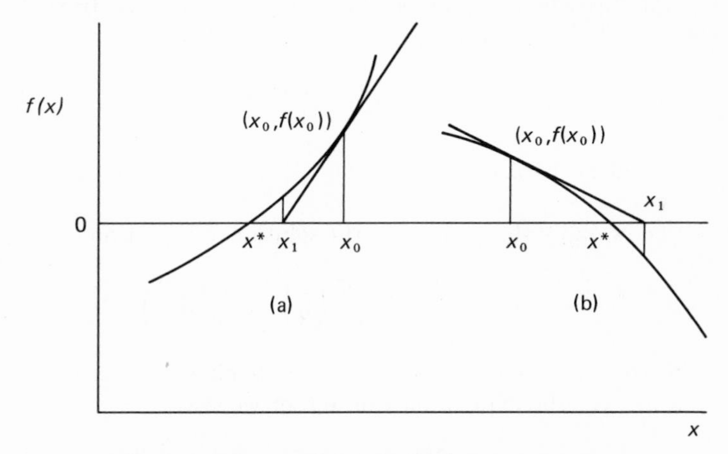

Fig. 3–5.1. Newton's method of approximation.

still yield values of x_i which converge to x^*. There are some situations in which the curve is so shaped that, if x_0 is not close to x^*, this method will not converge. However, this is not a serious limitation for us, and we shall find that Newton's method is extremely useful over a very wide range of applications.

The computational procedure is based on the relationship between the function being analyzed and its derivative (these may be, and often are, the *first* and *second derivatives*, respectively, of the original objective function being optimized).

In Figure 3–5.1, in both diagrams, the slope of the tangent to the curve at point $(x_0,f(x_0))$ is $f'(x_0)$, the derivative of the function expressed in terms of x_0. However, the slope is also

$$\text{Slope} = \frac{f(x_0)}{x_0 - x_1} \tag{3–5.2}$$

Note that, by writing the denominator as it is written in Equation (3–5.2), the sign of the slope is correct in both cases. Of course, in the diagram on the left, the slope is positive, indicating that the original function, for which this slope is the second derivative, has a minimum at the desired point. The diagram on the right represents a maximum. In either case,

$$f'(x_0) = \frac{f(x_0)}{x_0 - x_1}$$

Solving for x_1, the *second* estimate is

$$x_1 = x_0 - \frac{f(x_0)}{f'(x_0)} \tag{3-5.3}$$

The general formula for finding the $(i + 1)^{\text{th}}$ estimate from the ith estimate by successive iterations is

$$x_{i+1} = x_i - \frac{f(x_i)}{f'(x_i)} \tag{3-5.4}$$

and this Equation (3–5.4) is the basis of Newton's method of approximation.

We shall now apply this method to the solution of Equation (3–4.7)

$$0 = 2.5 - \frac{100}{n^2} + \frac{40.55}{n}\left(\frac{2}{3}\right)^n + \frac{100}{n^2}\left(\frac{2}{3}\right)^n \tag{3-4.7}$$

We ignore the fact that this expression is itself a derivative, and we identify it as $f(n)$, the expression whose root we seek.

$$f(n) = 2.5 - \frac{100}{n^2} + \left(\frac{40.55}{n} + \frac{100}{n^2}\right)\left(\frac{2}{3}\right)^n \tag{3-5.5}$$

Its derivative is

$$f'(n) = \frac{200}{n^3} + \left(\frac{40.55}{n} + \frac{100}{n^2}\right)\left(\frac{2}{3}\right)^n \ln\frac{2}{3} - \left(\frac{2}{3}\right)^n\left(\frac{40.55}{n^2} + \frac{200}{n^3}\right) \tag{3-5.6}$$

As a first approximation, even though we know from Table 3–3.1 that the optimal value of n is in the vicinity of $n = 5$, nevertheless, in order to demonstrate the method, we select $n_0 = 7$ as an arbitrary first estimate and substitute it into Equations (3–5.5) and (3–5.6) to yield 0.918 and 0.320, respectively.

Then from Equation (3–5.4)

$$n_1 = n_0 - \frac{f(n_0)}{f'(n_0)} = 7 - \frac{0.918}{0.320} = 7 - 2.87$$

$$= 4.13$$

Thus, the second estimate is 4.13.

Iterating again, for $n_1 = 4.13$, from Equation (3–5.4),

$$n_2 = n_1 - \frac{f(n_1)}{f'(n_1)} = 4.13 - \frac{-0.424}{0.670} = 4.13 + 0.633$$
$$= 4.74$$

Thus, the third estimate is 4.74.

Iterating again, for $n_2 = 4.74$,

$$n_3 = n_2 - \frac{f(n_2)}{f'(n_2)} = 4.74 - \frac{-0.474}{0.567} = 4.74 + 0.08$$
$$= 4.82$$

Thus, the fourth estimate is 4.82.

Iterating again, for $n_3 = 4.82$,

$$f(4.82) = 0.002$$
$$f'(4.82) = 0.555$$

Then

$$n_4 = n_3 - \frac{f(n_3)}{f'(n_3)} = 4.82 - \frac{0.002}{0.555} = 4.82$$

Therefore, further iteration does not change the result in the second decimal place. Actually, there was no need to iterate again. The low value of 0.002 for $f(4.82)$ indicated that 4.82 is very close to n^*, the desired root. Also, the very small adjustment in the previous iteration from 4.74 to 4.82 indicated that there was little to be gained by further iteration. We might also note that the positive value of $f'(4.82)$ indicates that, near this value of n, there is a *minimum* on the average cost curve, since $f'(n) = \frac{d^2}{(dn)^2}(AC)$, the second derivative of the average cost curve.

Therefore we can take 4.82 to be the root of the equation. If the machine is retired after 4.82 years of service, the average-annual-cost equation, (3–3.4), is slightly modified to take account of the partial year:

$$AC = \frac{1}{4.82}\left[\sum_{i=1}^{4}(20 + 5i) + 0.82\,[20 + (5)(4.82)] + 100 - 100\left(\frac{2}{3}\right)^{4.82}\right]$$
$$= (0.207)(80 + 50 + 36.16 + 100 - 14.169) = (0.207)(252)$$
$$= \$52.16$$
$$= 52.2 \text{ dollars (to three significant figures)}$$

The average cost with a 4.82-year replacement cycle is 52.2 dollars per year. This represents a saving over the $52.40 cost for a 5-year replacement period as found in Table 3–3.1. This seems to be a relatively small saving, indicating that the curve is relatively flat near this, the optimum point.

3–6. Reconciliation of Conflicting Objectives. It has been pointed out in Chapter 1 that in many business situations the objective function to be optimized is some combination of cost and benefit. This kind of cost vs. benefit analysis requires some transformation function making it possible to evaluate both the cost and the benefit on a single scale.

The Donsex County Electric Company serves a small residential area with electric power. Management finds that it is quite dissatisfied with the present rate of power failure. A study team finds that generating equipment deficiencies create an average of 200 customer-hours of electric power outage per day. Before deciding on the scope of new generating-equipment acquisition, management appointed a technical group to evaluate available appropriate new generating equipment and to analyze various new equipment purchase possibilities in terms of cost and associated expected levels of power failure. The technical group found that, for five selected typical equipment acquisitions, the cost and expected number of daily customer-hours of power outage were as given in Table 3–6.1. Management found this report completely unacceptable for two

TABLE 3–6.1

Donsex County Electric Company
Cost and Expected Performance of Additional Generating Equipment

New Equipment Cost ($ millions)	Approximate Number of Expected Daily Customer-Hours of Power Outage
0 (Present Equipment)	200
2	133
4	100
10	57
20	33
50	15

reasons: (1) discussion indicated that, rather than just these few selected equipment configurations, there was, in effect, a continuum of possible equipment costs with associated levels of power outage, but the technical team had presented only these five possible configurations; (2) there was no apparent way to resolve the conflicting objectives of cost savings and outage level reduction.

The technical team solved the first problem by further study leading to the following general relationship between power-outage level and equipment cost (C_e), of which the data in Table 3–6.1 are specific points.

$$H = 200 - \frac{200C_e}{4{,}000{,}000 + C_e} \tag{3–6.1}$$

where: H = expected daily outage in customer-hours
C_e = additional equipment cost in dollars

The second problem was met by ascertaining from discussions with management its feeling that a customer-hour of power outage was to be evaluated at a cost to the company of approximately $25. Since the equipment life was estimated to be eleven years, one hour per day is equivalent to 4,015 hours in 11 years. At $25 per hour, this is equivalent to approximately $100,000 over the life of the equipment. Once management agreed to this result, the rest was easy.

The total cost to the company (TC) was equal to the equipment cost C_e plus the customer waiting cost C_w,

$$TC = C_e + C_w$$

but

$$C_w = 100{,}000H = 100{,}000\left(200 - \frac{200C_e}{4{,}000{,}000 + C_e}\right)$$

$$TC = C_e + 10^7\left(2 - \frac{2C_e}{4 \times 10^6 + C_e}\right)$$

Differentiating this with respect to C_e,

$$\frac{d}{dC_e}(TC) = 1 + 10^7\left(0 - \frac{(4 \times 10^6 + C_e)(2) - 2C_e(1)}{(4 \times 10^6 + C_e)^2}\right)$$

Setting the derivative equal to zero,

$$0 = 1 - \frac{8 \times 10^{13}}{(4 \times 10^6 + C_e)^2}$$

$$(4 \times 10^6 + C_e)^2 = 80 \times 10^{12}$$

$$4 \times 10^6 + C_e = 8.94 \times 10^6$$

$$C_e = 4.94 \times 10^6$$

Thus, the optimal course of action is to spend approximately $5,000,000 for new generating equipment. This will provide a system with 89 expected daily customer-hours of outage:

$$H = 200 - \frac{200C_e}{4{,}000{,}000 + C_e} = 200 - \frac{(2 \times 10^2)(5 \times 10^6)}{4 \times 10^6 + 5 \times 10^6}$$

$$= 200 - \frac{10 \times 10^8}{9 \times 10^6} = 200 - 111 = 89 \text{ hours}$$

The total cost of this system, in terms of both capital costs and imputed customer dissatisfaction costs, is, at its minimum,

$$TC = C_e + C_w$$
$$= 5{,}000{,}000 + 8{,}900{,}000 = \$13{,}900{,}000$$

3–7. Interest Rates—Continuous Compounding. In many business problems, the cost of capital, either directly or in terms of its *opportunity cost,* is critical. The *opportunity cost* of any factor is the return which it can earn in its best alternative use. That is, even if a business uses its own internally generated capital for investment, it is not correct to assume that that is available at zero cost. If the going rate which that capital might earn in external investments is, say, 5%, then, if management wishes to maximize its return, management should not invest internally unless the expected earnings are at least equal to 5%. This is the opportunity cost of the capital. If it cannot earn 5% internally, it should be invested externally unless there is some other objective to be served by internal investment.

The question of opportunity cost arises constantly in business situations. Often it is related to capital cost and interest rates.

If a sum of money is drawing interest at the nominal rate of r per cent per year, and if the interest is compounded *annually* (i.e., *once* a year), then the sum does indeed grow at the rate of r per cent per year. However, if the interest is compounded twice a year, the *effective* rate of interest i is somewhat larger than r. The effective rate of interest i for *semiannual* compounding may be computed from the formula

$$1 + i = \left(1 + \frac{r}{2}\right)^2 \tag{3–7.1}$$

$$1 + i = 1 + r + \frac{r^2}{4}$$

$$i = r + \frac{r^2}{4}$$

If the *nominal* rate of interest is 5%, the *effective* rate i is, with *semiannual* compounding,

$$i = 0.05 + \left(\frac{0.05}{2}\right)^2 = 0.05 + 0.000625$$
$$= 0.050625$$

If compounding is more frequent, say, quarterly, the effective rate is larger. For quarterly compounding, the effective rate i is given by the formula

$$1 + i = \left(1 + \frac{r}{4}\right)^4 \tag{3–7.2}$$

The limiting case is where interest is compounded *continuously*, i.e., an infinitely large number of times per year. The effective rate in this case may be found from the same general formula. For any n, where n is the number of times per year interest is compounded, the effective rate of interest i is computed from the general formula

$$1 + i = \left(1 + \frac{r}{n}\right)^n \tag{3–7.3}$$

where r is the nominal rate of interest

From this it follows that, if n is very large, as is the case with *continuous compounding*, then the value of i may be determined from the relationship

$$1 + i = \lim_{n \to \infty} \left[\left(1 + \frac{r}{n}\right)^{n/r}\right]^r \tag{3–7.4}$$

and the term in the brackets is exactly the term which, according to Equation (2–9.2) has, as its limit, e. Therefore,

$$1 + i = e^r \tag{3–7.5}$$

Thus, the effective rate, when the nominal rate r is 5%, is (using the table of common logarithms and the relationship $e^x = \text{antilog}\,\frac{x}{2.303}$)

$$1 + i = e^{0.05} = \text{antilog}\,\frac{0.05}{2.303} = \text{antilog}\,0.02171$$

$$1 + i = 1.0513 \tag{3–7.6}$$

and the effective *annual* rate of interest is 5.13% per year. This value is the rate which is used in computing the present value of future sums of money. However, the *instantaneous* rate is 5% per year.

A sum of money under continuous compounding at 5% per year has a future value A such that, as shown in Figure 3–7.1, this future value at any time t is

$$A = P(1.0513)^t \tag{3–7.7}$$

where P is the *present value* of the sum.

The slope of the curve, i.e., the increase in A as a function of time, is

$$\frac{d}{dt}(A) = P(1.0513)^t \ln 1.0513 \tag{3–7.8}$$

but, from Equation (3–7.6) above,

$$1.0513 = e^{0.05}$$

and, therefore,

$$\ln 1.0513 = \ln e^{0.05} = 0.05 \tag{3–7.9}$$

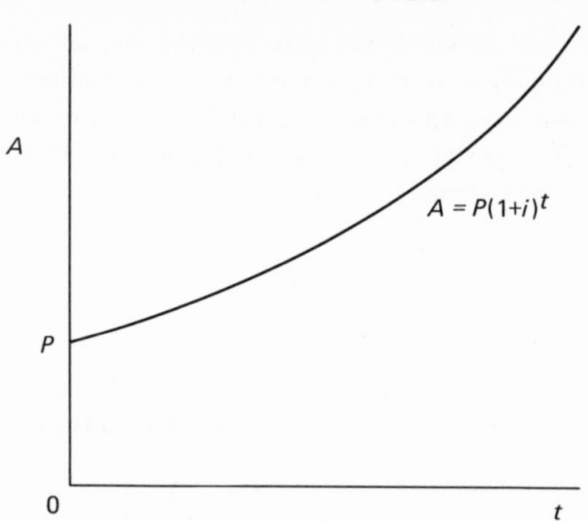

Fig. 3–7.1. The growth of a sum of money with present value P, at a continuously compounded rate of interest. Its future value A, at any time t, is $A = P(1 + i)^t$, where i is the effective rate of interest.

Thus, the slope is, from Equations (3–7.7), (3–7.8), and (3–7.9),

$$\frac{d}{dt}(A) = 0.05P(1.0513)^t = 0.05A \tag{3–7.10}$$

We shall use this result in the next section.

3–8. Timing the Sale of an Appreciating Asset. In this section we shall consider the problem of deciding when to sell an appreciating asset whose rate of appreciation is decreasing. Naturally, the decision to sell must be based on *both* the rate of appreciation of the asset and the opportunity cost of the invested capital. This is a purely financial problem in which the alternatively available interest rate is a controlling consideration, since it measures the opportunity cost.

The Sandy Burr Investment Company keeps a large sum of money in a trust account in which interest is being compounded *continuously* at 5% per year. A unique opportunity arose making it possible to buy a parcel of real estate for \$200,000, and it is just now being purchased with funds taken from the trust account. It is estimated that the realizable value of this purchase will increase from its present low disposal value (after fees, etc.) and approach \$400,000, according to the following function, where R is its value at any time t measured in years from the date of purchase:

$$R = 400{,}000(1 - 0.6^t) \qquad \text{for } t \geq 1 \tag{3–8.1}$$

In order to plan future acquisitions, it is necessary to decide now, at time $t = 0$, exactly when the parcel is to be sold and the proceeds of the sale returned to the trust account.

The decision is to be made on the basis of the present value of the investment. There has been an investment of \$200,000. Its disposal value, if it is sold a year from now, will be \$160,000, yielding a loss on the transaction of \$40,000, as well as the lost interest. However, there is no intention of selling so soon. Rather, the parcel of real estate is to be held for appreciation. The appreciation pattern, as given in Equation (3–8.1) and graphed in Figure 3–8.1, is one which levels off over time, and clearly

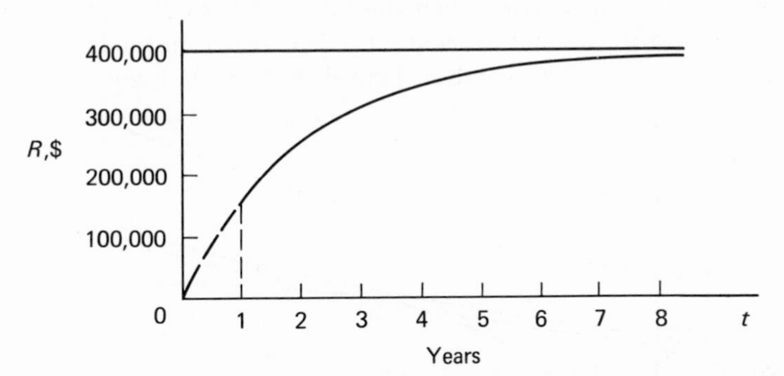

Fig. 3–8.1. Graph of the function $R = 400{,}000(1 - 0.6^t)$. The future value of a real estate investment. The Sandy Burr Investment Company.

it is possible to hold the asset too long in view of the opportunity cost. In this problem the opportunity cost is represented by the continuously compounded rate of 5%. The purpose of this analysis is to find the optimal time of sale.

The present value of any future sum of money is defined in terms of its opportunity cost, namely, its ability to earn 5% continuously com-

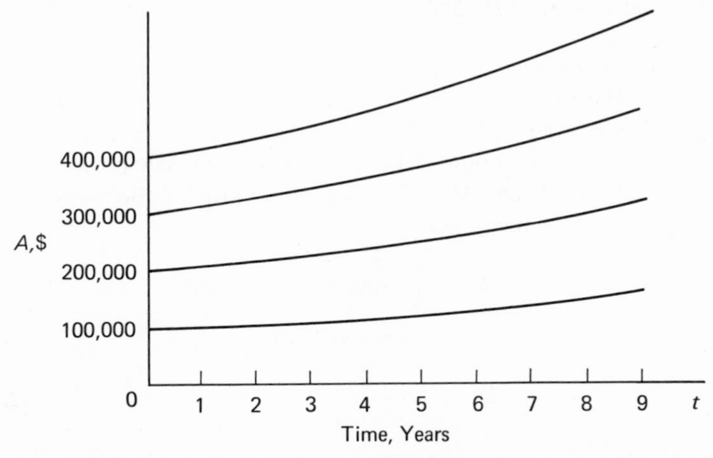

Fig. 3–8.2. Graph of the function $A = P(1.0513)^t$. The future values of various sums of money at a continuously compounded rate of interest of 5 per cent.

pounded in the trust fund. Figure 3–8.2 shows the future value of sums with various present values under a continuously compounded rate of interest of 5%. The optimal time to sell is when the curve for R, the value of the real estate parcel of Figure 3–8.1 is tangent to the curve on Figure 3–8.2 for the highest present value. The reasoning that leads to this conclusion is that there are two alternative investments available, the first with a higher but falling rate of return, and the second with a lower but constant rate of return. When the rate of return of the first becomes equal to that of the second, then any funds invested in the first should be shifted to the second. This combined graph is shown in Figure 3–8.3.

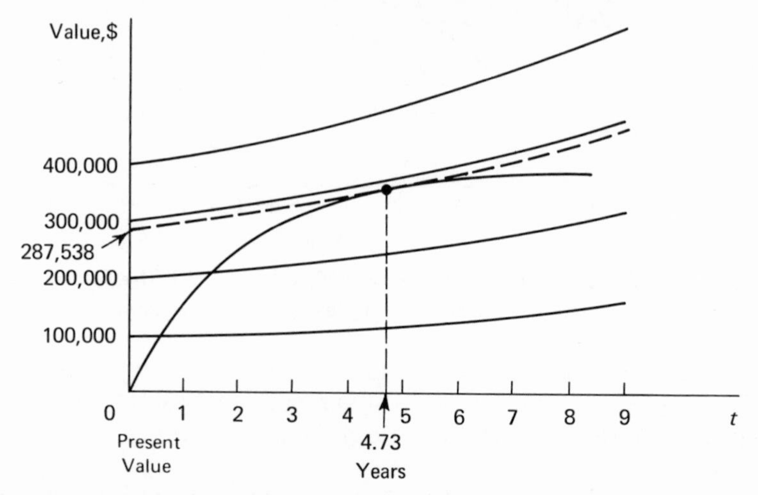

Fig. 3–8.3. The optimal timing of the sale of an appreciating asset. If sold at 4.73 years after purchase, it will yield $364,286 at that time, and that sum has a present value of $288,587.

The point of tangency is, of course characterized by the fact that both curves have the same slope at that point. Since the interest-rate curves of Figure 3–8.2 have a slope of $0.05A$ at all points, as demonstrated in Equation (3–7.10), the point of tangency will occur when the curve for R has a slope of $0.05R$, i.e., 5% of the current value of the asset.

The slope of the curve for R is

$$\frac{d}{dt}(R) = \frac{d}{dt}[400{,}000(1 - 0.6^t)]$$

$$= (-400{,}000)(0.6)^t \ln 0.6$$

$$\frac{d}{dt}(R) = (204{,}332)(0.6)^t \qquad (3\text{–}8.2)$$

Setting the two slopes equal to one another,

$$0.05A = (204{,}332)(0.6)^t$$

but, at the point of tangency, $A = R$. Therefore, from Equation (3–8.1),

$$(0.05)(400{,}000)(1 - 0.6^t) = (204{,}332)(0.6)^t$$

$$20{,}000 - (20{,}000)(0.6)^t = (204{,}332)(0.6)^t$$

$$(0.6)^t = 0.08915$$

$$t \log 0.6 = \log 0.08915$$

$$-0.22185t = -1.04988$$

$$t = 4.7324 \text{ years}$$

Thus, the optimal timing is to sell the asset after approximately $4\frac{3}{4}$ years. At that time, its selling price will be

$$\begin{aligned} R &= (400{,}000)(1 - 0.6^{4.7324}) \\ &= (400{,}000)(1 - 0.08915) = (400{,}000)(0.91085) \\ &= \$364{,}340 \end{aligned}$$

The present value of this sum is

$$P = \frac{A}{(1.0513)^{4.7324}} = \frac{364{,}340}{1.2671} = \$287{,}538$$

Thus, the optimal course of action is to sell in approximately $4\frac{3}{4}$ years for approximately \$364,000. The time, $4\frac{3}{4}$ years, is the time such that the real estate parcel has its *highest present value*, about \$288,000. The present value of the real estate parcel changes as a function of t, the time in the future at which it is viewed and evaluated, as may be seen in Figure 3–8.3. *If the optimal timing is observed in selling the asset*, then it has a present value of about \$288,000. Therefore, by purchasing the asset, the present value of the \$200,000 taken from the trust fund increased from \$200,000 to \$288,000, if appreciation occurs exactly as forecasted, and if the asset is sold in $4\frac{3}{4}$ years.

3–9. Decay of Advertising Effect. The Canel Company, which has advertised and promoted its product by sporadic television special programs and associated in-store promotion over the years, finds that its residual advertising effect on consumers, as measured on an awareness-attitude scale (called by the company, the "A-scale") and derived by psychologically oriented personal interview surveys, decreases from its value, arbitrarily called 100, just after a typical program, according to the following pattern.

$$A = 100\, e^{-0.07t}$$

where t is the time in weeks since the end of the advertising campaign

The company wishes to ascertain the maximum time which may be permitted to elapse between successive campaigns while maintaining a minimum level of 50 on the A-scale.

Figure 3–9.1 shows the pattern of A-scale decay and reinforcement over time, if the company maintains a minimum level of 50 by scheduling

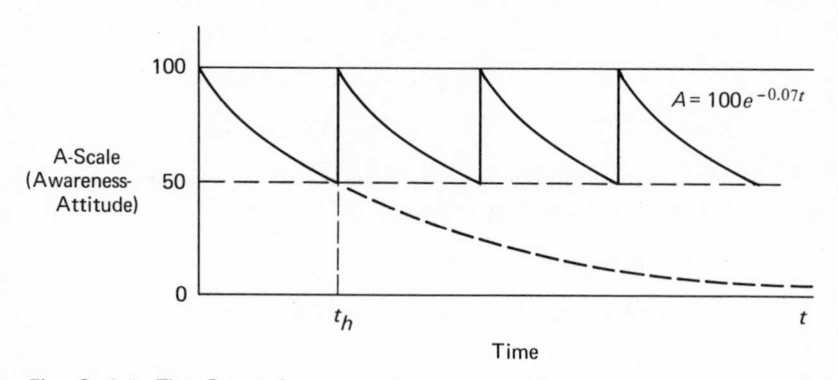

Fig. 3–9.1. The Canel Company. Decay of residual advertising effect with reinforcement at half-life.

programs to occur just when the A-scale measure reaches 50. Thus, the desired time interval between programs is the "half-life" of the residual advertising effect. It is the time interval in which the advertising effect decreases to half the level at which the interval began. This half-life time interval t_h is the time interval such that

$$e^{-0.07t_h} = 0.5 \tag{3–9.1}$$

Taking the reciprocal of both sides of equation (3–9.1),

$$e^{0.07t_h} = 2 \tag{3–9.2}$$

Then, using the familiar relationship, $\ln e^x = x$, and taking the natural logarithm of both sides of Equation (3–9.2),

$$0.07t_h = \ln 2 = (2.303)(0.30103) = 0.693272$$

$$t_h = 9.9 \text{ weeks}$$

Thus, programs should be scheduled at about 10-week intervals in order to cause the A-scale measure to follow the path shown in Figure 3–9.1.

Pursuing this problem, one might question the objective of maintenance of a minimum of 50 on the A-scale and ask what the proper minimum should be in the light of the costs and benefits of the advertising and promotion campaigns.

The company's research department has ascertained that the company sales level and associated profit on that product, *after all costs except the advertising and promotion campaigns,* is such that the annual profit under a program of equally-spaced campaigns is

$$P = 80 + 0.05A_{\min} \tag{3–9.3}$$

where: P is the annual profit in millions of dollars
$A_{\min}$ is the minimum A-scale level permitted

and that the total cost of each campaign is \$200,000. Then, the annual cost of advertising and promotion is 0.2 million dollars multiplied by the annual number of campaigns, which, since t is measured in weeks, is $\frac{52}{t}$. Then, since the residual A-scale measure is $100e^{-0.07t}$, the relationship between profit and the time interval t is

$$P = 80 + 5\,e^{-0.07t} - \frac{52}{t}(0.2) \tag{3–9.4}$$

and the optimal time interval is ascertained by differentiating the profit function with respect to t, and setting the derivative equal to zero:

$$\frac{dP}{dt} = -(0.07)(5)e^{-0.07t} + \frac{10.4}{t^2} = 0$$

$$0.35t^{*2}\,e^{-0.07t^*} = 10.4$$

$$t^{*2}\,e^{-0.07t^*} = 29.7$$

We can easily solve this rather difficult appearing equation for t^* by using Newton's approximation method

$$f(x) = x^2\,e^{-0.07x} - 29.7$$

$$f'(x) = -0.07x^2\,e^{-0.07x} + 2x\,e^{-0.07x} = x\,e^{-0.07x}\,(2 - 0.07x)$$

As a first approximation, let us arbitrarily select $x_0 = 10$, the current advertising practice. (Use Appendix F for e^{-x} when possible; elsewhere use $e^x = \text{antilog}\,\frac{x}{2.303}$.)

For $x_0 = 10$, $e^{-0.07} = 0.49659$,

$$f(x_0) = (100)(0.49659) - 29.7 = 49.7 - 29.7 = 20.0$$

$$f'(x_0) = (4.97)(1.3) = 6.46$$

Then

$$x_1 = x_0 - \frac{f(x_0)}{f'(x_0)} \tag{3–5.3}$$

$$x_1 = 10 - \frac{20}{6.46} = 10 - 3.1 = 6.9$$

For $x_1 = 6.9$, $e^{-0.483} = 0.61698$,

$$f(x_1) = (47.61)(0.61698) - 29.7 = 29.37 - 29.7 = -0.33$$

$$f'(x_1) = (6.9)(0.61698)(2 - 0.483) = (4.25716)(1.517) = 6.46$$

$$x_2 = 6.9 - \frac{-0.33}{6.46} = 6.95 \approx 7.0$$

For $x_2 = 7.0$, $e^{-0.49} = 0.61267$,

$$f(x_2) = (49)(0.61267) - 29.7 = 30.0 - 29.7 = 0.3$$

Clearly, since $f(6.9) = -0.33$ and $f(7.0) = 0.3$, the desired root lies between these values, and we need iterate no longer. For all practical purposes,

$$t^* = 7 \text{ weeks}$$

Under this optimal scheduling pattern of seven-week intervals between campaigns, the annual profit, from Equation (3–9.4), is (rounded to the nearest 0.1 million dollars):

$$P = 80 + 3.06 - 1.49 = 81.6 \text{ million dollars}$$

This may be compared with the annual profit of 81.4 million dollars earned under the current practice using ten-week intervals between campaigns.

3–10. Two Controllable Variables—Price and Advertising Budget. In the Do-Mor Frypan illustration of Chapter 2, it was found that, at a unit price (p) of \$10, with the sales function

$$S_{10} = (1{,}000{,}000)\left(1 - \frac{1}{x^2}\right) \qquad \text{for } x \geq 1.5 \qquad (3\text{–}10.1)$$

where: x is the advertising budget in millions of dollars
S_{10} is the annual sales in units at a price of \$10

and the annual production cost function, omitting the subscript for S,

$$C = 200{,}000 + 5S \qquad \text{for } S \leq 1{,}200{,}000$$

where S is the number produced per year (the same as sales)

the optimal advertising budget was \$2,154,400, which yielded sales of

$$S = (1{,}000{,}000)\left(1 - \frac{1}{4.6414}\right) = 784{,}500 \text{ units}$$

and profit of

$$P = \text{Revenue} - \text{Production Cost} - \text{Advertising Cost} \qquad (2\text{–}5.7)$$

$$P = pS - (200{,}000 + 5S) - 1{,}000{,}000x \qquad (3\text{–}10.2)$$

$$P = (10)(784{,}500) - 200{,}000 - (5)(784{,}500) - (1{,}000{,}000)(2.1544)$$

$$= 7{,}845{,}000 - 200{,}000 - 3{,}922{,}500 - 2{,}154{,}400$$

$$P = \$1{,}568{,}000 \text{ (to the nearest thousand dollars)}$$

Now the company has decided to try to find out whether the price of \$10 is optimal. The demand curve is found to be, for any price p, in the range between \$6 and \$15:

$$S_p = S_{10}\left(\frac{20 - p}{10}\right) \qquad \text{for } 6 \leq p \leq 15 \tag{3–10.3}$$

where: p is the unit price
S_{10} is the sales (number of units) at $p = \$10$
S_p is sales at price p

Then

$$S_p = (1{,}000{,}000)\left(1 - \frac{1}{x^2}\right)\left(\frac{20 - p}{10}\right) \tag{3–10.4}$$

and the profit function is

$$P = pS_p - (200{,}000 + 5S_p) - 1{,}000{,}000x$$

$$= S_p(p - 5) - 1{,}000{,}000x - 200{,}000$$

$$P = \left[(1{,}000{,}000)\left(1 - \frac{1}{x^2}\right)\left(\frac{20 - p}{10}\right)\right](p - 5) - 1{,}000{,}000x - 200{,}000 \tag{3–10.5}$$

In order to find the simultaneous optimal values of price and advertising budget, we shall differentiate P partially with respect to p and set that expression equal to 0. Next we shall differentiate P partially with respect to x and set that expression equal to 0. Then, we can find the values of p and x which satisfy both of those expressions by solving them simultaneously.

$$\frac{\partial P}{\partial p} = (1{,}000{,}000)\left(1 - \frac{1}{x^2}\right)\left[\left(\frac{20 - p}{10}\right)(1) + (p - 5)\left(-\frac{1}{10}\right)\right]$$

$$0 = 2 - \frac{p^*}{10} - \frac{p^*}{10} + 0.5$$

$$2p^* = (2.5)(10)$$

$$p^* = 12.5 \tag{3–10.6}$$

$$\frac{\partial P}{\partial x} = (1{,}000{,}000)\left(\frac{20 - p}{10}\right)(p - 5)\left(\frac{2}{x^3}\right) - 1{,}000{,}000$$

$$0 = \left(\frac{20 - p}{10}\right)(p - 5)\left(\frac{2}{x^{*3}}\right) - 1 \tag{3–10.7}$$

The two equations which must be solved simultaneously are Equations (3–10.6) and (3–10.7). This is particularly easy in this case because Equation (3–10.6) contains only variable p^*. The asterisks indicate that Equation (3–10.6) yields the optimal value of p, and Equation (3–10.7) yields the optimal value of x. Solving these equations simultaneously yields the simultaneous optimal values of both variables.

$$0 = \left(\frac{20 - 12.5}{10}\right)(12.5 - 5)\left(\frac{2}{x^{*3}}\right) - 1$$

$$1 = (0.75)(7.5)\left(\frac{2}{x^{*3}}\right)$$

$$x^{*3} = 11.25$$

$$x^* = 2.241$$

The reader should verify that, in both cases, the second derivative is negative, indicating that the extreme point is a maximum. Thus, the optimal configuration of the controllable variables is

$$p^* = \text{Price} = \$12.50$$

$$x^* = \text{Advertising Budget} = \$2.241 \text{ million dollars}$$

and the resulting sales level (in units), omitting the subscript for S, is, from Equation (3–10.4),

$$S = (1{,}000{,}000)\left(1 - \frac{1}{(2.241)^2}\right)\left(\frac{20 - 12.5}{10}\right)$$

but $(2.241)^2 = 5.022$, and $1 - \dfrac{1}{5.022} = 0.8009$:

$$S = (750{,}000)(0.8009) = 600{,}700 \text{ units}$$

The resulting optimum profit (in dollars) is, from Equation (3–10.2),

$$\begin{aligned} P &= (12.5)(600{,}700) - 200{,}000 - (5)(600{,}700) - 2{,}241{,}000 \\ &= 7{,}509{,}000 - 200{,}000 - 3{,}004{,}000 - 2{,}241{,}000 \\ &= \$2{,}064{,}000 \end{aligned}$$

as compared with $1,568,000 at the optimal advertising level but a predetermined price of $10.

Let us examine this problem graphically to see just what we have done.

From Equation (3–10.4) we can compute the unit sales at various arbitrarily selected price and advertising levels. These are shown in the matrix of Figure 3–10.1. Figure 3–10.2 shows the advertising response curve for a price of $10 (the $10 row of Figure 3–10.1), and Figure 3–10.3 shows the price–demand curve for an advertising budget of $2,000,000 (the $2,000,000 column of Figure 3–10.1).

		Annual Advertising Budget, $ Millions				
		1.5	2	3	4	5
	6	778	1,050	1,244	1,313	1,344
	8	667	900	1,067	1,126	1,152
Price, $	10	556	750	889	938	960
	12	449	600	711	750	768
	15	278	375	445	469	480

Fig. 3–10.1. Sales in thousands of units of Do-Mor Frypan Co. for selected levels of price and annual advertising budget. Source: Equation (3–10.4).

In Figure 3–10.4, the profit values are presented for all of the combinations of price and advertising budget shown in Figure 3–10.1. Equation (3–10.5) was used for this computation, but, since S was already computed, the equation was modified to the form of Equation (3–10.8) to simplify the arithmetic.

$$P = (p - 5)S - 1{,}000{,}000x - 200{,}000 \qquad (3\text{–}10.8)$$

It is clear from Figure 3–10.4 that we may plot profit against advertising budget at a constant price, or profit against price at a constant advertising budget, and, in either case, the curve will rise to a maximum and then descend as the controllable variable is increased. In Figure 3–10.5 we have plotted the relationship between profit and *both* controllable variables, using the technique commonly employed to represent

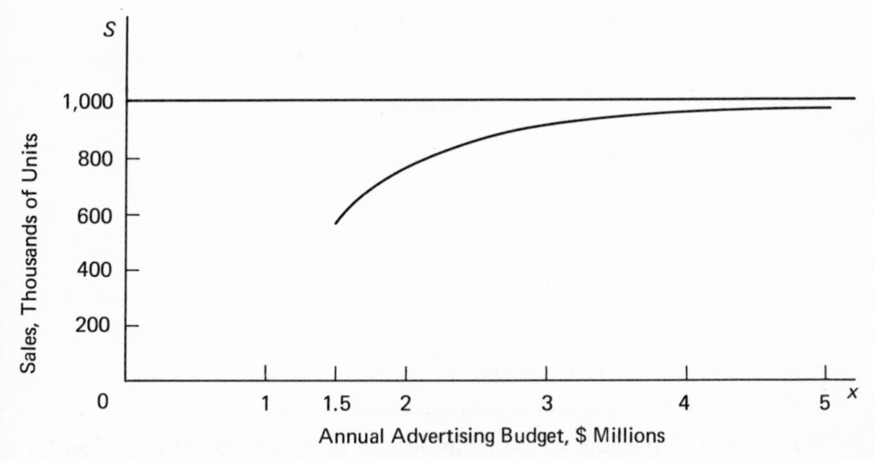

Fig. 3–10.2. Do-Mor Frypan Co. Advertising response curve at a fixed price of $10.

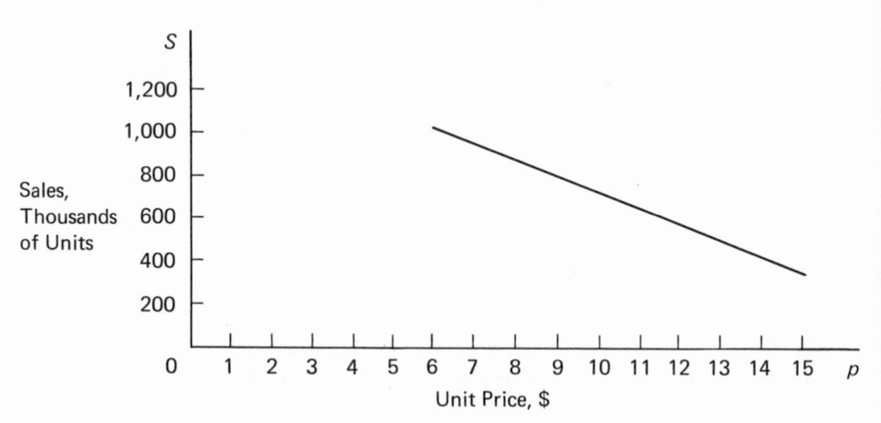

Fig. 3–10.3. Do-Mor Frypan Co. Demand curve at annual advertising budget of $2,000,000.

contour lines on a topographical map. The lines are "iso-profit" lines. They represent constant levels of profit. A cross section drawn horizontally at, say, $p = 10$, rises to a peak at about $x = 2.15$, and then decreases. Similarly, a vertical cross section at, say, $x = 3$ rises to a peak in the vicinity of $p = 12.5$, and then decreases. The diagram is to be imagined as depicting a curved surface whose height measures the profit. The surface rises to a peak of 2,064 at the optimal point, $x = 2.241$, $p = 12.5$. The lines are lines of constant height on the surface.

Note that lines have been drawn at $x = 1.5$, $p = 6$, and $p = 15$, to delineate the limits of validity of the analysis. These limits, as stated in Equations (3–10.1) and (3–10.3), indicate that there is no basis for assuming that the given functions apply beyond those limits. For that reason, all contour lines outside of the limits are shown as dashed lines.

	Annual Advertising Budget, $ Millions				
Price, $	1.5	2	3	4	5
6	−922	−1,150	−1,956	−2,887	−3,856
8	301	500	1	−822	−1,744
10	1,080	1,550	1,245	490	−400
12	1,443	2,000	1,777	1,050	176
15	1,080	1,550	1,250	490	−400

Fig. 3–10.4. Profit (annual) in thousands of dollars of Do-Mor Frypan Co. for arbitrarily selected levels of price and advertising. Source: Equatioı (3–10.8).

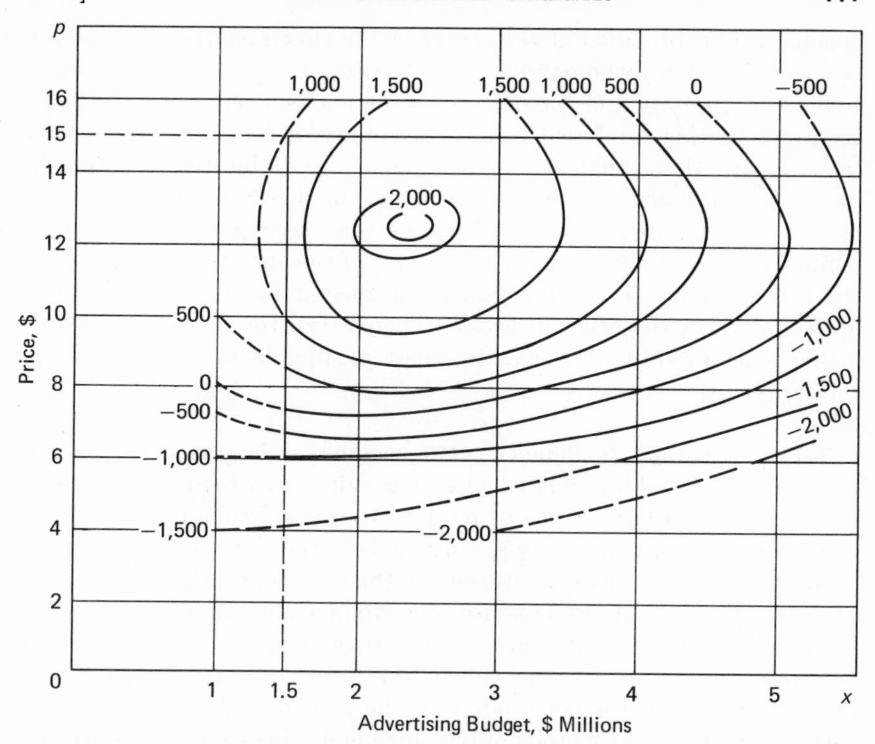

Fig. 3–10.5. Contour lines showing profit (in thousands of dollars) as a function of price and advertising budget. The optimum point is 2,064 at (2,241, 12.5). Source: Figure 3–10.4.

The significance of the fact that Equation (3–10.6)

$$p^* = 12.5 \tag{3–10.6}$$

is independent of x is seen in the contour diagram, in that the maximum on any vertical cross section line occurs at $p = 12.5$, and it is independent of the value of x. On the other hand, the maximum value for x is not independent of the value of p. This is evident in Equation (3–10.7) which includes both variables. It can also be seen in the contour diagram, in that the optimal value for x is 2.234 when $p = 12.5$, but when $p = 10$ the optimal value for x, as seen in Section 2–5 above, is 2.15, and when $p = 6$, the optimal value for x is 1.41. This last value may be verified by the reader as an exercise. (See Exercise 3–1 at the end of this chapter.)

The contour diagram of Figure 3–10.5 is particularly interesting for operations researchers. The contour lines are *lines of equal value of the objective function*. That is, every point on any line is exactly as desirable as any other point on the same line, since the value of the objective function is constant along each line. The value of the objective function can be improved by moving across these lines, in this case, toward the optimal course of action at the center of the closed contour lines at the point (2.241, 12.5), where profit is $2,064,000.

This interpretation of the objective function as a set of contour lines, each representing a different value of the objective function, may be contrasted with the graphical representation of the objective function in linear programming problems. In the case of linear programming, the objective function is represented, as we shall see, as a set of straight parallel lines, each representing some value of the objective function with the higher values in one direction perpendicular to these lines and the lower values in the other direction. There, also, the optimal course of action is achieved by moving across these parallel lines from nonoptimal solutions to the optimal.

3–11. Lagrange Multipliers. The method of Lagrange multipliers is a general method for finding an extreme value (maximum or minimum) of a function, subject to one or more restrictions. While the method of Lagrange multipliers is widely applicable, sometimes it is simpler to solve problems of this sort by substitution. In this section, we shall first solve a problem by substitution. This use of a familiar and simple method will serve to illustrate the general characteristics of problems requiring the determination of an extreme value subject to restrictions, and it will provide an intuitive understanding of the meaning of the result. Then we shall introduce the method of Lagrange multipliers and solve the same problem using the new method.

It is quite common in management science models to find that the model to be optimized is subject to certain restrictions on the controllable variables. When this is the case, the decision maker cannot be content to seek out the optimal values of the controllable variables, but rather he must find the optimal values *subject to the restricting conditions*. For example, in the Do-Mor problem of the last section, we found that the optimal values of the controllable variables, price and advertising budget, were, respectively, $12.50 and $2,241,000. Clearly, if there had been a restriction that, say, the advertising budget had to be $2,000,000, not only would the optimal value given above for advertising budget be impossible, but also the optimal price might be different.

Indeed, in the simplified version of the Do-Mor problem given in Section 2–5, the price was constrained to be $10. That value of price, if substituted into Equation (3–10.7), would yield the familiar equations of Section 2–5, with the resulting optimal advertising budget of $2,154,400.

From the last paragraph, it is clear that, if one of the controllable variables is restricted to some fixed value, the problem is simplified, since the fixed variable is no longer a *controllable* variable in the sense in which we use that term. It is an uncontrollable variable whose value is known, and the problem is solved merely by substituting the correct value of that variable into the equation which is the system model. Then, the problem is simplified in that it then requires only the determination of the optimal value of, say, the price along the specified column, as shown in Figure 3–10.4 or 3–10.5; or alternatively, the determination of the optimal value of advertising budget along the appropriate row of those figures. This last case is, of course, exactly the problem which was solved in Section 2–5, where the price was specified at $10, and the optimal advertising budget was found to be $2,154,400 yielding an annual profit of $1,568,000. This result may be seen to be consistent with the data given in Figures 3–10.4 and 3–10.5.

This substitution procedure may also be used when there is some simple fixed relationship among the controllable variables, e.g., in the Do-Mor problem of Section 3–10, if there had been a restriction that the advertising budget must be exactly 200,000 times the price, or, since x is in millions of dollars,

$$x = 0.2p \qquad \text{or} \qquad p = 5x \tag{3–11.1}$$

Then the system Equation (3–10.5)

$$P = (1{,}000{,}000)\left(1 - \frac{1}{x^2}\right)\left(\frac{20 - p}{10}\right)(p - 5) - 1{,}000{,}000x - 200{,}000 \tag{3–10.5}$$

may be simplified by substitution from Equation (3–11.1) to eliminate the controllable variable x:

$$P = (1{,}000{,}000)\left(1 - \frac{1}{(0.2p)^2}\right)\left(\frac{20 - p}{10}\right)(p - 5) - (1{,}000{,}000)(0.2p) - 200{,}000 \tag{3–11.2}$$

This equation may be simplified and differentiated to yield the optimal price level.

First, to simplify:

$$\left(1 - \frac{1}{0.04p^2}\right)\left(\frac{20 - p}{10}\right)(p - 5)$$

$$= \left(1 - \frac{25}{p^2}\right)\left(2 - \frac{p}{10}\right)(p - 5)$$

$$= \left(1 - \frac{25}{p^2}\right)\left(2p - \frac{p^2}{10} - 10 + \frac{p}{2}\right) = \left(1 - \frac{25}{p^2}\right)\left(-\frac{p^2}{10} + 2.5p - 10\right)$$

$$= -\frac{p^2}{10} + 2.5p - 10 + 2.5 - \frac{62.5}{p} + \frac{250}{p^2}$$

$$= -\frac{p^2}{10} + 2.5p - \frac{62.5}{p} + \frac{250}{p^2} - 7.5$$

Then, differentiating,

$$\frac{dP}{dp} = (1{,}000{,}000)\left(-\frac{2p}{10} + 2.5 + \frac{62.5}{p^2} - \frac{500}{p^3}\right) - 200{,}000$$

$$0 = (5)\left(-\frac{p^*}{5} + 2.5 + \frac{62.5}{p^{*2}} - \frac{500}{p^{*3}}\right) - 1$$

$$= -p^* + 12.5 + \frac{312.5}{p^{*2}} - \frac{2{,}500}{p^{*3}} - 1$$

$$= p^{*4} - 11.5p^{*3} - 312.5p^* + 2{,}500$$

(Here we shall present the detailed arithmetic of the solution so that the reader may, if he wishes, follow the step-by-step application of the method.) Solving by Newton's approximation method,

$$f(p) = p^4 - 11.5p^3 - 312.5p + 2{,}500$$

$$f'(p) = 4p^3 - 34.5p^2 - 312.5$$

Let $p_0 = 15$, then

$$f(15) = 50{,}625 - 38{,}813 - 4{,}688 + 2{,}500 = 9{,}624$$

$$f'(15) = 13{,}500 - 7{,}763 - 312.5 = 5{,}424$$

$$p_1 = p_0 - \frac{f(p_0)}{f'(p_0)} = 15 - \frac{9{,}624}{5{,}424} = 15 - 1.77 = 13.2$$

$$f(13.2) = 30{,}360 - 26{,}450 - 4{,}125 + 2{,}500 = 2{,}285$$

$$f'(13.2) = 9{,}200 - 6{,}011 - 312.5 = 2{,}876$$

$$p_2 = 13.2 - \frac{2{,}285}{2{,}876} = 13.2 - 0.79 = 12.4$$

$$f(12.4) = 23{,}642 - 21{,}926 - 3{,}875 + 2{,}500 = 341$$

$$f'(12.4) = 7{,}626 - 5{,}305 - 312.5 = 2{,}008$$

$$p_3 = 12.4 - \frac{341}{2{,}008} = 12.4 - 0.169 = 12.23$$

(Note that we have retained the second decimal place since we are now close to the answer.)

$$f(12.23) = 22{,}372 - 21{,}037 - 3{,}822 + 2{,}500 = 13$$

$$f'(12.23) = 7{,}317 - 5{,}160 - 312.5 = 1{,}844$$

since

$$\frac{f(12.23)}{f'(12.23)} < 0.01$$

we retain

$$p^* = \$12.23$$

Then

$$x^* = \frac{12.23}{5} = 2.446 \text{ million dollars}$$

and

$$P = \$2{,}033{,}000$$

These results, i.e., price equals \$12.23, advertising budget equals \$2,446,000, and profit equals \$2,033,000, may be read (with far less precision, of course!) on Figure 3–11.1, which is the same as Figure

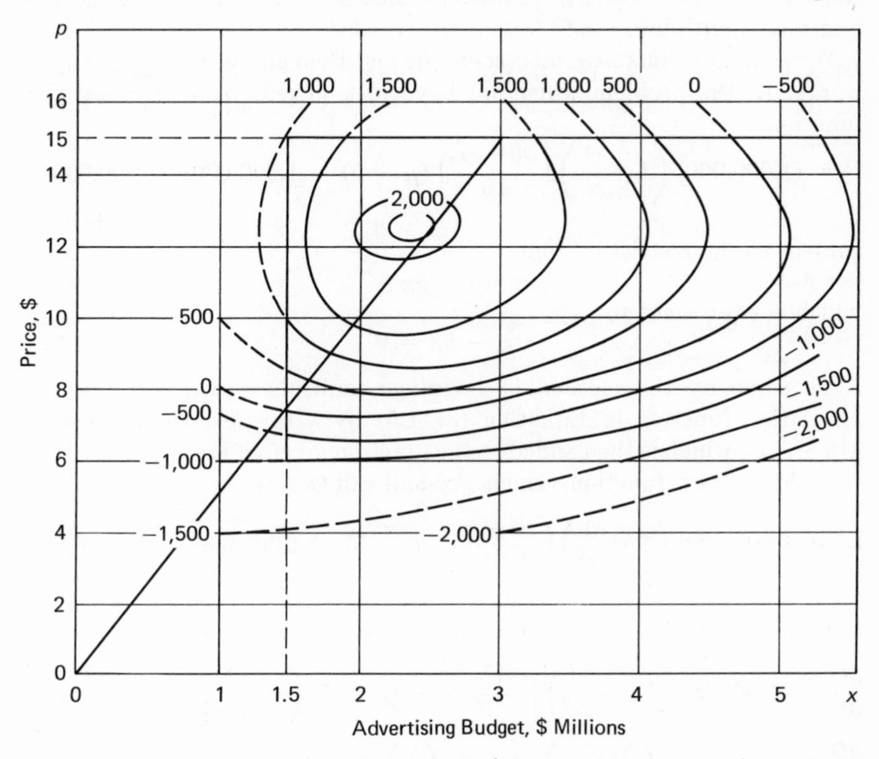

Fig. 3–11.1. Contour lines showing profit (in thousands of dollars) as a function of price and advertising budget. The straight line has the equation: $p = 5x$.

3–10.5, but with a line drawn for the restriction, $p = 5x$. The restriction, of course, required that the solution be on that line, and the problem was to find the maximum profit point along that line.

The method of Lagrange multipliers provides an alternative general technique for finding the extreme value of a function $E(x_1,x_2)$, subject to the restriction that

$$G(x_1,x_2) = 0 \qquad (3\text{–}11.3)$$

The technique involves the introduction of the "Lagrange multiplier" λ which is multiplied by the restriction function $G(x_1,x_2)$, and this product is added to the original function to be optimized, yielding a new function which we shall designate $F(x_1,x_2,\lambda)$.

$$F(x_1,x_2,\lambda) = E(x_1,x_2) + \lambda G(x_1,x_2) \tag{3–11.4}$$

The function $F(x_1,x_2,\lambda)$ may then be partially differentiated with respect to each of the three variables, x_1, x_2, and λ, in turn to yield three partial derivatives. When these are set equal to zero and solved simultaneously, the desired result, i.e., the extreme value of $E(x_1,x_2)$ subject to the condition that $G(x_1,x_2) = 0$, is obtained as well as the value of λ, the Lagrange multiplier.

We shall now illustrate this technique and then analyze it to see why it works. In the problem which we have just solved, we maximized the function

$$P = (1{,}000{,}000)\left(1 - \frac{1}{x^2}\right)\left(\frac{20 - p}{10}\right)(p - 5) - 1{,}000{,}000x - 200{,}000 \tag{3–10.5}$$

subject to the restriction that

$$p = 5x$$

which is equivalent to

$$p - 5x = 0 \tag{3–11.5}$$

To solve by the method of Lagrange multipliers, we multiply the restriction function of Equation (3–11.5) by λ to yield the expression $\lambda(p - 5x)$, which is then added to the function given in Equation (3–10.5) to yield the new function, which we shall call Q.

$$Q = (1{,}000{,}000)\left(1 - \frac{1}{x^2}\right)\left(\frac{20 - p}{10}\right)(p - 5) - 1{,}000{,}000x - 200{,}000 + \lambda(p - 5x) \tag{3–11.6}$$

Differentiating this expression with respect to p, x, and λ yields

$$\frac{\partial Q}{\partial p} = (1{,}000{,}000)\left(1 - \frac{1}{x^2}\right)\left[\frac{20 - p}{10} + (p - 5)\left(-\frac{1}{10}\right)\right] + \lambda \tag{3–11.7}$$

$$\frac{\partial Q}{\partial x} = (1{,}000{,}000)\left(\frac{20 - p}{10}\right)(p - 5)\left(\frac{2}{x^3}\right) - 1{,}000{,}000 - 5\lambda \tag{3–11.8}$$

$$\frac{\partial Q}{\partial \lambda} = p - 5x \tag{3–11.9}$$

Now the three equations to be solved simultaneously are (with asterisks omitted for simplicity),

$$(1{,}000{,}000)\left(1 - \frac{1}{x^2}\right)\left(2.5 - \frac{p}{5}\right) + \lambda = 0 \tag{3–11.10}$$

$$(1{,}000{,}000)\left(\frac{2}{x^3}\right)\left(-\frac{p^2}{10} + 2.5p - 10\right) - 1{,}000{,}000 - 5\lambda = 0 \tag{3–11.11}$$

$$p - 5x = 0 \tag{3–11.12}$$

Substituting $p = 5x$ into Equations (3–11.10) and (3–11.11) and changing signs in the second yields

$$(1{,}000{,}000)\left(1 - \frac{1}{x^2}\right)(2.5 - x) = -\lambda \qquad (3\text{–}11.13)$$

and

$$(1{,}000{,}000)\left(\frac{2}{x^3}\right)(2.5x^2 - 12.5x + 10) + 1{,}000{,}000 = -5\lambda \quad (3\text{–}11.14)$$

Then, substituting Equation (3–11.13) into (3–11.14) yields

$$\left(\frac{2}{x^3}\right)(2.5x^2 - 12.5x + 10) + 1 = (5)\left(1 - \frac{1}{x^2}\right)(2.5 - x) \qquad (3\text{–}11.15)$$

$$\frac{5}{x} - \frac{25}{x^2} + \frac{20}{x^3} + 1 = (5)\left(2.5 - x - \frac{2.5}{x^2} + \frac{1}{x}\right)$$

$$5x^2 - 25x + 20 + x^3 = 12.5x^3 - 5x^4 - 12.5x + 5x^2$$

$$5x^4 - 11.5x^3 - 12.5x + 20 = 0 \qquad (3\text{–}11.16)$$

This function may be solved by the use of Newton's approximation method, but that is not necessary here. Since we already know the answer to be $x = 2.446$, we can verify it by substitution:

$$(5)(2.446)^4 - (11.5)(2.446)^3 - (12.5)(2.446) + 20$$
$$= 179.0 - 168.3 - 30.6 + 20 = 000.1 \approx 0$$

Thus, the optimal solution, subject to the restriction, is $x^* = 2.446$, $p^* = 12.23$, $Q = P = \$2{,}033{,}000$, and from Equation (3–11.13),

$$-\lambda = (1{,}000{,}000)\left(1 - \frac{1}{(2.446)^2}\right)(2.5 - x)$$
$$= (1{,}000{,}000)(0.83286)(0.554)$$
$$\lambda = -461{,}404$$

or, to three places,

$$\lambda = -461{,}000$$

We shall discuss the meaning of λ presently, but first let us show why this method yields the desired result.

In Figure 3–11.1, there is some profit line, actually the 2,033 line (corresponding to \$2,033,000) which is just tangent to the restriction line. The point of tangency (x^*,p^*) is the optimal point, and at the point of tangency, both lines have the same slope. The slope of the profit line is, of course, $\frac{dp}{dx}$ in the xp plane as pictured. But the slope may also be viewed as

$$\frac{\frac{\partial P}{\partial x}}{\frac{\partial P}{\partial p}} = \text{Slope of profit line} \tag{3-11.17}$$

This follows, on reflection, from the fact that the numerator represents the relative rate at which profit changes as x changes. It is zero if the profit line at that point is parallel to the x-axis; and it is large if the profit line is sloped sharply upward, indicating that, for a given change in x, relatively many profit lines are cut. Also, the denominator is the relative rate at which profit lines are cut as p changes. Thus, if the profit lines are vertical, the denominator is zero, and it becomes large as the profit lines approach the horizontal.

In other words, for a given small change in profit, the denominator is inversely related to the p-distance, dp, necessary to effect that change, and the numerator is inversely related to the x-distance, dx, necessary to effect that change. Then, the ratio of Equation (3–11.17) is, for a small change in profit at some selected point, the ratio of the inverse of dx to the inverse of dp. And this is the slope of the profit line:

$$\frac{\frac{\partial P}{\partial x}}{\frac{\partial P}{\partial p}} = \frac{\frac{1}{dx}}{\frac{1}{dp}} = \frac{dp}{dx} \tag{3-11.18}$$

We can now prove the method. Using the profit function P and the restriction function G, we construct a new function. Writing G to represent $G(x,p)$, this new function Q is

$$Q = P + \lambda G \tag{3-11.19}$$

When we differentiate, we obtain

$$\frac{\partial Q}{\partial x} = \frac{\partial P}{\partial x} + \lambda \frac{\partial G}{\partial x} \tag{3-11.20}$$

$$\frac{\partial Q}{\partial p} = \frac{\partial P}{\partial p} + \lambda \frac{\partial G}{\partial p} \tag{3-11.21}$$

$$\frac{\partial Q}{\partial \lambda} = G \tag{3-11.22}$$

When we set these three partial derivatives equal to zero, we obtain

$$-\lambda = \frac{\frac{\partial P}{\partial x}}{\frac{\partial G}{\partial x}} \tag{3-11.23}$$

$$-\lambda = \frac{\dfrac{\partial P}{\partial p}}{\dfrac{\partial G}{\partial p}} \tag{3–11.24}$$

$$G = 0 \tag{3–11.25}$$

Now, when we solve the three equations, (3–11.23), (3–11.24), and (3–11.25), simultaneously, we assure that $G = 0$, i.e., that the original restriction is satisfied. Also, since these ratios are both equal to $-\lambda$, from Equations (3–11.23) and (3–11.24), it follows that

$$\frac{\dfrac{\partial P}{\partial x}}{\dfrac{\partial G}{\partial x}} = \frac{\dfrac{\partial P}{\partial p}}{\dfrac{\partial G}{\partial p}} \tag{3–11.26}$$

which is equivalent to

$$\frac{\dfrac{\partial P}{\partial x}}{\dfrac{\partial P}{\partial p}} = \frac{\dfrac{\partial G}{\partial x}}{\dfrac{\partial G}{\partial p}} \tag{3–11.27}$$

But these two ratios are, respectively, the slopes of the profit curve and the restriction curve, as demonstrated in Equation (3–11.18). Therefore, since at the simultaneous solution to the three equations, (3–11.23), (3–11.24), and (3–11.25), Equation (3–11.27) holds, it follows that, at that point on the xp plane, the slopes of the two functions, P and G, are equal, and therefore that point is a point of tangency and is an extreme point of P subject to the condition of Equation (3–11.25), i.e., $G = 0$.

This general method of Lagrange multipliers does not in any way require that the restriction line be a straight line as in our simple example. It works perfectly well for curved restriction lines and for more than two variables. The demonstration given above did not rely on or even refer to the fact that, in the Do-Mor illustration, the restriction function G was linear.

Thus, in the general case, the method of Lagrange multipliers is used to obtain an extreme value of the function $E(x_1,x_2)$ subject to the restriction that the function $G(x_1,x_2) = 0$. Then the function F is defined such that

$$F(x_1,x_2,\lambda) = E(x_1,x_2) + \lambda G(x_1,x_2) \tag{3–11.4}$$

The desired solution is obtained by differentiating F partially with respect to x_1, x_2, and λ, and setting the three partial derivatives equal to zero. The values of these three variables which satisfy the resulting three expressions constitute the desired solution.

With more than one restriction,

$$F = E + \lambda_1 G_1 + \lambda_2 G_2 + \cdots \tag{3-11.28}$$

Finally, we come to the interpretation of λ. From Equations (3–11.23) and (3–11.24), it is clear that λ is a constant of proportionality. It shows the magnitude and direction of the effect on P of a change in either of the controllable variables. If either x or p is altered to change G, the effect on P is 461,000 times as great (and in the same direction since $-\lambda$ is positive) as the effect on G. Thus, since G was defined as

$$G = p - 5x = 0 \tag{3-11.29}$$

G increases if p increases or if x decreases. The value of $-\lambda = 461{,}000$ tells us that the effect on P of small changes in p or x is 461,000 times as big.

This reasoning may be followed on the chart of Figure 3–11.1, where $G > 0$ occurs in the area above and to the left of the straight line for $G = 0$, and $G < 0$ occurs in the area below and to the right of the straight line.

If p is increased, G is increased, as may be seen in Equation (3–11.29). Then the value of $\lambda = -461{,}000$ tells us that profit will increase 461,000 times as much as G, as seen in Equation (3–11.30):

$$\frac{\dfrac{\partial P}{\partial x}}{\dfrac{\partial G}{\partial x}} = \frac{\dfrac{\partial P}{\partial p}}{\dfrac{\partial G}{\partial p}} = 461{,}000 \tag{3-11.30}$$

Similarly, if x is increased, G is decreased, as seen in Equation (3–11.29), and then from Equation (3–11.30), we can see that P is consequently also decreased and 461,000 times as much as G.

If G, the restriction, can be subject to change, this kind of analysis indicates in which direction change is desirable, and how desirable it is. Also, as we shall see in the next section, it serves to indicate when *inequality* restrictions are actually limiting and when they are not.

3–12. Inequality Restrictions. The interpretation of λ given above suggests a simple solution to problems in which the constraint is an inequality rather than an equality. It is clear that, in the solution given above (2.446, 12.23), as can be seen in Figure (3–11.1), profit will increase if either p is increased slightly or x is decreased slightly. However, the constraint $G = 0$ makes it impossible to change one without the other, and the solution given is the optimal solution subject to that equality constraint. If, however, the restriction had been, instead of the *equation*

$p = 5x$, the following *inequation*,

$$p \geq 5x$$

then

$$G = p - 5x \geq 0 \tag{3–12.1}$$

Then, the profit P could be increased above the value obtained in the preceding section by decreasing x below the value of $0.2p$ or by increasing p above the value of $5x$. On the other hand, if the inequality had been in the other direction, P could not be increased, since any change in x or p which decreases G from $G = 0$ also reduces P. In summary, then, when the objective function (to be maximized) and G, the restriction ($G \leq 0$) move in the same direction as a consequence of changes in the controllable variables, then the restriction is limiting, and the objective function cannot be increased above its value for $G = 0$ without violating the restriction.

Thus, the solution, when there is one inequality restriction of the form

$$G(x_1,x_2) \leq 0$$

is, first, to use the method of Lagrange multipliers as described above, treating the inequality restriction *as an equation*, and then, by examination of the sign of the Lagrange multiplier, to determine whether the constraint is actually limiting the optimum value of the objective function.

For the restriction $G \leq 0$, and an objective function to be maximized:

1. If $\lambda > 0$, the restriction is not a limitation, and the problem may be solved ignoring the restriction.
2. If $\lambda \leq 0$, the restriction does have a limiting effect, and therefore the result obtained by setting $G = 0$ is the optimum, subject to the inequality restriction $G \leq 0$.

We can illustrate this in the Do-Mor problem. If the inequality restriction had been

$$G = p - 5x \leq 0 \tag{3–12.2}$$

then, we would solve the problem as before, treating the restriction as if it were $p - 5x = 0$. Then the solution was

for $p - 5x = 0$

$$x^* = 2.446$$

$$p^* = 12.23$$

$$\lambda = -461{,}000$$

$$P = \$2{,}033{,}000$$

and the negative value of λ indicates that the optimum value of P is limited by the restriction. Therefore the result obtained here is the optimum obtainable, subject to the inequality restriction.

If, on the other hand, the restriction had been

$$G = p - 5x \geq 0 \tag{3-12.1}$$

then the negative value of λ would not constitute a limitation, in that now G can be increased above zero, and the positive value of $-\lambda$ indicates, from Equations (3–11.23) and (3–11.24), that increases in G are associated with increases in P. Thus, in that case, the value of P is not limited by the restriction. Thus the problem could be solved ignoring the restriction with the result of Section 3–10, the unrestricted optimal solution:

$$x^* = 2.241$$

$$p^* = 12.50$$

$$p - 5x = 1.33 > 0$$

$$P = \$2{,}064{,}000$$

In this solution, i.e., the optimal ignoring the restriction, the restriction is satisfied, indicating that the restriction $G \geq 0$ did not operate to limit our course of action in a way to diminish the achievable value of the objective function, whereas the restriction $G \leq 0$ did so limit us.

SUGGESTIONS FOR FURTHER READING

Baumol, W. J. *Economic Theory and Operations Analysis* (2d ed.). Englewood Cliffs, N.J.: Prentice-Hall, Inc., 1965.

Buffa, E. S. *Models for Production and Operations Management.* New York: John Wiley & Sons, Inc., 1963.

Dean, J. *Capital Budgeting.* New York: Columbia University Press, 1951.

Fabrycky, W. J., and P. E. Torgersen. *Operations Economy: Industrial Applications of Operations Research.* Englewood Cliffs, N.J.: Prentice-Hall, Inc., 1966.

Teichroew, D. *An Introduction to Management Science.* New York: John Wiley & Sons, Inc., 1964.

EXERCISES

3–1. Using Equation (3–10.5) find the optimal value for x, when $p = 6$.

3–2. Compute and construct the \$2,000,000 profit line for Figure 3–10.5.

3–3. The annual revenue R of the Sanro Company is given in dollars in the following equation:

$$R = 2400 \ln (q - 20)$$

where q is the number of units manufactured and sold during the year. The total yearly cost C to manufacture and sell q units is given by the equation:

$$C = 1000 + q^2$$

Find the optimal number to produce and sell for maximum profit.

3–4. The Chawol Stationery Company sells a desk calendar for $1.00. Studies indicate that they could sell an additional 2,000 calendars for every 5¢ by which they might decrease the price, and that, conversely, they would lose 2,000 sales for every 5¢ by which they might increase the price.

They now sell 30,000 units per season for a revenue of $30,000 and profit of $5,000, since the production cost is $25,000. The cost function is linear with a fixed cost of $10,000 and a unit variable cost of $.50.

a) What is the revenue maximizing price? How many would be sold at this price, and what is the profit and the revenue at this price?
b) What is the profit maximizing price? How many are sold at this price, and what is the profit and the revenue at this price?

3–5. The Arbur Company manufactures two grades of product. There is a cross elasticity of demand between these products such that, over the relevant range of prices, for the deluxe model, the demand is:

$$D_d = 5000p_s - 2000p_d - 100{,}000$$

and for the standard model:

$$D_s = 10{,}000p_d - 6000p_s - 50{,}000$$

Find the optimal prices for the deluxe model (p_d) and the standard model (p_s) for maximum revenue for the company.

3–6. The Necham Company wishes to maximize the effectiveness of its sales promotion budget of $1,000,000. This money is to be distributed between direct mail advertising and salesmen's calls in any proportion. How much of the $1,000,-000 should be spent on each of these two activities?

The Company wishes to maximize its net profit, which is 25% of sales. The relationship between sales and expenditures on these sales promotion activities, where a and c are expenditures on direct mail advertising and salesmen's calls, respectively, is:

$$\text{Sales (\$)} = \frac{50{,}000{,}000a}{500{,}000 + a} + \frac{25{,}000{,}000c}{1{,}000{,}000 + c}$$

3–7. The cost of operation of a small manufacturing firm is given by the function:

$$\text{Cost} = x^3 - 6x^2 + 250$$

where x is the number of units produced per day.

a) How many units of product should be produced per day to minimize the cost per day? What is the profit if the price is $200 per unit?
b) If the price is given by the function:

$$p = 170 - 5x$$

what is the profit maximizing price and production? (Note: The daily production need not be an integral number of units.)

3–8. Solve Equation (3–11.16) by Newton's method.

3–9. The Riap Company trains salesmen in groups, and the training cost is \$10,000 per group. After salesmen are trained, they are put on the payroll at \$833.33 per month at the home office, where they are unproductive. They are "kept busy" at the home office until they are sent to their newly assigned territory, where they are then productively used. The need for salesmen arises from the fact that the company is growing at such a rate that 5 additional salesmen are needed per month and, on the average, one experienced salesman leaves the firm each month and must be replaced. How large should the salesmen training groups be to minimize the home-office costs for training and salesmen's salaries?

Part II
PROBABILITY THEORY AND APPLICATIONS

4

Discrete Probability Distributions

4–1. Definition of Probability. In the real world there are many processes whose outcomes are not individually predictable with certainty, but whose outcomes may nevertheless be predicted with some degree of confidence. Probability theory enables us to assign a numerical value to our degree of confidence that a specified outcome will occur.

In its traditional meaning, probability refers to a repetitive process, one which may generate outcomes that are not identical and not individually predictable with certainty. However, the process may be described in terms of the relative frequencies of the various outcomes. These processes are called *probabilistic* or *stochastic* or *chance* processes, and the individual results of these processes are called *events.* An example of a stochastic or chance process would be the tossing of a coin. We do not know whether a particular toss of a coin will result in the event "heads" or the event "tails," but we may know something about the relative frequency of these events. The repetitive process in this example is the tossing of the coin; and what is observed (the face of the coin) is called a *stochastic variable,* or *chance variable* or *random variable.*

Strictly speaking, we usually think of a random variable as having a numerical value: e.g., in a coin-tossing experiment, we might assign the number 1 to the event "heads" and the number 0 to the event "tails." Indeed, a formal definition of a random variable is that it is a rule or function which assigns a numerical value to each of the possible outcomes of an experiment. Then, for practical purposes, *a random variable is a numerical variable whose numerical value depends upon the outcome of an experiment, and which may be different for different trials of the same experiment.*

The word *deterministic* is used to characterize processes that are not probabilistic, in which a set of values of the input variables produces exactly the same values of the output variables each time the process occurs. Such, e.g., is the relationship between cost and lot size in production planning. There, if the cost per setup is $100, then two setups will cost $200, three will cost $300, etc. In a stochastic process, such as, for example, the arrival of customers at a bank teller's window, if arrivals occur at the average rate of 2 per minute over the entire day, then an observation over a 5-minute period might yield the average or *expected value* of 10 arrivals, but it could also yield 9 or 11 or 8 or 12 or 7 or, indeed, any number from zero to a very large number. We can, by the use of probability theory, deal effectively with such stochastic processes as these, although we can not predict the outcome of any individual event.

Random variables may be divided into two classes: discrete and continuous. Discrete variables can assume only particular specific values, while continuous variables may assume any value within some appropriate range. An example of a discrete variable might be the "number of customer arrivals in a 5-minute interval." Clearly, the value of this variable must be an integer: 0, or 1, or 2, or 3, etc. It cannot take a value within the range, say, between 8 and 9, such as, for example, 8.3 or 8.75.

The relative frequencies which characterize chance processes are called probabilities. Probability may be most easily understood and conveniently handled if it is treated as a proportion. That is, if a population, either real or theoretical, i.e., one that does not now exist but could be generated by the operation of a chance process, consists of or can be imagined as consisting of N elements, all of which are equally likely to occur, A of which are classified as "success" and $N - A$ of which are classified as "failure," then the probability of success if one element is selected at random is $\frac{A}{N}$, the proportion of the number of successes to the number in the whole population. We shall comment later on the phrase "equally likely."

For example, in the theoretical distribution which would result from repetitively tossing a "fair" coin, half of the outcomes would be the event "heads," and half would be "tails"; therefore, we may say that the probability of heads is 0.5. This, by the way, is the definition of a "fair," or unbiased, coin.

If we know, from empirical evidence, such as census reports, that 40 per cent of the families in a given area have incomes in excess of $8,000 per year, then we can say that the probability of a randomly selected family's having an income over $8,000 per year is 0.4. If 600 families are selected at random from this area, the theoretical expectation would be that 240 of them would have annual incomes over $8,000. However, we would be very surprised if a real sample actually did yield *exactly* 240 "successes."

In both of these examples we know the true proportion of "successes" *in the population*. In this case of the coin we knew it from prior mathematical and definitional considerations (i.e., it was stipulated to be a "fair" coin), and in the family income case, we knew it from a complete census of the population.

However, we often also speak of "empirical probability" when we have empirical evidence covering only a part of the population. Mortality tables, insurance premiums, and often, climatological studies, are based on this sort of probability. Here, the general method is that of using the characteristics of an observed sample as empirical evidence leading to the assignment of probability values to the population as a whole. For example, if in our town rain has occurred on 30 per cent of the September days over the last 75 years, then one might say that the probability of rain on a random day next September is 0.3.

4–2. Objective and Subjective Probability. Probabilities, such as those discussed above, which are based on mathematical considerations or empirical evidence about relative frequencies, are often referred to as *objective* probabilities, while probabilities which are *not* based on such specific mathematical considerations or observational evidence are often called *subjective* probabilities. For example, the businessman might look at a new product and say that its probability of becoming a successful product (i.e., with sales in excess of some specified figure) is 0.9. He makes this statement although he has no specific experience with *this* product. However, he does presumably have some empirical evidence about the market for similar products, about other competitive products, and as to the extent to which this particular new product fills a need. He might even feel that he has seen many many new products over the years and that, of those which had this particular degree of promise, 90 per cent eventually turned out to be successful. If he reasoned this way, he might be described as trying to approach the relative frequency concept of objective probability.

Indeed, he may even define his class of events very broadly in that he may feel that, although he cannot be certain about the success of this new product, he feels about its likelihood of occurrence in such a way that he can classify this event in his mind as one of a class of widely varying situations, 90 per cent of which have resulted in a "successful" outcome. These might include certain political elections, athletic contests, weather situations, and many others. By reasoning in this way, he can try to make any subjective probability situation share some of the characteristics of the repetitive process concept of objective probability, and, indeed, this may well be what he means when he characterizes his subjective probability as his *degree of belief* measured on the scale between 0 and 1. Indeed, the very requirement "equally likely" used in the definition given above is a subjective judgment.

On the other hand, as we shall see, objective probabilities, when applied to decision making in the real world, are not basically different from subjective probabilities. We speak of "fair" coins and "random" samples; but who has ever seen a fair coin, and who can be sure that he knows how to take a random sample?

Whenever we assign probability values to *real-world phenomena* we are describing, in a quantitative expression, our degree of belief or intensity of conviction that a particular event will occur. The assignment of a specific numerical probability value to a real-world phenomenon raises two questions: first, what it means, and, second, whether it is correct.

First, the assignment of a probability value of, say, 0.9 to some event means that this is one of a class of phenomena, 90 per cent of which have some specified property. The class may be defined very closely, like the flipping of a coin; or it may be defined very broadly so as to include, in one class, the outcome of a strike, the quality of a bottle of wine, the degree of traffic congestion at rush hour, and the likelihood that a particular car will finish at Le Mans. In the first case (coin flipping), the repetitive trials are more nearly identical than in the second, but in a real sense they are not identical, and the difference between the two classes is one of degree rather than of kind.

The second question, that of the correctness of a probability value, is one which can be tested via the standard methods of statistical inference. We may flip a coin many times and conclude that it is not a fair coin, although, without testing, one might have been willing to treat it as if the probability of heads were 0.5. If our businessman says that the probability of success of the new product is 0.9, then, to test that, we must keep a record of all of the events to which he assigned the value 0.9 and observe the percentage in which the event actually occurred. If this turns out to be 90 per cent, then we can conclude that, if his skill is undiminished, we can use his 0.9 figure with confidence.

Summarizing, then, there are the probabilities which we, by agreement, assign to *theoretical models* such as a "fair" coin or die, or "random" samples taken from known populations such as normal populations, decks of cards, or other populations with known distributions and known parameters. These are called *objective probabilities.* When we apply probabilities to real phenomena in the real world, we must make certain assumptions with respect to either the population or the stochastic process, or both. That is, if we toss a coin and act as if the true probability of heads is 0.5, that is an assumption. It may be a good assumption, *but it is an assumption.* If we speak of sampling from a known population, then we are assuming that our sampling process is one which will generate "random" samples. This, too, is an assumption. Even if the sampling process involves drawing from a fishbowl, spinning a roulette wheel, or using a table of random numbers, *the "randomness" of samples is an assumption.* However, we tend to have considerable faith in the probabilities which are attached to these processes.

There are other processes in the real world of such nature that it is convenient to attach probabilities to them, but for which the actual probability number is not so seemingly self-evident, and which we may not be willing to accept so readily. For example, the weather forecaster makes "rain vs. shine" forecasts every day, and he is not absolutely positive every day; but he does, on the basis of the evidence available to him, have more faith in his forecast on some days than on others. He therefore finds it useful to assign a probability number to his forecast every day, indicating his estimate of the set of forecasts in which each forecast falls. That is, his over-all percentage of correct forecasts of rain may be 60 per cent; and, if we had no evidence but his unqualified forecast, we might be justified in treating this as a phenomenon with 0.6 probability. However, the forecaster may feel that a particular forecast is related to a weather phenomenon about which he can predict with more than his average degree of reliability. He, in fact, feels that this forecast belongs to a category, or *set,* of forecasts of rain, 90 per cent of them in fact followed by rain. He therefore assigns a probability of 0.9 to the forecast. If he is right, we are justified in behaving with respect to this value of 0.9 exactly as we would with any other probability number. *We call this probability, which he assigns in this way, subjective probability, because it comes from his subjective judgment, rather than from some objective counting process.* However, it may not really be very different from any other probability numbers when they are applied to real-world phenomena, since our acceptance of even these in the real world is based on faith rather than on objective fact.

If we can accept the application of probability numbers to weather forecasts referring to specific days, then we can expand the application of subjective probabilities to other, seemingly nonrepetitive processes. For example, we may speak of the probability that the President's party will gain in the next election, or the probability that a man will land on another planet and return before 1990. These are not repetitive processes, in any sense. There is only one *next* election, and there is only one date designated 1990. These things either will or will not happen. However, we may say that the probability that the President's party will gain in the next election is 0.8, and that the probability that a man will visit and return safely from a planet by the end of 1990 is 0.15. These figures are meaningful as subjective probabilities, if we understand them to mean that these statements belong, in the speaker's judgment, to sets of statements, of which 80 per cent and 15 per cent, respectively, are true. The judgment is involved in the classification of the statements. Some other person might classify these differently and arrive at figures of, say, 70 per cent and 20 per cent, respectively. Clearly, they cannot both be right; and certainly both may be wrong. The verification of the statement is not in whether either the President's party does gain or whether there is a successful expedition to a planet; the verification lies in the actual percentage of such statements which turn out to be true.

While it is not to be expected that two given people will agree on the exact subjective probability *value* which should be assigned to a particular phenomenon, it is possible to define the *interpretation* which should characterize their subjective probabilities. We refer back to the definition given early in this chapter, and with slight changes, present the following interpretation of subjective probabilities.

Any probability value may be expressed as a ratio of two positive integers, $\frac{A}{N}$, where $N > 0$, and $A \leq N$. The reader is asked to imagine a chance process which has N equally likely outcomes. We should not be troubled by the expression "equally likely," since it may be viewed as a theoretical model which need not exist in the real world; e.g., one may wish to think of a "perfect" roulette wheel divided into N equal sectors. Of these N possible outcomes, A are defined as *success*, and $N - A$ are defined as *not-success*. Then, the probability of success is $\frac{A}{N}$, and any subjective probability value which one assigns to a real world event should be interpreted as meaning that that event has the same likelihood of occurrence as has the occurrence of success in this imaginary process.

Let us illustrate this process by reference to a specific numerical example. The reader is now asked to imagine the "perfect" roulette wheel (or some other ideal chance process) with its circumference divided into 10 equal and equally likely sectors, 7 of which are labeled "success," and 3 of which are labeled "not-success." Now, if the wheel is to be spun in a way which meets all ideal requirements for a "fair spin," *the reader has some subjective feeling about the degree of intensity of conviction with which he expects the outcome to be "success."* This degree of intensity of conviction should be calibrated in his mind as *probability of 0.7*. Then, if he later encounters a situation in which he feels the same degree of intensity of conviction, he should characterize that situation as representing a subjective probability of 0.7.

Conversely, if he encounters a situation in which his degree of intensity of conviction is different, he can try to assign a numerical value to his subjective probability by visualizing again this ideal-chance process and asking himself how that ideal process must be defined in order to provide him with the same degree of intensity of conviction. He may, for example, feel that the imaginary roulette wheel counterpart with 10 divisions does not give him sufficient precision to express his feelings exactly. He may then prefer to think of the wheel with 100 divisions so that he can express his subjective probability to two decimal places, i.e., 0.74; or he may even, rarely, prefer to think in terms of 1,000 divisions, so that he can express his subjective probability to three decimal places, i.e., 0.735. Of course, there is no reason why the number of imaginary divisions must be a power of 10. For example, he may wish to think of the wheel with as having, say, only 3 divisions, 2 of which are "success," and thereby characterize his subjective probability as $\frac{2}{3}$ (or, in decimals, 0.6666 . . .).

This prescription for the assignment of subjective probabilities to real world events will be found to be useful in later chapters, especially Chapter 19, *Decision Theory*. Hopefully, this interpretation makes the concept more vivid and concrete than the mere statement that subjective probability measures the *degree of creditability* or the *degree of intensity of conviction*.

The mathematical methods, the rules and procedures, for manipulating and computing probability values are the same, regardless of the source of the original probability values and the interpretation people may wish to assign to them. The next sections will consider these rules and procedures.

4–3. Sets and Set Notation. In modern mathematics the name *set* is applied to *a collection of items which have some common specified property or properties*. Subject to this definition, a set may be a collection of numbers, cities, pencils, stars, students, automobiles, computations, attitudes, or any classification well defined by a criterion (or by inclusion in some specified list) which unambiguously specifies whether an item belongs to the collection. The items which make up a set are called the *elements* of the set.

A set may be a *finite set,* such as the letters of the English alphabet or the 500 largest corporations; or it may be an *infinite set,* such as the set of positive integers or the set of possible levels of concentration for our new liquid detergent.

If we define as the set A the even positive integers below 10, we may define this set by listing all of its members between braces as follows:

$$A = \{2, 4, 6, 8\} \tag{4–3.1}$$

or we may define it in a mathematical formula or a written statement, such as the following, in which the vertical line is to be read, "such that" or "given that":

$$A = \{x | x \text{ is an even positive integer less than } 10\} \tag{4–3.2}$$

or

$$A = \{2x | x \text{ is a positive integer less than } 5\} \tag{4–3.3}$$

Equation (4–3.3) is read, "A is the set of elements $2x$, such that x is a positive integer less than 5."

These three statements, Equations (4–3.1), (4–3.2), and (4–3.3), are all equivalent. They all say exactly the same thing.

If an element is a member of a set, that fact may be written

$$2 \in A \tag{4–3.4}$$

which is read, "2 belongs to the set A," or, "2 is an element of the set A." Conversely,

$$9 \notin A \tag{4–3.5}$$

is read, "9 is not an element of the set A."

An example of a mathematical formula as a definition of a set might be the following, where the set E is the set of all even positive integers and N is the set of all positive integers:

$$A = \{x | x \in E \text{ and } x < 10\} \tag{4–3.6}$$

or

$$A = \{2x | x \in N \text{ and } x \leq 4\} \tag{4–3.7}$$

Equations (4–3.6) and (4–3.7) obviously define the same set A as do Equations (4–3.1), (4–3.2) and (4–3.3). Note that we might equally well have written $x \leq 8$ or $x < 9$ in place of $x < 10$ in Equation (4–3.6). Clearly, there are many ways in which this particular set A may be defined.

The set B is a *subset* of another set A, *if every element in the set B is also an element of the set A*. For example, the set

$$B = \{2, 8\}$$

is a subset of the set

$$A = \{2, 4, 6, 8\}$$

A complete listing of the subsets of the set A includes the sets:

$$\{\ \}$$
$$\{2\} \quad \{4\} \quad \{6\} \quad \{8\}$$
$$\{2, 4\} \quad \{2, 6\} \quad \{2, 8\} \quad \{4, 6\} \quad \{4, 8\} \quad \{6, 8\}$$
$$\{2, 4, 6\} \quad \{2, 4, 8\} \quad \{2, 6, 8\} \quad \{4, 6, 8\}$$
$$\{2, 4, 6, 8\}$$

There are *sixteen* subsets of the four-element set A. It is important to note that the first and the last.sets enumerated above are included. That is, the entire set is considered a subset of A since it meets the criterion that all of its elements are also elements of A; and, also, the *empty* set, $\emptyset$, also called the *null* set

$$\emptyset = \{\ \}$$

is a subset since it also meets the criterion (i.e., it has no elements that are not elements of A). Indeed, *$\emptyset$ is a subset of every set.*

A general rule is that, if a set contains n elements, it has 2^n subsets as defined above. However, the term *proper subset* is applied to subsets which are not empty and not the entire set. Thus, the set A has fourteen proper subsets.

Subsets are designated by the symbol, $\subseteq$. Thus, the expression

$$B \subseteq A \tag{4–3.8}$$

indicates that every element of B is also an element of set A, and, therefore, set B is a subset of set A.

4–4. Complements, Intersections, and Unions. The *complement* of a set consists of those elements which do not belong to that set. This is a broad definition, and it requires some additional limitation. For example, if we say set $A = \{2, 4, 6, 8\}$, then its complement, according to the definition given above, would include all other numbers, all letters, all people, dogs, automobiles, houses, cities, rivers, planets, galaxies, etc. Clearly this is not what is intended. In any specific application, we have some *population* or *universe* in mind. This universe is the total category under consideration, and the *universal set* consists of all of the elements which are included in that category. The universal set may be all houses within the municipal limits, all automobiles manufactured last year, all families with incomes under $10,000 per year, all single-digit positive integers, etc. The universal set is designated by the symbol U. However, we shall not always use this symbol in our statements, but rather we shall understand that we are confining our attention to *the universe under consideration*. That is, we shall define the complement of A as A' according to the formula

$$A' = \{x | x \notin A\} \tag{4–4.1}$$

and we shall understand, of course, that our attention is limited to the particular universe under consideration. For example, if, for the purposes at hand, the universal set is defined as all single-digit positive integers and the set A is the set defined in Equation (4–3.1), then

$$U = \{1, 2, 3, 4, 5, 6, 7, 8, 9\} \tag{4–4.2}$$

and

$$A' = \{1, 3, 5, 7, 9\} \tag{4–4.3}$$

The formal statement of Equation (4–4.1) would be Equation (4–4.4),

$$A' = \{x | x \in U \text{ and } x \notin A\} \tag{4–4.4}$$

which explicitly states that, to be considered to be in the complement set, an element must be in the universal set which is under consideration.

The *union* of two sets A and B is written

$$A \cup B \tag{4–4.5}$$

which may be read, "A cup B" or "A union B." It is the set of elements which belong to A or B, or both. The *intersection* of two sets A and B is written

$$A \cap B \tag{4–4.6}$$

which may be read, "A cap B" or "A intersection B." It is the set of elements which belong to *both* A and B. These symbols, cup ($\cup$) and cap ($\cap$) are easy to remember if we think of the cup as having a large capacity and being able to hold all elements which impinge on it; it represents all elements in *either or both* sets. The cap symbol, on the other hand, is not capacious; it represents only those elements which occur in *both* sets.

Two sets are said to be *disjoint* if they have no common elements. If two sets are disjoint, membership in one set implies absence from the other. The events which characterize disjoint sets are *mutually exclusive;* i.e., if one event occurs, the other cannot. "Males" and "females" are disjoint subsets of the universal set "people."

We can illustrate all of these relationships by considering the employees of the Eastwood Manufacturing Company. It is a fact that exactly 50 per cent of the employees are male. Also, 70 per cent are residents of Eastwood City, where the plant is located, and 30 per cent commute from Walton which is a nearby city; all employees either reside in Eastwood or commute from Walton. Thus we have four classifications of employees and we can consider four sets of employees of the company:

$$M = \{x|x \text{ is a male}\}$$

$$F = \{x|x \text{ is a female}\}$$

$$R = \{x|x \text{ is a resident}\}$$

$$C = \{x|x \text{ is a commuter}\}$$

The set C is the complement of the set R:

$$C = R' \qquad \text{and} \qquad R = C'$$

and the set F is the complement of the set M:

$$F = M' \qquad \text{and} \qquad M = F'$$

The union of the set M and the set C includes all of the employees who are either male or commuters. These, by the way, are the only employees who can be seen on the streets and in the shops of Eastwood during the weekly luncheon meetings of the Eastwood League of Women Voters which all resident Eastwood women, employed or not, attend regularly.

The intersection of the set M and the set C includes only the male commuters. These, by the way, are the only people with permits to park cars in the Eastwood Company parking lot; for the female commuters do not drive (they are car pool passengers), and the local people, the residents, can walk to the plant.

4–5. Sample Space, Trials, and Events. In probability theory the word *trial* is used to describe a situation or experiment in which one or more *events* may or may not occur. It is an opportunity for the events to occur. The complete list of all of the possible outcomes or *sample points* of a trial is a set called the *sample space* of the experiment. The list must be exhaustive, and the elements must be mutually exclusive. When dealing with experiments, as we are doing here, we shall generally use the letter S to designate the set of sample points for the experiment at hand. Often we shall use subscripts to identify specific sample spaces.

For example, if our experiment is to select one employee's name from the rolls of the Eastwood Company and we are interested only in whether the selected employee is a resident or a commuter, then the sample space has only two points.

$$S_1 = \{R, C\}$$

We might, conversely, not be interested in whether the employee is a resident or a commuter, but only in whether the employee is male or female. Then the sample space is

$$S_2 = \{M, F\}$$

If, however, we are interested in both the residence criterion and the sex of the employee, then the sample space has four elements

$$S_3 = \{MR, MC, FR, FC\}$$

It is important to note that each of these possibility spaces or sample spaces is a perfectly valid sample space for this experiment, the usefulness or applicability of each depending upon the purpose of the experimenter at the particular time of the experiment. The only requirement for a sample space is that the set include elements such that one and only one of them represents the outcome of any and every trial. An *event* is a set of possible outcomes, i.e., a subset of the sample space.

4–6. Probability Values. If an experiment has n possible mutually exclusive outcomes, x_i, the sample space may be represented as

$$S = \{x_1, x_2, x_3, \ . \ . \ . \ , x_n\} \tag{4–6.1}$$

Then any trial will result in some outcome x_i. These outcomes are called *elementary events*. Since no two of them may occur in the same trial, for any $i \neq j$,

$$\{x_i \cap x_j\} = 0$$

To each outcome x_i we assign, either subjectively or objectively, or by some subjective-objective compromise, a measure which is called the *probability* of that outcome. The symbol used is $P(x_i)$ or p_i.

In this discussion and that which follows, we shall be thinking in terms of *discrete* probability distributions. Later we shall introduce *continuous* probability distributions and distinguish between these two types of probability distributions.

The maximum value which probability may take is 1. If an event is certain to happen, its probability is 1, and if it cannot occur, its probability is 0. This may be summarized by two mathematical requirements governing probability values.

Let the probabilities be represented by the symbol p_i, for the n possible events. That is, p_1 is the probability of the first event, p_2 is the probability of the second event, etc., and p_n is the probability of the nth event. Then, the first requirement is that no probability value may be less than 0 (i.e., it may not be negative) or greater than 1. That is, for all p_i:

$$0 \leq p_i \leq 1 \tag{4–6.2}$$

The second requirement is that the sum of all of the n probability values for the n possible events must equal 1:

$$p_1 + p_2 + p_3 + \cdots + p_n = 1 \tag{4–6.3}$$

or, more concisely,

$$\sum_{i=1}^{n} p_i = 1 \tag{4–6.4}$$

where the symbol Σ, the capital Greek letter "sigma," is used to represent the operation of summing. The equation may be read, "The sum of all of the probability values, from the first to the nth inclusive, is 1."

It is often convenient and helpful to represent probability relationships by means of Venn diagrams. To construct a Venn diagram, we first construct a closed shape which represents the sample space or possibility space. This shape encloses all of the elements or points in the set or classification under consideration, i.e., the specific universe or universal set for the chance process or experiment being studied. It is not necessary for the diagram to show each point (although often one may wish to do this), but we may imagine the points to be dispersed throughout the enclosed space but not necessarily uniformly distributed. These points may be imagined to be loosely or densely packed, depending upon whether the population is large or small. The diagram may be equally well used to represent finite populations or infinite populations. In the latter case, the space is viewed as containing an infinite number of points.

Some of the points represent "success" somehow defined, i.e., the fulfillment of some specified condition or statement, and the probability of success is the sum of the probability measures for the points for which the specified statement is true.

Consider the process of tossing a fair die. The sample space has six points as shown on the Venn diagram of Figure 4–6.1. The sample

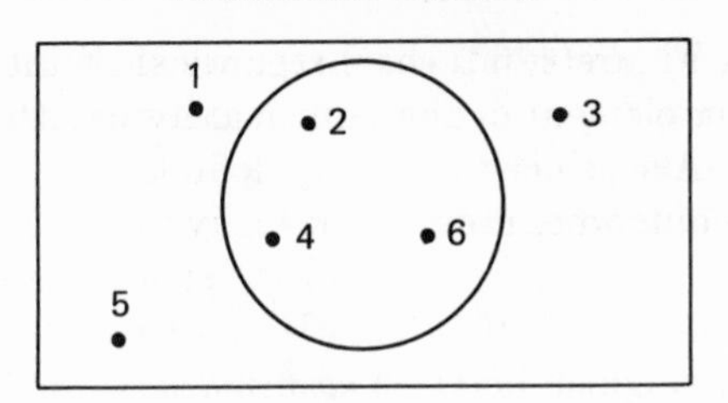

Fig. 4–6.1. Venn diagram. The outcomes of the tossing of a single die.

space is

$$S = \{1, 2, 3, 4, 5, 6\} \tag{4–6.5}$$

If we define success by the statement, "An even number turns up," and if we designate the sample points for which that condition is true as the set A,

$$A = \{2, 4, 6\} \tag{4–6.6}$$

The *event* A is a subset of the set S. The event A occurs if the outcome of the trial corresponds to a sample point in the subset A. The subset A is the union of the three sample points: $\{2\}$, $\{4\}$, and $\{6\}$. Since the die has been specified to be a fair die, then, by definition, the probability which we assign to each of these possible outcomes or *elementary events* is $\frac{1}{6}$.

Then, the *probability* of the event A is the sum of the probabilities of the elementary events whose union is the event A:

$$P(A) = P(\{2\}) + P(\{4\}) + P(\{6\}) \tag{4–6.7}$$

$$P(A) = \frac{1}{6} + \frac{1}{6} + \frac{1}{6} = \frac{1}{2} \tag{4–6.8}$$

As noted before, typically the individual points are not shown on a Venn diagram, and division of the universe into sets A and A' is usually shown as in Figure 4–6.2. Usually, in drawing Venn diagrams, it is helpful as a

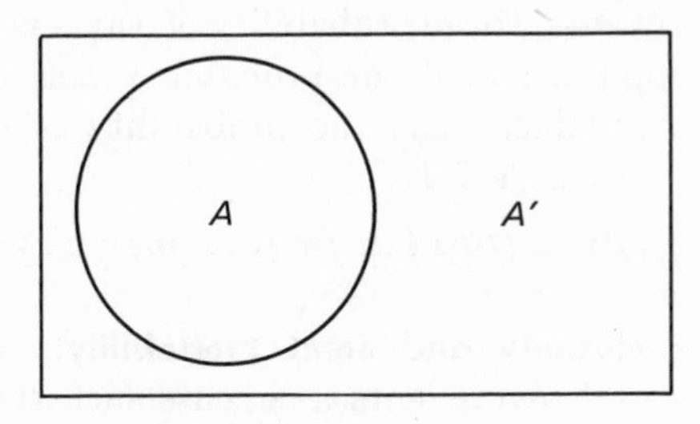

Fig. 4–6.2. Venn diagram. $P(A) + P(A') = 1$.

visual aid, but not essential, to draw the enclosed shapes so that the relative sizes of the enclosed areas approximate the probabilities of the respective events.

It is clear from Figure 4–6.2 that, regardless of the actual numerical value of $P(A)$, if an element of the universal set or sample space is not in A, it must be in A'. Also, since there is, by definition, a point in the universe for every possible outcome, then

$$P(A) + P(A') = 1 \tag{4–6.9}$$

We shall now distinguish between *elementary events* (the sample points) and *events* which may be various combinations of elementary events, and whose probabilities we can compute in terms of other events.

4–7. Complementary Events. From the Venn diagram of Figure 4–6.2 and its equivalent equation, (4–6.9), we can see that, if two events are mutually exclusive and exhaustive, that is, if either of them *but not both* must occur, then

$$P(A) = 1 - P(A') \tag{4–7.1}$$

Similarly, if there are many mutually exclusive events, one of which must occur, then the probability of any one may be computed as the complement of the probability of all of the others. Figure 4–7.1 depicts five

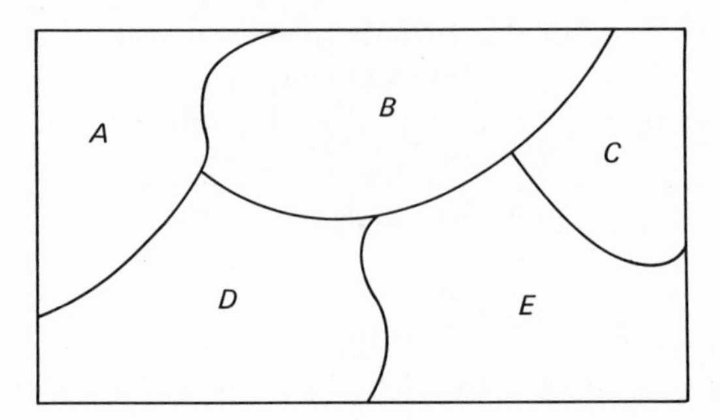

Fig. 4–7.1. Venn diagram. Five mutually exclusive events.

mutually exclusive events. If the probability of, say, event D were desired, but difficult to compute, and if the probability measures for the other four events were available, then the probability of event D could be computed from Equation (4–7.2):

$$P(D) = 1 - [P(A) + P(B) + P(C) + P(E)] \tag{4–7.2}$$

4–8. Mutual Exclusivity and Joint Probability. We have referred above to mutually exclusive events as events such that, if one of them occurs, the others do not. That is, for the set of sample points in the sample space, each point may represent the occurrence of only one of these events. There are no points common to more than one event. In the language of set theory, their sets are *disjoint,* and their statements, since they cannot both be true, are said to be *inconsistent.* For example, for the toss of a single die, there are six points in possibility (sample)

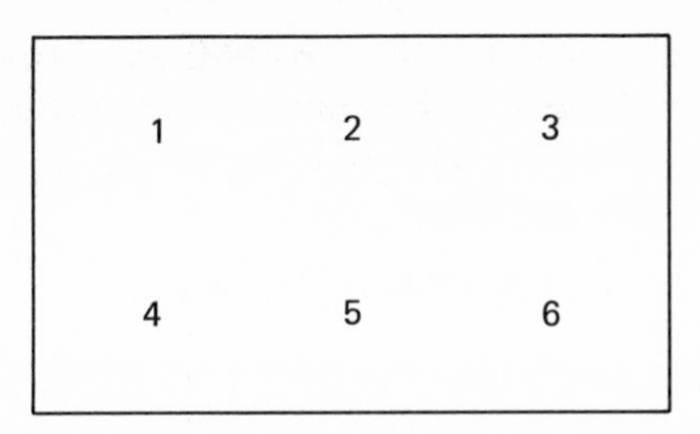

Fig. 4–8.1. Venn diagram. The toss of a fair die. Six equally likely sample points.

space, six elementary events, as seen in Figure 4–8.1. These are all mutually exclusive. That is, if one occurs the others cannot. Also, the statements, "The die shows two spots." and "The die shows three spots." are inconsistent. This is not new to us, since in Section 4–6 we defined elementary events as being mutually exclusive.

If we assume that the die is a "fair" die, then the six faces are all equally likely, and each of the six events has a probability of occurrence of $\frac{1}{6}$. Let us now define the event A by the statement "An even number shows." The event A, then, is the union of three elementary events:

$$A = \{2\} \cup \{4\} \cup \{6\} \tag{4–8.1}$$

and the probability of the event A is the union

$$P(A) = P(\{2\} \cup \{4\} \cup \{6\}) = P(\{2\}) + P(\{4\}) + P(\{6\}) \tag{4–8.2}$$

$$P(A) = \frac{1}{6} + \frac{1}{6} + \frac{1}{6} = \frac{1}{2}$$

Also, let us define the event B by the statement, "Either three or five shows." Then, the set of points for which the statement is true is the set $\{3, 5\}$ and the event B is the union of the two elementary events:

$$B = \{3\} \cup \{5\} \tag{4–8.3}$$

and the probability of the event B is

$$P(B) = P(\{3\} \cup \{5\}) = \frac{1}{6} + \frac{1}{6} = \frac{1}{3} \tag{4–8.4}$$

These relationships are shown in Figure 4–8.2.

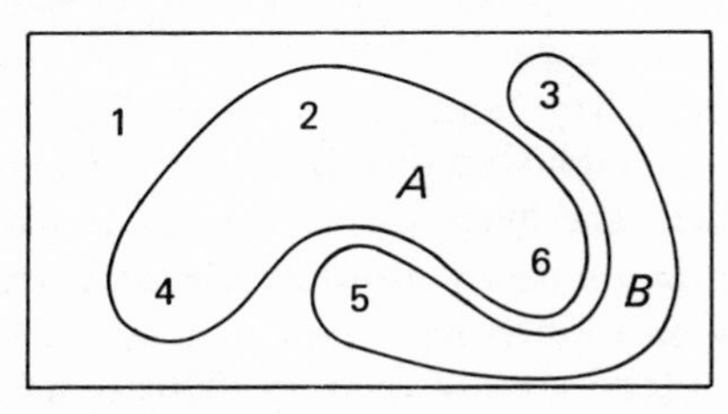

Fig. 4–8.2. Venn diagram. Event A represents "even number." Event B represents "either 3 or 5."

Finally, let us consider the event, "Either A or B occurs." The set of points for which this statement occurs is the union of sets A and B:

$$P(A \cup B) = P(A) + P(B) \tag{4–8.5}$$

$$P(A \cup B) = \frac{1}{2} + \frac{1}{3} = \frac{5}{6}$$

Equation (4-8.5) is valid only for mutually exclusive events; i.e., where the *intersection* is the empty set. Then

$$P(A \cap B) = 0 \tag{4–8.6}$$

Figures 4–8.3 and 4–8.4 are Venn diagrams which illustrate why Equation (4–8.5) does not hold when events are not mutually exclusive. It

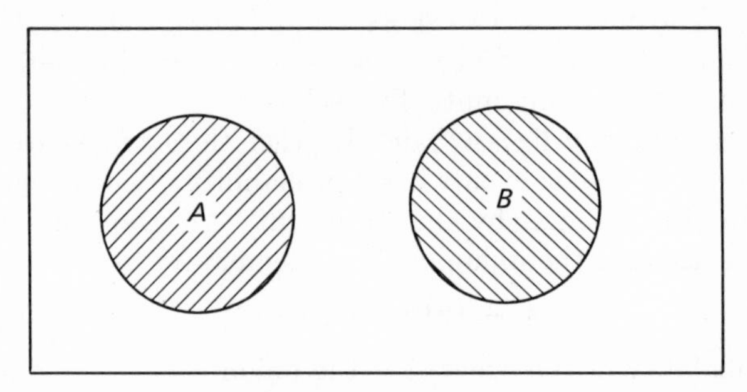

Fig. 4–8.3. Venn diagram. Events A and B are mutually exclusive. The union is the aggregate of the two shaded areas.

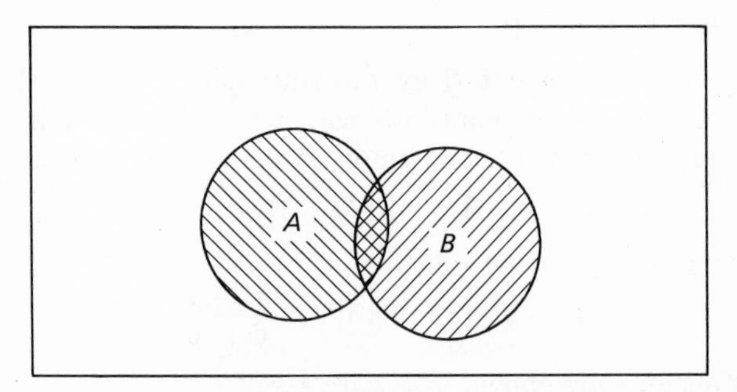

Fig. 4–8.4. Venn diagram. Events A and B are not mutually exclusive. The union is the entire shaded area. The intersection is the cross-hatched area.

holds for the mutually exclusive situation pictured in Figure 4–8.3, but, in Figure 4–8.4, where the events A and B are not mutually exclusive, the union, i.e., the probability of either A or B or both, is represented by the figure-eight-shaped shaded area and is smaller than the sum of the two circular areas by the area of overlap. This overlap area represents the intersection, where both A and B occur.

Thus, when events are not mutually exclusive, the probability of the intersection $(A \cap B)$ is not zero, and the probability of the union is decreased by the probability of the intersection since, otherwise, as seen in Figures 4–8.3 and 4–8.4, the intersection would be counted twice. The general formula for the probability of the union of two events is

$$P(A \cup B) = P(A) + P(B) - P(A \cap B) \tag{4–8.7}$$

Equation (4–8.7) holds for all pairs of events, mutually exclusive or not, since, if events A and B are mutually exclusive, then the last term is zero as indicated by Equation (4–8.6), and then Equation (4–8.7) reduces to Equation (4–8.5).

The occurrence of both A and B at the same time is referred to as a *compound event* and its probability, the probability of the intersection, $P(A \cap B)$, may also be referred to as the *joint probability* of A and B.

We can illustrate this situation by referring back to the toss of a fair die as pictured in Figures 4–8.1 and 4–8.2, and now let us again define event A as "The occurrence of an even number," but now let us define

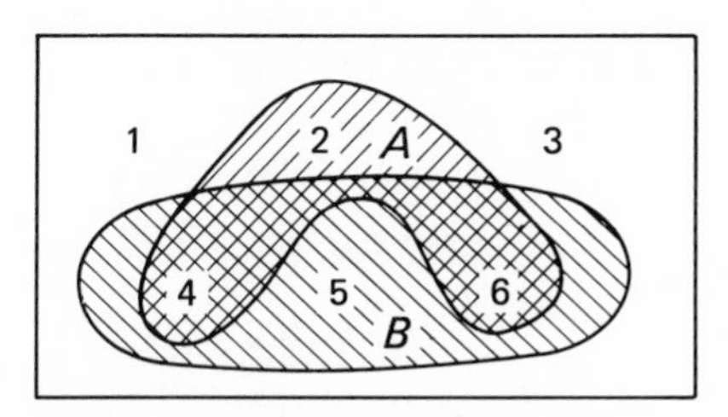

Fig. 4–8.5. Venn diagram. A toss of a fair die. A represents "even number," and B represents "greater than 3."

event B as "The occurrence of a number greater than three." This situation is pictured in Figure 4–8.5. There the compound event "A and B" can occur, and its probability, the probability of the *intersection*, is

$$P(A \cap B) = P(\{4\} \cup \{6\}) = \frac{1}{6} + \frac{1}{6} = \frac{1}{3}$$

$$P(A) = \frac{1}{2}$$

$$P(B) = \frac{1}{2}$$

and the probability of the *union* is

$$P(A \cup B) = P(A) + P(B) - P(A \cap B) \tag{4–8.7}$$

$$P(A \cup B) = \frac{1}{2} + \frac{1}{2} - \frac{1}{3} = \frac{2}{3}$$

4–9. Independence. Events are independent if the occurrence of any one of them provides no information about the probability of occurrence of any other. In the example which follows, we may speak of the event "female" or the event "commuter" to mean that a female is selected or a commuter is selected, and we shall examine two possible sets of facts. In the first, the events "female" and "commuter" are independent. That condition may be restated in terms of the classification criteria. That is, if the events "female" and "commuter" are independent, then the classification criteria "male-female" and "commuter-resident" are independent.

Returning to the Eastwood Manufacturing Co. illustration, if 50 per cent of a group of employees are male, and 30 per cent of the group commute from out of town to the city in which the plant is located (the remaining 70 per cent live in the city in which the plant is located), and if these two classification criteria, male–female and commuter–resident, are *independent*, then the probability of randomly selecting an employee and finding a female commuter is 0.5×0.3, or 0.15.

In this example, let the letters M, F, C, and R represent the characteristics male, female, commuter, and resident, respectively.

Then,

$$P(M) = 0.5$$

$$P(F) = 0.5$$

$$P(C) = 0.3$$

$$P(R) = 0.7$$

and, *if F and C are independent,* as described above,

$$P(F \cap C) = P(F)P(C) \qquad (4\text{–}9.1)$$

$$= (0.5)(0.3) = 0.15$$

This *compound* or *joint* event, i.e., a female commuter, represents the occurrence of two elementary events: a female, *and* a commuter. In this illustration, the probability that a randomly selected person will be a male (or a female) is independent of the matter of the selected person's being a commuter or a resident; and the probability that a randomly selected person will be a commuter is independent of the person's sex. On the diagram of Figure 4–9.1, straight parallel lines are used to delineate the areas in order to emphasize the *independence.* The two classification systems, "male–female" and "commuter–resident," are independent, since the percentage of commuters is 30 per cent of the entire plant—30 per cent of the males, and 30 per cent of the females. Similarly, the percentage of males is 50 per cent of the entire plant—50 per cent of the commuters, and 50 per cent of the residents.

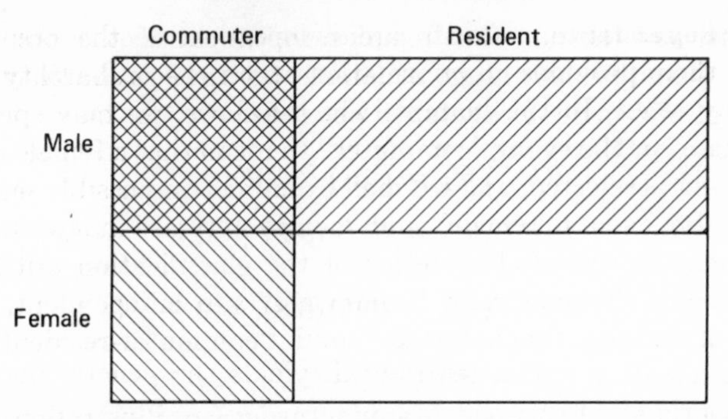

Fig. 4–9.1. Venn diagram. $P(M) = 0.5, P(C) = 0.3$. The classifications M–F and C–R are independent. $P(M \cap C) = 0.15$, $P(M \cap R) = 0.35$, $P(F \cap C) = 0.15$, $P(F \cap R) = 0.35$.

4–10. Conditional Probability. If these two classification criteria were not independent, there would be two probabilities of commuters; one for males, and one for females. The notational system for distinguishing between these two probabilities is, letting M and F represent "male" and "female," and C and R represent "commuter" and "resident":

$$P(C|M) \qquad \text{and} \qquad P(C|F)$$

The first is to be read, "the probability of a commuter, given that it is a male." It is referred to as the *conditional probability* of a commuter, given that it is a male. The second is read, "the probability of a commuter, given that it is a female."

We shall now examine a situation in which the classification systems are not independent. Figure 4–10.1 represents a situation in which, again,

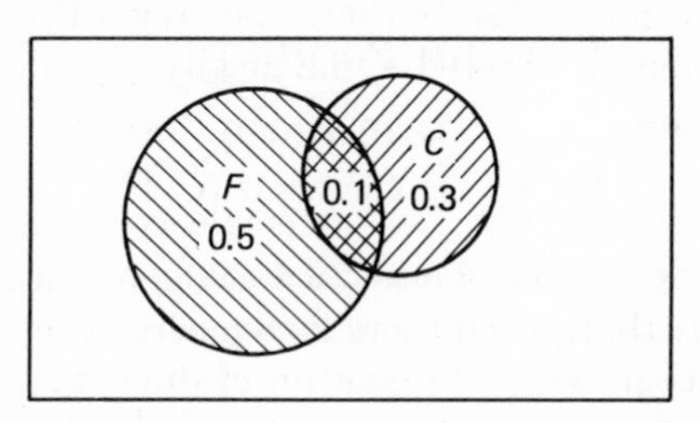

Fig. 4–10.1. Venn diagram. $P(F) = 0.5, P(C) = 0.3, P(C|F) = 0.2$.

$P(F) = 0.5$, and $P(C) = 0.3$, but the two classifications are not independent. In this new situation only $\frac{1}{5}$ of the females are commuters. This may be stated:

$$P(C|F) = 0.2$$

and, from this, it follows that

$$P(R|F) = 0.8$$

From this, and the fact that females are 50 per cent of the total, we can deduce that the percentage of female commuters in the plant is 10 per cent, and of female residents, 40 per cent:

$$P(F \cap C) = P(F)\,P(C|F) \tag{4–10.1}$$

$$P(F \cap C) = (0.5)(0.2) = 0.1$$

and

$$P(F \cap R) = (0.5)(0.8) = 0.4$$

Equation (4–10.1), when rearranged, yields the general definition of conditional probability:

$$P(C|F) = \frac{P(F \cap C)}{P(F)} \quad \text{for } P(F) > 0 \tag{4–10.2}$$

In dealing with conditional probabilities, and especially in dealing with their numerical values, it is helpful to think of a conditional probability as referring to a *reduced sample space*. That is, $P(C) = 0.3$, but $P(C|F) = 0.2$ for the reason that, in the latter case (the conditional probability of a commuter, given that it is a female) the sample space under consideration is *reduced* from *all employees* to *females*. Then, the second expression, the conditional probability, refers to the probability of a commuter, when only females are considered, and the first, $P(C)$, refers to the probability of a commuter when all employees are considered. It is helpful to look at Figure 4–10.1 with this interpretation in mind.

We can restate the definition of independence to say that, if the classification systems "male–female" and "commuter–resident" are independent, it follows that the probability of a randomly selected employee's being a commuter is the same, regardless of whether that person is male or female. Stated symbolically, if the classification systems are independent:

$$P(C) = P(C|F) = P(C|M) \tag{4–10.3}$$

Equation (4–10.3) is, in fact, a *definition of independence;* and, from this definition, it is clear that, when there is independence, Equation (4–10.1) simplifies to Equation (4–9.1). Equation (4–9.1), then, may be referred to as the formula for the *probability of compound independent events;* while Equation (4–10.1) is the general formula for the *probability of compound events*. Clearly, Equation (4–10.1) is the completely general statement, since it applies whether there is independence or not.

For conformity with symbol usage in previous definitional equations, the definition of conditional probability, Equation (4–10.2), and the formula for the probability of compound events, Equation (4–10.1), are restated here in terms of A and B.

The definition of *conditional probability*:

$$P(A|B) = \frac{P(A \cap B)}{P(B)} \qquad (4\text{–}10.4)$$

$$P(B|A) = \frac{P(A \cap B)}{P(A)} \qquad (4\text{–}10.5)$$

The general formula for *compound events*, the intersection:

$$P(A \cap B) = P(A)P(B|A) \qquad (4\text{–}10.6)$$

or

$$P(A \cap B) = P(B)P(A|B) \qquad (4\text{–}10.7)$$

These last two may also be referred to as the formulas for *joint probabilities.*

Finally, the general formula for *alternative events,* the union, is obtained by substituting Equation (4–10.6) into Equation (4–8.7):

$$P(A \cup B) = P(A) + P(B) - P(A)P(B|A) \qquad (4\text{–}10.8)$$

(Of course, Equation (4–10.7) could equally well have been used.) If events A and B are mutually exclusive, then $P(B|A) = 0$; and Equation (4–10.8) reduces to Equation (4–8.5), which is the formula for the probability of *alternative mutually exclusive events.* Indeed, the fact that the conditional probability is 0 is the essence of mutual exclusivity; and the equation

$$P(A|B) = P(B|A) = 0 \qquad (4\text{–}10.9)$$

is to be interpreted as a statement that events A and B are mutually exclusive.

If the classification schemes are independent, then the last term of Equation (4–10.8) becomes $P(A)P(B)$, since from Equation (4–9.1), for *compound independent events,*

$$P(A \cap B) = P(A)P(B) \qquad (4\text{–}10.10)$$

Then, when the classification schemes are independent, Equation (4–10.8) reduces to Equation (4–8.7), the formula for the probability of *alternative independent events.*

Now, all the quantities represented in Figure 4–10.1 may be computed. Given that

$$P(F) = 0.5$$

$$P(C) = 0.3$$

$$P(C|F) = 0.2$$

we may compute:

$$P(F \cap C) = P(F)P(C|F) = 0.5 \times 0.2 = 0.1$$
$$P(F \cap R) = P(F) - P(F \cap C) = 0.5 - 0.1 = 0.4$$
$$P(M \cap C) = P(C) - P(F \cap C) = 0.3 - 0.1 = 0.2$$
$$P(M \cap R) = 1 - P(F \cap C) - P(F \cap R) - P(M \cap C)$$
$$= 1 - (0.1 + 0.4 + 0.2) = 0.3$$

Also,

$$P(F \cup C) = P(F) + P(C) - P(F \cap C) = 0.5 + 0.3 - 0.1 = 0.7$$

The reader will see several alternative ways in which these and other quantities on the diagram might be computed.

4–11. Bayes' Theorem. A reconsideration of Equations (4–10.6) and (4–10.7) indicates that it is possible to combine them and compute $P(B|A)$, if $P(A|B)$ is known. The resulting equation is the very interesting and useful Bayes' theorem:

$$P(A \cap B) = P(A)P(B|A) \tag{4–10.6}$$

$$P(A \cap B) = P(B)P(A|B) \tag{4–10.7}$$

Combining these:

$$P(A)P(B|A) = P(B)P(A|B)$$

$$P(B|A) = \frac{P(B)P(A|B)}{P(A)} \tag{4–11.1}$$

Equation (4–11.1) is a simple statement of Bayes' theorem, about which much more will be said later. We can illustrate Bayes' theorem with the data given above. Given that:

$$P(F) = 0.5$$
$$P(C) = 0.3$$
$$P(C|F) = 0.2$$

The last equation states that, if a person is selected at random and found to be a female, the probability is 0.2 that she is a commuter. However, suppose a random person is found to be a commuter, what is the probability that that person is a female? This is exactly the kind of problem which Bayes' theorem can solve directly.

From Equation (4–11.1),

$$P(F|C) = \frac{P(F)P(C|F)}{P(C)} \tag{4–11.2}$$

$$P(F|C) = \frac{(0.5)(0.2)}{(0.3)} = \frac{0.1}{0.3} = 0.33$$

This result may be verified by examination of Figure 4–10.1.

In using Bayes' theorem, it is customary to refer to $P(F)$, as it appears in the numerator of Equation (4–11.2), as the *prior* probability of F; i.e., it is the probability of a female, before it is known that it is a commuter. Also, as used here, $P(F|C)$ is the *posterior* probability of F; i.e., it is the probability of a female, given the knowledge that it is a commuter. This use of the words *prior* and *posterior* serves to indicate that Bayes' theorem permits us to take account of additional knowledge about chance events by revising the probability values which we associate with these events.

Bayes' theorem is helpful in many situations; and, often, it helps to solve problems which, intuitively, would lead to the wrong answer. For example, the following problem is of a type which has, for generations of students of probability, been notorious for its counterintuitive answer.

There are three cars: A, B, and C. Car A contains two males, car B contains one male and one female, and car C contains two females. If one of these cars is selected at random, and one person is observed and found to be male, what is the probability that the other person in that car is male? Intuitively, students have traditionally rushed to the conclusion that the probability is 0.5, since the selected car must be either A or B, and the original selection among the cars was such that either one was equally likely to be selected. This is wrong, as we can see from Bayes' theorem, and as we can agree after due reflection on the fact that, after a person is observed as described above and found to be male, the two cars, A and B, are no longer equally likely to have been selected.

To solve the problem by Bayes' theorem,

$$P(A) = P(B) = P(C) = \tfrac{1}{3}$$

$$P(M|A) = 1 \qquad P(M|B) = 0.5$$

Since the other person in the car will be male if and only if the selected car is car A, the answer to the question is $P(A|M)$. From Bayes' theorem:

$$P(A|M) = \frac{P(A)P(M|A)}{P(M)}$$

But,

$$P(M) = P(A)P(M|A) + P(B)P(M|B) + P(C)P(M|C)$$

$$P(M) = (\tfrac{1}{3})(1) + (\tfrac{1}{3})(0.5) + (\tfrac{1}{3})(0) = 0.5$$

Therefore,

$$P(A|M) = \frac{(\frac{1}{3})(1)}{0.5} = \frac{2}{3}$$

We may have been a bit disturbed by the thought, implicit in the reasoning given above, that, *after* selecting one of the cars, we evaluated *the probability that we had* selected a particular one. This may suggest that the operation of Bayes' theorem can lead to results which seem to be quite justified and correct arithmetically and algebraically but may not be easy to explain or understand in terms of the traditional interpretation of probabilities. In any event, we have seen above that we may refer to the probability of choosing car A of $\frac{1}{3}$ as the *prior* probability that car A was chosen, and that the probability of $\frac{2}{3}$, the probability that car A was chosen, *after* one of the occupants has been noted to be male, may be referred to as the *posterior* probability that car A was chosen. It is posterior to the experimental evidence.

Let us examine one other problem in which we can use Bayes' theorem to arrive at a solution which is expressed in terms of a probability number, but in which the probability number is not readily interpreted in the traditional form of the percentage of successes in many repetitive trials. Dr. Damil, a competitive chap, engages in an athletic contest every Sunday morning with his friend Johow. From long experience, we know that they will toss a fair coin to decide whether to play chess or golf. If they play chess, the probability that Damil will win is 0.8; but, if they play golf, the probability that Damil will win is 0.1. Last Monday, Damil came to me and gleefully announced that he had triumphed over his opponent on the previous day. Then he asked, "What is the probability that we played golf yesterday?" The following computation led to the answer:

$$P(C) = P(G) = 0.5$$

$$P(W|G) = 0.1$$

$$P(W|C) = 0.8$$

where W represents "win" for Damil, and C and G represent "chess" and "golf," respectively. Then, by Bayes' theorem:

$$P(G|W) = \frac{P(G)P(W|G)}{P(W)}$$

and the probability of Damil's winning, $P(W)$, is the sum of the probability of "golf and Damil wins," $P(G \cap W)$, plus the probability of "chess and Damil wins," $P(C \cap W)$. Thus,

$$\begin{aligned} P(W) &= P(G \cap W) + P(C \cap W) \\ &= P(G)P(W|G) + P(C)P(W|C) \\ &= (0.5)(0.1) + (0.5)(0.8) = 0.45 \end{aligned}$$

therefore,

$$P(G|W) = \frac{(0.5)(0.1)}{0.45} = \frac{0.05}{0.45} = \frac{1}{9}$$

Clearly, the answer to Damil's question is that the probability that he played golf yesterday is $\frac{1}{9}$. The arithmetic is clear. However, this answer is not subject to the relative-frequency interpretation of probabilities. The only interpretation which would be consistent with that kind of interpretation of probabilities is to assert that it means that, if they follow their usual procedure of tossing the coin and then playing the game, then, for the occasions on which Damil wins, $\frac{1}{9}$ of them will occur when they play golf. This, however, is not the question which Damil asked. He asked, "What is the probability that we played golf yesterday?" In the relative-frequency interpretation of probabilities, this is a meaningless question. Yesterday has come and gone; a game was played; and there is no chance process associated with that unique event, which has already occurred. However, this question has meaning when probabilities are viewed from the so-called subjective point of view; and, then, using this interpretation of probabilities, Bayes' theorem can make very interesting and important contributions to decision theory. This matter will be discussed at length in Chapter 19. In any event, we may again note that the *prior* probability of playing golf was 0.5, but the *posterior* probability (posterior to the knowledge about the outcome of the game) is $\frac{1}{9}$.

We can review much of the subject matter of these sections by considering the results of throwing a pair of fair dice. The probability of throwing two dice and getting a *three* and a *five* is $\frac{2}{36}$. This may be computed in three ways. First, there are 36 possible events; and for fair dice, each of these has a probability of occurrence of $\frac{1}{36}$. The sample space for this experiment is shown in Table 4–11.1, in which each sample point is represented by a pair of numbers, the first representing the number of spots showing on the first die and the second representing the number of spots showing on the second die. Two of these sample points consist of a *three* paired with a *five*; therefore, the probability of the event, "a *three* paired with a *five*," is $\frac{2}{36}$.

TABLE 4–11.1

Sample Space for the Thirty-Six Possible Outcomes of a Throw of a Pair of Dice

$$S = \begin{Bmatrix} (1,1) & (1,2) & (1,3) & (1,4) & (1,5) & (1,6) \\ (2,1) & (2,2) & (2,3) & (2,4) & (2,5) & (2,6) \\ (3,1) & (3,2) & (3,3) & (3,4) & (3,5) & (3,6) \\ (4,1) & (4,2) & (4,3) & (4,4) & (4,5) & (4,6) \\ (5,1) & (5,2) & (5,3) & (5,4) & (5,5) & (5,6) \\ (6,1) & (6,2) & (6,3) & (6,4) & (6,5) & (6,6) \end{Bmatrix}$$

Second, using the rule for compound independent events, Equation (4–9.1), the probability of a *three* on the first die is $\frac{1}{6}$, and the probability of a *five* on the second die is $\frac{1}{6}$; and, therefore, the probability of a *three* on the first and a *five* on the second is $\frac{1}{36}$. Similarly, the probability of a *five* on the first and a *three* on the second is $\frac{1}{36}$. Thus, by the equation for the probability of alternative mutually exclusive events, Equation (4–8.5), the probability of a *three* and a *five* in either order is $\frac{2}{36}$.

A third way of arriving at the same result is to consider the probability of either a *three* or a *five* on the first die. That, by Equation (4–8.5) is $\frac{2}{6}$. Then, if we have thus fixed the first die, there is only one face on the second die which will produce the desired combination to yield "success." Its probability is $\frac{1}{6}$; and the probability of success (i.e., a *three* and a *five*) is $\frac{2}{6} \times \frac{1}{6}$, or $\frac{2}{36}$.

The probability of throwing either a *six* (as the total of the two faces) or *a pair* is an example of events which are not mutually exclusive. From Table 4–11.1,

The probability of a *six* is $\frac{5}{36}$.
The probability of *a pair* is $\frac{6}{36}$.

The probability of a *six* or *a pair* is the sum of these, less the probability of a *six and a pair*, i.e., (3,3), the probability of which is $\frac{1}{36}$. Thus, from Equation (4–8.7),

$$P(six \cup a\ pair) = P(six) + P(a\ pair) - P(six \cap a\ pair)$$

$$= \frac{5}{36} + \frac{6}{36} - \frac{1}{36} = \frac{10}{36}$$

This figure, $\frac{10}{36}$, may easily be verified by counting the number of elements which are either *six* or *a pair*. There are ten of these as seen in Table 4–11.1. The last term on the right side, $P(six \cap a\ pair)$, may be formed more formally, using Equation (4–10.6). $P(six) = \frac{5}{36}$, and $P(a\ pair|six) = \frac{1}{5}$,

$$P(six \cap a\ pair) = P(six)P(a\ pair|six)$$

$$= (\tfrac{5}{36})(\tfrac{1}{5}) = \tfrac{1}{36}$$

This procedure was hardly necessary in this trivial case, since it is quite obvious that, of the 36 possible outcomes, only one is both a *six* and *a pair*. The student will find that careful study of these last paragraphs in conjunction with the table will contribute a great deal to the understanding of probability computations.

4–12. Permutations. The study of permutations and combinations enables us to compute the number of ways in which a specified event may occur. We shall find that it is extremely important in deriving various probability values.

A *permutation* is an *order* or an *arrangement* of all or part of some number of elements. For example, there are six permutations of the three letters: *a*, *b*, *c*.

abc *bac* *cab*
acb *bca* *cba*

This result can be obtained by reasoning as follows:

1. There are 3 places to fill (the first, second, and third positions).
2. The first place can be filled in 3 ways (a, b, or c).
3. For each of the three selections for the first place, there are two ways to fill the second place (either of the remaining two letters may be used). This yields $3 \cdot 2 = 6$ ways to fill the first two places.
4. For each of the six selections for the first two places, there is only one way to fill the last place. Thus, there are $3 \cdot 2 \cdot 1 = 6$ ways to arrange 3 elements.

From this reasoning, a very simple and universally applicable rule can be derived:

If one thing can be done in k_1 ways and, after it is done, a second thing can be done in k_2 ways, and, after it is done, a third thing can be done in k_3 ways, etc. . . . and after the $(n - 1)th$ thing is done, the nth thing can be done in k_n different ways; then the number of different ways in which the n things can be done is

$$k_1 \cdot k_2 \cdot k_3 \cdot \cdot \cdot k_n$$

From this rule, it follows that the number of permutations of, say, five elements is

$$5(5-1)(5-2)(5-3)(5-4) = 5 \cdot 4 \cdot 3 \cdot 2 \cdot 1 = 120$$

Thus, the number of permutations of n elements is $n!$ However, often it is necessary to determine the number of permutations of subsets of size r taken from the n elements, where r is equal to or less than n. Traditionally, this is referred to as "the number of permutations of n elements taken r at a time." For example, how many 3-digit numbers can be constructed from the 5 digits (1, 2, 3, 4, 5), using each digit only once in each 3-digit number? There are 5 ways to select the first, 4 ways to select the second, and 3 ways to select the third. Therefore, there are $5 \cdot 4 \cdot 3 = 60$ possible three-digit numbers.

(It must be noted that this problem is quite different from the determination of the number of three-digit numbers which can be constructed from the first 5 digits, using each *as many times as we wish*. Then the possible number of three-digit numbers is $5 \cdot 5 \cdot 5 = 5^3 = 125$. When we discuss permutations and combinations here and elsewhere, we always intend that each element may be used only once.)

The number of permutations of n things taken r at a time is written ${}_nP_r$. There is a general formula for this which may be derived as follows. We have seen that the number of permutations of 5 elements is

$$\text{Five-factorial} = 5! = 5 \cdot 4 \cdot 3 \cdot 2 \cdot 1 = 120$$

but the number of permutations of 5 elements taken only 3 at a time is

$$5 \cdot 4 \cdot 3 = 60$$

There is no simple symbol for this, but it is clearly equivalent to

$$\frac{5!}{(5-3)!} = \frac{5!}{2!} = \frac{5 \cdot 4 \cdot 3 \cdot 2 \cdot 1}{2 \cdot 1} = 5 \cdot 4 \cdot 3 = 60$$

Thus,

$${}_5P_3 = \frac{5!}{(5-3)!} = 60$$

As a general rule, the number of permutations of n elements taken r at a time is

$${}_nP_r = n(n-1)(n-2) \cdots (n-r+1)$$

and this is clearly equivalent to

$${}_nP_r = \frac{n(n-1)(n-2)\cdots(n-r+1)(n-r)(n-r-1)\cdots 3 \cdot 2 \cdot 1}{(n-r)(n-r-1)\cdots 3 \cdot 2 \cdot 1}$$

$${}_nP_r = \frac{n!}{(n-r)!} \tag{4–12.1}$$

4–13. Combinations. A group of elements considered without reference to the order of the individuals in the group is a *combination.* Clearly there is only one combination of n elements taken all at a time. Also, for any combination of n elements, there are $n!$ permutations. From this fact that there are $n!$ permutations possible with any combination of n elements, we can see that the number of combinations of n things taken r at a time, designated $\binom{n}{r}$ or, by some writers ${}_nC_r$, is smaller than ${}_nP_r$. In fact, the number of permutations of n elements taken r at a time is: $r!$ times the number of combinations of n things taken r at a time:

$${}_nP_r = r!\binom{n}{r} \tag{4–13.1}$$

$$\binom{n}{r} = \frac{{}_nP_r}{r!} \tag{4–13.2}$$

$$\binom{n}{r} = \frac{n!}{r!(n-r)!} \tag{4–13.3}$$

From Equation (4–13.3) it should also be clear that

$$\binom{n}{r} = \binom{n}{n-r} \tag{4–13.4}$$

If the Board of Trustees has 10 members, how many possible slates of 4 officers (president, vice-president, secretary, treasurer) may be selected? The statement of this question illustrates a commonly occurring ambiguity in that it is not explicit in stating whether the desired answer is the number of combinations or the number of permutations. If it is the former, then the desired answer is merely the number of possible different executive committees (the four officers constitute the executive committee) without regard to the specific office held by each member. If it is the latter, then each possible executive committee actually represents 4! different arrangements, since that question considers any change in any office as creating a different slate of officers. That is, if one slate had Smith as president and Hayes as vice-president, and another was identical except that Hayes was president and Smith was vice-president, then that is a different permutation, although it is not a different combination. The answers to the two questions are:

$$\binom{n}{r} = \binom{10}{4} = \frac{10!}{4!\,6!} = \frac{10 \cdot 9 \cdot 8 \cdot 7}{4 \cdot 3 \cdot 2 \cdot 1} = 210$$

$$_nP_r = {}_{10}P_4 = \frac{10!}{6!} = 10 \cdot 9 \cdot 8 \cdot 7 = 5{,}040$$

4–14. Distinct Permutations. Sometimes, in examining permutations, we do not wish to consider all of the elements as distinct, but rather wish to classify them into categories. For example, the number of permutations of the first five letters of the alphabet $\{a, b, c, d, e\}$ is $5! = 120$. However, suppose for some purpose we are interested in distinguishing only between consonants and vowels. In that case, the permutations *abcde* and *acbde* are not distinct, since they both represent: vowel, consonant, consonant, consonant, vowel. How many distinct permutations, then, are there?

First, we can rewrite the set as $\{v, c, c, c, v\}$ or $\{v, v, c, c, c\}$. We can see that for each distinct permutation, there will be 2! ways of rearranging the two vowels and 3! ways of rearranging the three consonants, so that there are $2!\,3! = 12$ true permutations for each *distinct* permutation.

Clearly, then, if D is the number of distinct permutations,

$$2!\,3!\,D = 5!$$

$$D = \frac{5!}{2!\,3!} = 10 \qquad (4\text{–}14.1)$$

The general rule is:

The number of distinct permutations of n things taken all at a time when n_1 are alike, n_2 others are alike, etc., is

$$D = \frac{n!}{n_1!\,n_2!\,\cdots} \qquad (4\text{–}14.2)$$

If five fair coins are tossed, what is the probability of 0, 1, 2, 3, 4, or 5 heads? This can easily be computed from the rules for manipulating permutations and combinations. There are $2^5 = 32$ different ways in which the five coins may fall. This follows from the fact that there are two ways the first coin may fall, two ways the second coin may fall, etc. If these 32 elementary events are all equally likely, then the *probability* of each possible compound event is $\frac{1}{32}$ times the *number* of these elementary events which are included in that compound event. Consider, for example, the event, two heads. This is another aspect of the problem solved in Equation (4–14.1). That is, it is the number of distinct permutations of the objects $\{H, H, T, T, T\}$.

Thus

$$P(\text{two heads}) = \frac{\frac{5!}{2!\,3!}}{32} = \frac{10}{32}$$

Similarly, the probabilities for all possible values of x, where x is the number of heads, are derived in Table 4–14.1.

TABLE 4–14.1

Computation of Probabilities of All Possible Numbers of Heads in Five Tosses of a Fair Coin

x	$P(x)$
0	$\frac{5!}{0!\,5!\,(32)} = \frac{1}{32} = 0.03125$
1	$\frac{5!}{1!\,4!\,(32)} = \frac{5}{32} = 0.15625$
2	$\frac{5!}{2!\,3!\,(32)} = \frac{10}{32} = 0.31250$
3	$\frac{5!}{3!\,2!\,(32)} = \frac{10}{32} = 0.31250$
4	$\frac{5!}{4!\,1!\,(32)} = \frac{5}{32} = 0.15625$
5	$\frac{5!}{5!\,0!\,(32)} = \frac{1}{32} = 0.03125$
	$\frac{32}{32} = 1.00000$

4–15. Probability Distributions. Table 4–14.1 represents a *probability distribution.* A discrete probability distribution such as is displayed in the table is a mutually exclusive and exhaustive list of all of the events which may result from a chance process, and the probability associated with each. Since the random variable "number of heads" may take only discrete values, the probability distribution which characterizes that random variable is a *discrete probability distribution.* Discrete probability distributions may be represented in tabular fashion as in

Table 4–15.1 or in graphic form as in Figure 4–15.1 or 4–15.2. Clearly, the first column in tables such as Table 4–15.1 is a list of the set of sample points in the sample space for some specified experiment.

TABLE 4–15.1

Probability Distribution of the Outcomes of Five Tosses of a Fair Coin

Number of Heads x	Probability $P(x)$
0	0.03125
1	0.15625
2	0.31250
3	0.31250
4	0.15625
5	0.03125
	1.00000

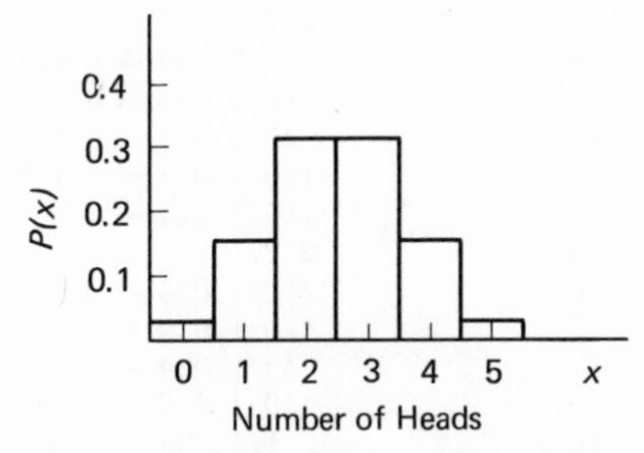

Fig. 4–15.1. Histogram representing probability distribution for five tosses of a fair coin (or a single toss of five fair coins).

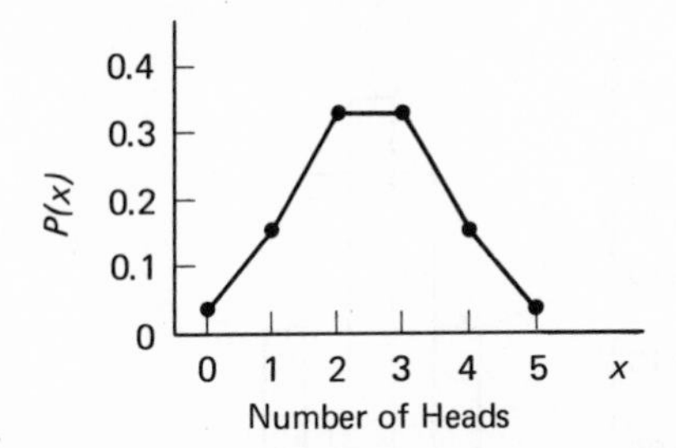

Fig. 4–15.2. Probability polygon representing probability distribution for five tosses of a fair coin (or a single toss of five fair coins).

For a single toss of a coin, the probability distribution is shown in Table 4–15.2, and, for ten tosses, it is shown in Table 4–15.3. The histogram for the distribution of Table 4–15.3 is shown in Figure 4–15.3.

TABLE 4–15.2

Probability Distribution of the Outcomes of a Single Toss of a Fair Coin

Event	Probability
Heads	0.5
Tails	0.5
Total	1.0

TABLE 4–15.3

Probability Distribution of the Outcomes of Ten Tosses of a Fair Coin

Number of Heads x	Probability $P(x)$
0	1/1,024 = 0.001
1	10/1,024 = 0.010
2	45/1,024 = 0.044
3	120/1,024 = 0.117
4	210/1,024 = 0.205
5	252/1,024 = 0.246
6	210/1,024 = 0.205
7	120/1,024 = 0.117
8	45/1,024 = 0.044
9	10/1,024 = 0.010
10	1/1,024 = 0.001
	1,024/1,024 = 1.000

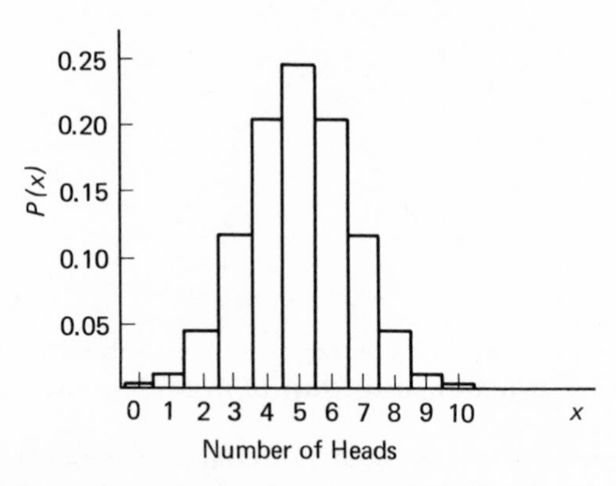

Fig. 4–15.3. Histogram representing the probability distribution for the outcomes of ten tosses of a fair coin.

A discrete probability distribution may be defined as a collection of pairs $[x_i, P(x_i)]$ in which the first element describes an event, and the second is the number representing the probability of occurrence of that event.

For the illustration of Section 4–10, Figure 4–10.1, the probability distribution for the four compound events is shown in Table 4–15.4.

TABLE 4–15.4

Probability Distribution For Random Selection of Employees Classified by Sex and Residence

Event	Probability
Female–Commuter	0.1
Female–Resident	0.4
Male–Commuter	0.2
Male–Resident	0.3
	1.0

SOURCE: Figure 4–10.1.

4–16. Expected Values. The *expected value* or *expectation* of a random variable (the outcome of chance process) is the weighted average of all of the values of the variable, each weighted by its probability of occurrence. This, of course, is *identical with the arithmetic average.*

Thus, if a chance process can be described by a probability distribution, i.e., two or more possible events, each of which has or is assigned a *numerical value,* and each of which has a definite probability of occurrence, the *expected value* of a trial is the sum of the products of the value of each event multiplied by the associated probability. If each of n outcomes is associated with a payoff or value, x_i, and a probability, $P(x_i)$, the expected value of the random variable x, written $E(x)$, is

$$\text{Expected value} = \mu = E(x) = \sum_{i=1}^{n} x_i P(x_i) \qquad (4\text{–}16.1)$$

For example, in tossing a fair coin, if the payoff is \$10 for heads and zero for tails, the expected value of this process is \$5.

$$\text{Expected value} = (10)(0.5) + (0)(0.5) = \$5$$

Consider the decision problem of a speculator faced with the choice between two courses of action: A_1, sell a particular asset now for \$10,000; and A_2, hold the asset for speculation. If he holds it, there are four possible events, each of which will result in a different selling price, and each of which has a different probability of occurrence. The payoff values and the probabilities are shown below.

Events	I	II	III	IV
Probabilities	0.2	0.4	0.3	0.1
Payoffs for A_2 ($ thousands)	8	5	12	30

The expected value of the course of action A_2 (holding the asset for speculation), written $E(A_2)$, is

$$\begin{aligned} E(A_2) &= (8)(0.2) + (5)(0.4) + (12)(0.3) + (30)(0.1)] \\ &= 1.6 + 2.0 + 3.6 + 3.0 = 10.2 \text{ thousand dollars} \\ &= \$10{,}200 \end{aligned}$$

Thus, A_2, with its expected return of $10,200, is preferable to A_1, with its assured return of $10,000, under the psychological and philosophical assumptions that the value or *utility* of a sum of money is exactly proportional to its size, that there is no additional utility or disutility from the act of gambling itself, and that people behave in the way which maximizes their expected values.

The first assumption means that $10,000 is twice as valuable or desirable as $5,000, and $30,000 is six times as desirable as $5,000, etc. Clearly, in the real world, this may not be the case for all persons at all times. The second assumption means that the decision maker does not enter into gambles because he likes the act of gambling, and he does not avoid them because he dislikes the act of gambling. The third assumption is a critical one for decision theory. In order for us to predict how people will behave in any particular situation, we must have a model. The model which is most commonly used to describe how people behave in decision situations is that, wherever applicable, people behave in the way which maximizes the expected values of their utilities (or, of course, minimizes the expected values of disutilities such as costs, etc.). This is probably a good assumption in that it tends, in most cases, to make reasonably accurate predictions about how people actually do behave. However, it is not necessarily always dependable, as we shall see in Chapter 19, under "event matching."

If these assumptions did not hold, then, in the case above, the decision maker might prefer to take the certain $10,000 rather than run the risk of having to accept $8,000 or $5,000, if events I or II were realized. On the other hand, he might like to gamble; and he might choose to speculate for the large gain, $30,000, under event IV, even if the probability distribution of the outcomes were such that the expected value turned out to be less than $10,000. Throughout this book we assume that people make decisions according to these three assumptions, which may be restated as: (1) The utility of money is linear. (2) There is no utility or disutility in gambling. (3) People will make decisions in a way such as to maximize the expected value of the monetary payoff or to minimize the expected monetary cost. This is exactly what we have had our decision maker do in the illustration above.

The expected value of a random variable is the arithmetic mean of the probability distribution of that variable. This follows from the fact that the arithmetic mean is computed by summing the products of each of the values of the variable multiplied by the frequency or weight assigned to it, and then dividing by the sum of the weights. In the case of a probability distribution, the weights are the probabilities associated with each of the values of the variable; and the need to divide by the sum of the weights is satisfied by the fact that the sum of the probabilities is exactly 1, thus avoiding the necessity for a separate division step. The reader may verify the identity between the expected value and the arithmetic mean by reference to Tables 4–15.2 and 4–15.3.

4–17. The Binomial Distribution. The *binomial distribution* is, in reality, a family of distributions, all of which have certain characteristics in common. The distribution of the number of heads in n tosses of a fair coin, which is presented in Tables 4–15.1, 4–15.2, and 4–15.3 and graphed in Figures 4–15.1, 4–15.2, and 4–15.3, is a binomial distribution; that is, its probability values may be derived, given the probability of success in one trial, p, and the number of trials, n, by the use of the familiar binomial expansion formula $(q + p)^n$, where $q = 1 - p$.

The binomial distribution is of great importance, because it enables us to compute the probability that a sample of n observations (or "trials") will result in any specified number of successes from 0 to n, given the probability of success in the population. For example, if in a particular suburb of a large city, 80 per cent of the housewives shop in the city's central business district at least once a week, what is the probability that a sample of 10 housewives selected at random will contain exactly 7 members who so shop?

Clearly, one way in which such a sample may occur is to select, by chance, seven shoppers followed by three nonshoppers. The probability of this event, since successive selections of individuals are assumed to be independent is:

$$[P(\text{shopper})]^7[P(\text{nonshopper})]^3$$

or

$$(0.8)(0.8)(0.8)(0.8)(0.8)(0.8)(0.8)(0.2)(0.2)(0.2) = (0.8)^7(0.2)^3 = 0.001677$$

However, there are many other ways in which seven "successes" and three "failures" may be drawn. The number of these is precisely equal to the number of distinct permutations of ten things, seven of which are the same and three others of which are the same. This, from Equation (4–14.2), is

$$\frac{10!}{7!\,3!} = \frac{10 \cdot 9 \cdot 8}{3 \cdot 2 \cdot 1} = 120$$

Since each of these 120 different ways of getting seven successes and three failures has the probability of p^7q^3, where p is the probability of success and q is the probability of failure, the probability of seven successes and three failures *in any order* is the union of all of these, or

$$P(\text{seven successes and three failures in ten trials in any order}) = 120p^7q^3 = (120)(0.001677) = 0.2012$$

This result agrees with what may be found in Appendix B.

From this we can construct the general rule for the probability of x successes in n trials, where p is the probability of success and q is the probability of failure:

$$P(x) = \frac{n!}{x!\,(n-x)!}\,p^x q^{(n-x)} \tag{4–17.1}$$

The first part of this expression, the *coefficient*, is the familiar expression for the number of distinct permutations, and the second part, $p^x q^{(n-x)}$, is the probability of each of these possible distinct permutations, each of which represents x successes and $(n - x)$ failures. It should also be noted that, in the expression for distinct permutations when there are, as in this case, only two kinds of distinct elements, the expression is the same as for the number of combinations of n things taken x at a time, and Equation (4–17.1) may be written using the form $\binom{n}{x}$ as follows:

$$P(x) = \binom{n}{x} p^x q^{(n-x)}$$

This expression is the general formula for finding individual terms of the binomial expansion. Since it is obviously also the basic formula for evaluating probabilities in the binomial distribution, let us examine the relationship between the familiar binomial expansion and the binomial probability distribution. First, we shall briefly review the binomial expansion.

The binomial expansion results from raising to the nth power a binomial in the form $(q + p)$. If $n = 2$, the expansion is the familiar:

$$(q + p)^2 = q^2 + 2qp + p^2$$

and, if, for example, $n = 5$, the expansion is:

$$(q + p)^5 = q^5 + 5q^4p + 10q^3p^2 + 10q^2p^3 + 5qp^4 + p^5$$

From the above binomial expansions, the following general relationships should be noted:

1. The *number of terms* in a binomial expansion is always $n + 1$.
2. The *exponents* of p and q, for any single term, when added together, always sum to n. This is because the two exponents are always x for p, and $(n - x)$ for q. The sum of these is clearly n.
3. The *exponents* of q are n, $(n - 1)$, $(n - 2)$, . . . , 1, 0, respectively; and the exponents of p are 0, 1, 2, . . . , $(n - 1)$, n, respectively (note: $p^0 = 1$; $q^0 = 1$).
4. The *coefficients* for the $n + 1$ terms of the distribution are always symmetrical, ascending to the middle of the series and then descending. When n is an odd number, $n + 1$ is even and the coefficients of the two central terms are identical. These coefficients may be derived in several different ways:
   a) *For single terms:*
      The term in which the coefficient of p is x (i.e., the $(x + 1)$th term) has as its coefficient $\dfrac{n!}{x!(n - x)!}$.
   b) *For the complete expansion:*
      The coefficient of each term may be obtained from the previous term by the following rule. Consider the terms to be numbered consecutively, beginning with 1. *For any term, multiply its coefficient by the exponent of q and divide by the number of the term to obtain the coefficient of the next term.*
5. Every term in the expansion is in the form of Equation (4–17.1), and, therefore, if $q + p = 1$, the binomial expansion will generate $(n + 1)$ terms, which represent, respectively, the probability of 0, 1, 2, . . . , n successes in an experiment consisting of n random trials in a population characterized by a probability of success of p.

Therefore, any term of the binomial expansion $(q + p)^n$ may be found by the use of Equation (4–17.1) and, clearly then, each term of the expansion may be seen to represent the probability of some number of successes in n trials. There are $(n + 1)$ terms to the expansion of the binomial $(q + p)^n$, and these represent, in order, the probability of 0 success, 1 success, 2 successes, . . . , etc., up to and including n successes. Like most other distributions, real and theoretical, the binomial distribution has an arithmetic mean and standard deviation. These parameters may be computed by the use of the familiar computational formulas with the slight change that, for theoretical distributions, such as the binomial, probabilities are used in place of the frequencies used in a sample. The formulas for discrete probability distributions are:

For the arithmetic mean (the "expected value"),

$$\mu = \frac{\Sigma x P(x)}{\Sigma P(x)} \tag{4–17.2}$$

in place of the familiar sample formula

$$\bar{x} = \frac{\Sigma f x}{\Sigma f}$$

For the standard deviation,

$$\sigma = \sqrt{\frac{\Sigma (x - \mu)^2 P(x)}{\Sigma P(x)}} \tag{4–17.3}$$

in place of the sample formula

$$s = \sqrt{\frac{\Sigma f (x - \bar{x})^2}{\Sigma f}}$$

Since the sum of the probabilities is 1,

$$\Sigma P(x) = 1 \tag{4–17.4}$$

the denominators of Equations (4–17.2) and (4–17.3) drop out, leaving

$$\mu = \Sigma x P(x) \tag{4–17.5}$$

$$\sigma = \sqrt{\Sigma (x - \mu)^2 P(x)} \tag{4–17.6}$$

These *general* formulas may be used to compute the mean and standard deviation of a binomial distribution or any probability distribution. However, they are seldom used with the binomial distribution, because there are theoretical formulas which are *specifically applicable to the binomial distribution* and are much easier to use. These formulas, which are derived below in Section 4–21, are

$$\mu = np \tag{4–17.7}$$

$$\sigma = \sqrt{npq} \tag{4–17.8}$$

For example, for the binomial distribution, $(0.2 + 0.8)^{10}$, $p = 0.8$, $q = 0.2$, and $n = 10$:

$$\mu = np = (10)(0.8) = 8$$

$$\sigma = \sqrt{npq} = \sqrt{(10)(0.8)(0.2)} = \sqrt{1.6} = 1.26$$

The use of the general equations (4–17.5) and (4–17.6) would, of course, yield the same results, but in order to use those equations in the problem dealing with the shoppers, it would first be necessary to obtain $P(x)$ for all eleven possible values of x, either from a table such as Appendix B or by computation, as we have done in Table 4–14.1 for $x = 5$ and Table 4–15.3 for $x = 10$.

As an illustration, consider the binomial distribution of Tables 4–14.1 and 4–15.1. The mean and standard deviation may be computed as in Table 4–17.1, using Equations (4–17.5) and 4–17.6) as follows:

TABLE 4–17.1

Computation of μ and σ of Binomial Distribution

($p = q = 0.5$, $n = 5$)

x	$P(x)$	$xP(x)$	$x - \mu$	$(x - \mu)^2$	$(x - \mu)^2 P(x)$
0	1/32	0	−2.5	6.25	6.25/32
1	5/32	5/32	−1.5	2.25	11.25/32
2	10/32	20/32	−0.5	0.25	2.5/32
3	10/32	30/32	0.5	0.25	2.5/32
4	5/32	20/32	1.5	2.25	11.25/32
5	1/32	5/32	2.5	6.25	6.25/32
		80/32 = 2.5			40/32 = 1.25

$$\mu = \Sigma xP(x) \tag{4–17.5}$$

$$= 2.5$$

$$\sigma = \sqrt{\Sigma(x - \mu)^2 P(x)} \tag{4–17.6}$$

$$= \sqrt{1.25} = 1.118$$

The alternative method of computation, using the specific formulas for the binomial distribution, is much simpler. It requires only p, q, and n:

$$\mu = np \tag{4–17.7}$$

$$= (5)(0.5) = 2.5$$

$$\sigma = \sqrt{npq} \tag{4–17.8}$$

$$= \sqrt{(5)(0.5)(0.5)} = \sqrt{1.25} = 1.118$$

4–18. Symmetry and the Binomial Distribution. In the binomial distribution, when p, the probability of success, equals 0.5, i.e., $p = q$, then the distribution is symmetrical. The binomial distribution of Tables 4–14.1, 4–15.1, 4–15.2, and 4–15.3 and Figures 4–15.1, 4–15.2, and 4–15.3 are all symmetrical about their arithmetic mean, μ. That is because, in all these cases, $p = q = 0.5$.

However, when p and q are not equal, the binomial distribution is not symmetrical; it is said to be *asymmetrical*, or, more commonly, *skewed*. For example, the binomial distribution for $p = \frac{2}{3}$, $n = 6$, is skewed. This distribution will have seven terms, referring to the probabilities of 0, 1, 2, 3, 4, 5, and 6 successes, respectively. The expansion $(q + p)^n$ for $q = \frac{1}{3}$, $p = \frac{2}{3}$, $n = 6$ is given below.

$$(\tfrac{1}{3} + \tfrac{2}{3})^6 = (\tfrac{1}{3})^6 + 6(\tfrac{1}{3})^5(\tfrac{2}{3}) + 15(\tfrac{1}{3})^4(\tfrac{2}{3})^2 + 20(\tfrac{1}{3})^3(\tfrac{2}{3})^3 + 15(\tfrac{1}{3})^2(\tfrac{2}{3})^4 + 6(\tfrac{1}{3})(\tfrac{2}{3})^5 + (\tfrac{2}{3})^6$$

This distribution is arranged in the form of a probability distribution in Table 4–18.1, and its frequency polygon is given in Figure 4–18.1. In

TABLE 4–18.1

Skewed Binomial Probability Distribution

($p = \frac{2}{3}$, $q = \frac{1}{3}$, $n = 6$)

x	$P(x)$		
0	$(\frac{1}{3})^6$	= 1/729	= 0.001
1	$6(\frac{1}{3})^5(\frac{2}{3})$	= 12/729	= 0.017
2	$15(\frac{1}{3})^4(\frac{2}{3})^2$	= 60/729	= 0.082
3	$20(\frac{1}{3})^3(\frac{2}{3})^3$	= 160/729	= 0.220
4	$15(\frac{1}{3})^2(\frac{2}{3})^4$	= 240/729	= 0.329
5	$6(\frac{1}{3})(\frac{2}{3})^5$	= 192/729	= 0.263
6	$(\frac{2}{3})^6$	= 64/729	= 0.088
	$(\frac{1}{3} + \frac{2}{3})^6$	729/729	1.000

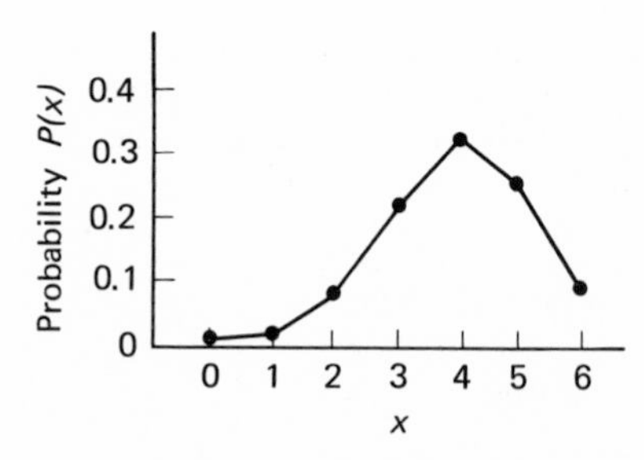

Fig. 4–18.1. Frequency polygon, skewed binomial distribution: $p = \frac{2}{3}$, $q = \frac{1}{3}$, $n = 6$.

understanding the frequency polygon for a *discrete* distribution such as the binomial distribution, it must be remembered that *only the plotted points have meaning*. The lines connecting the points are an aid to visual presentation, but they have no statistical meaning. They should not be interpreted to suggest that interpolation between points is possible or meaningful.

The mean and standard deviation may again be computed by the two alternative techniques: first, the general computational technique which is applicable to any kind of distribution; and second, using the specific formulas for the binomial distribution. Both of these techniques are illustrated in Table 4–18.2 and the computations which follow it, using Equations (4–17.5) and (4–17.6).

TABLE 4–18.2

Computation of the Mean and Standard Deviation of a Skewed Binomial Distribution

$(p = \frac{2}{3},\ q = \frac{1}{3},\ n = 6)$

x	$P(x)$	$xP(x)$	$x - \mu$	$(x - \mu)^2$	$(x - \mu)^2P(x)$
0	1/729	0	−4	16	16/729
1	12/729	12/729	−3	9	108/729
2	60/729	120/729	−2	4	240/729
3	160/729	480/729	−1	1	160/729
4	240/729	960/729	0	0	0
5	192/729	960/729	1	1	192/729
6	64/729	384/729	2	4	256/729
		2,916/729			972/729

$$\mu = \Sigma xP(x) = \frac{2{,}916}{729} = 4$$

$$\sigma = \sqrt{\Sigma(x - \mu)^2P(x)} = \sqrt{\frac{972}{729}} = \sqrt{\frac{4}{3}} = 1.2$$

Again, of course, the same result could be obtained much more easily by the use of the specific formulas for the parameters of the binomial distribution, Equations (4–17.7) and (4–17.8):

$$\mu = np = 6 \cdot \frac{2}{3} = 4$$

$$\sigma = \sqrt{npq} = \sqrt{6 \cdot \frac{2}{3} \cdot \frac{1}{3}} = \sqrt{\frac{4}{3}} = 1.2$$

4–19. Approximations to the Binomial Distribution. The binomial distribution, as we have seen, is a discrete distribution. That is, the values of the random variable are discrete integral numbers; and the frequency polygon and the histogram have a broken line character. Furthermore, there is no interpolation between points on the frequency polygon, because there are no intermediate points. However, as n increases, of course the number of possible outcomes increases similarly, and the frequency poly-

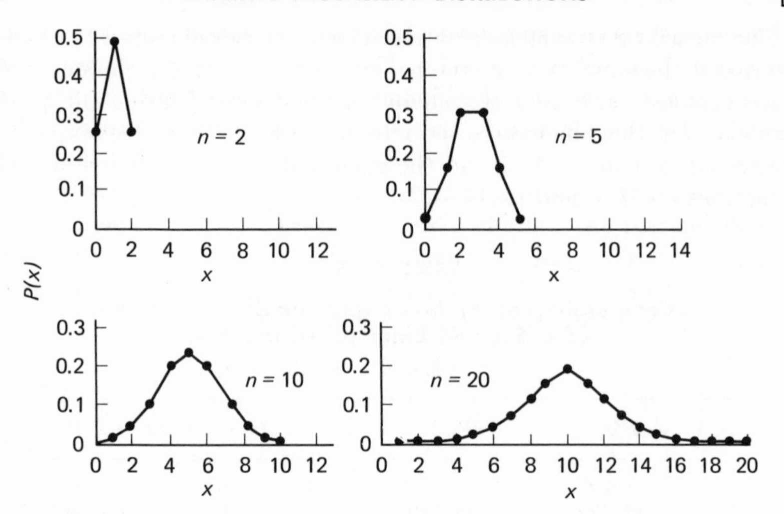

Fig. 4–19.1. Frequency polygons for binomial distributions with $p = q = \frac{1}{2}$; and $n = 2, 5, 10$, and 20, respectively.

gon approaches a smooth curve. The shape of this smooth curve is suggested by the series of frequency polygons in Figure 4–19.1, which represent binomial distributions for $p = q = \frac{1}{2}$, and $n = 2, 5, 10$, and 20, respectively.

The distribution which the binomial distribution resembles when n is large is called the *normal distribution;* and as suggested by the binomial distributions above, its graph has the characteristic shape of Figure 4–19.2. The normal distribution, which has also been known as the

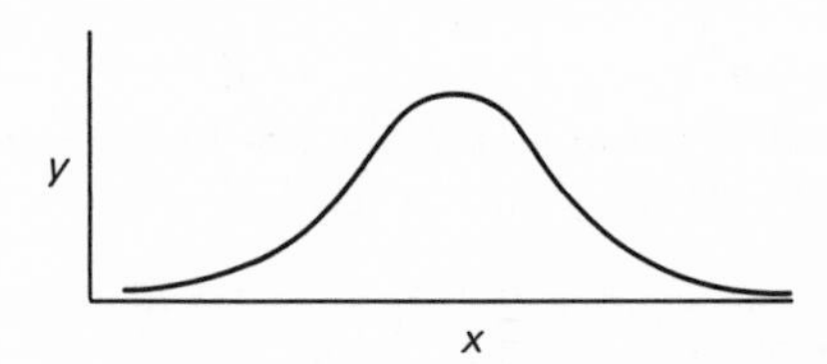

Fig. 4–19.2. The graph of the normal distribution.

Gaussian or *Laplacian* distribution, is a theoretical probability distribution, which was first derived by Abraham DeMoivre in 1733 and, then, independently by Gauss and Laplace about a hundred years later, DeMoivre's work having been unpublished and undiscovered during this time. The normal distribution was derived from the standardized form of the binomial distribution, using the variable in the form $(x - \mu)/\sigma = (x - np)/\sqrt{npq}$, and letting n increase without limit. The mathematics of the derivation are beyond the scope of this book, but the conclusions are extremely important to us.

The normal curve is symmetrical, but the derivation made no assumption about the equality of p and q. Therefore, it is seen that, *even though p and q be not equal*, and the binomial distribution therefore not symmetrical, still, as n increases, the binomial distribution changes to look more and more like the normal distribution, which is symmetrical. If n is extremely large, the binomial distribution becomes indistinguishable from the normal distribution. This may be expressed mathematically by saying that, as n increases, the binomial distribution *approaches the normal distribution as its limit.* This relationship is suggested by the graphs of Figure 4–19.3 which show the binomial distributions for $p = 0.25$,

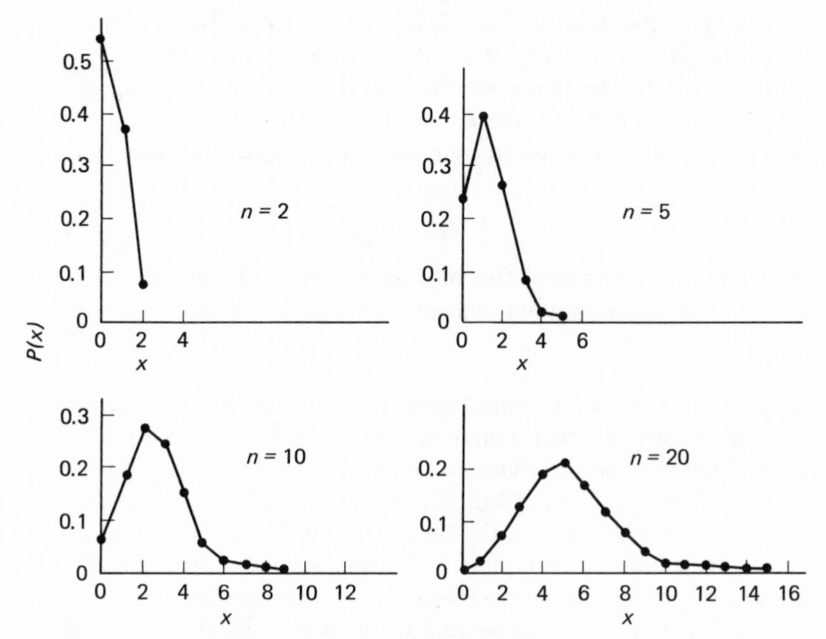

Fig. 4–19.3. Frequency polygons for binomial distributions with $p = 0.25$; $q = 0.75$; and $n = 2, 5, 10$, and 20, respectively.

$q = 0.75$; and $n = 2, 5, 10$, and 20, respectively. Clearly, as n increases, the shape of the distribution tends toward symmetry.

We shall discuss the normal distribution in detail in Chapter 6, which deals with continuous probability distributions. For the present, we merely note that the normal distribution, because of its mathematical properties, is extremely easy to use, and its ready availability in tables such as Appendix A makes it unnecessary for us to evaluate the large factorial numbers which would otherwise be required for the binomial distribution.

If p and q are not equal, or not nearly equal, then, if n is not large enough, the resulting binomial distribution may not be sufficiently close to the normal distribution to permit the use of the normal distribution as an approximation. In such cases, the Poisson distribution may be used.

4–20. The Poisson Distribution. As we have seen, the binomial distribution approaches the normal distribution as its limit as n increases, and the approach to normality occurs rapidly enough that the normal distribution is a satisfactory approximation to the binomial distribution even when n is not very large and when p and q are not equal. However, if p is very small, and n is not large enough, then the normal distribution may not be satisfactorily close. Then, the Poisson distribution, named for Seméon D. Poisson who described it in 1837, provides a very useful approximation to the binomial distribution. Like the binomial distribution, the Poisson distribution is a discrete distribution.

The probability distribution for the Poisson distribution is given by:

$$P(x) = \frac{e^{-m}m^x}{x!} \tag{4–20.1}$$

where: m = the mean, the only parameter of the distribution
e = the familiar constant (2.71828)
$x = 0, 1, 2, \ldots$

Values of e^{-m} may be computed from a table of logarithms or directly from tables such as that found in Appendix F. A direct table of the Poisson distribution is given in Appendix C. (See also the author's *Statistical Analysis*, Second Edition, Appendix M for a *cumulative* table.)

The relationship between the binomial and Poisson distributions may be easily seen, and the complete derivation is given in Section 14–2. The derivation appears there because of the extreme importance of the Poisson distribution in queueing theory. Since the derivation there is given in terms of the queueing theory symbols, we shall here indicate the nature of that derivation in terms of the familiar symbols of Equation (4–17.1), the expression for the binomial probability distribution:

$$P(x) = \frac{n!}{x!\,(n-x)!}\,p^x q^{(n-x)} \tag{4–17.1}$$

The operations indicated in equation (4–17.1) are such that that equation may be rewritten as

$$P(x) = \frac{n(n-1)(n-2)\cdots(n-x+1)}{x!}\,p^x(1-p)^n(1-p)^{-x} \tag{4–20.2}$$

But, if n is very large, and x is some relatively small finite number,

$$n \cong (n-1) \cong \cdots \cong (n-x+1)$$

and therefore

$$n(n-1)(n-2)\cdots(n-x+1) \cong n^x$$

Then

$$P(x) = \frac{(np)^x}{x!}(1-p)^n(1-p)^{-x}$$

but, if p is very small, $1-p$ is close to 1, and for $(1-p)^{-x}$, where x is not extremely large,

$$(1-p)^{-x} \cong 1$$

However, $(1-p)^n$ is *not* approximately 1, because n *is* very large. It may be rewritten as

$$(1-p)^n = [(1-p)^{-1/p}]^{-np}$$

and, from Equation (2–9.2), the limit of this last term, as p is very small, is e^{-np}. Therefore,

$$P(x) = \frac{(np)^x}{x!}e^{-np} = \frac{e^{-m}m^x}{x!} \tag{4–20.3}$$

which is the expression for the Poisson probability distribution as given in Equation (4–20.1), with mean $m = np$.

We shall show in the next section that, like the binomial distribution, the mean of the Poisson distribution is np, or m, as it is usually designated. However, the variance (the square of the standard deviation) of the Poisson distribution is also m. This may be seen intuitively from the fact that the variance of the binomial distribution is npq; and, in the Poisson distribution, since p is small, q is large. If q is taken to be close to 1, it may be dropped from the binomial formula, with the result that the variance then is np, or m.

The Poisson distribution is extremely easy to use. For example, a manufacturer of gymnasium equipment ships his equipment unassembled but accompanied by the parts necessary for assembly by the purchaser. The apparatus requires 198 bolts for assembly, but the manufacturer packs a box containing 200 bolts with the apparatus. The bolts are made by an automatic machine which turns out defective, unusable bolts with a probability of 0.01. What is the probability that a purchaser will not have enough usable bolts to complete the assembly?

$$m = np = 200 \times 0.01 = 2$$

From the table of e^{-m}, Appendix F,

$$e^{-2} = 0.13534$$

Then, from Equation (4–20.1)

$$P(x) = e^{-2}\frac{2^x}{x!} \qquad = (0.13534)\frac{2^x}{x!}$$

$$P(0) = (0.13534)\frac{2^0}{0!} = 0.13534$$

$$P(1) = (0.13534)\frac{2^1}{1!} = 0.27068$$

$$P(2) = (0.13534)\frac{2^2}{2!} = 0.27068$$

$$P(x \leq 2) = \ldots\ldots\ldots\ldots\ 0.67670$$

$$P(x > 2) = 1.00000 - 0.67670 = 0.32330$$

Thus, the probability that the supply of bolts will be inadequate is 0.32330.

This problem can be solved even more easily by the use of tables of the Poisson distribution. These figures for the probability of various values of x may be found directly in Appendix C; and in that table, the values given above may be read in the column for $m = 2$.

From the data for this distribution, with $m = 2$, as given in Appendix C, the distribution may be plotted, as is shown in Figure 4–20.1.

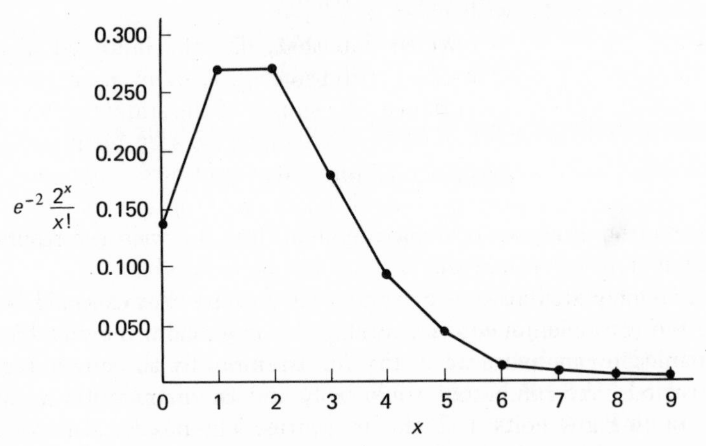

Fig. 4–20.1. Poisson distribution; $m = 2$.

The Poisson distribution is widely used in queueing theory. Suppose that aircraft are arriving at an airport at random times, but at an over-all average rate of 12 per hour. The facilities at the airport are such that, if more than 20 aircraft arrive in any one hour, the systems cannot cope with the situation. What is the probability that more than 20 aircraft will arrive in any one hour?

Here we use the Poisson distribution with $m = np = 12$. We can see why this is so by imagining the hour to be made up of many (n) small increments of time, each having the property that the probability of an aircraft arriving in that interval is p. Since these time intervals are very short, p is therefore very small. (The probability of more than one arrival in the small interval is insignificantly small, and it is ignored.) Then, for the n small increments of time making up the hour, the expected number of arrivals (the average number of arrivals) is np. In this case, $np = 12$. Then, from Appendix C:

$$P(0) = 0.0000$$

$$P(1) = 0.0001$$

$$P(2) = 0.0004$$

.

.

etc.

.

.

$$P(19) = 0.0161$$

$$P(20) = \underline{0.0097}$$

$$0.9885$$

and the probability of more than 20 arrivals in one hour is

$$1.0000 - 0.9885 = 0.0115$$

This distribution is shown in Figure 4–20.2. Thus, for just over 1 per cent of the time (1.15 per cent), this airport will be in trouble.

It is extremely easy to consider and analyze time intervals of different lengths. For example, for a 30-minute period, m would be equal to 6; and the distribution can be found in the Appendixes just as before. For 10-minute periods, the value of m would be 2; and the distribution would be that shown in Figure 4–20.1. That distribution is markedly skewed; and, for still shorter time intervals, the distribution would be even more skewed, approaching a reverse J-shape, where the highest value of $P(x)$ occurs when $x = 0$. As the time interval considered becomes longer; i.e., as the value of m increases, the Poisson distribution approaches the normal distribution as its limit. This effect of changing m may be seen from examination of Appendix C for, say, $m = 0.1$ and for $m = 20$. The former distribution has the shape of the reverse J, and the latter is almost symmetrical. In the distribution of Figure 4–20.2, where m is 12, the approach to normality is quite marked, as compared with Figure 4–20.1. As m increases, the Poisson distribution, like the binomial distribution, approaches the normal distribution as its limit. However, it must be emphasized that the Poisson distribution, like the binomial distribution, is a *discrete* distribution; and that, on the diagrams of Figures 4–20.1 and 4–20.2 (like Figures 4–18.1, 4–19.1, and 4–19.3), only the plotted points

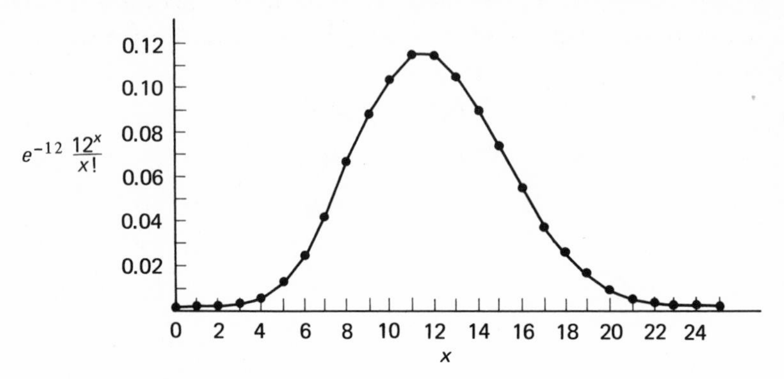

Fig. 4–20.2. Poisson distribution; $m = 12$.

are meaningful. The straight lines connecting these points are added for visual-aid purposes, and they have no mathematical or statistical meaning. That is, they are not to be interpreted to suggest that interpolation between the points is meaningful or possible.

4–21. The Mean and Variance of the Poisson and Binomial Distributions. We shall find that the Poisson distribution is extremely useful in queueing theory, and there we shall have use for both the mean and the variance of the Poisson distribution. Therefore, we shall now derive the expressions for these parameters.

First, the arithmetic average, the *expected value*, μ, is, from Equation (4–16.1):

$$\mu = E(x) = \sum_{i=1}^{n} x_i P(x_i) \tag{4–21.1}$$

It is the sum of the products of each possible value of x multiplied by its respective probability. For the Poisson distribution, this is

$$\mu = \sum_{x=0}^{\infty} x\,\frac{e^{-m}m^x}{x!} = 1\,\frac{e^{-m}m^1}{1} + 2\,\frac{e^{-m}m^2}{2!} + 3\,\frac{e^{-m}m^3}{3!} + \cdots \tag{4–21.2}$$

$$= me^{-m}\left(1 + m + \frac{m^2}{2!} + \frac{m^3}{3!} + \cdots\right)$$

But the term in the parentheses is e^m, as we have seen in Equation (2–9.4); therefore,

$$\mu = me^{-m}e^m$$

$$\mu = m \tag{4–21.3}$$

Now, we can proceed to derive the expression for the variance of the Poisson distribution using a familiar relationship in statistics. Looking back at Equation (4–17.6) and the definition of the expected value given in Equation (4–21.1), we can see that the term under the square root sign is nothing more than the expected value of the expression $(x - \mu)^2$. Therefore, for any distribution with mean μ, the variance is

$$\sigma^2 = E(x - \mu)^2 \tag{4–21.4}$$

$$= E(x^2 - 2x\mu + \mu^2)$$

but the expected value of a sum is equal to the sum of the expected values:

$$\sigma^2 = E(x^2) - E(2x\mu) + E(\mu^2)$$

but again, since the expected value of a constant is merely the constant,

$$\sigma^2 = E(x^2) - 2\mu E(x) + \mu^2$$

and since by definition,

$$E(x) = \mu$$

then

$$\sigma^2 = E(x^2) - 2\mu^2 + \mu^2$$

$$\sigma^2 = E(x^2) - \mu^2 \tag{4–21.5}$$

or, its equivalent

$$\sigma^2 = E(x^2) - [E(x)]^2 \tag{4–21.6}$$

This last expression is extremely important, and it has been seen in many forms:

1. For computation of a sample variance (or standard deviation),

$$s^2 = \frac{\Sigma x^2}{n} - \left(\frac{\Sigma x}{n}\right)^2 \tag{4–21.7}$$

2. For a discrete probability distribution,

$$\sigma^2 = \Sigma\, x^2P(x) - [\Sigma\, xP(x)]^2 \tag{4–21.8}$$

$$\sigma^2 = \Sigma\, x^2P(x) - [E(x)]^2 \tag{4–21.9}$$

$$\sigma^2 = \Sigma\, x^2P(x) - \mu^2 \tag{4–21.10}$$

3. For a continuous probability distribution, the same formula is used with the integral sign of calculus in place of the summation sign. We shall use this form below in Chapter 6, Equation (6–7.3).

For the Poisson distribution, the variance, then, is, from Equation (4–21.10):

$$\sigma^2 = \sum_{x=0}^{\infty} x^2 \frac{e^{-m}m^x}{x!} - m^2 \qquad (4\text{–}21.11)$$

$$= \left(1\,\frac{e^{-m}m^1}{1} + 4\,\frac{e^{-m}m^2}{1\cdot 2} + 9\,\frac{e^{-m}m^3}{1\cdot 2\cdot 3} + \cdots\right) - m^2$$

$$\sigma^2 = me^{-m}\left(1 + 2m + \frac{3m^2}{2!} + \frac{4m^3}{3!} + \cdots\right) - m^2 \qquad (4\text{–}21.12)$$

We can evaluate the term in the parenthesis by recalling from Equation (2–9.4) that

$$e^m = 1 + m + \frac{m^2}{2!} + \frac{m^3}{3!} + \frac{m^4}{4!} + \cdots$$

Therefore

$$me^m = m + m^2 + \frac{m^3}{2!} + \frac{m^4}{3!} + \frac{m^5}{4!} + \cdots$$

and

$$\frac{d}{dm}(me^m) = 1 + 2m + \frac{3m^2}{2!} + \frac{4m^3}{3!} + \cdots$$

But this is exactly the term in the parentheses in Equation (4–21.12):

$$\sigma^2 = me^{-m}\left[\frac{d}{dm}(me^m)\right] - m^2 \qquad (4\text{–}21.13)$$

Therefore, differentiating the term in the brackets:

$$\frac{d}{dm}(me^m) = me^m + e^m \qquad (4\text{–}21.14)$$

Then

$$\sigma^2 = me^{-m}[me^m + e^m] - m^2$$

$$= m^2 + m - m^2$$

$$\sigma^2 = m \qquad (4\text{–}21.15)$$

Thus, the variance of the Poisson distribution is equal to m, and it is therefore exactly equal to the mean. That is, the mean and the variance of the Poisson distribution are both equal to m. The standard deviation, of course, is $\sqrt{m}$. Thus, the Poisson distribution has, in effect, only one parameter, m, which is both the mean and the variance, and that single number describes completely a Poisson distribution.

The mean and variance of the binomial distribution may also be derived by the use of these same formulas, namely Equations (4–21.1) and

(4–21.10). For the binomial distribution, where x may take only integral values from 0 to n, the general formula for the mean is

$$\mu = \sum_{x=0}^{n} xP(x) \tag{4–21.16}$$

$$= 0q^n + 1[npq^{n-1}] + 2\left[\frac{n(n-1)}{2!}\,p^2q^{n-2}\right]$$

$$+ 3\,\frac{n(n-1)(n-2)}{3!}\,p^3q^{n-3} + \cdots + n(n-1)\,\frac{p^{n-1}q}{1!} + np^n$$

$$= np\left[q^{n-1} + \frac{(n-1)}{1!}\,pq^{n-2} + \frac{(n-1)(n-2)}{2!}\,p^2q^{n-3} + \cdots + (n-1)p^{n-2}q + p^{n-1}\right]$$

but the term in the brackets is the expansion of the binomial:

$$(q+p)^{n-1} = q^{n-1} + (n-1)pq^{n-2} + \frac{(n-1)(n-2)}{2!}\,p^2q^{n-3} + \cdots$$

and the sum of these terms, as with any probability distribution, is 1. Indeed, since $q + p = 1$, $(q + p)^n = 1$, for any n. Therefore,

$$\mu = np \tag{4–21.17}$$

This is the familiar formula for the mean of the binomial distribution, Equation (4–17.7).

Similarly, the variance may be derived using Equation (4–21.10), with $\mu = np$. Thus, for the binomial distribution,

$$\sigma^2 = \Sigma x^2P(x) - (np)^2 \tag{4–21.18}$$

For the derivation of the variance of the binomial distribution, we shall find it convenient to use the mathematical trick of solving, first, for $\Sigma x(x-1)P(x)$:

$$\sum_{x=0}^{n} x(x-1)P(x) = 0(-1)q^n + 1\cdot 0\cdot npq^{n-1} + \frac{2\cdot 1\cdot n(n-1)}{2!}\,p^2q^{n-2}$$

$$+ \frac{3\cdot 2\cdot n(n-1)(n-2)}{3!}\,p^3q^{n-3} + \cdots + n(n-1)(n-2)p^{n-1}q + n(n-1)p^n$$

$$\sum_{x=0}^{n} x(x-1)P(x) = n(n-1)p^2\,[q^{n-2} + (n-2)pq^{n-3} + \cdots + (n-2)p^{n-3}q + p^{n-2}]$$

Again, the term in the brackets is equal to 1, and the left side of the equation may also be rewritten omitting the summation limits for convenience, yielding

$$\Sigma x^2P(x) - \Sigma xP(x) = n(n-1)p^2$$

$$\Sigma x^2P(x) - \Sigma xP(x) = n^2p^2 - np^2 \qquad (4\text{–}21.19)$$

but, the second term on the left side of Equation (4–21.19) is the arithmetic mean, np:

$$\Sigma x^2P(x) - np = n^2p^2 - np^2$$

$$\Sigma x^2P(x) = n^2p^2 - np^2 + np$$

$$= n^2p^2 + np - np^2$$

$$= n^2p^2 + np(1-p)$$

but $(1 - p) = q$. Then, from Equation (4–21.18),

$$\sigma^2 = \Sigma x^2P(x) - (np)^2 \qquad (4\text{–}21.18)$$

$$= n^2p^2 + npq - n^2p^2$$

$$\sigma^2 = npq \qquad (4\text{–}21.20)$$

This is the familiar formula for the variance of the binomial distribution, corresponding to Equation (4–17.8), which was given as the standard deviation:

$$\sigma = \sqrt{npq} \qquad (4\text{–}17.8)$$

SUGGESTIONS FOR FURTHER READING

FELLER, W. *An Introduction to Probability Theory and Its Applications,* Vol. 1 (2d ed.). New York: John Wiley & Sons, Inc., 1957.

GOLDBERG, S. *Probability, An Introduction.* Englewood Cliffs, N.J.: Prentice-Hall, Inc., 1960.

GOOD, I. J. *The Estimation of Probabilities.* Cambridge, Mass.: M.I.T. Press, 1965.

RICHMOND, S. B. *Statistical Analysis* (2d ed.). New York: The Ronald Press Company, 1964.

SAVAGE, L. J. *The Foundations of Statistics.* New York: John Wiley & Sons, Inc., 1954.

SCHLAIFER, R. *Probability and Statistics for Business Decisions.* New York: McGraw-Hill Book Co., Inc., 1959.

EXERCISES

4–1. An ordinary coin is tossed four times. What is the probability of getting exactly three heads? At most three heads? At least three heads?

4–2. Garlow, a shopkeeper, has just received a shipment of canned soups, which he stores in his cellar. During the night the cellar is flooded and all labels are washed off the cans, which are identical in shape, size and weight. The shipment contained the following quantities and types of soup:

Abalone, 1000 cans
Bean, 750 cans
Chicken, 500 cans
Duck, 250 cans
Total 2500 cans

a) If a can is chosen at random and opened, what is the probability that it contains either abalone or duck soup? Neither abalone nor chicken soup?

b) If two cans are chosen at random and opened, what is the probability that both contain chicken soup? That both contain the same soup? Assume that drawing two cans from the pile has a negligible effect on the size of the pile and the distribution of soups.

4–3. The Sidro Company has opened a new branch of its rent-a-car business with a stock of three cars. The company estimates the following use pattern:

(1) Convertible sports: in use 80%; daily rate; $20
(2) Sedan: in use 75%; daily rate: $15
(3) Hardtop sports: in use 50%; daily rate; $25

Assume that all cars are rented one at a time and independently of one another.

a) What is the probability that a customer entering the office will be able to rent a car immediately?

b) What is the probability that he will be able to rent a sports car immediately?

c) What is the expected revenue per day for the new branch?

4–4. A task force of 8 men has to select from their own membership a committee of four, consisting of Chief, Deputy, Treasurer, and Secretary.

a) How many different committees can be selected, assuming that each person is selected for and identified with his particular position on the committee?

b) How many different committees can be selected, without attention given to who holds a particular office? That is, the task force just selects a group of four.

c) In (*b*), assuming that a group has been chosen, how many different ways can the four positions be allocated?

d) What do you notice about your answers to (*a*), (*b*), and (*c*)?

4–5. The Dabo Game Company has developed a new game in which 3 "Buckies" are tossed simultaneously and the sum of the numbers of the sides that lie face down on the table is called the score. (A Bucky is a tetrahedron, that is, a four-sided geometric solid, each side of which is an equilateral triangle. The sides are numbered 1 to 4, and the solid is so symmetrical that each side has the same chance as any other of coming to rest face down on the table.) Buckies are used in a betting game with the following payoff rules. The individual player plays against the bank, and all bets are of 50¢ per play.

Score	Payoff
3 or 12	$3
4 or 11	$2
5 or 10	$1
All other scores	0

a) If x is the score on one play of the game, what is the probability distribution of x? What is the expected value of x?

b) What is the expected value of the game to a player? If the payoff for "3 or 12" had been \$5, would you prefer to play or be the bank? What payoff rule for "3 or 12" (all other rules the same) would make you indifferent about playing or being the bank? (Assume that there are no outside considerations influencing your decision.)

4–6. A Bucky is tossed 5 times (see 4–5). If the "4-side" is called success, what is the probability distribution of the number of successes? What is the expected value of the number of successes? What is the standard deviation?

4–7. The Dime Food Corporation is recruiting housewives for its cake-mix testing panel. For this purpose it has devised the following test of the candidates' ability to discriminate. Each applicant is presented with four samples of cake, three of them baked from mix A and one from mix B. The applicant is to identify the sample from mix B. This procedure is repeated 10 times, and the passing score is seven or more correct choices.

a) If a housewife cannot discriminate and guesses the answer each time, what is the probability that she will be admitted to the panel?

b) Suppose that the applicant does possess the ability to discriminate cake mixes and has a certain probability p of making a correct choice on each trial. Using the binomial table in Appendix B, what is the smallest value of p that will guarantee the applicant at least a probability of 0.88 of being admitted to the panel? (Solve, using Appendix B.)

4–8. A teacher sets a midterm exam consisting of 20 multiple-choice questions. Each question has four choices, only one of which is correct. Assume that a student taking the exam guesses on every question.

a) What is the probability that the student gets at least 4 questions right? At least 8 questions right?

b) What is the minimum passing grade (i.e., number correct), such that the probability of getting the grade or exceeding it by guessing only is less than or equal to 0.005?

4–9. Two production lines, gidgets and widgets, feed into a single conveyor that takes all the products to the testing area. Equal amounts of both products are made, with items dropping onto the conveyor at random time intervals. From past experience it is known that 20% of gidgets are defective while only 5% of widgets are defective.

a) What is the probability that an item selected at random from the conveyor will be a defective widget?

b) If an item is selected at random from the conveyor, what is the probability that it is defective?

c) If an item, selected at random, is found to be defective, what is the probability that it is a gidget?

4–10. The Bendri Auto Agency handles two models of cars, a family sedan and a sports coupé. The dealer has found that 80% of married-men customers buy the family sedan, whereas 90% of the single-men customers buy the sports coupé; 75% of all the customers are married men.

a) In preparing his weekly orders to the factory, what ratio of sedans to sports coupés should the dealer plan for? That is, on the average, what will be the ratio of sedans to sports models sold?

b) What is the probability that a sedan car that was just driven out of the showroom was bought by a single man?

4–11. The major departments of the Winrin Research Corporation are staffed as follows:

Department	Ph.D.	M.A.	B.A.
Systems Analysis	15	20	5
Consumer Behavior	5	10	15
City Planning	20	15	10

One department is selected at random, and a man's personnel record is withdrawn from the department's files. The man holds a Ph.D. degree. What is the probability that the department selected is Consumer Behavior?

4–12. At the Wilhef Rocket Control Company, 5% of the production of controls has been found to be defective. If these defective controls are installed and cause a rocket to misfire, the Company suffers a penalty of $500 per defective. An inspector is hired at $50 per day to test the controls before they are installed. He can test and repair 10 units per day. Assuming that his testing and repairing are perfect, what are the average daily savings to the Company?

4–13. A local chess club with 12 members begins a round robin tournament in which every member has to play every other member. How many games are played in the tournament?

4–14. A survey of leading weekly magazines was made to determine the percentage of households that had read the current issue. The results of the survey were as follows:

Read	Percentage
At least A	31
At least B	33
At least C	40
At least A and B	9
At least A and C	11
At least B and C	6
All three magazines	4

a) How many read none of these three magazines?
b) How many read only C?

4–15. A product manager sent his Vice President a report of a survey of consumer reactions to the company's new product now in test market. The survey results were reported as follows:

Liked product, 50%
Liked package, 30%
Liked advertising, 23%
Liked product and package, 8%
Liked product and advertising, 20%
Liked package and advertising, 10%
Liked all three aspects, 5%

The product manager was called into the V.P.'s office and reprimanded. Why?

4–16. A study of bridge traffic obtained the following data on the arrival of cars at the toll booth over 957 1-minute periods.

No. of Cars Arriving During 1 Minute Period	0	1	2	3	4	5
Observed frequency	202	329	242	126	43	15

a) Find the average number (λ) of cars arriving per minute.

b) Find the appropriate Poisson distribution, and compare it with the empirical probabilities found from the table above; do this by plotting both distributions on the same graph as well as by tabular presentation.

4–17. Three disgruntled officers of the Ruritarian army, Cols. Jash, Mish, and Risch, decide to play the game of Russian roulette in that order. In that game, as you may recall, one live bullet is placed in a pistol that holds six bullets; the chamber is spun, the gun placed to the head, and the trigger pulled. If the live bullet is in the chamber, the game is over. If the chamber is empty, the pistol is passed to the next man in turn.

a) What is the probability that each man loses the game (i.e., is killed), assuming that the chamber is not spun again once the game is set up? What is the probability that no one loses the game, i.e., all three are left alive?

b) If, after each time the trigger is pulled (and the game continues), the chamber is spun before the next man pulls the trigger, what is the probability that each man loses? No man loses?

4–18. Fraed, an advertising executive who works on lower Madison Avenue can go home to his uptown apartment either by subway or bus. He varies his method of transportation at random, choosing the subway 40% of the time and the bus 60% of the time. If he takes the subway home the probability that he gets there before his dinner is burnt is 80%; if he takes the bus, the probability of this is only 50%. One day he gets home late and his dinner is burnt to a crisp. What is the probability he came home by subway?

4–19. The Goshil Auto Sales Company finds that its daily sales pattern is well represented by a Poisson distribution and that the probability of zero sales on any day is essentially the same as the probability of two sales on any day. What is the probability of one sale on any day? (Show how you obtained your results.)

5

Introduction to Integral Calculus

5–1. The Meaning of Integration. Integration is the name given to the mathematical operation which is the reverse of differentiation. In Chapter 2 we saw that we could *differentiate* a function and obtain, as the result, the derivative. For example, let

$$\frac{d}{dx}(F(x)) = f(x)$$

If we now reverse the process and take the *antiderivative*, the antiderivative of a function $f(x)$ being that function whose derivative is $f(x)$, then, of course, we obtain, as the result, the original function $F(x)$. This process of finding the antiderivative is called *integration*. If we *integrate* a function, the result is called the *integral*. We can summarize the terminology by the trivial but correct statement that the derivative of the integral of a function is the original function, as is the integral of the derivative. These statements are much the same as the trivial statement that the square root of the square of a function is the original function.

The symbol for the operation of integration is the *integral sign*, $\int$. Its use is illustrated by the following equations. We have seen in Chapter 2, following Equation (2–5.4), that

$$\frac{d}{dx}(x^2) = 2x \tag{5–1.1}$$

Then, the reverse process yields

$$\int 2x\, dx = x^2 \tag{5–1.2}$$

The dx which appears in the left side of Equation (5–1.2) must *always* be present to accompany the integral sign, and, indeed, one should regard the integral sign as including the symbol dx as a necessary part.

Using the symbols introduced in Section 2–6, if

$$\frac{dy}{dx} = y' \tag{2–6.2}$$

then

$$\int y'\, dx = y \tag{5–1.3}$$

In the symbol form introduced in Section 2–6, which uses the prime sign to represent the derivative but retains the function expression, these relations may be expressed as follows:

$$y = f(x) \tag{2–3.1}$$

$$\frac{dy}{dx} = \frac{d}{dx}(f(x)) = f'(x) \tag{2–6.3}$$

$$\int f'(x)\, dx = f(x) \tag{5–1.4}$$

The results given above in Equations (5–1.2), (5–1.3), and (5–1.4) are not quite complete, in that the integral should have an additional term called the *constant of integration*, C. This is because the derivative of x^2 as shown in Equation (5–1.1) is indeed $2x$; but also

$$\frac{d}{dx}(x^2 + 1) = 2x \tag{5–1.5}$$

$$\frac{d}{dx}(x^2 + 5) = 2x \tag{5–1.6}$$

$$\frac{d}{dx}(x^2 + C) = 2x \tag{5–1.7}$$

where C may be any constant.

Conversely, then,

$$\int 2x\, dx = x^2 + C \tag{5–1.8}$$

where C is the *constant of integration*. Its value can usually be determined in real problems on the basis of other information which may be available. Clearly, then, to be completely accurate, we should rewrite Equations (5–1.3) and (5–1.4) to show this constant.

$$\int y'\, dx = y + C \tag{5–1.9}$$

and

$$\int f'(x)\, dx = f(x) + C \tag{5–1.10}$$

Because the integral, as defined above, has this as yet undetermined constant term, it is called the *indefinite integral*. In a later section we shall introduce the *definite integral*, which does not require the constant term. For the present, however, the constant term is essential.

5-2. Evaluating the Indefinite Integral. The integral of a function is that expression which, when differentiated, yields that function. From this rule, we can, by inspection, perform the following integrations and many more:

$$\int 5\,dx = 5x + C \tag{5-2.1}$$

$$\int x\,dx = \frac{x^2}{2} + C \tag{5-2.2}$$

$$\int x^2\,dx = \frac{x^3}{3} + C \tag{5-2.3}$$

$$\int (3x^2 + 4x + 1)\,dx = x^3 + 2x^2 + x + C \tag{5-2.4}$$

Since, also,

$$\int 3x^2\,dx + \int 4x\,dx + \int dx = x^3 + 2x^2 + x + C \tag{5-2.5}$$

it can be seen that the integral of a sum (or difference) is the sum (or difference) of the integrals. That is, the left sides of Equations (5-2.4) and (5-2.5) are equal.

$$\int (3x^2 + 4x + 1)\,dx = \int 3x^2\,dx + \int 4x\,dx + \int dx \tag{5-2.6}$$

Also, referring to the extremely important general equation from Section 2-5,

$$\frac{d}{dx}(ax^n) = nax^{n-1} \tag{2-5.4}$$

we can deduce the equally important reverse rule to be

$$\int ax^n dx = \frac{ax^{n+1}}{n+1} + C \qquad \text{for } n \neq -1 \tag{5-2.7}$$

We shall later see a few other rules for evaluating integrals, but, in general, the process of integration is much more difficult than the process of differentiation, and therefore tables of integrals are widely available and widely used. Our attention here will not be on methods of integration, but rather on the meaning and uses of integrals.

5-3. Differential Equations. We can illustrate the use of the indefinite integral by referring to the problem of continuously compounded interest, which was discussed in Section 3-7.

There it was found that, when interest is compounded continuously at 5 per cent per year, the future value of a sum of money, with present value P, changes according to the relationship

$$\frac{d}{dt}(A) = 0.05A \qquad (3\text{–}7.10)$$

However, we could have started our analysis by reasoning that this statement, Equation (3–7.10), must be what is meant by continuous compounding. Then we can find what the effective rate of interest is by integrating and letting $t = 1$.

First, writing the expression in differential form and collecting the terms with A on one side of the equation and t on the other,

$$\frac{dA}{A} = 0.05\,dt \qquad (5\text{–}3.1)$$

Then, integrating both sides of the equation (note that the left side may alternatively be viewed as $\left.\frac{1}{A}\,dA\right)$,

$$\int \frac{dA}{A} = \int 0.05\,dt \qquad (5\text{–}3.2)$$

$$\ln A = 0.05t + C \qquad (5\text{–}3.3)$$

Since, when $t = 0$, the "future" value *is* the present value, i.e., $A = P$, we can use this relationship to evaluate C. At time $t = 0$,

$$\ln P = (0.05)(0) + C$$

$$C = \ln P \qquad (5\text{–}3.4)$$

Then, since C is a constant, its value at any value of t is its value at all values of t, and Equation (5-3.3) becomes

$$\ln A = 0.05t + \ln P$$

$$\ln\left(\frac{A}{P}\right) = 0.05t$$

$$\frac{A}{P} = e^{0.05t}$$

$$A = Pe^{0.05t} \qquad (5\text{–}3.5)$$

Equation (5–3.5) gives the future value A of the present sum P for any time t into the future (where t is measured in years).

We can find the *equivalent* annual rate of interest by letting $t = 1$, and noting the increase in A after one year. Letting $t = 1$, then,

$$A = Pe^{0.05}$$

but

$$e^{0.05} = 1.0513$$

therefore, after one year,

$$A = 1.0513P$$

and the equivalent rate of interest is 5.13 per cent.

Equations such as (3–7.10) are called *differential equations;* that is, a differential equation is an equation which involves a derivative. Differential equations may arise in operations research models when the information available to the analyst comes to him in terms of *changes.* In such cases the problem is to find the unknown function, given information about its rate of change. Equation (3–7.10) is such a differential equation. It is, of course, the algebraic statement of the condition that the time rate of increase of the future value of a sum of money at any time is 5 per cent of the current value of that sum; i.e., it is growing at a rate which is proportional to its own size. This growth pattern, of course, also characterizes radioactive decay, as described above in Chapter 3.

Another familiar illustration of a differential equation might have arisen in the inventory problem involving the Courbro Company, discussed in Sections 1–2, 2–5, and 3–2. If the information available to the company involved the *marginal cost* of additions to the lot size instead of the *total cost,* the total cost for any lot size could be computed.

Thus, if the information available to the company indicated that the marginal cost in dollars of additions to the lot size x was

$$\frac{d}{dx}(TC) = 0.02 - \frac{500{,}000}{x^2} \tag{5–3.6}$$

then, the cost at any lot size could be determined by integration. First, collect terms in TC and x:

$$d(TC) = 0.02dx - 500{,}000\frac{dx}{x^2}$$

$$\int d(TC) = 0.02\int dx - 500{,}000\int x^{-2}\,dx$$

$$TC = 0.02x - 500{,}000\left(\frac{x^{-1}}{-1}\right) + C$$

$$TC = 0.02x + \frac{500{,}000}{x} + C \tag{5–3.7}$$

This last equation resembles the equation used in previous chapters for the total cost in this problem. However, here we have the constant of integration, which must be evaluated. In this case it is very simple. We know that, if $x = 0$, the total cost is zero; i.e., there is no setup cost and no holding cost. Therefore, $C = 0$, and the total cost equation becomes the familiar

$$TC = 0.02x + \frac{500{,}000}{x} \tag{1–2.4}$$

and from this equation, the total cost at any value of x may be computed.

In summary, then, in marginal analysis problems, the marginal cost function is the derivative of the total-cost function, and conversely, the total cost function is the integral of the marginal cost function (this relationship also holds for marginal revenue vs. total revenue, marginal product vs. total product, etc.).

In general, differential equations are difficult to solve, and we shall not here devote much time and attention to that subject. Most standard references in calculus discuss various types of differential equations and the methods available for solving them. The differential equations which we have seen above are of the simplest variety; namely, those which may be solved by *separation of the variables;* i.e., separating all of the variables so that only one variable occurs in any one term. If this can be done, and if it is a first-order differential equation (no second or higher derivatives), then we need only integrate both sides of the equation as we have done above. Even equations of this type are not always easy to solve.

However, if the integration can be performed, the problem of evaluating the constant of integration remains. In order to evaluate this, there must be available at least one numerical value of the integrated function, so that it may be substituted into the final expression to evaluate the constant and complete the analysis.

A familiar illustration of this simplest type of differential equation arises in economic theory in connection with the concept of elasticity of demand. Elasticity is the ratio of the relative changes of two mutually interdependent variables. Elasticity of demand is the relative change in the quantity sold (demanded) for a given relative change in price. If the elasticity is ϵ,

$$-\epsilon = \frac{\frac{dq}{q}}{\frac{dp}{p}} \tag{5-3.8}$$

where: q is the quantity sold, and
p is the price

For unit elasticity, the relationship between q and p is that of a rectangular hyperbola, where pq, the total revenue, is independent of p, as seen in the following derivation. For unit elasticity,

$$\frac{\frac{dq}{q}}{\frac{dp}{p}} = -1 \tag{5-3.9}$$

$$\frac{dq}{q} = -\frac{dp}{p} \tag{5-3.10}$$

But, from Equation (2-9.5), this is equal to

$$d \ln q = -d \ln p \tag{5-3.11}$$

Equations (5-3.10) and (5-3.11) say that the change in demand associated with a change in price is such that the changes are proportional and in opposite directions. That is, if price increases by, say, 1 per cent, demand decreases by 1 per cent.

This also says that the revenue R is constant as price changes. Integrating both sides of Equation (5-3.11),

$$\int d \ln q = -\int d \ln p \tag{5-3.12}$$

$$\ln q = -\ln p + C$$

$$\ln q + \ln p = C$$

$$pq = C' \tag{5-3.13}$$

but pq is the total revenue R. Thus, with unit elasticity, the revenue is constant. This result can also be obtained by differentiating R with respect to p. From Equation (5-3.13),

$$R = pq \tag{5-3.14}$$

Differentiating with respect to p,

$$\frac{dR}{dp} = p\frac{dq}{dp} + q \tag{5-3.15}$$

but, from Equation (5-3.10),

$$p\frac{dq}{dp} = -q \tag{5-3.16}$$

therefore Equation (5-3.15) becomes

$$\frac{dR}{dp} = -q + q = 0 \tag{5-3.17}$$

and the revenue is independent of changes in price.

If the demand curve is linear, then the elasticity of demand varies along the demand curve. This follows from the fact that, then, the *absolute* change in sales volume as a consequence of a given price change is constant and independent of the sales level or price level. For example, if the Wilne Corporation has annual sales of 15 million units at a price of \$10, and if

$$\frac{dq}{dp} = -\frac{1}{2} \tag{5-3.18}$$

where: q is in millions of units
p is in dollars.

then the demand curve may be computed as follows:

$$dq = -\frac{1}{2}\,dp \tag{5-3.19}$$

Integrating both sides of Equation (5–3.19) yields

$$\int dq = -\frac{1}{2}\int dp$$

$$q = -\frac{p}{2} + C \tag{5-3.20}$$

Then the constant C may be evaluated by substituting for the current values of p and q:

$$15 = -\frac{10}{2} + C$$

$$C = 20$$

and the demand curve is

$$q = 20 - \frac{p}{2} \tag{5-3.21}$$

and at a price of, say, \$8,

$$q = 20 - \frac{8}{2} = 16 \text{ million units}$$

and revenue = (16)(8) = \$128,000,000, as compared with the current value of \$150,000,000. However, the expression for the revenue is,

$$R = pq = p\left(20 - \frac{p}{2}\right) = 20p - \frac{p^2}{2} \tag{5-3.22}$$

$$\frac{dR}{dp} = 20 - p$$

This indicates that, at a price of \$8, $\frac{dR}{dp} = 12$, indicating that the revenue increases as price increases or that the demand is *inelastic* at that point, and that the price should be raised to increase the revenue.

Clearly, the *revenue-maximizing price level* is where the derivative of R with respect to p is 0. From Equation (5–3.22),

$$\frac{dR}{dp} = 20 - p = 0$$

$$p^* = \$20$$

Then,

$$R = p\left(20 - \frac{p}{2}\right) = (20)(10) = \$200{,}000{,}000$$

As a final illustration, consider the Jalo Company, whose sales trend (in millions of dollars) is such that annual sales S increases continuously according to the relationship

$$\frac{dS}{dt} = \sqrt{t}$$

where t is the time in years from the end of 1966, and sales were at the rate of 15 million dollars at the end of 1966.

Sales at any time in the future may be found by integrating to yield

$$S = \frac{2}{3}t^{3/2} + C$$

but, when $t = 0$, $S = 15$. Therefore, $C = 15$, and

$$S = 15 + \frac{2}{3}t^{3/2}$$

and the rate of sales at the end of 1975, for example, can be predicted to be

$$\text{Sales (1975)} = 15 + \frac{2}{3}(9)^{3/2} = 15 + 18$$

$$= 33 \text{ million dollars}$$

5–4. The Definite Integral. An important use of integral calculus is in the determination of areas. This widely applicable procedure is based on the fact that the integral calculus enables us to compute the area between a curve and the x-axis, i.e., the area under a curve. In Figure 5–4.1, $f(x)$ is some continuous function. The area under the curve between

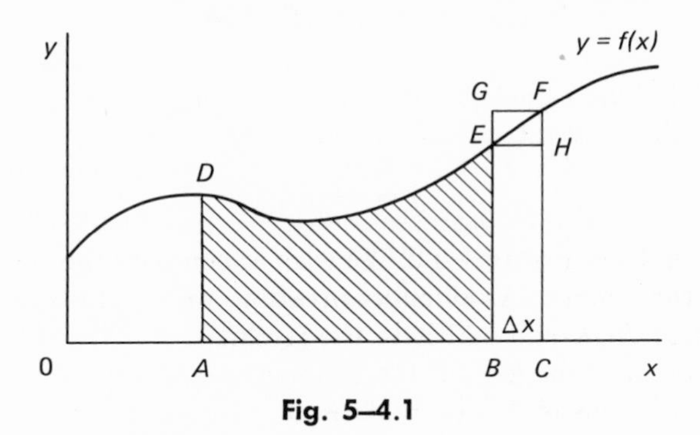

Fig. 5–4.1

A and B is the shaded area $ABED$. We would like to know the size of this area.

Consider now the increment to this area which results when we inquire about the area under the curve between A and C. This results from moving along the x-axis from B to C, the distance Δx. The size of the incremental area, $BCFE$, lies between that of the smaller rectangle $BCHE$ and that of the larger rectangle $BCFG$:

$$BE \cdot \Delta x < \Delta \text{ Area} < CF \cdot \Delta x$$

As Δx becomes very small, we represent it by dx, and the increment to the area is $d(\text{Area})$. When Δx is very small, BE and CF are very close to each other and are equal to y. Then

$$d(\text{Area}) = y\, dx \tag{5–4.1}$$

$$= f(x)\, dx \tag{5–4.2}$$

Integrating this, we find that

$$\text{Area} = \int f(x)\, dx \tag{5–4.3}$$

If we represent $\int f(x)\, dx$ by $F(x)$, then

$$\text{Area} = F(x) + C \tag{5–4.4}$$

However, from Figure 5–4.1, we can see that the area we seek is zero when $x = A$. Therefore,

$$0 = F(A) + C$$

$$C = -F(A) \tag{5–4.5}$$

Then, the area we seek, between A and B, is:

$$\text{Area} = F(B) - F(A) \tag{5–4.6}$$

This is the desired shaded area. It may be represented by the *definite integral*,

$$\int_A^B f(x)\, dx = F(B) - F(A) \tag{5–4.7}$$

where A and B are called the *limits of integration*.

We may illustrate the definite integral by considering the function

$$y = x^2 + 2 \tag{5–4.8}$$

which is graphed in Figure 5–4.2. We wish to compute the area under this curve between 0 and 3. As an approximation, we could compute the area of the triangle PQR and add it to the rectangle $PRSO$. The area of the rectangle is 6, and the area of the triangle is $(\frac{1}{2})(3)(9) = 13\frac{1}{2}$. The total area is $19\frac{1}{2}$, but this is clearly too large.

The true desired area obviously lies between the rectangle with area 6 and the shape $PQSO$ with area $19\frac{1}{2}$. A closer approximation may be obtained by dividing the x-axis into thirds, as shown in Figure 5–4.3.

The sum of the areas of the three vertical rectangles is another approximation to the desired area. The areas of the rectangles are, respectively 2,

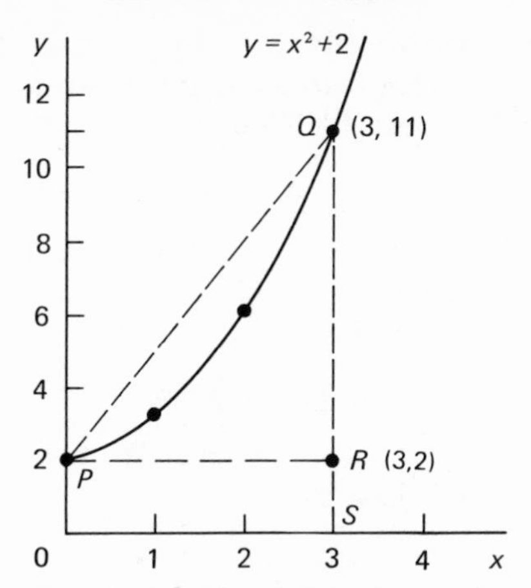

Fig. 5–4.2. The definite integral.

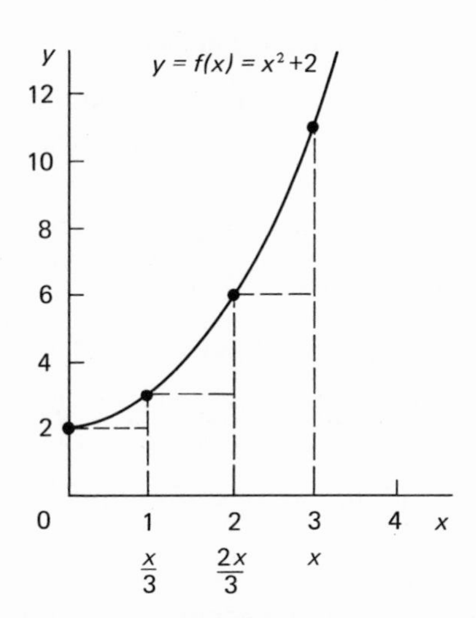

Fig. 5–4.3

3, 6, and their sum is 11. In symbols, these areas are:

$$\text{Area of rectangles} = \frac{x}{3}f(0) + \frac{x}{3}f\left(\frac{x}{3}\right) + \frac{x}{3}f\left(\frac{2x}{3}\right)$$

but

$$f(x) = x^2 + 2$$

Therefore,

$$f(0) = 0^2 + 2 = 2$$

$$f\left(\frac{x}{3}\right) = \frac{x^2}{9} + 2$$

$$f\left(\frac{2x}{3}\right) = \frac{4x^2}{9} + 2$$

and

$$\text{Area of rectangles} = \left(\frac{x}{3}\right)(2) + \left(\frac{x}{3}\right)\left(\frac{x^2}{9} + 2\right) + \left(\frac{x}{3}\right)\left(\frac{4x^2}{9} + 2\right)$$
$$= \frac{x}{3}\left(2 + \frac{x^2}{9} + 2 + \frac{4x^2}{9} + 2\right)$$
$$= \frac{x}{3}\left(\frac{5x^2}{9} + 6\right)$$
$$= \frac{5x^3}{27} + 2x = \frac{x^3}{27/5} + 2x$$
$$= \frac{x^3}{5.4} + 2x$$

and, for $x = 3$,

$$\text{Area of rectangles} = 5 + 6 = 11$$

If the rectangles had been erected at smaller intervals, so that there were, say, five rectangles as seen in Figure 5–4.4, then their total area would be

$$\text{Area of rectangles} = \frac{x}{5}f(0) + \frac{x}{5}f\left(\frac{x}{5}\right) + \frac{x}{5}f\left(\frac{2x}{5}\right) + \frac{x}{5}f\left(\frac{3x}{5}\right) + \frac{x}{5}f\left(\frac{4x}{5}\right)$$
$$= \frac{x}{5}(2) + \frac{x}{5}\left(\frac{x^2}{25} + 2\right) + \frac{x}{5}\left(\frac{4x^2}{25} + 2\right)$$
$$+ \frac{x}{5}\left(\frac{9x^2}{25} + 2\right) + \frac{x}{5}\left(\frac{16x^2}{25} + 2\right)$$
$$= \frac{x}{5}\left(\frac{x^2 + 4x^2 + 9x^2 + 16x^2}{25} + 10\right) = \frac{x}{5}\left(\frac{30x^2}{25} + 10\right)$$
$$= \frac{x^3}{25/6} + 2x = \frac{x^3}{4.167} + 2x$$

and, for $x = 3$,

$$= 6.48 + 6 = 12.48$$

Clearly, as the rectangles become thinner and thinner, the denominator of the first term changes. It can be shown that this denominator, which is

$$\frac{k^3}{\sum_{n=1}^{k-1} n^2}$$

approaches 3 as k, the number of rectangles, becomes very great, and that is exactly the result which integration yields directly:

$$\text{Area} = \int_0^x (x^2 + 2)\,dx = \frac{x^3}{3} + 2x$$

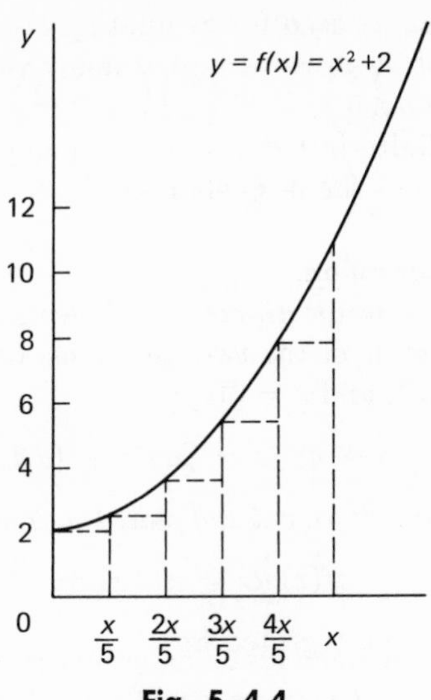

Fig. 5–4.4

Then, for $x = 3$,

$$\text{Area} = \frac{3^3}{3} + (2)(3) = 9 + 6 = 15$$

Similarly, we might find the area under the curve between $x = 2$ and $x = 3$:

$$\text{Area} = \int_2^3 (x^2 + 2)\, dx = \left[\frac{x^3}{3} + 2x\right]_2^3 \tag{5–4.9}$$

This last expression means that the quantity within the brackets is to be evaluated at $x = 3$ and at $x = 2$, and the latter subtracted from the former:

$$\text{Area} \doteq \left[\frac{3^3}{3} + (2)(3)\right] - \left[\frac{2^3}{3} + (2)(2)\right] = 15 - \frac{8}{3} - 4 = \frac{25}{3}$$

$$= 8.333$$

This is a general relationship. *The area under a continuous function $f(x)$ between any two points,* A and B, may be found by taking the definite integral of $f(x)$ between those two points:

$$\text{Area under } f(x) \text{ between } A \text{ and } B = \int_A^B f(x)\, dx = F(x)\Big|_A^B \tag{5–4.10}$$

$$\int_A^B f(x)\, dx = F(B) - F(A) \tag{5–4.7}$$

The vertical line in the last term of Equation (5–4.10) serves the same purpose as the brackets in Equation (5–4.9). That is, it indicates the limits over which the function $F(x)$ is to be evaluated.

The definite integral, as used for evaluating areas in this way, may be imagined as the sum of the areas of a great many very thin rectangles with height $f(x)$ and width dx.

This use of the definite integral is of great importance in probability theory, as we shall see in the next chapter.

5–5. Rules for Integration.

1. *The integral of a sum (or difference) of two functions is the sum (or difference) of the integrals of the two functions.* Let u and v be two functions of x; i.e., $u = f(x)$, and $v = g(x)$:

$$\int (u + v)\, dx = \int u\, dx + \int v\, dx \tag{5–5.1}$$

2. *A constant may be factored out and placed in front of the integral sign:*

$$\int af(x)\, dx = a\int f(x)\, dx \tag{5–5.2}$$

3. *Powers of x* may be integrated by

$$\int x^n\, dx = \frac{x^{n+1}}{n+1} + C \tag{5–5.3}$$

4. *Integral of* $\frac{1}{x}$:

$$\int \frac{dx}{x} = \ln x + C \tag{5–5.4}$$

5. *Integration of* $\ln x$:

$$\int \ln x\, dx = x \ln x - x + C \tag{5–5.5}$$

As with the other integrals given above, this result may be verified by taking the derivative of the integral.

6. *Integration by parts.* From the familiar expression for the derivative of the product of two functions, u and v, where $u = f(x)$ and $v = g(x)$,

$$\frac{d}{dx}(uv) = u\frac{dv}{dx} + v\frac{du}{dx} \tag{2–7.3}$$

Multiplying both sides by dx and integrating both sides yields

$$\int d(uv) = \int u\, dv + \int v\, du$$

$$uv = \int u\, dv + \int v\, du$$

$$\int u\, dv = uv - \int v\, du \tag{5–5.6}$$

This extremely valuable rule may be illustrated as follows. To integrate the following expression,

$$\int x^3(x + 2)^2\, dx$$

let

$$(x + 2)^2 = u$$

and

$$x^3\,dx = dv$$

Then

$$v = \frac{x^4}{4}$$

and

$$du = 2(x + 2)\,dx$$

Then, from Equation (5–5.6),

$$\begin{aligned}\int (x + 2)^2 \cdot x^3\,dx &= (x + 2)^2 \cdot \frac{x^4}{4} - \int \frac{x^4}{4}(2)(x + 2)\,dx \\ &= \frac{x^4}{4}(x + 2)^2 - \frac{1}{2}\int x^5\,dx - \int x^4\,dx \\ &= \frac{x^4}{4}(x + 2)^2 - \frac{x^6}{12} - \frac{x^5}{5} + C \\ &= \frac{x^4}{4}(x^2 + 4x + 4) - \frac{x^6}{12} - \frac{x^5}{5} + C \\ &= \frac{x^6}{4} + x^5 + x^4 - \frac{x^6}{12} - \frac{x^5}{5} + C \\ &= \frac{x^6}{6} + \frac{4x^5}{5} + x^4 + C\end{aligned}$$

This method is not, in this case, easier than the more direct method of squaring and multiplying followed by integration of the separate terms. However, in many cases, it is the easiest and sometimes the only method available.

7. *Integration of a function of a function.* If u is some function of x, then

$$\int u^n\,du = \frac{u^{n+1}}{n + 1} + C \qquad (5\text{–}5.7)$$

$$\int \frac{du}{u} = \ln u + C \qquad (5\text{–}5.8)$$

$$\int e^u\,du = e^u + C \qquad (5\text{–}5.9)$$

$$\int a^u\,du = \frac{a^u}{\ln a} + C \qquad (5\text{–}5.10)$$

$$\int \ln u\,du = u \ln u - u + C \qquad (5\text{–}5.11)$$

$$\int \sin u \, du = -\cos u + C \tag{5–5.12}$$

$$\int \cos u \, du = \sin u + C \tag{5–5.13}$$

These results, all of which also appear in Appendix E, provide extremely useful techniques for integrating functions which seem, at first glance to be very difficult to integrate. The key to the process is the *conversion of the expression to one of the standard forms* given above.

This conversion technique may be illustrated by the following. To integrate the expression,

$$\int \frac{2x \, dx}{\sqrt{5 - 3x^2}}$$

we shall convert it to the standard form of Equation (5–5.7):

Let

$$u = 5 - 3x^2$$

Then

$$du = -6x \, dx$$

and

$$dx = \frac{du}{-6x}$$

Then the original expression becomes

$$\int \frac{2x \, du}{-6x\sqrt{u}} = -\frac{1}{3}\int u^{-\frac{1}{2}} \, du = -\frac{2u^{\frac{1}{2}}}{3} + C$$

$$= -\frac{2}{3}\sqrt{5 - 3x^2} + C$$

We can similarly illustrate the use of Equation (5–5.8). If the expression to be integrated is

$$\int \frac{6x^2 \, dx}{x^3 + 3}$$

let

$$u = x^3 + 3$$

then

$$du = 3x^2 \, dx$$

and

$$dx = \frac{du}{3x^2}$$

then the original expression becomes

$$\int \frac{6x^2\,du}{3x^2u} = 2\int \frac{du}{u} = 2\ln u + C$$
$$= 2\ln(x^3 + 3) + C$$

Illustrating Equation (5–5.10), we integrate

$$\int x a^{x^2}\,dx$$

let

$$u = x^2$$

then

$$du = 2x\,dx$$

and

$$dx = \frac{du}{2x}$$

then the expression to be integrated becomes

$$\int \frac{x a^u\,du}{2x} = \frac{1}{2}\int a^u\,du = \frac{a^u}{2\ln a} + C$$
$$= \frac{a^{x^2}}{2\ln a} + C$$

Of course it may not always be possible to convert the expression to one of the standard forms represented by Equations (5–5.7) through (5–5.13), and often in such cases, we can integrate by parts, using Equation (5–5.6). However, frequently integration is extremely difficult to perform. For our purposes, a table of integrals, such as may be found in most calculus books and any book of mathematical tables, can and should be used. A very brief table of integrals may be found in Appendix E.

SUGGESTIONS FOR FURTHER READING

See suggested readings for Chapter 2.

EXERCISES

5–1. Integrate the following:

1. $\int x^4\,dx$
2. $\int x^{-2}\,dx$
3. $\int x^{\frac{1}{2}}\,dx$
4. $\int x^{-1}\,dx$
5. $\int 3x^{-\frac{1}{2}}\,dx$
6. $\int 3x^2\,dx$
7. $\int 5^x\,dx$
8. $\int (2x^3 - 3x^{-1})\,dx$

5–2. Evaluate the following definite integrals:

1. $\int_1^3 x\,dx$
2. $\int_0^e \ln x\,dx$
3. $\int_2^3 (x + x^2 + x^3)\,dx$
4. $\int_0^1 e^x\,dx$
5. $\int_1^2 \left(\frac{1}{x} + x^2\right) dx$
6. $\int_1^2 xe^{-x^2}\,dx$

5–3. Integrate the following:

1. $\int (2x + 3)^2\,dx$
2. $\int (1 - x)^{-1}\,dx$
3. $\int \frac{x\,dx}{\sqrt{4x^2 - 5}}$
4. $\int 3xe^{x^2}\,dx$
5. $\int e^{2x+3}\,dx$
6. $\int \sin 2x\,dx$
7. $\int x \cos (3x^2)\,dx$
8. $\int \ln (2x + 5)\,dx$
9. $\int x \ln (x^2 - 1)\,dx$
10. $\int \ln \left(\frac{2x + 2}{x}\right) dx$
11. $\int \left(\frac{3x^2 - x^{-\frac{1}{2}}}{x^3 - 2x^{\frac{1}{2}}}\right) dx$
12. $\int \left(\frac{6x + 3}{x^2 + x + 1}\right) dx$
13. $\int axe^{-ax}\,dx$
14. $\int \frac{\ln x}{x}\,dx$

5–4. Consider the rectangle with the x-axis as base and with diagonal from the origin to the point (4,20). The curve of the equation $y = 18 - x^2$ divides the rectangle into two areas. The curve of the equation $y = x^2$ further divides the rectangle, producing four areas in all. Draw the graph and compute the sizes of all four areas.

5–5. The Lensayl Commercial Institute is now 1 year old, and it has 100 students. It plans to increase its student enrolment continuously at an annual rate that is its present enrolment (100) times the reciprocal of its current age (in years). What is the expected enrolment 5 years from now?

5–6. The Jakuh Advertising Agency finds that the residual advertising effect of its advertising campaigns decays continuously at the monthly rate of $1/t^2$, where t is the time in months since the last campaign. If the level after one month is arbitrarily called 1.00, what is the level after n months?

6

Continuous Probability Distributions

6–1. Continuous Distributions. As we have seen, when a random variable may take only certain specified numerical values, such as the number of successes in n trials, the probability distribution that characterizes the process which generates that random variable is called a *discrete distribution*. However, sometimes the chance variable is one which may take all values in some interval. Examples of these are: the height or weight of a person or object; the time taken to complete a task; the distance covered or the speed of a moving object subject to chance forces. In these cases, the probability distribution is *continuous*. Continuous distributions are frequently very easy to deal with, and for this reason, we often treat a discrete random variable as if it were continuous, especially when it may take a large number of values. An excellent illustration of this relationship is the use of the normal distribution as an approximation to the binomial distribution.

With a continuous distribution, where the number of possible values of the random variable is infinite, we do not speak of the probability of the occurrence of *some specific value*. Rather we speak of the probability that the value of the random variable (x) lies between two specified points, say A and B. If $B > A$, this probability is $P(A \leq x \leq B)$.

Also, the general formula for the curve describing a continuous probability distribution is usually written

$$y = f(x) \tag{6–1.1}$$

and it is called a *probability density function* (*pdf*).

6–2. The Probability Density Function, *pdf*, and the Cumulative Distribution Function, *cdf*. In the following general discussion, the reader may find it helpful to make frequent reference to the graphs of Figure 6–2.1, which show a probability density function (upper graph)

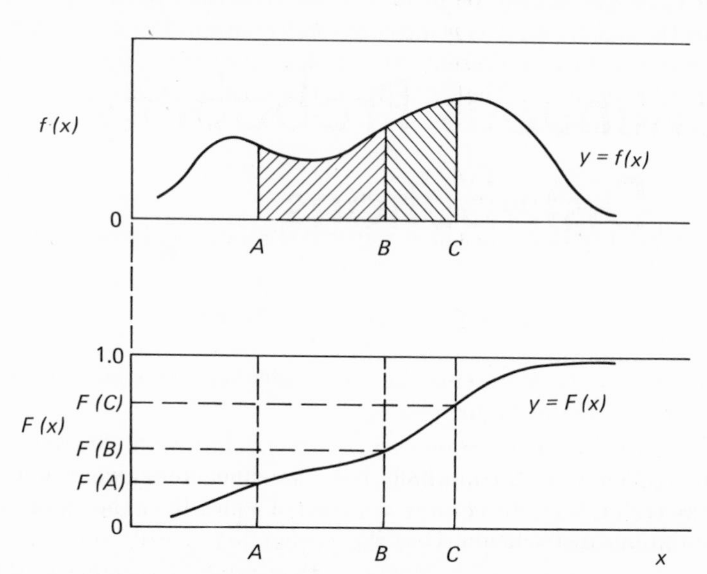

Fig. 6–2.1. Portion of a probability density function and a cumulative distribution function.

and the corresponding cumulative distribution function (lower graph) for some hypothetical probability distribution in which x is continuously distributed.

All probability density functions must meet these two conditions.

1. *Nonnegativity:*

$$f(x) \geq 0 \qquad \text{for all } x \tag{6–2.1}$$

2. *Area under the curve must total to* 1:

$$\int_{-\infty}^{+\infty} f(x)\, dx = 1 \tag{6–2.2}$$

Also, as a consequence of the nonnegativity condition, *the cumulative distribution function (cdf) must be nondecreasing as x increases.* If $A < B < C$,

$$\int_A^C f(x)\, dx \geq \int_A^B f(x)\, dx \tag{6–2.3}$$

This condition assures that the *cumulative distribution function, fcd,* rises from left to right. The *cdf* is generally represented by $F(x)$, where

$$F(x) = \int_{-\infty}^{x} f(x)\,dx \tag{6–2.4}$$

Clearly, its graph may be level in some intervals, but it never slopes down to the right; i.e., it is *monotonic nondecreasing*. It rises from 0 to 1. The expression $F(A)$ represents the probability that x lies at or below some specific value, A. That is, $F(A)$ is the area under the $f(x)$ curve to the left of the value A.

$$F(A) = \int_{-\infty}^{A} f(x)\,dx \tag{6–2.5}$$

The probability that x lies in any specified range, say between A and B, is, if $A < B$,

$$P(A \leq x \leq B) = \int_{A}^{B} f(x)\,dx \tag{6–2.6}$$

and this probability represents the area under the curve between $x = A$ and $x = B$, as seen in Figure 6–2.1.

We have used the expression $P(A \leq x \leq B)$, but we could equally well have used $P(A < x < B)$, which has the same numerical value. The difference is $P(x = A)$ and $P(x = B)$, both of which have the value of zero in a continuous distribution. Clearly

$$P(x = A) = \int_{A}^{A} f(x)\,dx = 0 \tag{6–2.7}$$

This result; i.e., $P(x = A) = 0$ in a continuous distribution, does not mean that the value of the variable *cannot* be exactly A. Naturally, it must take *some* value, and all values are possible. However, there is an infinitely large number of possible values, so the probability associated with any one of them is zero.

6–3. The Uniform Distribution. The simplest case of a continuous distribution is the uniform distribution, $y = k$. Consider the random variable which may take all values in the interval between 0 and 4 and whose *pdf* is

$$\begin{aligned} f(x) &= 0.25 \qquad \text{for } 0 \leq x \leq 4 \\ &= 0 \qquad \text{elsewhere} \end{aligned} \tag{6–3.1}$$

This is graphed in the upper half of Figure 6–3.1. Equation (6–3.1) is a *pdf* since it meets the two requirements given in Section 6–2, i.e., non-negativity and area under the curve equal to 1:

$$\int_{0}^{4} f(x)\,dx = \int_{0}^{4} 0.25\,dx = 0.25x \Big|_{0}^{4} = 1 - 0 = 1$$

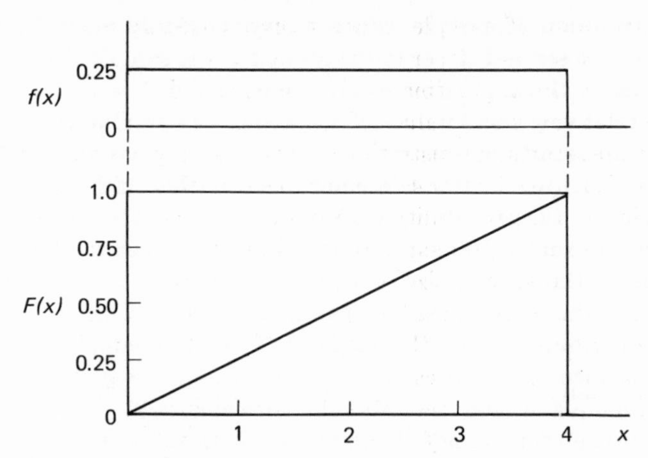

Fig. 6–3.1. The *pdf* and *cdf* for $y = 0.25$, for $0 \leq x \leq 4$.

It must be noted that, in the *pdf*, the range of possible values is specified *as part of the equation*. This is *essential* when the range is other than $-\infty$ to $+\infty$, or when it is not inherently specified by the mathematical form of the expression.

The lower half of Figure 6–3.1 is the cumulative distribution function, the *cdf*:

$$F(x) = \int_0^x 0.25\,dx = 0.25x \tag{6–3.2}$$

The general expression for the *pdf* for the uniform distribution, i.e., a continuous random variable which is uniformly distributed over the interval from a to b, is

$$\begin{aligned} f(x) &= \frac{1}{b-a} \qquad \text{for } a \leq x \leq b \\ &= 0 \qquad \text{elsewhere} \end{aligned} \tag{6–3.3}$$

6–4. The Normal Distribution. The most important of the continuous distributions in statistics is the normal distribution. Its importance stems, not primarily from its occurrence in natural phenomena in the real world, although some physical phenomena do seem to be distributed normally, but rather from two other factors. First, the already-noted close approximation between the binomial distribution and the normal distribution, and second, the central-limit theorem. The central-limit theorem asserts that certain statistics, most important of which is the arithmetic mean, tend to be normally distributed as the sample size becomes large. Thus, if samples of large size, n, are drawn from a population that is not normally distributed, nevertheless, the successive sample means will form, themselves, a distribution that is approximately normal.

The distribution of sample means is *asymptotically* normal; that is, it approaches closer and closer to the normal as the sample size, n, increases and, actually, the approximation to the normal distribution is very good for even relatively small values of n, the sample size. One very interesting and, perhaps, startling illustration of this tendency has already been seen in Table 4–11.1 in Chapter 4. There we can see that, although for the toss of a single die, the probability distribution of the outcomes is *rectangular*, i.e. there is exactly the same probability ($\frac{1}{6}$) for each of the possible outcomes, if the sample size is increased to only 2, the probability distribution of the eleven possible outcomes, the *sum* of the two faces, is a peaked distribution with the mode at 7. As the sample size, i.e., the number of dice tossed in each trial, is increased, the distribution of the sum will more and more resemble the normal curve.

The equation for the *pdf* of the normal distribution is

$$y = f(x) = \frac{1}{\sigma\sqrt{2\pi}} e^{-\frac{1}{2}\frac{(x-\mu)^2}{\sigma^2}} \qquad (6\text{–}4.1)$$

where π and e are the familiar constants, and μ is the arithmetic mean of the distribution, with σ as its standard deviation. The formula, then, is in the form

$$y = f(x,\mu,\sigma) \qquad (6\text{–}4.2)$$

or, in order to compute the various values of y from values of x, we need to know the mean and the standard deviation. On the other hand, this indicates that when we do know these two parameters, we know all that we need to know to compute the curve for the entire distribution. More technically, the mean and the standard deviation define completely a normal distribution.

The equation also indicates that the distribution is symmetrical about μ. This follows from the fact that, whether $(x - \mu)$ is positive or negative, its absolute size is all that matters, since it is squared. Clearly, then, the arithmetic mean of the normal distribution must be the center of symmetry, μ.

There is no single normal distribution. It is a family of distributions. All have the same shape; but they may be wider or narrower, depending on the standard deviation. Figure 6–4.2 shows three different distributions, all normal, and all with the same mean but with different standard deviations.

For the normal distribution and, indeed, for any probability distribution, the total area under the curve is treated as being exactly equal to one square unit. In the next section, when we speak of the area under the curve, we shall not worry about just what the size of the unit is; but we shall define the total area under the curve as being equal to 1, the area under the curve to the left of a vertical line erected through the arithmetic mean as equal to 0.5, etc. This and many other area relationships hold true, regardless of the size of the unit, since they always deal with *relative* areas, i.e., relative to the total area under the curve, which is defined as being equal to 1.

The general shape of the *pdf* and the *cdf* of the normal distribution are shown in Figure 6–4.1.

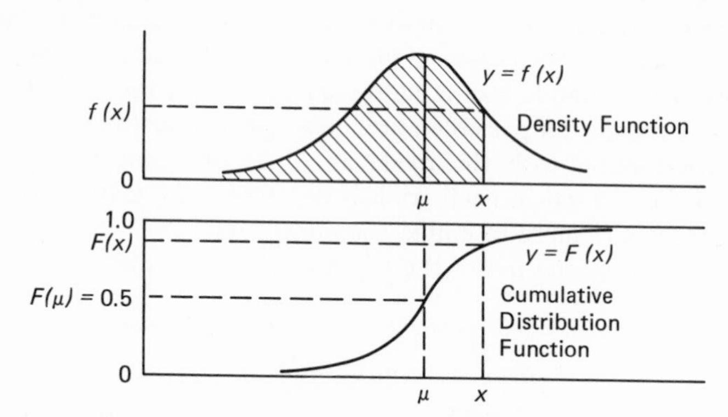

Fig. 6–4.1. The normal distribution. The upper curve is the *pdf*, and the lower curve is the *cdf*. The height of the upper curve, the *pdf*, or *density function*, is $f(x)$ at any point x. $F(x)$ is the area under the upper curve to the left of any point x. $F(x)$ is also the height of the lower curve at any point x. The total area under the upper curve is 1, and the height (ordinate) which the lower curve approaches as it moves to the right is also 1.

We have referred above to the *sampling distribution of the arithmetic mean*, when we noted the reasons for the importance of the normal distribution. This is the distribution which would result if many samples were drawn from some population and the arithmetic means of these samples computed. It is the distribution of these sample arithmetic means.

If a population is normal, then random members selected from that population will be normally distributed, since, obviously, they will merely reproduce the original population. Thus, we might say that the means of samples of size $n = 1$, drawn from a normal population, will be normally distributed. This is merely a trivial restatement of the last sentence, but it is in a more useful form. It is also a fact that means of samples of size $n = 2$ or 3 or 4 or 10 or 100, or any size at all, will be normally distributed. That is, if a parent population is normally distributed, the population which is the arithmetic means of very many samples of size n is itself a normal population.

However, the arithmetic means of samples of size $n = 1$ will, of course, reproduce identically the original normal population, that is, the parent population. But, if the sample size is larger than just a single observation, the population of the arithmetic means of such samples will not be identical with the parent population. It will, as we have seen above, be normally distributed; and, indeed, it will have the same arithmetic mean; but it will not have the same standard deviation. A moment's reflection will suggest that large samples will tend to yield arithmetic means that are closer to the mean of the parent population than will small samples. Thus, the arithmetic means of small and large samples alike will tend to cluster about the true arithmetic mean of the parent population; but the arithmetic means derived from the larger samples will tend to cluster *more closely* about that population mean than will the comparable statistics obtained from the smaller samples. Figure 6–4.2 shows graphically the

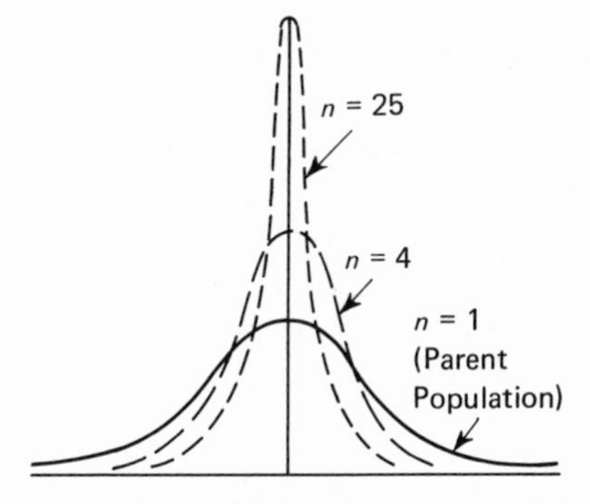

Fig. 6–4.2. Distribution of a normal population and the sampling distributions of the arithmetic means of samples of size $n = 4$ and $n = 25$.

distributions of sample means from samples of size $n = 4$ and $n = 25$, compared with the distribution of the parent normal population. Note that all these sampling distributions of arithmetic means are normal distributions. Also note that they all have the same arithmetic mean. They differ only with respect to their dispersion, which, of course, decreases as the sample size increases.

The dispersion of a sampling distribution of arithmetic means depends upon two factors:

1. *The dispersion of the parent population.* The more variable the parent population, the more variable will be the sample means.
2. *The size of the sample.* As we have seen, the variability of the sample means decreases with increasing size of the sample.

Thus, the standard deviation of the sampling distribution of arithmetic means may be said to increase with increasing standard deviation of the parent population and with decreasing size of the sample. Actually, the mathematical relationship is that the standard deviation of the distribution of sample arithmetic means, which is also called the *standard error of the arithmetic mean,* varies directly with the standard deviation of the parent population and inversely with the square root of the size of the sample. Its symbol is $\sigma_{\bar{x}}$, and the equation is

$$\sigma_{\bar{x}} = \frac{\sigma}{\sqrt{n}} \qquad (6\text{–}4.3)$$

6–5. Areas Under the Normal Curve. Another property of the normal distribution is that its range is infinite. No matter how far from μ we go in either direction, $f(x)$ is never equal to 0. As x departs more and more from μ, $f(x)$ approaches the x-axis *asymptotically;* that is, it keeps getting closer and closer but it never actually touches it. However, it gets very close, within a relatively short distance from μ.

The rapidity with which the normal curve approaches the x-axis is seen from the fact that, in the range from 2 standard deviations below the mean to 2 standard deviations above the mean, lies 95.5 per cent of the area of the distribution; that is, 95.5 per cent of the members of the distribution lie within that range; or, to use probability terminology, the probability is 0.955 that a random member of a normal distribution will lie within 2 standard deviations on either side of the mean of the distribution. This is illustrated in Figure 6–5.1.

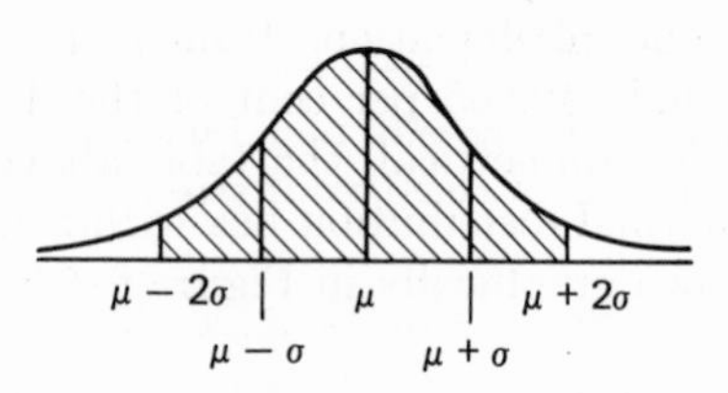

Fig. 6–5.1. **95.5 per cent of the area of a normal distribution lies in the range from $\mu - 2\sigma$ to $\mu + 2\sigma$.**

The percentage of the normal distribution which lies within any range may be computed from the equation for the normal distribution, Equation (6–4.1). However, it is not necessary for us to be able to perform these computations, because they have all been worked out and tabulated. For such a *table of areas* see Appendix A; a portion of that table is reproduced in Table 6–5.1 and illustrated in Figure 6–5.2.

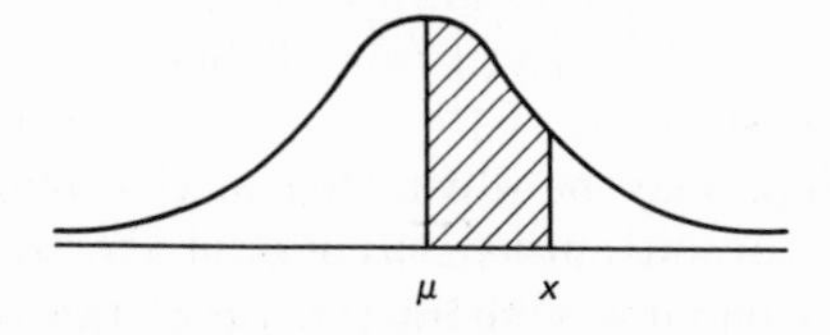

Fig. 6–5.2. **Area under the normal curve as given in Table 6–5.1. and Appendix A.**

TABLE 6–5.1

Areas Under the Normal Curve

$\frac{x - \mu}{\sigma}$	Area Under Normal Curve Between μ and x
1.0	0.34134
2.0	0.47725
3.0	0.49865
4.0	0.49997

This table is called a *table of areas,* because it gives the proportion of the area under the curve which lies between the vertical lines erected at two points along the x-axis. The left column is the distance from the mean expressed in terms of standard deviations. The area given in the right column corresponds to the area of the normal distribution lying between the two lines. The table above tells us that if x is $\mu + \sigma$, or in other words, if the distance between x and μ is 1 standard deviation, and, hence, $(x - \mu)/\sigma = 1$, then 34.134 per cent of the distribution lies between μ and x and is represented by the shaded area in Figure 6–5.2. Similarly, if x is at, say, 3 standard deviations from μ, i.e., $(x - \mu)/\sigma = 3$, the shaded area will include 49.865 per cent of the distribution. Since the normal distribution is symmetrical, the table above tells us that about 68 per cent of the normal distribution lies within the range from $\mu - \sigma$ to $\mu + \sigma$. This is shown graphically in Figure 6–5.3.

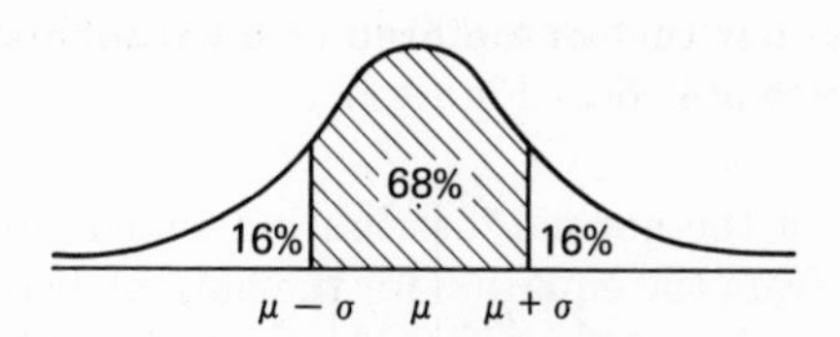

Fig. 6–5.3. Normal distribution showing that 68 per cent of the area under the curve lies within 1 standard deviation of the mean.

The relationships, which are shown in Table 6–5.2 and are pictured in Figure 6–5.4, are similarly derived from Table 6–5.1. These may well be kept in mind by the student.

These relationships may be illustrated in the following way. A steel fabricating plant is turning out lengths of steel wire to be used for suspension purposes. The important characteristic of the wire is its breaking strength, i.e., the load that it will bear before it breaks. Long experience has shown that the breaking strengths of these lengths of steel wire are

TABLE 6–5.2

Percentage of the Area of the Normal Distribution Lying Within the Range Defined by Integral Numbers of Standard Deviations on Either Side of the Mean

Number of Standard Deviations from Mean $\left\lvert \frac{x-\mu}{\sigma} \right\rvert$	Approximate Percentage of the Normal Distribution in the Range $\mu - x$ to $\mu + x$
1	68
2	95.5
3	99.7
4	99.99

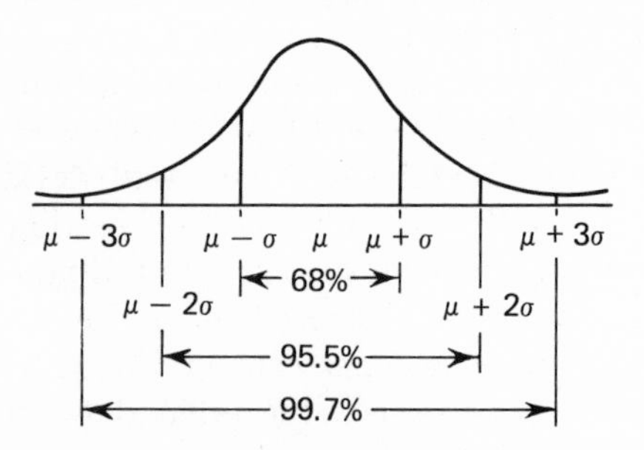

Fig. 6–5.4. Normal distribution showing percentages lying within 1, 2, 3 standard deviations of the mean.

normally distributed with mean 200 lb., and standard deviation 10 lb. This distribution is graphed in Figure 6–5.5.

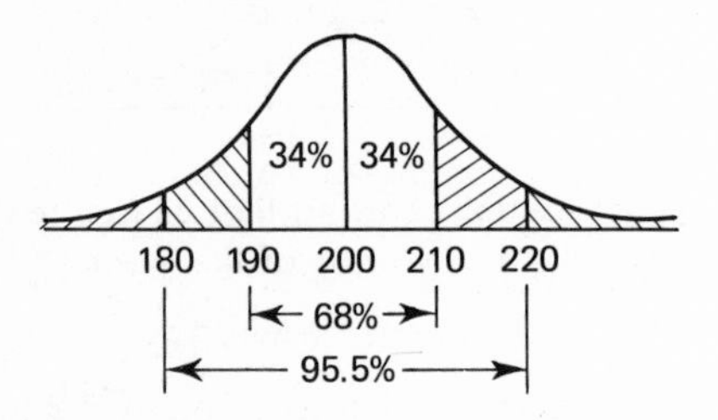

Fig. 6–5.5. Normal distribution of the breaking strengths of lengths of steel wire with $\mu = 200$ lb, and $\sigma = 10$ lb.

From the table of areas under the normal curve, we can ascertain the percentage of the distribution which has a breaking strength between any two desired limits. For example, 68 per cent of the lengths of wire have breaking strengths between 190 and 210 lb. Also, we know that only about 2.25 per cent of them cannot support more than 180 lb., whereas 16 per cent can support 210 lb. or more.

On the other hand, if we had a requirement that the wire be able to support 175 lb., and we therefore wanted to find the proportion of the output of the plant which would be unsatisfactory, we would want to find the area shown as a shaded area in Figure 6–5.6.

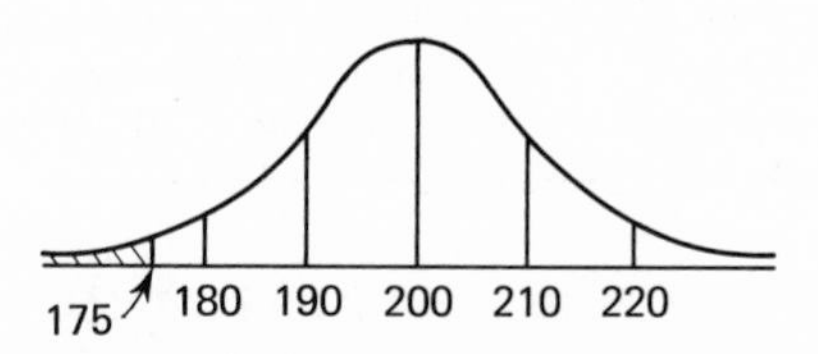

Fig. 6–5.6. Distribution of the breaking strength of lengths of steel wire, showing the portion with breaking strength less than 175 lb.

To find the desired percentage, we must first translate the 175-lb. figure to deviations from the mean in terms of standard deviations. The formula to be used is

$$\frac{x - \mu}{\sigma} \tag{6–5.1}$$

$$\frac{175 - 200}{10} = -2.5$$

Thus, 175 lb. is 2.5 standard deviations away from the mean. Looking up 2.5 in Appendix A, we obtain 0.49379. This means that 49.379 per cent of the distribution lies within 2.5 standard deviations of the mean on either side of the mean, and 0.621 per cent of the distribution lies beyond 2.5 standard deviations on either side. Therefore, 0.621 per cent of the lengths of steel wire, or 6 in 1,000, will be unsatisfactory in that they will not be able to support 175 lb.

If we wanted to find the percentage of the distribution lying between 212 and 224 lb., we should have to resort to subtraction, since this cannot be found directly. First, the 212 and the 224, respectively, must be transformed to deviations from the mean as measured in standard deviations, using Equation (6–5.1):

For 212,

$$\frac{x - \mu}{\sigma} = \frac{212 - 200}{10} = 1.2$$

For 224,

$$\frac{x - \mu}{\sigma} = \frac{224 - 200}{10} = 2.4$$

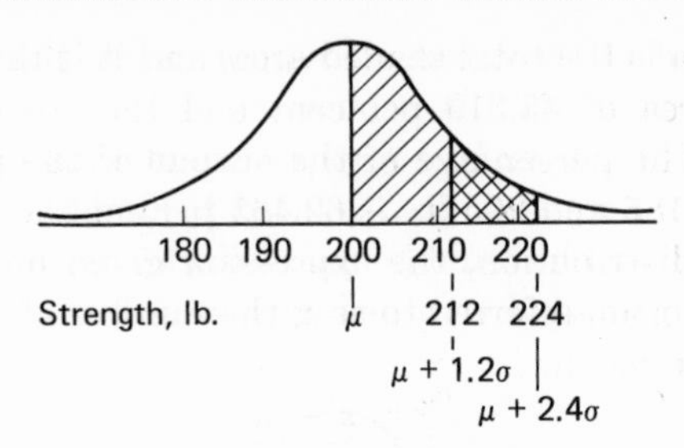

Fig. 6–5.7. Determination of the percentage of the output of lengths of steel wire with breaking strength between 212 and 224 lb.

The table of areas gives 0.38493 for 1.2 and 0.49180 for 2.4. Figure 6–5.7 shows that these two numbers, respectively, refer to the areas lying between the mean and vertical lines erected at 1.2 and 2.4 standard deviations on either side of the mean.

The total shaded area, lying between the mean and 224 lb., is 49.180 per cent; and the diagonally hatched area, that lying between the mean and 212 lb., is 38.493 per cent. The desired area, the cross-hatched area between 212 and 224 lb., is the difference, 10.687 per cent of the distribution.

If we wanted to find the percentage of the distribution lying between, say, 185 and 205 lb., we would have to add the areas on both sides of the mean, since this cannot be found directly. Again, using Equation (6–5.1):

For 185,

$$\frac{x - \mu}{\sigma} = \frac{185 - 200}{10} = -1.5$$

For 205,

$$\frac{x - \mu}{\sigma} = \frac{205 - 200}{10} = +0.5$$

The table of areas gives 0.43319 for 1.5 and 0.19146 for 0.5. Figure 6–5.8 shows that these two numbers, respectively, refer to the areas lying between the mean and the vertical lines erected at -1.5 and $+0.5$ standard deviations on either side of the mean. Since 185 is less than 200 and, therefore, the -1.5 is negative, that area appears to the left of the mean.

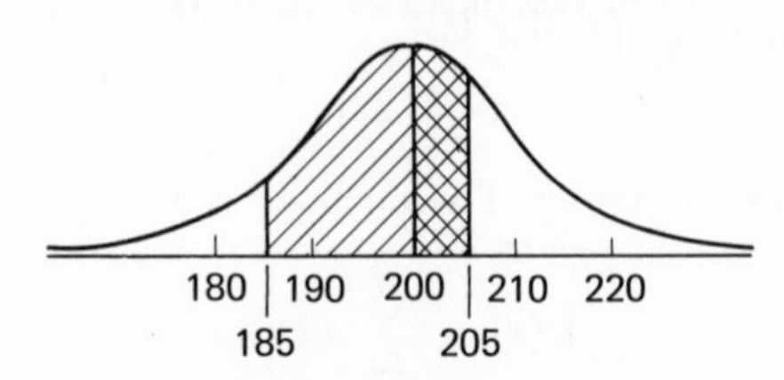

Fig. 6–5.8. Determination of the output of lengths of steel wire with breaking strength between 185 and 205 lb.

The desired area is the total shaded area, and it is the sum of the diagonally hatched area of 43.319 per cent and the cross-hatched area of 19.146 per cent. The percentage of the output of the plant with tensile strength between 185 and 205 lb. is 62.465 per cent.

In the normal distribution, the expression given in Equation (6–5.1) and used above is often referred to as z, the number of standard errors of departure from the mean.

$$z = \frac{x - \mu}{\sigma} \tag{6–5.2}$$

6–6. Mathematics of the Normal Distribution. The availability of tables such as Appendix A makes it unnecessary to solve Equation (6–6.1), the *pdf* of the normal distribution, for specific numerical values. However, let us briefly examine the *pdf* for the normal distribution and demonstrate that, for the normal distribution, the area under the curve is equal to 1:

$$\int_{-\infty}^{\infty} f(x)\, dx = 1$$

From Equation (6–4.1), the area under the curve is

$$A = \int_{-\infty}^{\infty} \frac{1}{\sigma\sqrt{2\pi}} e^{-\frac{1}{2}\left(\frac{x-\mu}{\sigma}\right)^2} dx \tag{6–6.1}$$

let

$$z = \frac{x - \mu}{\sigma} \tag{6–6.2}$$

then

$$x = \sigma z + \mu \tag{6–6.3}$$

also

$$\frac{dz}{dx} = \frac{1}{\sigma}$$

therefore

$$dz = \frac{dx}{\sigma} \tag{6–6.4}$$

Then

$$A = \frac{1}{\sqrt{2\pi}} \int_{-\infty}^{\infty} e^{-\frac{z^2}{2}} dz \tag{6–6.5}$$

From Equation 19 of Appendix E,

$$A = 1$$

Now, let us look at the mean. The mean of a discrete distribution is

$$E(x) = \sum_{i=1}^{n} x_i P(x_i) \tag{6–6.6}$$

where there are n possible values of x.

Similarly, for a continuous distribution,

$$E(x) = \int_a^b xf(x)\,dx \tag{6–6.7}$$

where the domain of x is from a to b.

Thus, for the normal distribution,

$$E(x) = \int_{-\infty}^{\infty} xf(x)\,dx \tag{6–6.8}$$

$$E(x) = \int_{-\infty}^{\infty} x \frac{1}{\sigma\sqrt{2\pi}} e^{-\frac{1}{2}\left(\frac{x-\mu}{\sigma}\right)^2} dx \tag{6–6.9}$$

Utilizing the relationship of Equation (6–6.2), it is simple to prove that $E(x) = \mu$. This is left as an exercise for the reader (see Exercise 6–1). However, it is obvious from the symmetry characteristics of the normal curve that the mean is μ.

6–7. The Exponential Distribution. Another important continuous distribution is the exponential distribution. We shall find that it is particularly useful in queueing theory. The *pdf* for the exponential distribution is

$$\begin{aligned} f(x) &= \alpha e^{-\alpha x} && \text{for } x \geq 0 \\ &= 0 && \text{elsewhere} \end{aligned} \tag{6–7.1}$$

This distribution, the *exponential distribution*, is referred to by many authors as the *negative exponential distribution*. These names are used almost interchangeably to refer to the distribution discussed here.

The graph of the density function (*pdf*) for the distribution slopes downward to the right from its maximum at $x = 0$, where $f(x) = \alpha$, as seen in Figure 6–7.1.

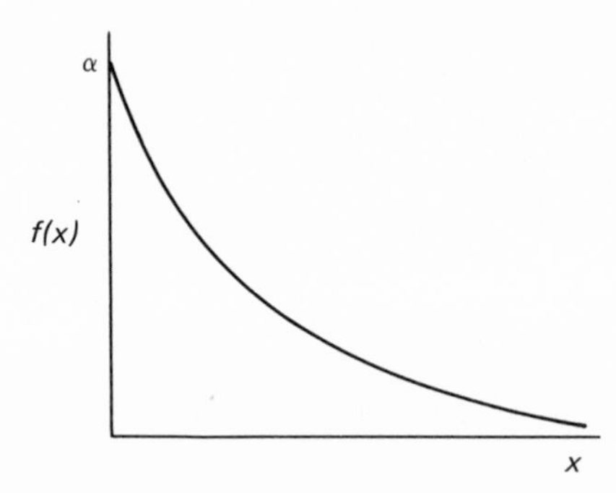

Fig. 6–7.1. The exponential distribution *pdf*. $f(x) = \alpha e^{-\alpha x}$.

As we did with the normal distribution, we can easily demonstrate that the area under the curve is equal to 1.

$$A = \int_0^\infty f(x)\,dx = 1$$

$$A = \int_0^\infty \alpha e^{-\alpha x}\,dx = \left[-\frac{1}{\alpha}\,\alpha e^{-\alpha x}\right]_0^\infty$$

$$A = 0 - (-1) = 1$$

We shall now show that the mean of the exponential distribution is $\frac{1}{\alpha}$ and that the variance is $\frac{1}{\alpha^2}$, and, finally, we shall derive the expression for the *cdf* of the exponential distribution.

To find the mean:

$$E(x) = \int_0^\infty x\alpha e^{-\alpha x}\,dx$$

Integrating by parts, letting $u = x$ and $dv = \alpha e^{-\alpha x}\,dx$, then $du = dx$, and $v = -e^{-\alpha x}$:

$$\int u\,dv = uv - \int v\,du \tag{5–5.6}$$

$$\int_0^\infty x\alpha e^{-\alpha x}\,dx = [-xe^{-\alpha x}]_0^\infty - \int_0^\infty - e^{-\alpha x}\,dx$$

$$E(x) = 0 - 0 - \left[\frac{1}{\alpha}\,e^{-\alpha x}\right]_0^\infty$$

$$= 0 - 0 - 0 + \frac{1}{\alpha}$$

$$E(x) = \frac{1}{\alpha} \tag{6–7.2}$$

We shall later have use for the variance of the exponential distribution, and we shall therefore now proceed to derive the expression for the variance of the exponential distribution using the basic relationships of statistics derived and discussed in Section 4–21 above.

There we saw that the general formula for the variance of a probability distribution is

$$\sigma^2 = E(x^2) - [E(x)]^2 \tag{4–21.6}$$

For a discrete probability distribution, this equation was used in the form

$$\sigma^2 = \Sigma x^2 P(x) - [E(x)]^2 \tag{4–21.9}$$

Here, for a continuous distribution, it takes the form

$$\sigma^2 = \int x^2 f(x)\, dx - [E(x)]^2 \tag{6–7.3}$$

and, applying this last equation to the exponential distribution,

$$\sigma^2 = \int_0^\infty x^2 \alpha e^{-\alpha x}\, dx - \left(\frac{1}{\alpha}\right)^2 \tag{6–7.4}$$

Integrating by parts, letting $u = x^2$ and $dv = \alpha e^{-\alpha x}\, dx$, then $du = 2x\, dx$ and $v = -e^{-\alpha x}$. Using the general equation for integration by parts,

$$\int u\, dv = uv - \int v\, du \tag{5–5.6}$$

$$\int_0^\infty x^2 \alpha e^{-\alpha x} = [-x^2 e^{-\alpha x}]_0^\infty - \int_0^\infty - 2x e^{-\alpha x}\, dx$$

$$= 0 - 0 + \frac{2}{\alpha} E(x) = \frac{2}{\alpha^2}$$

$$\sigma^2 = \int_0^\infty x^2 \alpha e^{-\alpha x} - \left(\frac{1}{\alpha}\right)^2 = \frac{2}{\alpha^2} - \frac{1}{\alpha^2}$$

$$\sigma^2 = \frac{1}{\alpha^2} \tag{6–7.5}$$

This is the variance of the exponential distribution.

The *cdf* of the exponential distribution is

$$F(x) = \int_0^x \alpha e^{-\alpha x}\, dx = [-e^{-\alpha x}]_0^x$$

$$F(x) = 1 - e^{-\alpha x} \tag{6–7.6}$$

This *cdf* is graphed in Figure 6–7.2. The equation for the *cdf*, Equation (6–7.6) is widely used, and its applications go far beyond its usefulness in probability theory as a *cdf*. It is commonly used, for example, in model

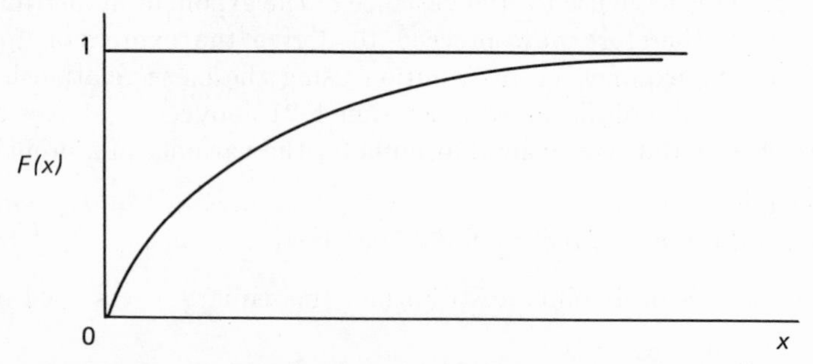

Fig. 6–7.2. The *cdf* of the exponential distribution. $F(x) = 1 - e^{-\alpha x}$.

building to represent a *saturation* phenomenon such as, for example, the effect of advertising, where the horizontal asymptote represents the maximum sales possible, x is the size of the advertising effort, and y is the resulting sales. This expression has very desirable characteristics for this kind of model. Not only does it show diminishing returns, but it also recognizes a ceiling or saturation level beyond which it cannot go. That is, the effect of successive increments of the input x diminishes as the total amount of x increases, and, eventually, additional input increments have no effect. These characteristics may be found in many real-world phenomena.

6–8. The Gamma Distribution. In this section and Section 6–10, we shall discuss the gamma and beta distributions, both of which have been found to be very useful in management science models. Both of these distributions share a common characteristic with the normal distribution. That is, the *pdf*'s for all three of these distributions are relatively simple mathematical functions, multiplied by constants which are not necessarily so simple. The simple mathematical functions are, for these three respective distributions:

normal	$e^{-z^2/2}$
gamma	$x^a e^{-bx}$
beta	$x^a(1 - x)^b$

For each of these functions shown above, the integral over some interval of the function is some constant, as may be seen in Appendix E, Equations 19, 20, and 21, respectively. Consequently, multiplying each of these functions by the reciprocal of the respective constant yields a new function which is a *pdf*; i.e., its integral over the specified interval is 1. The reader will note that this is exactly what has been done to produce the *pdf*'s for these three continuous distributions.

The gamma distribution has two parameters, a and b, and its *pdf* is

$$\begin{aligned} f(x) &= \frac{b^{a+1}}{\Gamma(a+1)} x^a e^{-bx} \qquad \text{for } x > 0 \\ &= 0 \qquad\qquad\qquad\qquad \text{elsewhere} \end{aligned} \tag{6–8.1}$$

where $b \geq 0$ and $a > -1$

The capital Greek letter gamma, which appears in the denominator, designates the *gamma function*, a mathematical relationship which has the value

$$\Gamma(n) = (n - 1)! \tag{6–8.2}$$

(see Exercises 6–2 and 6–3). Therefore, the gamma probability distribution function (the *pdf*) may be written

$$f(x) = \frac{b^{a+1}}{a!} x^a e^{-bx} \qquad \text{for } x > 0$$
$$= 0 \qquad \text{elsewhere} \tag{6–8.3}$$

We shall see that this distribution is closely related to the exponential distribution, and later we shall see that it is also related to the Poisson distribution (see Exercise 6–5). To see the relationship to the exponential distribution, rearrange Equation (6–8.1) to

$$f(x) = \frac{b}{\Gamma(a+1)} (bx)^a e^{-bx} \tag{6–8.4}$$

Then, if $a = 0$,

$$f(x) = be^{-bx} \tag{6–8.5}$$

and this is the familiar *pdf* for the exponential distribution, Equation (6–7.1). Thus, the exponential distribution is the special case of the gamma distribution, where $a = 0$.

The general shapes of the graphs of the density functions (*pdf*'s) for the gamma distributions for $b = 1$ and selected values of a are shown in Figure 6–8.1.

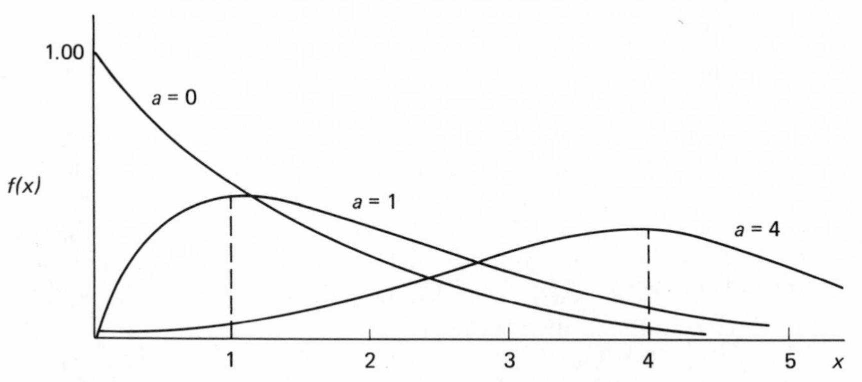

Fig. 6–8.1. Gamma distribution *pdf*'s for $b = 1$, where $a = 0$, 1, and 4, respectively.

It can easily be demonstrated (see Exercise 6–4) that the area under the curve is equal to 1 for all values of a. In the *pdf* for the gamma distribution, the parameter b changes the relative scales of the two axes, and the parameter a determines the location of the peak of the curve; but, for all values of these two parameters, the area under the curve is equal to 1. Equation (6–8.1) is a *pdf*. The peak of the curve, the mode, is at $x = \frac{a}{b}\cdot$ This may be shown by differentiating Equation (6–8.1) and setting the derivative equal to zero (see Exercise 6–8 at the end of this chapter).

Values for the *cdf*, called the *incomplete gamma function*,

$$F(m) = \int_0^m \frac{b^{a+1}}{\Gamma(a+1)} x^a e^{-bx}\, dx \tag{6–8.6}$$

where m is any selected value of x, have been tabulated for values of m and a. However, this may also be evaluated by the use of the Poisson distribution (see Exercise 6–5).

The mean and variance of the gamma distribution are $\dfrac{a+1}{b}$ and $\dfrac{a+1}{b^2}$, respectively. These derivations are left as exercises for the student (see Exercises 6–6 and 6–7). In these exercises the student will show that

$$E(x) = \frac{a+1}{b} \tag{6–8.7}$$

and that

$$\sigma^2 = \frac{a+1}{b^2} \tag{6–8.8}$$

6–9. The Chi-Square Distribution. The *chi-square distribution* is the name given to a special case of the gamma distribution which has particular importance in certain statistical tests and which also may have considerable usefulness in model building.

If, in the gamma distribution, $a = \frac{n}{2} - 1$ and $b = \frac{1}{2}$, the *pdf* becomes

$$f(x) = \frac{1}{2^{\frac{n}{2}}\Gamma\left(\frac{n}{2}\right)} x^{\frac{n}{2}-1} e^{-\frac{x}{2}} \tag{6–9.1}$$

This distribution is known as the *chi-square distribution with n degrees of freedom*. It has only one parameter, n, and as a consequence of some of the applications of this distribution in statistical tests, this parameter has been dubbed *degrees of freedom*.

For the purposes of model building, the *chi-square* distributions are just a particular subset of gamma distributions, but they do have the important simplifying virtue that they have only one parameter. Thus, of course, the mean, mode, and variance are defined in terms of n.

From the expressions for the gamma distribution, the chi-square distribution mean, mode, and variance may be derived by substitution for a and b.

For the chi-square distribution:

$$E(x) = n \tag{6–9.2}$$

$$\sigma^2 = 2n \tag{6–9.3}$$

$$\text{mode} = n - 2 \tag{6–9.4}$$

The chi-square distribution for various values of n is plotted in Figure 6–9.1.

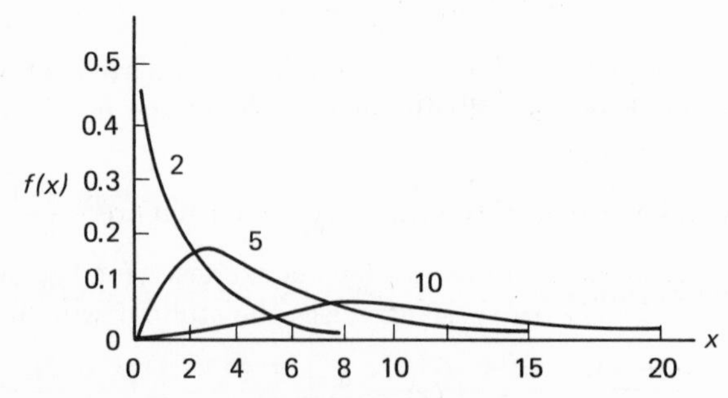

Fig. 6–9.1. Chi-square distribution for n = 2, 5, 10.

6–10. The Beta Distribution. The beta distribution, which is quite useful in management science, particularly in certain kinds of scheduling problems, has the *pdf*:

$$f(x) = \frac{(a+b+1)!}{a!\,b!}x^a(1-x)^b \qquad \text{for } 0 < x < 1 \tag{6–10.1}$$
$$= 0 \qquad \text{elsewhere}$$

where both a and b are greater than -1.

The area under the curve is

$$A = \int_0^1 \frac{(a+b+1)!}{a!\,b!}x^a(1-x)^b\,dx \tag{6–10.2}$$

We shall show that this area is equal to 1. However, we shall not integrate this expression ourselves, but we can use the table of integrals, Appendix E. There, Formula 21 tells that

$$\int_0^1 x^a(1-x)^b\,dx = \frac{a!\,b!}{(a+b+1)!} \tag{6–10.3}$$

Therefore

$$A = 1 \tag{6–10.4}$$

Similarly we can solve for the mean and variance of the beta distribution

$$E(x) = \frac{(a+b+1)!}{a!\,b!}\int_0^1 x^{a+1}(1-x)^b\,dx \tag{6–10.5}$$

Again using Formula 21 from Appendix E, or Equation (6–10.3) above

$$E(x) = \frac{(a+b+1)!}{a!\,b!}\cdot\frac{(a+1)!\,b!}{(a+b+2)!}$$

Therefore the mean of the beta distribution is

$$E(x) = \frac{a+1}{a+b+2} \tag{6–10.6}$$

To solve for the variance, first we solve for $E(x^2)$

$$E(x^2) = \frac{(a+b+1)!}{a!\,b!} \int_0^1 x^{a+2}(1-x)^b\,dx \tag{6–10.7}$$

Again using Formula 21 from Appendix E, or Equation (6–10.3) above,

$$E(x^2) = \frac{(a+b+1)!}{a!\,b!} \cdot \frac{(a+2)!\,b!}{(a+b+3)!} = \frac{(a+1)(a+2)}{(a+b+2)(a+b+3)} \tag{6–10.8}$$

Then, from Equation (4–21.6)

$$\sigma^2 = E(x^2) - [E(x)]^2 \tag{4–21.6}$$

$$\sigma^2 = \frac{(a+1)(a+2)}{(a+b+2)(a+b+3)} - \left(\frac{a+1}{a+b+2}\right)^2 \tag{6–10.9}$$

$$\sigma^2 = \frac{(a+b+2)(a^2+3a+2) - (a+1)^2(a+b+3)}{(a+b+2)^2(a+b+3)} \tag{6–10.10}$$

The numerator of Equation (6–10.10) is

$$a^3 + 3a^2 + 2a + a^2b + 3ab + 2b + 2a^2 + 6a + 4 - a^3 - 5a^2 - 7a - a^2b - 2ab - b - 3$$

which simplifies to

$$a + ab + b + 1 = (a+1)(b+1)$$

Therefore, the variance of the beta distribution is

$$\sigma^2 = \frac{(a+1)(b+1)}{(a+b+2)^2(a+b+3)} \tag{6–10.11}$$

From Equation (6–10.1), it is clear that if $a = b = 0$, the beta distribution is the uniform distribution where $f(x) = 1$.

Also, from Equation (6–10.6) it is clear that, if $a = b$, $E(x) = 0.5$.

The mode of the beta distribution may easily be shown to be equal to $\frac{a}{(a+b)}\cdot$ (See Exercise 6–10 at the end of this chapter.)

Figure 6–10.1 shows the general shapes of the density functions (*pdf*'s) for the beta distribution for selected values of a and b.

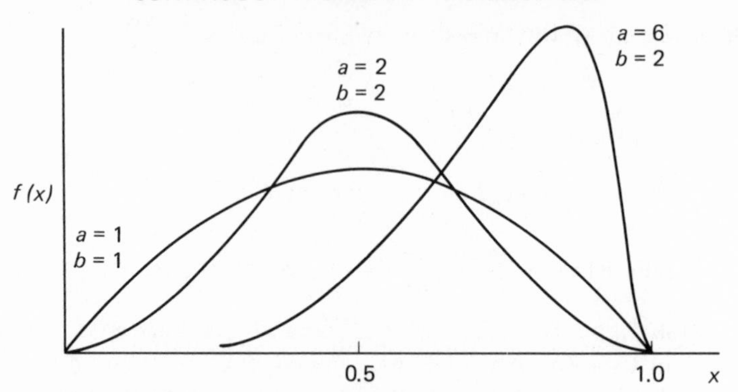

Fig. 6–10.1. Beta distribution *pdf*'s for selected values of a and b.

The means and variances for the beta distributions shown in Figure 6–10.1 may be readily computed from the formulas of Equations (6–10.6) and (6–10.11):

$$E(x) = \frac{a+1}{a+b+2} \tag{6–10.6}$$

$$\sigma^2 = \frac{(a+1)(b+1)}{(a+b+2)^2(a+b+3)} \tag{6–10.11}$$

For the beta distributions shown in Figure 6–10.1: for $a = 1$, $b = 1$,

$$E(x) = \frac{1+1}{1+1+2} = \frac{2}{4} = 0.5$$

$$\sigma^2 = \frac{(1+1)(1+1)}{(1+1+2)^2(1+1+3)} = \frac{4}{80} = \frac{1}{20} = 0.05$$

$$\sigma = 0.224$$

for $a = 2$, $b = 2$,

$$E(x) = \frac{3}{6} = 0.5$$

$$\sigma^2 = \frac{9}{(36)(7)} = \frac{9}{252} = 0.0357$$

$$\sigma = 0.189$$

for $a = 6$, $b = 2$,

$$E(x) = \frac{7}{10} = 0.7$$

$$\sigma^2 = \frac{21}{1{,}100} = 0.0191$$

$$\sigma = 0.138$$

We shall find this ease of computation to be of great use in Chapter 17 below.

Values of the *cdf* of the beta distribution,

$$F(x) = 0 \qquad \text{for } x < 0$$

$$= \int_0^x \frac{(a+b+1)!}{a!\,b!} x^a(1-x)^4\,dx \qquad \text{for } 0 < x < 1 \quad (6\text{–}10.12)$$

$$= 1 \qquad \text{for } x > 1$$

have been tabulated as tables of the *incomplete beta function.*

6–11. Probability Distributions and Operations Research. In this chapter and in Chapter 4, we have examined most of the distributions which we are likely to find important in operations research applications. That is, the probability distributions which we have seen: the binomial, Poisson, uniform, normal, exponential, gamma, and beta, are able to fill most needs which commonly arise in model building.

The binomial and Poisson distributions can produce almost any desired configuration for a discrete distribution. This has been illustrated in Chapter 4.

The continuous distributions which we have seen in this chapter can, similarly, produce configurations of most shapes which we are likely to require. As we have noted, the *cdf* for the exponential distribution, in addition to its great usefulness in describing probability distributions, has considerable usefulness in describing saturation phenomena in management science models.

The normal distribution, of course, is always symmetrical. In addition, it has the property that its tails extend infinitely far in both directions. Of course, it is possible to use the normal distribution to describe a probability distribution whose tails do not run to infinity, but which do extend, say, three or more standard deviations from the mean.

If it is desired to describe a probability distribution which is skewed to the right, the gamma distribution may be used. Since the arithmetic mean of the gamma distribution is $\frac{a+1}{b}$, while the mode is $\frac{a}{b}$, clearly the skewness of the shape of the gamma distribution may be controlled by setting a. For $a = 0$, the distribution, of course, is the same as the exponential distribution. Then, as a takes larger and larger values, the right skewness of the distribution decreases, and, for large values of a, the gamma distribution approaches symmetry. The gamma distribution also has the characteristics that its minimum value is zero, while the maximum extends as far as one may desire. This gives the gamma distribution a very great usefulness in describing real-world phenomena. That is, most real-world phenomena tend to be skewed to the right. If one thinks for a moment about prices, price changes, sizes of firms, sums of money, years of employment, ages, and many other phenomena, one realizes that all of these have a floor at zero, but no necessary ceiling, or, at least, a relatively very high potential ceiling. Therefore, distributions of phenomena such as these and, of course, many others tend to be skewed to the right.

We have seen that, for the gamma distribution, we can create many shapes ranging from near symmetry to extreme right skewness, that we can easily compute its mean, mode, and standard deviation from the values of a and b, and that we can compute the probability of any interval under the gamma distribution by using the very simple device noted above and described in detail in Exercise 6–5 at the end of this chapter, whereby tables of the Poisson distribution may be used for this purpose. (This technique is also illustrated in Section 7–8 below.)

The beta distribution, on the other hand, may be used when either limited-range symmetry or skewness to the left is desired. While left skewness is not so common as right skewness, there are situations when it does arise, and then the beta distribution is extremely convenient to use. Like the gamma distribution, the mean, mode, and standard deviation may be computed very easily from the values of the parameters a and b. The beta distribution differs from the other distributions also in that its range is fixed between 0 and 1. Some operations researchers, when they desire a distribution which is skewed to the *right*, but which runs from 0 to 1, use the mirror image of the beta distribution for this purpose. This is generally a relatively convenient device. Similarly, of course, one could use the mirror image of the gamma distribution for a distribution which is skewed to the left and which is not limited on the left. However, this need arises very seldom indeed.

Table 6–11.1 summarizes the most important parameters: the arith-

TABLE 6–11.1

Parameters of Probability Distributions

Distribution	Arithmetic Mean	Variance	Mode*
Binomial (4–17.1)	np	npq	$(n+1)p - 1 < M \leq (n+1)p$
Poisson (4–20.1)	m	m	$m - 1 < M \leq m$
Uniform (6–3.3)	$\frac{(a+b)}{2}$	$\frac{(b^2 - ab + a^2)}{3}$	
Normal (6–4.1)	μ	σ^2	μ
Exponential (6–7.1)	$\frac{1}{\alpha}$	$\frac{1}{\alpha^2}$	0
Gamma (6–8.1)	$\frac{(a+1)}{b}$	$\frac{(a+1)}{b^2}$	$\frac{a}{b}$
Beta (6–10.1)	$\frac{(a+1)}{(a+b+2)}$	$\frac{(a+1)(b+1)}{(a+b+2)^2(a+b+3)}$	$\frac{a}{a+b}$
Chi-Square (6–9.1)	n	$2n$	$n - 2$

* For the binomial and Poisson distributions, M, the mode, is the *integer* which satisfies the stated condition.

metic mean, the variance, and the mode of the distributions which we have discussed. The variance is used in the table rather than its square root, the standard deviation, in order to avoid the extensive use of the square root sign which might be distracting in the table.

SUGGESTIONS FOR FURTHER READING

FELLER, W. *An Introduction to Probability Theory and Its Applications*, Vol. 2. New York: John Wiley & Co., Inc., 1966.

MEYER, P. L. *Introductory Probability and Statistical Applications*. Reading, Mass.: Addison-Wesley Publishing Co., Inc., 1965.

MOOD, A. M., and F. A. GRAYBILL. *Introduction to the Theory of Statistics* (2d ed.). New York: McGraw-Hill Book Co., Inc., 1963.

EXERCISES

6–1. Prove that, for the normal distribution, $E(x) = \mu$. (Hint: Use the relationships of Equations (6–6.2), (6–6.4), and (6–6.3), respectively, to transform Equation (6–6.9) into such a form that it can be split into two terms. The first term can be integrated by parts with the help of Equation 19 of Appendix E and shown to be equal to zero. The second term can be shown to be equal to μ, again by the use of Equation 19 of Appendix E.)

6–2. The gamma function is:

$$\Gamma(n) = \int_0^\infty x^{n-1}e^{-x}\,dx \tag{6–8.1}$$

Show that:

$$\Gamma(1) = 1$$

$$\Gamma(2) = 1$$

$$\Gamma(3) = 2$$

(Hint: Integrate by parts for $\Gamma(2)$ and $\Gamma(3)$.)

6–3. Show that

$$\Gamma(n) = (n-1)! \tag{6–8.2}$$

(Hint: Integrate by parts, letting $u = x^{n-1}$ and show that

$$\Gamma(n) = (n-1)\int_0^\infty x^{n-2}e^{-x}\,dx$$

which is $\Gamma(n) = (n-1)\,\Gamma(n-1)$. What happens if this technique is applied successively?)

6–4. Show that Equation (6–8.1) for the gamma distribution is a *pdf*, by showing that the area under the curve is equal to 1 for all a. (Hint: Let $bx = y$. Then $dy = b\,dx$. Substitute this into Equation (6–8.1) to obtain the following equation, where $A(a) =$ the area under the curve for some value of a.

$$A(a) = \frac{1}{\Gamma(a+1)}\int_0^\infty y^a e^{-y}\,dy \tag{6–E4.1}$$

Then integrate by parts, letting $y^a = u$. Show that $A(a) = A(a-1)$.) What does this suggest about successive applications of this procedure with respect to the relationship between $A(a)$ and $A(0)$? But what is the value of $A(0)$?

6–5. Show that the incomplete gamma function (Equation (6–8.6)) can be evaluated by the cumulative Poisson distribution with parameter m for $x = 0$ through $x = a$. (Hint: Let $bx = y$. Then $dy = b\,dx$. The resulting integral, Equation (6–E4.1), from 0 to ∞, is equal to 1, as has been shown by Exercise 6–4. However, it is the integral from 0 to m that we seek to evaluate. Rewrite $F(m)$ to equal 1 minus the integral from m to ∞. Integrate by parts to get:

$$F(m) = 1 - \frac{m^a e^{-m}}{a!} - \frac{1}{(a-1)!}\int_m^\infty y^{a-1}e^{-y}\,dy$$

The similarity of the last term to the equation before integration should suggest that successive integrations will yield

$$F(m) = 1 - \sum_{x=0}^{a} \frac{m^x e^{-m}}{x!} \tag{6–E5.1}$$

6–6. Show that the mean of the gamma distribution is $\frac{a+1}{b}\cdot$ (Hint: Integrate the function:

$$E(x) = \int_0^\infty x \frac{b^{a+1}}{\Gamma(a+1)} x^a e^{-bx}\,dx$$

by parts, after letting $bx = y$ and $dy = b\,dx$. For the integration, let $u = y^{a+1}$. Derive as a result:

$$E(x) = \frac{a+1}{b}\int_0^\infty \frac{y^a e^{-y}}{\Gamma(a+1)}\,dy$$

What is the value of the integral? See Exercise 6–4.)

6–7. Show that the variance of the gamma distribution is $\frac{a+1}{b^2}\cdot$ (Hint:

$$\sigma^2 = \int_0^\infty x^2 \frac{b^{a+1}}{\Gamma(a+1)} x^a e^{-bx}\,dx - [E(x)]^2$$

Using the same substitutions as before, evaluate $\sigma^2 + [E(x)]^2$. Show that:

$$\sigma^2 + [E(x)]^2 = \frac{(a+1)(a+2)}{b^2}\int_0^\infty \frac{y^{a+1}e^{-y}}{\Gamma(a+2)}\,dy$$

But this integral is also equal to 1 (see Exercise 6–4). Then substitute for $E(x)$ its value, and solve for σ^2.)

6–8. Show that the mode of the gamma distribution occurs at $x = \frac{a}{b}\cdot$ (Hint: differentiate Equation (6–8.1), and set the derivative equal to 0.)

6–9. Starting with Equation (6–9.1), derive for the chi-square distribution: (a) the mode; (b) the arithmetic mean; (c) the variance.

6–10. Show that the mode of the beta distribution is $\frac{a}{a+b}\cdot$ (Hint: differentiate the *pdf* and set it equal to 0.) We shall use this result in Chapter 17.

6–11. Sketch roughly the *pdf* for the gamma distribution with the following parameters; label your axes:

(i) $b = 1$, $a = 2, 4, 6$, (i.e., 3 curves)
(ii) $b = 2$, $a = 2, 4, 6$, (i.e., 3 curves)
(iii) $b = 3$, $a = 2, 4, 6$, (i.e., 3 curves)

6–12. Sketch roughly the *pdf* for the beta distribution with the following parameters; label your axes:

(i) $b = 1$, $a = 2, 4, 6$, (i.e., 3 curves)
(ii) $b = 2$, $a = 2, 4, 6$, (i.e., 3 curves)
(iii) $b = 3$, $a = 2, 4, 6$, (i.e., 3 curves)

7

Inventory, Maintenance, and Replacement Models

7–1. Introduction. In this chapter we shall introduce system models that require and apply many of the techniques which have been introduced in early chapters, particularly Chapters 4, 5, and 6. We are now in a position to analyze systems which have stochastic inputs and to use integral calculus where necessary. This, as we shall see, broadens immensely our problem-solving capability beyond that utilized in Chapter 3, which considered only deterministic models.

Also, in this chapter we shall introduce such new mathematical techniques as we may need to take full advantage of the tools developed in previous chapters. One of the important tools which we shall require is the technique for differentiating an integral.

7–2. Inventory Problems. In the inventory (or economic lot size) problem which we considered above (i.e., the Courbro problem of Sections 1–2, 2–5, 3–2, and 5–3), the demand was known with certainty. Obviously, in most real-world inventory-management situations, demand is not so conveniently predictable. However, if the expected demand can be described in probabilistic terms, it is possible to determine optimal inventory policies.

In this and the following sections we shall extend the traditional economic-lot-size model to take account of the fact of probabilistic demand.

When there is probabilistic demand, there exists the possibility of shortages under almost any reasonable inventory policy, and therefore it is necessary to have a measure of shortage cost. Thus, in addition to the holding costs and setup costs, the cost of shortage must be included in the analysis. The cost of shortage may vary widely from situation to situation. As a minimum, it is the inconvenience of back ordering and customer waiting, but it may be the opportunity cost of lost sales, the loss of customer goodwill, the idleness of equipment, or at worst, defeat in battle, bankruptcy, or death. This out-of-stock cost is often extremely difficult to measure, but it must always somehow be included in the model.

We shall consider two basic classes of inventory problems; the *single episode* and the *continuing system.* The single episode inventory problem is one such as the Marchand problem discussed in Sections 7-3 and 7-4 below in which there is a single selling season during which the shortages or overages will occur and after which the excess or leftover stock (if any) is disposed of at some kind of loss. The essence of this kind of problem is the difficulty or impossibility of carrying over inventories from one period to the next. This is the class of problem often referred to as the "Christmas tree problem" or the "newsboy problem" for obvious reasons. This class of problem includes a wide range of possible situations extending far beyond the retail situation to which it owes its name. For example, it might include the determination of the best level of cash to carry on a purchasing venture, or the optimal number of spare parts to purchase with a new piece of equipment, or the optimal number of spare parts to carry on a trip or in a repair truck. In the latter case, the cost of shortage is not lost sales, but the cost of equipment idleness or emergency orders.

In the continuing system, such as that of the Courbro problem referred to above, the inventory policy is one of repetitive reordering with reordering policy defined according to some inventory-level or time-interval criterion. In the Courbro problem, where the demand was fixed and known, the reorder time and the reorder quantity were both determined, and they were found to be constant, i.e., regular intervals and constant ordering quantities.

In continuing systems with probabilistic demand, especially with delivery lags, there are two alternative general kinds of inventory policies. In the first, the reorder criterion is the *current stock level;* i.e., when the stock on hand reaches the *reorder level,* an order is placed with adequate lead time to provide a properly calculated risk of outage before delivery. In these cases, the reorder quantity is often some fixed amount. Alternatively, in the second kind of system, the *reorder interval* is fixed, in which case the reorder quantity is variable, depending on the amount on hand at the reorder date. In this kind of system, usually the order size is computed to bring the inventory to some desired level at delivery time. The first kind of system tends to be the more desirable with automatic computerized inventory control.

We shall not here attempt to explore all or even most of the kinds of inventory problems which may arise. There are several excellent books available dealing exclusively with this subject, some of which are listed at the end of this chapter. However, we shall examine some interesting examples of inventory problems. In the following section we shall consider a single episode system with a continuous probability distribution of demand, and we shall find that the general result which we obtain may, with slight modification, be applied to discrete probability distributions.

7–3. Single Episode System. The Marchand Ladies Specialty Shop forecasts, in April, that its demand (potential sales) for a particular bathing suit model will be in the vicinity of 300 units over the coming season; but this is an *expected value*, and actually the manager's anticipation is some probability distribution with mean 300 units. We shall proceed to analyze this problem for the *general case*, and then, after we have constructed the general model, we shall inquire into the *specific* probability distribution of demand which describes his expectations.

The Marchand manager must decide how many bathing suits should be ordered in April, if the entire stock must be ordered then, and if no supplemental ordering is possible later in the season. These suits sell for \$10.00 per unit. Their wholesale cost is \$6.00, and their distress clearance value at the end of the season is \$1.00.

The first matter to be noted in this case is that the objective of the analysis cannot be maximization of *actual* profits, since with probabilistic demand, actual profits cannot be known in advance. Therefore, the objective function is *expected* profit, and the analysis will seek to maximize it. Again, we find ourselves making the assumption that people behave in the way which maximizes their expected values. We shall say more about this assumption in Chapter 19, where general aspects of decision theory are discussed. For the present, we shall assume that people do act to maximize their expected values. In this case, the *expected profit* is to be maximized.

In constructing the appropriate model for this system we shall use the general notation for continuous probability distributions, $f(y)$, so that the result may be applied to any probability distribution which may be appropriate.

Let y be the demand, and let x be the quantity ordered. The profit R is

$$\begin{aligned} R &= 10y + 1(x - y) - 6x = 9y - 5x \qquad \text{for } y \leq x \\ &= 10x - 6x \qquad\qquad\quad\;\; = 4x \qquad\qquad\;\; \text{for } y > x \end{aligned}$$

The *expected* profit, if x items are to be ordered, is, from the general definition of the expected value given in Equation (6-6.7):

$$E(R) = \int_0^x (9y - 5x)f(y)\,dy + \int_x^\infty 4xf(y)\,dy \tag{7-3.1}$$

$$= \int_0^x 9yf(y)\,dy - \int_0^x 5x\,f(y)\,dy + \int_x^\infty 4x\,f(y)\,dy$$

The quantity to be ordered for maximum expected profit can be found by taking the derivative of this function with respect to x and setting it equal to 0.

$$0 = \frac{d}{dx}E(R) = \frac{d}{dx}\left[\int_0^x 9yf(y)\,dy - \int_0^x 5xf(y)\,dy + \int_x^\infty 4xf(y)\,dy\right] \tag{7-3.2}$$

The last term may be simplified by removing the infinity limit, using the relationship

$$\int_0^\infty f(y)\,dy = 1$$

Therefore

$$\int_0^x f(y)\,dy + \int_x^\infty f(y)\,dy = 1$$

and

$$\int_x^\infty f(y)\,dy = 1 - \int_0^x f(y)\,dy$$

Then the last term in Equation (7-3.2) becomes

$$\int_x^\infty 4xf(y)\,dy = 4x\int_x^\infty f(y)\,dy = 4x\left[1 - \int_0^x f(y)\,dy\right]$$

and Equation (7-3.2) becomes

$$\frac{d}{dx}E(R) = \frac{d}{dx}\left[\int_0^x 9yf(y)\,dy - 5x\int_0^x f(y)\,dy + 4x - 4x\int_0^x f(y)\,dy\right]$$

$$= \frac{d}{dx}\left[\int_0^x 9yf(y)\,dy - \int_0^x 9xf(y)\,dy + 4x\right]$$

$$\frac{d}{dx}E(R) = \frac{d}{dx}\left[\int_0^x 9(y - x)f(y)\,dy + 4x\right] \tag{7-3.3}$$

The carrying forward of the indicated differentiation process, requiring differentiation of an integral, can generally be performed in two alternative ways. The first and usually more difficult and tedious method, is to perform the indicated integrations and differentiate the result. The second method, which is usually far easier to perform, is to differentiate the integral directly. We shall now introduce that latter technique.

7–4. Differentiation of an Integral. The process which we are investigating is the differentiation of an integral expression with respect to a variable x, *not* the variable of integration, where *the limits of integration are functions of x.* The general expression is

$$F(x) = \int_{a(x)}^{b(x)} g(x,y)\, dy \tag{7–4.1}$$

where: $a(x)$ and $b(x)$, the limits of integration, are functions of x

The solution to this form of equation is given below without proof:[1]

$$\frac{d}{dx}F(x) = \int_{a(x)}^{b(x)} \frac{\partial}{\partial x} g(x,y)\, dy + g(x,b(x))\frac{d}{dx}b(x) - g(x,a(x))\frac{d}{dx}a(x) \tag{7–4.2}$$

In applying this formula to Equation (7–3.3), $a(x) = 0$, $b(x) = x$, $g(x,y) = 9(y - x)f(y)$, and $g(x,b(x))$ and $g(x,a(x))$ in Equation (7–4.2) merely mean that $b(x)$ or $a(x)$ should be substituted for y in the expression $g(x,y)$. The derivative is

$$\frac{d}{dx}E(R) = \int_0^x 9(-1)f(y)\, dy + 9(x - x)(1) - 9(0 - x)(0) + 4$$

$$0 = -9\int_0^{x*} f(y)\, dy + 4$$

$$\int_0^{x*} f(y)\, dy = \frac{4}{9} = 0.4444 \tag{7–4.3}$$

where x^* is the optimal ordering quantity

This final form of the equation may now be applied to whatever probability distribution describes the expectation of the manager with respect to the demand for the bathing suits. In this problem, we now find, on interrogating the manager, that his anticipation distribution of demand is essentially normal with mean 300 units and standard deviation 50 units. Actually, this distribution cannot be strictly normal, since the demand can not be less than zero, and indeed, in the modification of Equation (7–3.2), we removed the infinity upper limit of the last integral by substituting for its equivalent under the assumption that the demand could not be less than zero, i.e., that the integral from zero to infinity was 1. However, in this problem, this is not a serious limitation or practical difficulty, since zero is six standard deviations away from the mean, and for the normal distribution, $F(-6)$ is essentially zero. Thus, in this problem, we can accept the assumption of normality even though the lower limit is zero rather than minus infinity.

[1] The derivation of this expression is beyond the scope of this book. A discussion may be found in Dean, Sasieni, and Gupta, *Mathematics for Modern Management* (New York: John Wiley & Sons, Inc., 1963), pp. 249–50.

Thus, the optimal quantity to be ordered, x^*, is that for which the integral of the specified normal distribution ($\mu = 300$, $\sigma = 50$) from zero to x^* is 0.4444. Let $F(z)$ be the *cdf* of the normal distribution, where z is the standard normal deviate

$$z = \frac{x - \mu}{\sigma} \qquad (6\text{–}5.2)$$

$$F(z) = 0.4444$$

Then, from Appendix A,

$$z = -0.14$$

This indicates that the optimal ordering quantity is 0.14 standard deviations below the mean of the specified normal distribution:

$$x^* = \mu - 0.14\sigma = 300 - (0.14)(50)$$
$$= 293 \text{ units}$$

Actually, examination of Equation (7–4.3) and the prior steps in its derivation indicates that there is a general formula for solving problems of this type, regardless of the form of the distribution. That general and extremely valuable formula is

$$\int_0^{x^*} f(y)\, dy = \frac{p - c}{p - d} \qquad (7\text{–}4.4)$$

where: p is the selling price
c is the wholesale cost
d is the distress clearance (salvage) value
y is the demand
x^* is the optimal ordering quantity

If, for example, the selling price had been \$10.00, but the cost had been \$5.00, and the distress salvage value had been \$2.00, then from Equation (7–4.4), the optimal ordering quantity, x^*, would be that for which

$$\int_0^{x^*} f(y)\, dy = \frac{10 - 5}{10 - 2} = \frac{5}{8} = 0.625$$

From Appendix A,

$$\text{for } F(z) = 0.625, \qquad z = 0.32$$

then

$$x^* = 300 + (0.32)(50) = 316 \text{ units}$$

As a further illustration, if the anticipation distribution had been the *uniform distribution* between 275 and 375,

$$f(y) = 0.01 \qquad \text{for } 275 \leq y \leq 375$$

then, for $p = \$10.00$, $c = \$6.00$, and $d = \$1.00$,

$$\int_0^{x^*} f(y)\,dy = \frac{4}{9} = 0.4444$$

but the lower limit is now 275 rather than 0. Then,

$$\int_{275}^{x^*} 0.01\,dy = 0.01 \Big|_{275}^{x^*} = 0.01x^* - (0.01)(275)$$

then

$$0.01x^* - (0.01)(275) = 0.4444$$

$$x^* = \frac{0.4444 + (0.01)(275)}{0.01} = 44.44 + 275$$

$$= 319 \text{ units (to the nearest unit)}$$

The important general result of this and the preceding section is the formulation given in Equation (7–4.4). We shall see an alternative technique for arriving at this same result in Section 7–12, below.

The method embodied in Equation (7–4.4) may be applied to discrete distributions with the slight modification shown in the following expression, where x^*, the optimal ordering quantity, is the *smallest* quantity such that

$$P(y \leq x^*) \geq \frac{p - c}{p - d} \tag{7–4.5}$$

or

$$\sum_{y=0}^{x^*} P(y) \geq \frac{p - c}{p - d} \tag{7–4.6}$$

This result is not very widely used. With discrete probabilities, problems of this sort are usually solved by computing the expected values of all of the possible alternative ordering quantities and treating the problem according to the techniques for discrete decision problems under risk. However, this method works perfectly well and yields the same solution to the decision problem.

7–5. Continuing System. The Jaz Camera Shop stocks an expensive reflex camera of which it sells, on the average, 1 per week. The weekly distribution of demand for the camera is essentially Poisson, except that the demand never exceeds 4 per week. (Therefore, in the computations, we shall accumulate all probabilities for demand greater than 3 and allocate them to demand of 4.) This pattern of demand may be assumed to be constant over time.

Mr. Jaz, the owner, orders these cameras once a week (late Saturday evening, after closing the shop). He sends an employee to his supplier to pick them up, making his ordering cost \$5 per order. His gross margin on the camera is \$40 per camera, and his carrying cost is \$4 per camera per week based on the number of cameras on hand at the start of the week (immediately after filling his weekly order). This carrying cost is for capital cost, insurance, shelf space, risk of obsolescence, and wear and tear.

Whenever Jaz is short (that is, whenever a customer wants a camera but there is none in stock), his unit shortage cost in lost goodwill, reputation, and future film and film processing revenues is \$20 per camera.

We shall now seek to ascertain Jaz's optimal ordering policy under the assumption that he will order at the same time every week, and that he will always order the number of units necessary to restore his inventory level to some desirable *replenishment level,* the level at which he wishes to start each week. We shall find later that this restriction may be inconsistent with a truly optimal policy under certain cost conditions, but we shall for the present assume that he orders each week, whenever the inventory level at ordering time is below the optimal replenishment level. Thus, for the present, the only question to be answered is, how many items should he order, or what should be the replenishment level?

In general, we shall use the symbol v to represent the inventory level at any time, and x to represent the replenishment level, the *controllable* variable.

From Appendix C, the probability distribution of weekly demand is (to two decimal places) as given in Table 7–5.1.

TABLE 7–5.1

Jaz Camera Shop
Probability Distribution of Weekly Demand
for Reflex Camera

Demand y	Probability $P(y)$
0	0.37
1	0.37
2	0.18
3	0.06
4 (i.e., 4 or more)	0.02

Let x be the number of units at full inventory at the start of the selling week (after replenishment). The demand during the week is y. If $y \geq x$, his inventory is depleted, and he will reorder the amount x. If $y < x$, he will carry over the amount $x - y$ and will order at the end of the week only the amount y, the number sold during the week. Also, if $y > x$, he has been short by the amount $y - x$.

The number of cameras sold each week will be

$$\text{Sales} = y \qquad \text{for } y \leq x$$
$$= x \qquad \text{for } y > x$$

Therefore, the *expected gross margin,* with a unit gross margin of \$40, is

$$E(\text{Gross Margin}) = 40 \sum_{y=0}^{x} yP(y) + 40 \sum_{y=x+1}^{4} xP(y) \qquad (7\text{–}5.1)$$

The *expected shortage cost,* with a unit shortage cost of \$20, is

$$E(\text{Shortage Cost}) = 20 \sum_{y=x+1}^{4} (y - x)P(y) \qquad (7\text{–}5.2)$$

The *expected order cost* is \$5 times the probability that an order will be required, and orders will be required following weeks in which at least one camera was sold.

$$E(\text{Order Cost}) = 5(1 - P(y = 0)) = (5)(0.63) = \$3.15$$

The *expected net profit,* R, on this item (in dollars) is

$$E(R) = E(\text{Gross Margin}) - E(\text{Shortage Cost}) - \text{Holding Cost} - E(\text{Order Cost})$$

In the analysis which follows, we shall, in the intermediate stages, omit consideration of the E(Order Cost) since that is \$3.15 for *all* ordering policies consistent with a decision to order whenever $v < x$, and we shall insert it into the final answer. The holding cost is, of course $4x$ dollars per week.

The expected gross margin, Equation (7–5.1), is evaluated in Table 7–5.2, and the expected shortage cost is evaluated in Table 7–5.3 for each replenishment level from $x = 1$ to $x = 4$.

The expected net profit, R, for the various values of x is computed below from Equations (7–5.2) and (7–5.3), using the data developed in Tables 7–5.2 and 7–5.3.

$$E(R) = E(\text{Gross Margin}) - E(\text{Shortage Cost}) - \text{Holding Cost} - E(\text{Order Cost})$$

$$E(R|x = 1) = 25.20 - 7.20 - 4.00 - 3.15 = \$10.85$$
$$E(R|x = 2) = 35.60 - 2.00 - 8.00 - 3.15 = \$22.45$$
$$E(R|x = 3) = 38.80 - 0.40 - 12.00 - 3.15 = \$23.25 \text{ (optimal)}$$
$$E(R|x = 4) = 39.60 - 0 - 16.00 - 3.15 = \$20.45$$

The optimal inventory policy is to replenish the inventory level to three units at the start of each week.

There is an alternative way to solve this problem, using the format of

TABLE 7–5.2

Jaz Camera Shop
Computation of Expected Gross Margin

Inventory Level at Beginning of Week (Replenishment Level) x	Demand y	0	1	2	3	4		E(Gross Margin)
	$P(y)$	0.37	0.37	0.18	0.06	0.02	$\sum_{y=0}^{x} y\,P(y) + \sum_{y=x+1}^{4} x\,P(y)$ (Sum of (2) to (6))	((7) × 40)
(1)		(2)	(3)	(4)	(5)	(6)	(7)	(8)
1		0	0.37	0.18	0.06	0.02	0.63	$25.20
2	$y\,P(y)$ for $y \leq x$	0	0.37	0.36	0.12	0.04	0.89	35.60
3	$x\,P(y)$ for $y > x$	0	0.37	0.36	0.18	0.06	0.97	38.80
4		0	0.37	0.36	0.18	0.08	0.99[1]	39.60[1]

The numbers in the shaded area were computed from the expression in the shaded area. The other numbers in columns (4), (5), and (6), representing situations in which $y > x$, were computed from the lower, unshaded expression.

[1] Rounding error. Correct values are 1.00 and 40.00.

TABLE 7–5.3

Jaz Camera Shop
Computation of Expected Shortage Cost

Replenishment Level x	Demand y	0	1	2	3	4	$\sum_{y=x+1}^{4} (y-x)P(y)$ (Sum of (2) to (6))	E(Shortage Cost) = $20 \sum_{y=x+1}^{4} (y-x)P(y)$
	$P(y)$	0.37	0.37	0.18	0.06	0.02		
(1)		(2)	(3)	(4)	(5)	(6)	(7)	(8)
1		–	0	0.18	0.12	0.06	0.36	$7.20
2	$(y-x)P(y)$	–	–	0	0.06	0.04	0.10	2.00
3		–	–	–	0	0.02	0.02	0.40
4		–	–	–	–	0	0	0

the decision matrix, in which the net profit is computed for each combination of x_i and y_j. Then the x_i are the courses of action A_i, and the y_j are the states of nature, and it is a simple problem in decision making

	$P(y_j)$	0.37	0.37	0.18	0.06	0.02	
	y_j	0	1	2	3	4	
A_i	$x_1 = 1$	−4	31	11	−9	−29	$E(A_1) = \$10.85$
	$x_2 = 2$	−8	27	67	47	27	$E(A_2) = \$22.45$
	$x_3 = 3$	−12	23	63	103	83	$E(A_3) = \$23.25$*
	$x_4 = 4$	−16	19	59	99	139	$E(A_4) = \$20.45$

Fig. 7–5.1. Decision matrix formulation of Jaz Camera Shop problem. The optimal solution is to replenish the inventory level to $x = 3$ at the start of each week.

under risk. The matrix is shown in Figure 7–5.1, where the cell entries, R_{ij}, are computed from the formulas:

$$R_{ij} = -4x_i \qquad \text{for } y = 0 \tag{7–5.3}$$

$$R_{ij} = 40y_j - 4x_i - 5 \qquad \text{for } 0 < y_j \leq x_i \quad \text{(shaded area in Figure 7-5.1)} \tag{7–5.4}$$

$$R_{ij} = 40x_i - 20(y_j - x_i) - 4x_i - 5 \quad \text{for } y_j > x_i \tag{7–5.5}$$

The result $x^* = 3$ is, of course, the same via both methods of computation. This latter, shorter, method is far more efficient for solving this specific problem, but the former, longer, method is more general and provides more insight, since it yields, as intermediates, the expected values of the individual cost items.

Thus, the optimal replenishment level is three units, and if ordering to the replenishment level takes place every week, then the optimal policy is to order the amount $(3 - v)$ each week, where v is the amount on hand. Under this policy, ordering takes place whenever the inventory level, v, falls below the optimal replenishment level x^*, i.e., in this case, whenever the number on hand is fewer than three. This policy is optimal when the ordering and holding costs are relatively small.

However, there is an alternative policy. The manager could consider not ordering even when the inventory level is below x^*. This would be preferable when the added risk of outage is smaller than the cost of ordering. For example, if the quantity on hand at ordering time is $v = 2$, then if he orders, the ordering cost is \$5, but if he does not order, there is no ordering cost. This \$5 ordering cost plus the added holding cost must then be compared with the difference in the expected gross margin and shortage cost.

The standard ordering cost of \$3.15 which was derived and used above was arrived at on the assumption that ordering frequency was independent of the course of action selected (the replenishment level), but depended only on the pattern of demand. That was the case then, since the courses of action considered above were solely the various possible replenishment levels, and ordering was assumed to occur at the end of a week in which one or more sales occurred, i.e., when $v < x^*$. If, however, we now include as controllable the decision whether or not to order when the inventory level is below x^*, then the ordering cost is not constant for all courses of action.

Let us now consider the alternative courses of action when the inventory is at various levels at ordering time. We can now not be sure that $x^* = 3$, since under this new policy in which there is a *reorder level* r as well as a *replenishment level* x, the replenishment level may be different from that which we found with a policy of always reordering when $v < x^*$.

We have seen above that the expected value of the gross margin and shortage cost for various levels of inventory at the start of the week are as given in Table 7–5.4. It can also be noted that, for higher values of x, the

TABLE 7–5.4

Jaz Camera Shop
Expected Gross Margin Less Shortage Cost for Various Replenishment Levels

Replenishment Level x (1)	E(Gross Margin) (2)	E(Shortage Cost) (3)	((2) − (3)) (4)
1	\$25.20	\$7.20	\$18.00
2	35.60	2.00	33.60
3	38.80	0.40	38.40
4	39.60	0	39.60

column (4) figure will be unchanged. That is, the shortage cost is zero for all values of x greater than 4 and the expected gross margin will also remain at \$39.60, since there is never a weekly demand in excess of four units.

If the inventory level v at ordering time is *three* units, then the optimal course of action is to keep the inventory level at three, since ordering additional cameras will add ordering costs and carrying costs of \$9.00, and the expected gain in gross margin and shortage cost is only \$1.20, as seen in Table 7–5.4.

If the inventory level v at ordering time is *two* units, then the manager has the following courses of action open to him.

A_0: Do not order; keep inventory level at 2
A_1: Order 1 unit
A_2: Order 2 units
A_3: etc.

The expected net profit R for the subsequent week, under each of these courses of action, is:

$$E(R) = E(\text{Gross Margin}) - E(\text{Shortage Cost}) - \text{Holding Cost} - \text{Order Cost}$$

$$E(R|A_0) = 35.60 - 2.00 - 8.00 - 0 = \$25.60^*$$

$$E(R|A_1) = 38.80 - 0.40 - 12.00 - 5.00 = 21.40$$

$$E(R|A_2) = 39.60 - 0 - 16.00 - 5.00 = 18.60$$

Clearly, replenishing to a level higher than four is not desirable, since that would have the effect of further reducing the expected profit by the amount of the holding cost. Thus, the optimal course of action, when $v = 2$ is A_0: *do not reorder*.

If the inventory level v at ordering time is *one* unit, then, the manager has the same courses of action open to him. Now, however, ordering one unit replenishes his level to two units, etc. The expected values of these courses of action are, when $v = 1$, and where A_i is the course of action, *order i units:*

$$E(R) = E(\text{Gross Margin}) - E(\text{Shortage Cost}) - \text{Holding Cost} - \text{Order Cost}$$

$$E(A_0) = 25.20 - 7.20 - 4.00 - 0 = \$14.00$$

$$E(A_1) = 35.60 - 2.00 - 8.00 - 5.00 = 20.60$$

$$E(A_2) = 38.80 - 0.40 - 12.00 - 5.00 = 21.40^*$$

$$E(A_3) = 39.60 - 0 - 16.00 - 5.00 = 18.60$$

Clearly, the optimal course of action with $v = 1$ is to reorder two items, restoring the inventory level to three.

Finally, if the inventory level is reduced to zero at ordering time, the courses of action open to the manager look very much as do those above, except that A_{i+1} replaces A_i, and now ordering one unit to restore to a level of 1 will have an expected profit of only \$9.00 since the ordering cost would then be incurred, and the expected profit of remaining at zero is, of course, zero. Then the optimal policy is to order three units with expected profit of \$21.40.

Thus, the optimal over-all policy is to reorder when the inventory level falls to the reorder level $r^* = 1$ and to reorder to a replenishment level $x^* = 3$. In other words, he should order the quantity $3 - v$, when v, the amount on hand, is 1 or 0, and not order, when the amount on hand is either 2 or 3.

The over-all expected value (for the subsequent week; including ordering cost, if any) of this policy is \$24.10, which, as expected, makes this policy clearly preferable to the previously analyzed policy of ordering whenever the inventory level is below three at ordering time. The expected value, it will be recalled, of that policy was found to be \$23.25.

This result (\$24.10) is obtained by the application of the methods of Chapter 15, *Markov Chains* (see Exercise 15–1 at the end of that chapter). By those methods it can be shown that, if this policy is followed, 37 per cent of the weeks will start with $v = 2$, and 63 per cent of the weeks will start with $v = 3$. Proceeding from that result, we can see that, of the 63 per cent of the weeks which start with $v = 3$ units: 37 per cent, or 23 per cent of all weeks, will finish with $v = 3$ and not require ordering; the same number of weeks will start with $v = 3$ and end with $v = 2$. Also, of the 37 per cent of the weeks which start with $v = 2$ units, 37 per cent, or 14 per cent of all weeks ($0.37 \times 0.37 = 0.14$), will end with $v = 2$. Thus, over all, for any week,

$$
\begin{aligned}
&P(\text{start with 3, end with 2}) &&= 0.23, &&\text{and } E(R) = \$25.60\\
&P(\text{start with 3, end with 3}) &&= 0.23, &&\text{and } E(R) = 26.40\\
&P(\text{start with 2, end with 2}) &&= 0.14, &&\text{and } E(R) = 25.60\\
&P(\text{require replenishment to 3}) &&= 0.40, &&\text{and } E(R) = 21.40
\end{aligned}
$$

These individual expected values have been derived above as the expected value, under the optimal policy, of the profit of the subsequent week, including ordering cost, if any. The expected profit under this entire system is

$$E(R) = (25.60)(0.37) + (26.40)(0.23) + (21.40)(0.40) = \$24.10$$

This optimal policy, it should be noted, specified *both* a *reorder level* r and a *replenishment level* x. That is, the reorder level was not just *any* level below the replenishment level, but rather was some specified lower level because of the importance of the ordering cost and the holding cost.

There is one additional ramification of this problem which may occur to some readers. That is, it may sometimes be that the optimal course of action is to order more than $x^* - v$ when $v \leq x^*$. This may be the case if the ordering cost is large, and then, although that course of action (ordering more than $x^* - v$) will not maximize the expected profit for the next week, it may maximize the expected profit over a longer period by avoiding future ordering costs. This would be the case if the expected savings in ordering costs exceeded the expected additional holding costs. That is not the case in this problem, since the additional holding cost is \$4.00 per item per week, and the ordering cost is \$5.00 per order, with a probability of 0.37 of selling zero items in any week. Thus, if the replenishment level is brought to *four items,* the additional holding cost is \$4.00 for the first week, and the probability of saving an order after 1 week is the probability of selling two items (if fewer than two are sold, there will be no order under either policy, and if more than two are sold, there will be an order under either policy). Since, in that case, no new order would be required if the week had started with four units. But $P(y = 2) = 0.18$, and the expected savings is $(5.00)(0.18) = \$0.90$. This cannot balance the additional holding cost of \$4. Also, the possibility of saving an order over two weeks is the probability of selling exactly two items in two weeks. Then the expected saving over two weeks is, where the numbers in the parentheses represent sales in the first and second weeks, respectively,

$$P(0 \cap 2) + P(1 \cap 1) = (0.37)(0.18) + (0.37)(0.37)$$
$$= 0.07 + 0.14 = 0.21$$

and the expected savings in ordering cost is $(5.00)(0.21) = \$1.05$, which is far more than offset by the additional holding cost of \$8.00. Similar reasoning may be used to extend the time consideration further into the future with the same result.

This whole problem may be solved in a different way by using the procedures of Chapter 15 to evaluate the *expected values* of all policies, i.e., all combinations of x and r, and thereby select the optimal (see Exercise 15–1 at the end of that chapter). The procedure is far too tedious to be practical, but the result would be the same as that which we have derived, $x^* = 3$, $r^* = 1$.

7–6. Lags in Delivery Time. When there is probabilistic demand, and when delivery or manufacture for inventory replenishment is not instantaneous (as we have assumed above), then the reorder level or reorder quantity must take into account the possibility of outage between the time of ordering and the time of delivery.

Under a *reorder-level* system, with lags in delivery, there are again two variables to be determined; the reorder quantity and the reorder criterion. Usually, the reorder quantity is fixed, and the reorder criterion is some predetermined inventory level, computed so that, at the time of delivery, there will still be some *expected safety stock* level on hand. The ideal general system is shown in Figure 7–6.1, which depicts the course of the inventory level if the *average demand* pattern always prevailed with no variance. Figure 7–6.2 shows what might occur in practice under the policy described in Figure 7–6.1. In the figure, the descending dashed lines indicate expectations at reorder time. The three cycles in Figure

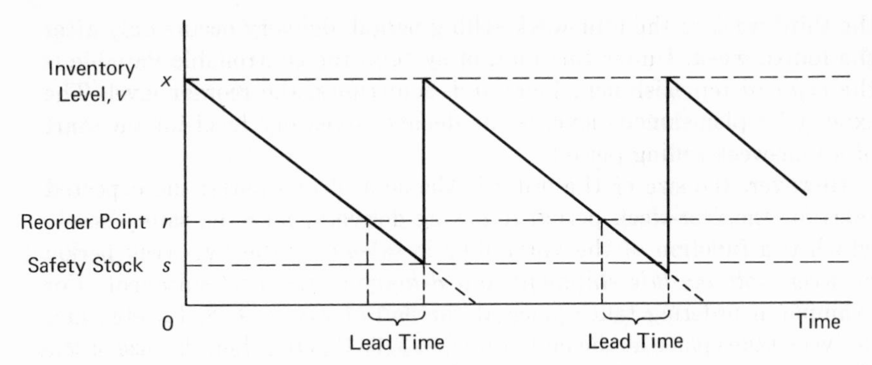

Fig. 7–6.1. Planned inventory-control policy. Always order the amount $(x - s)$ when the inventory level reaches r.

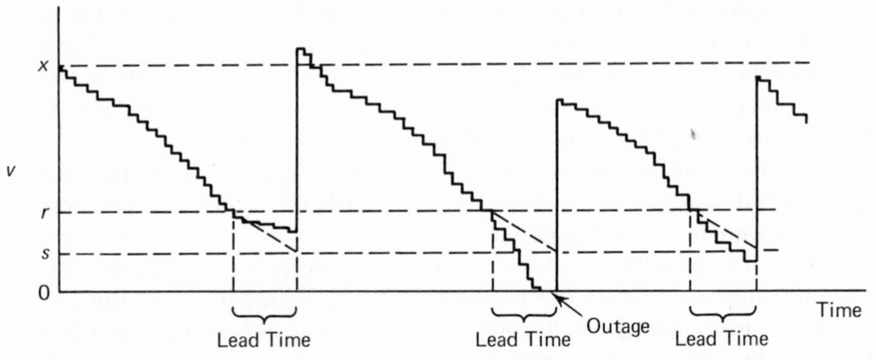

Fig. 7–6.2. Actual inventory levels under control system of Figure 7–6.1.

7–6.2 show the three possible eventualities other than the ideal of Figure 7–6.1. In the first cycle, sales were below expectations during the lead-time period, with the result that inventories did not reach the safety stock level, and after delivery, inventories were at a level somewhat higher than x, the desired replenishment level. In the second cycle, sales were very high in the lead-time period, with the result that stocks were depleted before delivery, and outage occurred. In the third cycle, sales were above average in the lead-time period, but the existence of the safety stock prevented the occurrence of outage.

Under a *reorder-interval* or *periodic* system with lags in delivery, the replenishment level must take into account future sales over the entire period from the ordering of a shipment until the receipt of the next shipment. That is, if ordering is done once every four weeks, for example, and if delivery requires one week, then the replenishment level must be determined as the optimal inventory to have on hand for a four-week selling period. That is because, although ordering occurs at the end of the third week of the four-week selling period, delivery occurs only after the fourth week. Under this kind of system, the controllable variable is the *expected* replenishment level and, sometimes, the reorder level. The expected replenishment level is the desired inventory level for the start of a four-week selling period.

However, the size of the order is the sum of two parts: the expected sales for the four-week period following delivery, *plus* the safety stock, which is a function of the variability in sales over the five-week period between *ordering this* shipment and *delivery* of the *next* shipment. For example, if ordering takes place at the end of weeks: 4, 8, 12, etc., and delivery takes place at the end of weeks: 5, 9, 13, etc., then the size of the shipment ordered at the end of week 4 must take into account the expected sales in the four-week period from the end of week 5 to the end of week 9, but the safety stock must be based on the variability in sales over the five-week period from the end of week 4 to the end of week 9, since the management is powerless to modify the actual stock on hand between the time of ordering this shipment and the actual delivery of the next shipment. True, there is a delivery at the end of week 5, but this is not subject to control after it is ordered at the end of week 4.

Thus, we must be careful to refer here to an *expected* replenishment level, because the replenishment level is a random variable when there is a lead time and variable demand. This is shown in Figure 7–6.2 for a *reorder-level* or *perpetual* system. For a *reorder-interval* or *periodic* system, the only difference from the representation of Figure 7–6.2 is that, in the latter case, the cycles are all of equal length, the reordering takes place at the specified *times*, and the reorder quantity is variable, depending on the quantity on hand at each specified reorder time.

Let us redefine the Jaz Camera Shop problem by adding a new assumption. We shall now assume that there is a delivery lag of one week between ordering and delivery. That is, cameras ordered on any Saturday night are delivered on the *next* Saturday night, at which time a new order may be placed for delivery a week later. The ordering cost of $5 per order is incurred each time an order is placed, and not by acceptance of delivery of items previously ordered.

We shall now seek to ascertain the optimal reordering policy by comparing various possible alternative policies. This comparison is presented in Tables 7–6.1 to 7–6.3.

Table 7–6.1 shows the expected inventory level v at the end of a selling week for each of the possible starting inventory levels. For starting inventory levels higher than 4, the expected inventory level at the end of the selling week before replenishment is 1 less than the starting inventory since the expected number sold in a week, when there are no shortages, is 1. These figures are computed from the distribution of demand given in Table 7–5.1.

TABLE 7–6.1

Jaz Camera Shop
Expected Inventory Level at End of Week Before Replenishment for Various Starting Inventory Levels

Inventory Level at Start of Week After Replenishment	Possible Inventory Levels at End of Week Before Replenishment, v	$P(v)$	$vP(v)$	Expected Inventory Level at End of Week Before Replenishment
	0	0.02	0	
	1	0.06	0.06	
4	2	0.18	0.36	
	3	0.37	1.11	
	4	0.37	1.48	3.01[1]
	0	0.08	0	
3	1	0.18	0.18	
	2	0.37	0.74	
	3	0.37	1.11	2.03
	0	0.26	0	
2	1	0.37	0.37	
	2	0.37	0.74	1.11
1	0	0.63	0	
	1	0.37	0.37	0.37
0	0	1.00	0	0

[1] Rounding error; correct value is 3.00.

Table 7–6.2 uses the last column of Table 7–6.1 to compute the expected inventory *after* replenishment for each of the various reordering policies considered. From this the expected holding cost for the following week is computed and combined with the ordering cost.

Table 7–6.3 compares the effectiveness of the various alternative inventory policies. The analysis, of course, considers the system performance for the week starting a week after the order is placed (or not placed). The expected gross margin less shortage cost is computed as the average over all of the possible inventory levels at the start of that week, each weighted by its probability of occurrence under the given policy, again using the probability distribution of demand given in Table 7–5.1 and the *expected gross margin less shortage cost* from Table 7–5.4. To this is added the holding cost for that week and the order cost for the order placed a week earlier for delivery for that selling week.

TABLE 7-6.2

Jaz Camera Shop
Computation of Expected Holding Cost Plus Order Cost of Alternative Inventory Policies

Alternative Policies					
Inventory after Replenishment	Reorder Quantity	Expected Inventory on Hand a Week Later after Replenishment	Expected Holding Cost	Order Cost	Expected Holding Cost Plus Order Cost
	5	5	20.00	5	25.00
0	4	4	16.00	5	21.00
	3	3	12.00	5	17.00
	2	2	8.00	5	13.00
	4	4.37	17.48	5	22.48
1	3	3.37	13.48	5	18.48
	2	2.37	9.48	5	14.48
	3	4.11	16.44	5	21.44
2	2	3.11	12.44	5	17.44
	1	2.11	8.44	5	13.44
	2	4.03	16.12	5	21.12
3	1	3.03	12.12	5	17.12
	0	2.03	8.12	0	8.12
4	1	4.01	16.04	5	21.04
	0	3.01	12.04	0	12.04

The over-all optimal inventory policy is indicated by the asterisks in Table 7-6.3 and summarized in Table 7-6.4. The ordering criterion is the end-of-the-week inventory *after* receipt of the order placed a week earlier. This is the *effective* inventory at ordering time.

It is important to note that all of the computations deal with the situation one week after the decision is made. That is because the decision does not take effect until that time. The net revenue for the current week is considered to be already out of the control of the inventory policy, since nothing can be done to change the inventory within the week. The decision to be made has to do with the situation and events of the following week, and therefore it is with that week that we have been concerned.

The expected net revenue under this policy is \$20.91. Again the derivation of this result requires the techniques of Chapter 15, *Markov Chains* (see Exercise 15-2 at the end of that chapter). This expected value of \$20.91 is less than the expected value under the optimal policy without lag, which, it will be recalled, was \$24.10. The difference, \$3.19, is the cost of the uncertainty introduced by the one-week lag in the delivery

TABLE 7–6.3

Jaz Camera Shop
Comparison of Alternative Inventory Policies

Alternative Policies			Inventory Level a Week Later after Replenishment, x								
			0	1	2	3	4	5			
			Expected Gross Margin less Shortage Cost, M								
Inventory after Replenishment	Reorder Quantity		−20.00	18.00	33.60	38.40	39.60	39.60	Expected Gross Margin less Shortage Cost	Expected Holding Cost plus Order Cost	Expected Net Revenue
0	5	$P(x)$	0	0	0	0	0	1.00			
		$MP(x)$	0	0	0	0	0	39.60	39.60	25.00	14.60
0	4	$P(x)$	0	0	0	0	1.00	0			
		$MP(x)$	0	0	0	0	39.60	0	39.60	21.00	18.60
0	3	$P(x)$	0	0	0	1.00	0	0			
		$MP(x)$	0	0	0	38.40	0	0	38.40	17.00	21.40*
0	2	$P(x)$	0	0	1.00	0	0	0			
		$MP(x)$	0	0	33.60	0	0	0	33.60	13.00	20.60
1	4	$P(x)$	0	0	0	0	0.63	0.37			
		$MP(x)$	0	0	0	0	24.95	14.65	39.60	22.48	17.12
1	3	$P(x)$	0	0	0	0.63	0.37	0			
		$MP(x)$	0	0	0	24.19	14.65	0	38.84	18.48	20.36*
1	2	$P(x)$	0	0	0.63	0.37	0	0			
		$MP(x)$	0	0	21.17	14.21	0	0	35.38	18.48	16.90

TABLE 7–6.3 (*Continued*)

Alternative Policies			Inventory Level a Week Later after Replenishment, x						Expected Gross Margin less Shortage Cost	Expected Holding Cost plus Order Cost	Expected Net Revenue
			0	1	2	3	4	5			
Inventory after Replenishment	Reorder Quantity		Expected Gross Margin less Shortage Cost, M								
			−20.00	18.00	33.60	38.40	39.60	39.60			
2	3	$P(x)$	0	0	0	0.26	0.37	0.37			
		$MP(x)$	0	0	0	9.98	14.65	14.65	39.28	21.44	17.84
2	2	$P(x)$	0	0	0.26	0.37	0.37	0			
		$MP(x)$	0	0	8.74	14.21	14.65	0	37.60	17.44	20.16*
2	1	$P(x)$	0	0.26	0.37	0.37	0	0			
		$MP(x)$	0	4.68	12.43	14.21	0	0	31.32	13.44	17.88
3	2	$P(x)$	0	0	0.08	0.18	0.37	0.37			
		$MP(x)$	0	0	2.69	6.91	14.65	14.65	38.90	21.12	16.78
3	1	$P(x)$	0	0.08	0.18	0.37	0.37	0			
		$MP(x)$	0	1.44	6.05	14.21	14.65	0	36.35	17.12	19.23
3	0	$P(x)$	0.08	0.18	0.37	0.37	0	0			
		$MP(x)$	−1.60	3.24	12.43	14.21	0	0	28.28	8.12	20.16*
4	1	$P(x)$	0	0.02	0.08	0.18	0.37	0.37			
		$MP(x)$	0	0.36	2.69	6.91	14.65	14.65	39.26	21.04	18.22
4	0	$P(x)$	0.02	0.06	0.18	0.37	0.37	0			
		$MP(x)$	−0.40	1.08	6.05	14.21	14.65	0	35.59	12.04	23.55*

* Indicates optimal q for each v.

TABLE 7–6.4

Jaz Camera Shop
Optimal Inventory Policy

Inventory Level	Optimal Reorder Quantity	Expected Net Profit
0	3	$21.40
1	3	20.36
2	2	20.16
3	0	20.16
4	0	23.55

time. It would be worth $3.19 per week to find a supplier who holds a large enough stock to provide immediate delivery.

This of course is an illustration of a well-known phenomenon of the business world. Most businessmen would like their *suppliers* to carry inventories large enough and provide delivery rapidly enough to free them from the need to carry large inventories; and at the same time, they would like their *customers* to carry inventories large enough and to reorder regularly enough to free them from wide variations in demand. Thus, each businessman would like to avoid the need for inventory problems by pushing them in either or both directions in the channels of distribution. These "inventories" may, of course, be in the form of stocks of goods or, in many ways its equivalent, in excess production capacity.

7–7. Replacement and Maintenance Problems. There is a large class of problems which involve primarily the timing of the replacement of capital equipment or other earning assets. Although these "other" assets may be any kind of earning assets, such as for example the real estate investment of Section 3–8, typically this class of problems and the solutions to them have been thought of as applying primarily to physical equipment. We shall, however, attempt in the next few sections to illustrate applications beyond the realm of production equipment. For example, the real estate investment of The Sandy Burr Company had deteriorating earnings in the same sense as does a motor vehicle whose operating cost increases with age, or an aircraft or a manufacturing machine which is subject to competition by ever-improved equipment in the hands of competitors. Also, we shall see that a television commercial is also a deteriorating asset with an initial acquisition cost and a diminishing effectiveness over time, as the viewing public becomes progressively more inured to its blandishments.

Thus, some assets must be replaced because they deteriorate progressively over time, either because of absolutely or relatively diminishing effectiveness, increasing costs, or both. There are other assets about which replacement decisions must be made because they *break down;* i.e., they *ail completely* after some period of use, and the probability of failure ncreases as a function of time in service or time since last overhaul. Light ulbs are an excellent example of this kind of asset. In such cases, the ecision to be made is primarily when, if ever, to replace the asset (or roup of assets) because, although it is still working, its probability of ailure has become so large that it is economic to repair or replace it in ome orderly scheduled way at relatively low cost, rather than wait for it o break down, in which case the cost of repair or replacement, including own time for the equipment, may be relatively very large.

In Chapter 3, we discussed two cases of a deteriorating asset, the Sandy Burr investment of Section 3–8, and the Gethom Company equipment f Section 3–3. In both cases, the pattern of deterioration was given by a ime-dependent relationship, and the replacement timing was computed o maximize earnings or to minimize costs. Probability considerations did ot enter into those problems. In this chapter, we shall examine situations nvolving probabilities, particularly the probability of failure for assets which break down after some period of use.

7–8. Preventive Maintenance. Often, items that may fail in service nd then must be repaired, replaced, or overhauled, can and do incur epair costs, including the cost of equipment down time, which are ufficiently high to merit preventive maintenance, i.e., servicing of the quipment *before* it fails, thereby avoiding excessive down-time costs and aking advantage of planned and scheduled maintenance service with its ttendant efficiencies.

If the probability of failure of any item is a function of its age since its ast overhaul (or replacement), and if the costs of overhaul both before nd after failure are known, then it is possible to determine the optimal reventive maintenance period.

If there is no preventive maintenance, that is, if items are replaced when nd as they fail, and if the probability density function for the probability f failure is $y = f(t)$, i.e., P(failure in the time interval between t and $+ dt) = f(t)\,dt$, then the average life before failure is

$$\mu = \int_0^\infty tf(t)\,dt$$

nd the expected maintenance cost per operating item per unit time is

$$\text{Cost} = \frac{A}{\mu} \qquad (7\text{–}8.1)$$

where A is the cost of overhaul after failure

However, if there is preventive maintenance after T time units, the verage life *for those which fail* is the same integral as given above, but with upper integration limit T, the preventive maintenance period; and for those which do not fail in the preventive maintenance period, life is exactly T. The average life $\bar{t}$, under a system of preventive maintenance, is

$$\bar{t} = \int_0^T tf(t)\,dt + T\int_T^\infty f(t)\,dt \tag{7–8.2}$$

Letting

$$A = \text{Cost of overhaul after failure}$$

and

$$B = \text{Cost of overhaul before failure}$$

the expected annual maintenance cost per item is the weighted average: A multiplied by the probability that the item will fail in service, plus B multiplied by the probability that the item will survive through the preventive maintenance period and be overhauled before failure, all divided by the average life $\bar{t}$. This cost is

$$C = \left[A\int_0^T f(t)\,dt + B\int_T^\infty f(t)\,dt\right]\frac{1}{\bar{t}} \tag{7–8.3}$$

We can simplify Equations (7–8.2) and (7–8.3) by letting

$$p = P(\text{Failure before time } T) = \int_0^T f(t)\,dt$$

and

$$q = 1 - p = \int_T^\infty f(t)\,dt$$

Then, from Equation (7–8.2), the average life is seen to be

$$\bar{t} = \int_0^T tf(t)\,dt + Tq \tag{7–8.4}$$

and Equation (7–8.3) becomes

$$C = \frac{Ap + Bq}{\bar{t}} = \frac{Ap + B(1 - p)}{\bar{t}}$$

$$C = \frac{(A - B)p + B}{\bar{t}} \tag{7–8.5}$$

Thus, C is the *expected unit maintenance cost per time unit under a program of preventive maintenance with preventive maintenance period T*. We differentiate C with respect to T to find the *optimal* preventive maintenance period. Since both p and $\bar{t}$ are functions of T, the derivative is from Equation (7–8.5),

$$\frac{dC}{dT} = \frac{\bar{t}\dfrac{d}{dT}[(A - B)p + B] - [(A - B)p + B]\dfrac{d\bar{t}}{dT}}{\bar{t}^2}$$

Setting the derivative equal to 0,

$$\bar{t}\,\frac{d}{dT}\,[(A - B)p + B] - [(A - B)p + B]\,\frac{d\bar{t}}{dT} = 0 \qquad (7\text{–}8.6)$$

Now, evaluating each term of Equation (7–8.6) in turn, for the first term,

$$\frac{d}{dT}\,[(A - B)p + B] = (A - B)\,\frac{dp}{dT}$$

but

$$p = \int_0^T f(t)\,dt$$

Then, from Equation (7–4.2) for differentiating an integral,

$$\frac{dp}{dT} = 0 + f(T) - 0 = f(T) \qquad (7\text{–}8.7)$$

therefore,

$$\frac{d}{dT}\,[(A - B)p + B] = (A - B)f(T) \qquad (7\text{–}8.8)$$

Now, evaluating the second term of Equation (7–8.6), from Equation (7–8.4),

$$\bar{t} = \int_0^T tf(t)\,dt + Tq \qquad (7\text{–}8.4)$$

$$\frac{d\bar{t}}{dT} = \frac{d}{dT}\left[\int_0^T tf(t)\,dt + Tq\right]$$

Differentiating the integral,

$$\frac{d\bar{t}}{dT} = 0 + Tf(T) - 0 + T\,\frac{dq}{dT} + q$$

$$\frac{d\bar{t}}{dT} = Tf(T) + T\,\frac{dq}{dT} + q \qquad (7\text{–}8.9)$$

but,

$$\frac{dq}{dT} = \frac{d}{dT}\,(1 - p) = 0 - \frac{dp}{dT}$$

and, from Equation (7–8.7),

$$\frac{dq}{dT} = -f(T) \qquad (7\text{–}8.10)$$

Therefore, from Equations (7–8.9) and (7–8.10),

$$\frac{d\bar{t}}{dT} = q \qquad (7\text{–}8.11)$$

Now, Equation (7–8.6) may be rewritten, using the results of Equations (7–8.8), (7–8.11), and (7–8.4):

$$\left[\int_0^T tf(t)\,dt + Tq\right](A - B)f(T) - [(A - B)p + B]q = 0 \quad (7\text{–}8.12)$$

and, dividing by $q(A - B)$, we arrive at the final form of the general equation for the *optimal replacement interval.*

$$\frac{f(T)}{q}\int_0^T tf(t)\,dt + Tf(T) - p = \frac{B}{A - B} \quad (7\text{–}8.13)$$

(For simplicity, we have omitted the asterisks and have written T in place of T^*.) This is an important and useful equation. It is perfectly general, and it may be applied to any continuous distribution.

Before looking at a specific problem, let us examine Equation (7–8.13) and see how it can yield the desired solution, i.e., the value of T, the preventive maintenance period, for which the cost is minimized. Equation (7–8.13) tells us that, at the optimum, the expression on the left is equal to the cost ratio, $\frac{B}{A - B}$. One way to solve Equation (7–8.13) is to try various possible values of T to find that value for which the equation is most closely satisfied. We shall now illustrate this technique.

For this first illustration we shall ignore aspects of the problem dealing with the cost of money (the interest rate). Clearly, for some cases involving large equipment, this may be a serious omission. A more complete exnression, taking the cost of money into account is Equation (7–9.12).

The Hutchinson & Wilkinson Shipping Company finds that one of its shipboard power-transmission components has a life span before failure which may be described by the distribution shown in Figure 7–8.1, with

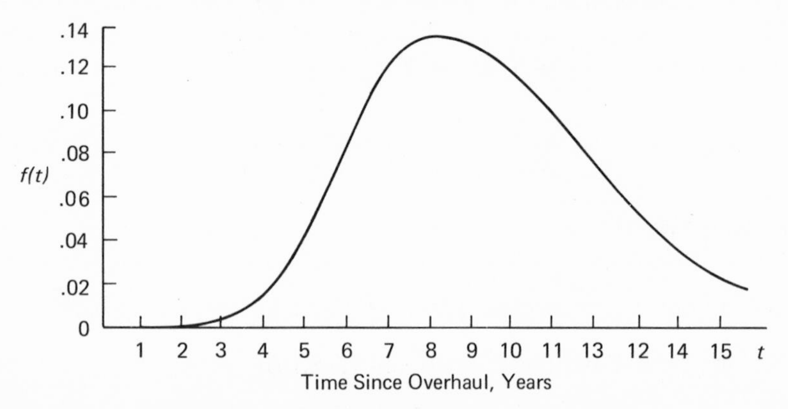

Fig. 7–8.1. Distribution of failures of power-transmission components. Hutchinson & Wilkinson Shipping Company.

discrete points given in column (3) of Table 7-8.1. (Actually, this is a gamma distribution with mean 9 years and standard deviation 3 years. The reader may, if he wishes, treat this distribution as an empirical discrete distribution with no necessary theoretical counterpart. However, in Exercise 7-8 at the end of this chapter, the reader is asked to derive the discrete points of the distribution given in column (3) of Table 7-8.1, using the mathematical device introduced in Exercise 6-5 at the end of Chapter 6.)

At its home port, the component can be replaced and overhauled at a cost of $1,300. However, the cost of failure *in service* is actually $1,000 more than that, since then the component must be replaced away from its home port with attendant inefficiencies and accompanying disruption of the shipping schedule. Thus, the cost of overhaul and replacement, if the component fails in use, is $2,300, but it is only $1,300 if the component is routinely overhauled before failure. The company wishes to ascertain the optimal *preventive maintenance period* so that it can follow the policy of routinely replacing and overhauling all components which attain that age since their last overhaul.

In the Hutchinson & Wilkinson Shipping Company, the shipping schedules are such that a preventive maintenance period computed to the nearest year is the most precise result which can be used. Therefore, it is a relatively simple matter to evaluate Equation (7-8.13) for, say, twelve values of T (1 year through 12 years) to find the optimal.

The required computations for the optimal preventive maintenance period are most easily performed in a worksheet table such as is shown in Table 7-8.1, in which Equation (7-8.13) is solved for various values of T. Actually, in the computations, we have used an approximation for simplification. That is, since the result is needed only to the nearest year, we have evaluated the probability of failure in any given year $f(t)$ as the difference between the cumulative probability of failure in that year and that for the previous year, and the resulting value p_t is used in place of $f(t)$ in Equation (7-8.13). This equation then becomes

$$\frac{p_T}{q}\sum_{t=1}^{T} tp_t + Tp_T - p = \frac{B}{A-B} \qquad (7\text{-}8.14)$$

which is the equation evaluated in Table 7-8.1. In the table, the last column is the value of the left side of Equation (7-8.14), and the value in that column which is closest to $\frac{B}{A-B}$ represents the optimal preventive maintenance period T.

Since

$$\frac{B}{A-B} = \frac{1{,}300}{2{,}300 - 1{,}300} = 1.3$$

TABLE 7–8.1

Computation of Optimal Preventive Maintenance Period Hutchinson & Wilkinson Shipping Company

Preventive Maintenance Period T	Cumulative Probability of Failure $F(T) = p$	Probability of Failure in t^{th} year p_t	$q = 1 - p$	tp_t	Cumulative of (5) Σtp_t	(3) ÷ (4)	(7) × (6)	Value of Left Side of Equation (7–8.14) (8) + (5) − (2)
(1)	(2)	(3)	(4)	(5)	(6)	(7)	(8)	(9)
1	0.0000	0.0000	1.0000	0.0000	0.0000	0.0000	0.0000	0.0000
2	0.0002	0.0002	0.9998	0.0004	0.0004	0.0002	0.0000	0.0002
3	0.0038	0.0036	0.9962	0.0108	0.0112	0.0036	0.0000	0.0070
4	0.0213	0.0175	0.9787	0.0700	0.0812	0.0179	0.0015	0.0502
5	0.0680	0.0467	0.9320	0.2335	0.3147	0.0501	0.0158	0.1813
6	0.1526	0.0846	0.8474	0.5076	0.8223	0.0998	0.0821	0.4371
7	0.2709	0.1183	0.7291	0.8281	1.6504	0.1623	0.2679	0.8251
8	0.4074	0.1365	0.5926	1.0920	2.7424	0.2303	0.6316	1.3162
9	0.5444	0.1370	0.4556	1.2330	3.9754	0.3007	1.1954	1.8840
10	0.6671	0.1227	0.3329	1.2270	5.2024	0.3686	1.9176	2.4775
11	0.7680	0.1009	0.2320	1.1099	6.3123	0.4349	2.7452	3.0871
12	0.8450	0.0770	0.1550	0.9240	7.2363	0.4968	3.5950	3.6740

the optimal value of T is approximately 8 years. That is, the optimal preventive maintenance policy is to replace and overhaul all components which have been in use for eight years since their last overhaul. Of course, individual items which fail before that interval will be replaced as they fail. The average life under this policy is, from Equation (7–8.4) and the data of Table 7–8.1, for $T = 8$,

$$\bar{t} = \sum_{t=1}^{T} tp_t + Tq \tag{7–8.15}$$

$$= 2.7424 + (8)(0.5926) = 7.48 \text{ years}$$

and the cost of maintenance per operating component under this eight-year policy is, from Equation (7–8.5),

$$C = \frac{(A - B)p + B}{\bar{t}}$$

$$= \frac{(1{,}000)(0.4074) + 1{,}300}{7.48} = \$228 \text{ per year}$$

which should be compared with the annual cost of \$256 without preventive maintenance as obtained from Equation (7–8.1), where $\frac{2{,}300}{9} = 256$.

In Table 7–8.2, the average annual maintenance cost per operating component for all integral preventive maintenance periods is computed,

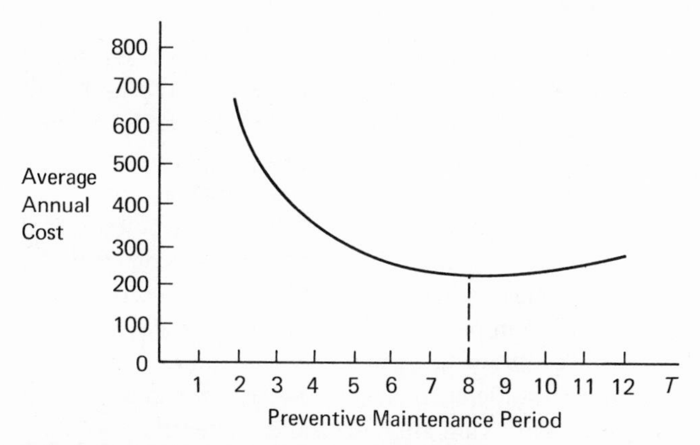

Fig. 7–8.2. Average costs under all integral-year preventive maintenance policies. Hutchinson & Wilkinson Shipping Company.

and the results are plotted in Figure 7–8.2. The computations are based on Equations (7–8.15) and (7–8.5), using data from Table 7–8.1.

It must be emphasized that Equations (7–8.13) and (7–8.14) are per-

TABLE 7–8.2

Computation of Costs for All Integral-Year Preventive Maintenance Periods Hutchinson & Wilkinson Shipping Company

T	$\bar{t}$	$1{,}300 + 1{,}000p$	C
(1)	(2)	(3)	(4)
1	1.00	1,300	1,300
2	2.00	1,300	650
3	3.00	1,304	435
4	4.00	1,321	330
5	4.97	1,368	275
6	5.91	1,453	246
7	6.75	1,571	233
8	7.48	1,707	228.21*
9	8.08	1,844	228.22
10	8.53	1,967	231
11	8.86	2,068	233
12	9.10	2,145	236

fectly general and can be easily applied to any given probability distribution. The tabular computation technique of Table 7–8.1 is extremely fast and easy to apply. The reader should note from column (4) of Table 7–8.2 and from Figure 7–8.2 that the curve is very flat in the vicinity of the optimum, indicating that the average cost is not sensitive to small changes in the length of the preventive maintenance period within that range.

7–9. Replacement of a Deteriorating Asset. We have noted above that some earning assets tend, not to breakdown and become suddenly unusable, but rather to deteriorate progressively over time. Such deteriorating assets must be replaced after some interval, even though they still are in operating condition. The criteria for the timing of such replacement decisions may be increasing cost, decreasing productivity, or increasing obsolescence of some other kind as indicated by other measures of effectiveness and compared with similar measures for newer equipment. Thus, an asset may be retired because new substitute assets are available which are sufficiently more effective to cause the older asset to be uneconomic even though its absolute effectiveness both in costs and in physical productivity is undiminished. Often, indeed, such replacements occur even though the older asset has its capital costs completely written off. Clearly, in such cases the new asset must be more effective on a fully allocated cost basis than the old asset with only its operating costs to cover. And this, of course, is often the case. Excellent examples of this kind of situation are the retirement by many airlines of the

DC-3 aircraft and the general retirement of steam locomotives by most railroads.

Let us examine an illustration in which the deteriorating earning asset is not a physical machine. In this particular illustration, the deteriorating asset is a television commercial message, but the general applicability of the analysis technique to a variety of other kinds of deteriorating assets will be evident to the reader.

The Loen Merchandising Company runs spot commercials every day, advertising its products on television. The company policy is to run only one commercial message during any time interval and then to replace it with another after some appropriate period of use. Careful consumer studies have led the company to its present advertising spending level of $10,000 per week for air time and have indicated that the benefit derived from the advertising is about double the air-time cost, when the commercial messages are new and at maximum effectiveness. The difficulty arises because the commercials lose their effectiveness over time. The company has just ascertained that the deterioration in effectiveness of the commercials is linear, and that they deteriorate by an amount that would lead to zero effectiveness in one year. Now the company seeks to determine how long a commercial should be run if new commercials cost $25,000 to produce.

This problem can be solved by enumeration quite easily, since the deterioration is linear. It can also be solved analytically by methods which are adaptable to any deterioration or decay function. We shall solve it analytically.

If a commercial loses $\frac{1}{52}$ of its effectiveness each week, then its loss in effectiveness over T weeks is $\frac{T}{52}$, and its relative effectiveness in the Tth week is $\left(1 - \frac{T}{52}\right)$, and its *average* effectiveness over T weeks is $\left(1 - \frac{T}{(2)(52)}\right)$.

Then, the average benefit derived per week over the T weeks is, if the benefit at 100% effectiveness is $20,000 per week,

$$\text{Average Weekly Benefit} = 20{,}000\left(1 - \frac{T}{(2)(52)}\right) \tag{7–9.1}$$

The only relevant variable cost in the system is the cost of production of commercials. The average cost per week, where the commercial is used for T weeks, is

$$\text{Cost} = \frac{25{,}000}{T} \tag{7–9.2}$$

And the average weekly effectiveness is

$$E = \text{Effectiveness} = \text{Benefit} - \text{Cost} \tag{7–9.3}$$

$$= 20{,}000\left(1 - \frac{T}{(2)(52)}\right) - \frac{25{,}000}{T}$$

$$E = 20{,}000 - \frac{20{,}000T}{(2)(52)} - \frac{25{,}000}{T} \tag{7–9.4}$$

Differentiating to find the maximum,

$$\frac{d}{dT}(E) = -\frac{20{,}000}{(2)(52)} + \frac{25{,}000}{T^2} \tag{7–9.5}$$

Setting the derivative equal to zero,

$$T^{*2} = \frac{(25{,}000)(2)(52)}{20{,}000} = 130$$

$$T^* = 11.4 \approx 11 \text{ weeks} \tag{7–9.6}$$

Thus, the commercials should be used for eleven weeks and then replaced.

The general analytic formula, where average weekly benefit is $f(t)$, is

$$\text{Average Weekly Effectiveness} = \frac{B}{T}\int_0^T f(t)\,dt - \frac{C}{T} \tag{7–9.7}$$

where: B is the weekly benefit when the asset is new
T is the replacement interval
C is the replacement cost (after salvage value, if any, is deducted)

This formula, Equation (7–9.7), may be reconciled with the expression used above in Equation (7–9.1) as follows. Equation (7–9.1) measures the average benefit by considering the triangle shown in Figure 7–9.1. The

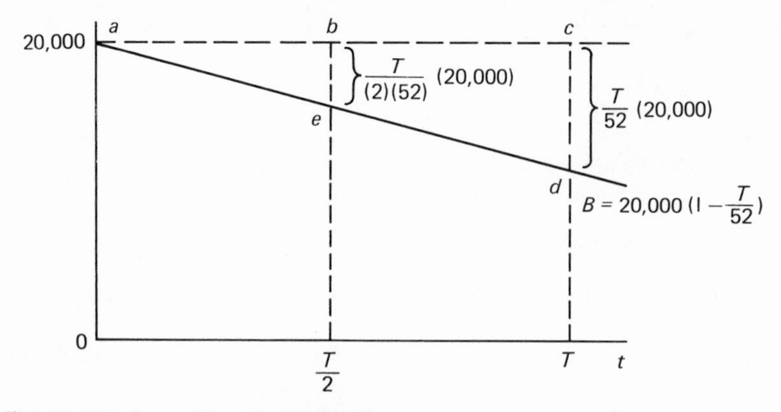

Fig. 7–9.1. Loen Merchandising Company. Linear deterioration in benefit derived from a television commercial.

total benefit over the period is $20{,}000T$ minus the triangle *acd*, whose area is $\frac{1}{2}\left(\frac{T}{52}\right)(20{,}000)T$. Thus the total benefit is

$$\text{Total Benefit} = 20{,}000T - \frac{1}{2}\left(\frac{T}{52}\right)(20{,}000)T$$

and the *average weekly* benefit over T weeks is

$$\text{Benefit} = \frac{1}{T}\left(20{,}000T - \frac{T^2}{(2)(52)}(20{,}000)\right) \tag{7–9.8}$$

This last equation is in the form of the first term of Equation (7–9.7) in that it is $\frac{1}{T}$ multiplied by the total benefit over the replacement period of T unit time periods. Also Equation (7–9.8) reduces to Equation (7–9.1).

Using Equation (7–9.7) in the Loen problem, the average weekly benefit function is

$$\text{Benefit} = \frac{20{,}000}{T}\int_0^T \left(1 - \frac{1}{52}t\right) dt$$

Then the average weekly effectiveness function, expressed in the form of Equation (7–9.7), is

$$E = \text{Effectiveness} = \frac{20{,}000}{T}\int_0^T \left(1 - \frac{1}{52}t\right) dt - \frac{25{,}000}{T} \tag{7–9.9}$$

$$E = \frac{20{,}000}{T}\left(T - \frac{T^2}{(2)(52)}\right) - \frac{25{,}000}{T} \tag{7–9.10}$$

We now find the optimal value of T by differentiating and setting the derivative equal to 0.

$$\frac{d}{dT}(E) = \frac{d}{dT}\left(20{,}000 - \frac{20{,}000T}{(2)(52)} - \frac{25{,}000}{T}\right) \tag{7–9.11}$$

$$0 = -\frac{20{,}000}{(2)(52)} + \frac{25{,}000}{T^{*2}}$$

$$T^{*2} = \frac{(25{,}000)(2)(52)}{20{,}000} = 130$$

$$T^* = 11.4 \approx 11 \text{ weeks}$$

This is, of course, the same result as that obtained in Equation (7–9.6) above.

The general formula of Equation (7–9.7) may be extended in generality to take account of the cost of capital and any change in salvage value or replacement cost. If the interest rate is r, then the effectiveness of the system, as measured in *present values* at time $t = 0$, i.e., just after a replacement, is

$$E = \frac{1}{T}\left[\int_0^T e^{-rt}f(t)\,dt + e^{-rt}(c(T) - s(T))\right] \qquad (7\text{–}9.12)$$

where: r is the discount rate
T is the replacement interval
$f(t)$ is the net current benefit at time t (i.e., the revenue less the operating and maintenance costs)
$c(t)$ is the replacement (including installation) cost at time t
$s(t)$ is the salvage value at time t

The first term in Equation (7–9.12) represents the present value of the stream of benefits derived from the asset between the present and time T. The second term is the present value of the difference between the replacement cost and the salvage value at time T, and the entire expression is reduced to an average value per unit time. The complete expression then yields the present value of the incomes and costs involved in a policy of replacement at time intervals of length T. Then, differentiating the equation with respect to T yields the optimal time interval between replacements.

7–10. Group Replacement. In the previous sections we considered the problem of replacement of individual items which may fail or deteriorate. In the cases to which the techniques of those sections apply, individual histories of individual items must be available, and decisions are made about *individual items* on the basis of their own individual histories and characteristics. In some situations, it is preferable to consider *groups* of items and investigate the desirability of replacing *entire groups* consisting of some new and some old items.

In such problems involving *group replacement* the solution is most readily obtained by considering time to be divided into discrete intervals and by evaluating the various possible replacement policies by enumeration. It is, however, possible to solve group replacement problems analytically, given the probability distribution of failure as a function of time, but the mathematics required is often beyond the scope of this book.

In Section 15–8, we shall see that Markov analysis provides a convenient tool for analysis of certain kinds of group replacement problems.

As a general rule, group replacement is desirable when the unit cost of individual replacement after failure is relatively large and when the probability of such failure increases with time. If the cost of group replacement, i.e., replacement of *all* items in the group, is G, and if the cost of individual replacement of all failed items as they fail is $I(t)$, where t is the time since the last group replacement; then, if individual items which fail within the group replacement interval are replaced, the total cost per group replacement cycle is

$$\text{Total Cost} = G + I(t) \tag{7–10.1}$$

and, if T is the selected group replacement interval, the average cost per unit time of that group replacement policy is

$$\text{Cost} = \frac{1}{T}\,(G + I(T)) \tag{7–10.2}$$

These relationships are shown in Figure 7–10.1, where the cost of the group replacement is represented by the rectangular hyperbola labeled $\frac{G}{T}$, and the cost of individual replacement within the time period is the rising curve labeled $\frac{I(T)}{T}$. If this second curve rises sufficiently rapidly to cause the sum to rise after reaching a minimum, then a policy of group replacement is desirable. On the other hand, if the cost of individual replacement does not rise sufficiently rapidly to cause the sum to reach a minimum and then increase, then individual replacement is superior to group replacement.

In group replacement problems, the data required and the mathematics for forecasting the individual replacement costs often make the problem extremely complex. Sometimes, in practice, when the functions are believed to have the general shape shown in Figure 7–10.1, it is possible to

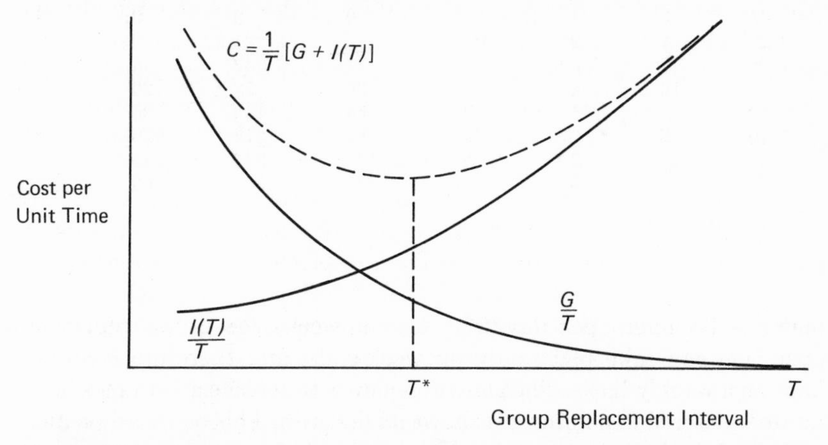

Fig. 7–10.1. Group replacement cost is the sum of the cost of group replacement (G/T) *plus* the costs of individual replacement of items which fail during the replacement interval.

observe and record the failure rates and make *ad hoc* decisions to perform group replacement. Let us examine an illustration of this kind.

The Da-Hi Beverage Corporation uses 150 special-purpose high-intensity lamps in its various inspection procedures. These lamps cost $1.00 each and they can all be replaced over a week end for a labor cost of $50. Thus the group replacement cost G is $200. However, when a lamp burns out in use, the labor cost for replacement and downtime is estimated to be $2.00, yielding an individual replacement cost of $3.00 per lamp. The production manager knows from experience that the cost of individual replacement tends to follow the general shape of the curve labeled $\frac{I(T)}{T}$ in Figure 7–10.1, and he therefore has his maintenance people keep a tracking record such as that shown in Table 7–10.1. Since the plant

TABLE 7–10.1

Da-Hi Beverage Company
Worksheet for Determination of Group Replacement Time

Week Ending	Number of Bulbs Replaced	Serial T	Average Cost of Group Replacement, $\frac{200}{T}$	Cost of Individual Replacement, (2) × 3	Cumulative (5)	(6) ÷ (3)	(7) + (4)
(1)	(2)	(3)	(4)	(5)	(6)	(7)	(8)
July 15	3	1	200	9	9	9	209
22	4	2	100	12	21	10	110
29	7	3	67	21	42	14	81
Aug. 5	12	4	50	36	78	20	70
12	18	5	40	54	132	26	66
19	28	6	33	84	216	36	69*
26	40	7	29	120	336	48	77
Sept. 2	55	8	25	165	501	63	88
9							
16							

operates 24 hours per day five days a week, the group replacement operation can take place only on week-ends, and therefore records are kept on a weekly basis. The general policy is to replace all lamps when the number entered in column (8) shows its first rise. This occurred on July 8, and all of the bulbs were replaced. It obviously occurred again on August 19, as indicated by the asterisk, at which time the group replacement should have been ordered. However, the worksheet in this illustration is continued to the end of August because the manager and his maintenance chief were away on vacation, and their respective assistants had failed to consult this worksheet. When the manager returned on September 5, he found the worksheet as shown in Table 7–10.1, ordered a group bulb replacement at the earliest opportunity, and said a few choice words to his assistant.

Their error was, however, fortunate for us, and we can see that the data of Table 7–10.1 do conform to the general configuration of Figure 7–10.1 and that the group replacement policy of the Da-Hi Manager is a good one. Actually, the optimal group replacement time was at the end of the previous week when the entry in column (8) was at its minimum. If the characteristics of the bulbs can be treated as being constant over time, then there should be group replacement every five weeks. If this assumption can not be made, then the present policy of the company is wise and safe. For example, it is a good policy to use if the bulbs are not always obtained from the same manufacturer. It makes no assumptions about the parameters of the distribution of bulb lives, and assumes only that the probability of bulb failure increases with increasing age of the bulb. However, it does not produce the *optimal* group replacement interval, but rather it produces a somewhat longer-than-optimal interval, since the signal for replacement is the rising of the cost curve. However, if the curve tends to be relatively flat near its minimum, as it often does, this solution is quite satisfactory.

7–11. A Note on the Exponential Distribution. If, in a replacement problem, the individual items are found to have their probability of breakdown such that it is described by the exponential distribution, then the probability of breakdown in the next time interval is independent of the current age. For example, in a group replacement situation, if breakdowns are random with probability of failure of 0.1 in the next time interval, then 10 per cent will be expected to fail in the next time interval, and 10 per cent of those which remain will fail in the following time interval, etc. If, as is to be expected, the new items added as replacements have the same probability of failure, then there is no possible gain from group replacement or, in the case of individual items, no gain from preventive maintenance. Expenditures for preventive maintenance or group replacement are wasted.

Clearly, with exponential failure distributions, the optimal policy is to allow items to fail at random and to replace or repair them at that time. In the diagram of Figure 7–10.1, if the failure probabilities had been exponential, the curve for individual replacement at failure, i.e., the curve labeled $\frac{I(T)}{T}$, would not rise, but would be horizontal, since the same number of items would fail in each time period. Then the curve for the sum of the costs would be ever decreasing, asymptotic to the horizontal line for individual replacement, and, indeed, it would be this horizontal line which describes the cost under the optimal policy of individual replacement.

This characteristic of the exponential distribution will be noted again in Chapter 14 on queueing theory. There we shall see that, if intervals between arrivals at a service facility are exponentially distributed, then the probability of an arrival within the next short interval is the same, regardless of the time which has passed since the last arrival. This, we shall see, is precisely what we mean by "random" arrivals.

7–12. The Marginal Decision Technique. Many of the important results derived in this chapter may be derived by a very simple technique using the concept of the regret matrix of decision theory introduced in Section 1–11. This ingenious technique will be seen to have a very broad applicability.[1] However, as we shall also see, it has its limitations, and it must be used with care.

In applying this *marginal decision technique* to inventory, maintenance, or replacement problems, the decision maker considers the decision problem at the margin. That is he addresses himself to the two-alternative decision problem of *stocking or not stocking* the marginal item or of *waiting or not waiting* one more time unit before preventive maintenance or replacement.

Looking first at the inventory problem, the decision maker must decide to adopt either the course of action A_1: not order the ith unit, or A_2: order the ith unit. If he orders only $i - 1$ units, and there is demand for the ith unit, his regret will be equal to his unit lost profit plus any shortage (penalty) cost. On the other hand, if he orders the ith unit and it is not needed, then his regret as a consequence of ordering the ith unit will be equal to the unit overage cost, i.e., his cost less salvage value. He will order the ith unit until the expected value of the regret associated with ordering is smaller than or equal to the expected value of the regret associated with not ordering.

We shall apply this technique to the general single-episode inventory problem (newsboy problem) treated above in Section 7–4. There we found, after a lengthy derivation, that the optimal quantity to be stocked x^*, is given by

$$\int_0^{x^*} f(y)\, dy = \frac{p - c}{p - d} \qquad (7\text{–}4.4)$$

where: p is the selling price
c is the wholesale cost
d is the distress clearance (salvage) value
y is the demand
x^* is the optimal ordering quantity

[1] For the basic idea of this section, I am indebted to three graduate students Claude Le Bon, Terrence V. O'Brien, and Joel R. Jankowski, who as students in my course, demonstrated the generality of the technique.

This may be alternatively derived from the decision theoretic regret atrix shown in Figure 7–12.1. There, of course, there is no regret associted with the marginal decision if the ith unit is not ordered and not eeded, or if it is ordered and needed. However, if it is ordered and not

		Demand $y<i$	Demand $y \geq i$
Order $i-1$ units	A_1	0	$p-c$
Order i units	A_2	$c-d$	0

Fig. 7–12.1. Regret matrix for single-episode inventory problem.

eeded, the overage cost $c - d$ measures the regret. On the other hand, if e i^{th} unit is not ordered but needed, the opportunity cost (the lost rofit) $p - c$ measures the regret.

The expected values of the regret are:

$$E(A_1) = (p - c)P(y \geq i)$$
$$E(A_2) = (c - d)[1 - P(y \geq i)]$$

The decision maker is indifferent between A_1 and A_2 when these xpected values are equal. Setting them equal to one another,

$$(p - c)P(y \geq i) = (c - d) - (c - d)P(y \geq i)$$
$$(p - c + c - d)P(y \geq i) = (c - d)$$
$$P(y \geq i) = \frac{c - d}{p - d} \qquad (7\text{–}12.1)$$

This result indicates that the ith unit should be ordered if the probaility that the demand will be for i *or more* is equal to the ratio $\frac{c - d}{p - d}$. n terms of discrete probabilities, then, the optimal quantity to be ocked is x^*, such that

$$\sum_{y=x^*}^{\infty} P(y) = \frac{c - d}{p - d} \qquad (7\text{–}12.2)$$

nd, for continuous probabilities,

$$\int_{x^*}^{\infty} f(y)\, dy = \frac{c - d}{p - d} \qquad (7\text{–}12.3)$$

These two expressions may be put into the more familiar form involvin $F(x^*)$. Equation (7–12.3) becomes the familiar

$$\int_0^{x^*} f(y)\,dy = 1 - \frac{c-d}{p-d} = \frac{p-c}{p-d} \qquad (7\text{–}12.4$$

which is the same result as in Equation (7–4.4) above. It clearly lead to the same solution of the Marchand problem as that obtained i Section 7–3.

For the discrete case, the optimal quantity to order is x^*, where x is the smallest quantity such that

$$\sum_{y=0}^{x^*} P(y) \geq \frac{p-c}{p-d} \qquad (7\text{–}4.6$$

This marginal decision technique may also be applied to the Jaz Camer problem of Section 7–5. In this problem dealing with the replenishmen level for a particular camera model, instead of developing a genera model, we shall solve the specific problem for the optimal replenish ment level. Ordering is done at the start of each week and the gross profi margin per unit is \$40, the penalty cost of shortage is \$20 per unit and the holding cost is \$4 per unit. We shall ignore the ordering cost fo the moment. Then, the regret matrix is as shown in Figure 7–12.2. Th

		Demand	
		$y<i$	$y \geq i$
Order $i-1$ units	A_1	0	56
Order i units	A_2	4	0

Fig. 7–12.2. Regret matrix for Jaz Camera Shop problem.

regret, if there is a shortage of one unit, is \$56, which is the sum of \$4 lost profit plus \$20 penalty shortage cost, less \$4 saved holding cost. Th regret, if there is overage of one unit, is, in this problem, merely th holding cost of \$4.

Then, the value of $P(y < i)$ at the point of indifference, where $E(A_1) =$ $E(A_2)$, i.e., where the expected values of the regrets are equal, may b found by setting the expected regrets equal to one another:

$$56P(y \geq i) = 4P(y < i)$$

$$56[1 - P(y < i)] = 4P(y < i)$$

$$56 = (4 + 56)P(y < i)$$

$$P(y < i) = \frac{56}{60} = 0.933$$

Thus the optimal replenishment level x^* is the *smallest* number such that $P(y < x^*)$ is 0.933 *or more*. (This may be reasoned by the reader since it can be seen from Figure 7–12.2 that if $P(y < x^*)$ is *smaller* than this indifference level, the $x^{*\text{th}}$ unit should *not* be ordered.)

The probabilities in the problem, from Table 7–5.1, are given in Table 7–12.1. The optimal replenishment level is thus 3 units. This is the same result as that obtained above in Section 7–5.

TABLE 7–12.1

Jaz Camera Shop
Probability Distribution of Weekly Demand for Reflex Camera

Demand y	$P(y)$	$F(y)$
0	0.37	0.37
1	0.37	0.74
2	0.18	0.92
3	0.06	0.98
4 (or more)	0.02	1.00

It should be noted that the ordering cost in the problem, which was given as $5 per order, is ignored in the above analysis. This is because this technique cannot deal easily with this kind of cost. The ordering cost is associated with the act of *ordering* rather than with the ith unit. It attaches to the ith unit only if the ith unit alone is to be ordered, and it does not attach to the ith unit if it is not the only unit being ordered. Since this technique deals only with the costs attached to the marginal unit, it would have to be applied twice, once to the situation wherein the ith unit is the only unit ordered and also to the alternative situation in which the ith unit is not the only unit ordered. This does not constitute an insurmountable problem, but it does indicate that the application of this technique is somewhat limited.

This limitation on this decision-theoretic marginal matrix technique suggests that there may be many other kinds of situations which similarly may not be readily treated by this technique. The technique thus is extremely valuable and useful, but it must be applied with care.

Finally we shall apply this marginal decision technique to the general problem of which the Hutchinson & Wilkinson Shipping Company problem of Section 7–8 is an illustration. This problem is the general situation in which there is a cost of replacement or maintenance *before* failure of $$B$ and a higher cost of $$A$ for replacement or maintenance *after* failure. The decision maker may be viewed as making the marginal decision to conduct preventive maintenance or to wait for one more time unit. This decision situation is depicted in the regret matrix of Figure 7–12.3. Letting t represent the life of the item and T some specific value of

		Failure in T^{th} period: $P(t \leq T)$ yes	$P(t > T)$ no
Replace before Tth period	A_1	0	B
Not replace before T^{th} period	A_2	A−B	0

Fig. 7–12.3. Regret matrix for preventive-maintenance problem.

t, then the regret, at the margin, for premature maintenance is the cost of the preventive maintenance B, and the cost of erroneous delay is the *excess* cost for maintenance *after* failure, $A - B$.

At the point of indifference, again,

$$BP(t > T) = (A - B)P(t \leq T)$$

$$B[1 - P(t \leq T)] = (A - B)P(t \leq T)$$

$$B = (A - B + B)P(t \leq T)$$

$$P(t \leq T) = \frac{B}{A}$$

Thus, the optimal preventive maintenance period is T^* such that, for continuous probabilities,

$$\int_0^{T^*} f(t)\,dt = \frac{B}{A} \tag{7–12.5}$$

and, for discrete probabilities,

$$P(t \leq T^*) \leq \frac{B}{A} \tag{7–12.6}$$

and the optimal policy is to replace *before* T^*, where T^* is the *greatest* age meeting the condition of Equation (7–12.6).

In the Hutchinson & Wilkinson problem, the probabilities of failure are given as discrete probabilities in Table 7–8.1, and the desired cumulative probabilities are given in column (2) of that table. From Equation (7–12.6), since the cost of maintenance is \$1,300 before failure and \$2,300 after failure,

$$P(t \leq T^*) \leq \frac{B}{A} = \frac{1300}{2300} = 0.566$$

Thus, the optimal policy is to replace *before* the 9th year, i.e., *after* 8 years.

Again this is the same result as that obtained above in Section 7–8 after a much more complex development.

In each case in which this technique has been applied here, it has obtained the correct solution far more easily than have the more traditional methods introduced in earlier sections. The reader then might well ask, why use those other methods? The answer is that those methods are perfectly general and they illustrate the basic model building techniques which constitute the very heart of Management Science. This marginal decision method is often tricky to use and not always applicable, but it can, as we have seen, sometimes provide a startlingly simple way to arrive at a perfectly correct solution.

SUGGESTIONS FOR FURTHER READING

Buffa, E. S. *Models for Production and Operations Management.* New York: John Wiley & Sons, Inc., 1963.

Dean, B. V. "Replacement Theory," Chapter 8 in *Progress in Operations Research,* Vol. 1 (R. L. Ackoff, ed.). New York: John Wiley & Sons, Inc., 1961.

Hanssman, F. "A Survey of Inventory Theory from the Operations Research Viewpoint," Chapter 3 in *Progress in Operations Research,* Vol. 1 (R. L. Ackoff, ed.). New York: John Wiley & Sons, Inc., 1961.

Magee, J. F. *Production Planning and Inventory Control.* New York: McGraw-Hill Book Co., Inc., 1958.

Sasieni, M., A. Yaspan, and L. Friedman. *Operations Research: Methods and Problems.* New York: John Wiley & Sons, Inc., 1959.

Starr, M. K., and D. W. Miller. *Inventory Control: Theory and Practice.* Englewood Cliffs, N.J.: Prentice-Hall, Inc., 1962.

EXERCISES

7–1. The number of passengers carried by Eastwestern Airlines is growing at the continuous rate of 10% per year. (That is, 10% is the *nominal* rate. The *equivalent* rate is, of course, higher.) The company was carrying passengers at the rate of 3,000,000 per year at the end of 1960 (i.e., December 31, 1960). How many total passengers will the airline carry in the 10.5-year period from January 1, 1963, through June 30, 1973, if growth continues at the 10% rate? (Note: This problem is to be solved analytically. Numerical solutions should be used for checking only.)

7–2. The Stadil Garden Shop buys Christmas trees at $2 per tree and sells them at $5 per tree. The manager has orders for 50 trees, but he wants to protect against the possibility of cancellations or possible new additional sales. The probability of one new additional order is 0.6, and the probability of more than one new additional order is 0. Unsold trees can be sold for firewood at $1 each. How many should he order if his expectation is that the probability of one cancellation is 0.5, the probability of two cancellations is 0.2, and the probability of more than two cancellations is 0? What is his expected profit?

7–3. Derive (in the symbolic terms in which it is stated) the general equation (7–4.4), using the methods of Sections 7–3 and 7–4.

7–4. The Hermot Shipping Company has, in its communications system, an electronic component whose life is distributed according to the *pdf*

$$f(t) = ae^{-at}$$

a) What is the probability that a new component will fail within n years?
b) What is the probability that a new component will be alive after t_1 years?
c) What is the probability that a component whose present age is t_1 will fail in the next n years?
d) What do these results tell you about this probability distribution?
e) What should be replacement policy of the company if the cost of replacement after failure is exactly double the cost of replacement before failure?

7–5. The Ririt Bookstore is about to stock a sensational new book written by a controversial person who is currently in the news. The book costs the company \$2.50 and it sells for \$5.00. After a short selling season, the book will be stale, and it will have a salvage value of 0. How many should be stocked if the anticipated distribution of expected sales is chi-square with mean 4 (in hundreds of books)? (Solve the problem using a table of the chi-square distribution available in most statistics books.)

As an extra optional exercise, try to solve it using the Poisson approximation to the gamma distribution. See Exercise 6–5.

7–6. A turbine part in the Hartob Manufacturing Company's main plant shows the following pattern of breakdown probabilities. It is sure to break down within 600 hours, and its probability of breakdown, in hundred-hour periods, is as given below. The cost of replacement after failure is \$300, including various downtime costs; but it is only \$100 if replacement takes place on a scheduled basis without unexpected downtime, inconvenience, and expense.

a) Find the optimal preventive maintenance policy (to the nearest 100 hours).
b) Compute the cost per hundred hours for each of the five possible preventive maintenance periods, and plot these to show that your solution is indeed the minimum cost policy.

Hours of Operation	Probability of Breakdown
100	0.1
200	0.1
300	0.2
400	0.3
500	0.2
600	0.1

7–7. The Tofer Swimming Pool Company sells a particular model for \$500. It costs the company \$300, and its salvage price is \$200. (All residual stock is sold in the August Sale at \$200 per unit.) The probability distribution of demand is as shown below.

Demand (Number of Pools), y	$P(y)$
0	0.10
1	0.20
2	0.30
3	0.15
4	0.10
5	0.10
6	0.05

How many pools should the manager stock for the coming season? Solve: (a) using the marginal decision method of Section 7–12; (b) using the decision-theoretic method of decision making under risk.

7–8. Derive the discrete points, given in column (3) of Table 7–8.1, of the gamma distribution with mean 9 years and standard deviation 3 years. (Hint: Use Equation (6–E5.1), which, using the terminology of this problem, where t is the number of years, becomes, for $F(t)$, the cumulative probability of breakdown in t years:

$$F(t) = 1 - \sum_{x=0}^{a} \frac{t^x e^{-t}}{x!} \qquad (7\text{–E8.1})$$

where a is the parameter of the gamma distribution. Then, from Equations (6–8.7) and (6–8.8), show that $a = 8$ and $b = 1$.

The reader should notice that in Equation (7–E8.1) the parameter b of the gamma distribution is absent. This is because the technique which we are using here assumes that $b = 1$. Since, in our problem, it is the case that $b = 1$, we shall obtain directly the probabilities which we desire. If b had been other than 1, we would have to scale the T units in order to obtain the probabilities. That is, we would scale the T units to make the average of the gamma distribution coincide with the average of the real distribution of the ages of the components. For example, if $a = 8$ but b had been 3, that would mean that the mean of the life spans was 3 years and the standard deviation 1 year. Then the T values used in Equation (7–E8.2) would have to be $\frac{1}{3}$ of their actual value so that the derived gamma distribution will have the proper mean of 3, rather than the mean value of 9 which this technique would otherwise generate, since it automatically yields probabilities for a gamma distribution with mean equal to $a + 1$. In our problem, this works out exactly right with no extra scaling step required.

Now, using the table of Appendix C, the values of $F(T)$ may be computed from the relationship[2]

$$F(T) = 1 - \sum_{x=0}^{8} \frac{T^x e^{-T}}{x!} \qquad (7\text{–E8.2})$$

In Appendix C, for $T = 1$, $F(T) = 0.0000$, since $P(x \geq 9) = 0.0000$. For each value of T, the Poisson probability, $P(x \geq 9)$ is computed by adding either the probabilities for 1 through 8 and subtracting from 1, or by adding the probabilities for all values of x greater than 8. In this way, column (2) and, from it, column (3)of Table 7–8.1 was prepared.)

[2] The desired cumulative values may be obtained directly from tables of the summed Poisson distribution. See Richmond, S. B., *Statistical Analysis* (2d ed.; New York: The Ronald Press Company, 1964), Appendix M.

Part III

ALLOCATION PROBLEMS

8

The Assignment Problem

8–1. Decision Making Under Certainty—Allocation Problems. In this part of the book, we shall examine additional types of problems involving decision making under certainty. Under certainty, the decision maker is certain about the state of nature. That is, he has full knowledge about the configuration of the uncontrollable inputs. His problem is, as always, to ascertain the optimal configuration of the controllable variables (course of action), and for this he requires only understanding of the system. Thus, the relevant variables are all under his control, and he must ascertain their optimal configuration. That is,

$$E_i = f(A_i) \tag{8–1.1}$$

and the problem is to select the A_i which yields the optimum value of the effectiveness function. The payoff matrix consists of a single column.

A familiar and recurring class of problems consists of allocation problems. These arise when there are two or more activities to perform, but there are limitations or restrictions on the available resources, such that each activity may not be able to be performed optimally. The problem then is to *allocate* the available resources in such a way that the effectiveness *over the entire system* is optimized, within the given restrictions.

8–2. The Assignment Problem. The simplest of the allocation problems is the assignment problem. This owes its simplicity to the fact that, in the assignment model, there are n tasks and n facilities, and we must assign *exactly one facility to each task*. The problem arises from the fact that the various facilities have different efficiencies in the various tasks. Examples of this situation are: employees and jobs, employees and machines, tractors and trailers, some traffic management problems, i.e., origins and destinations, and many others.

8–3. Solution by Enumeration. We can illustrate this kind of problem by looking at a simple problem where $n = 3$. That is, we wish to assign three facilities, one each to three jobs, and our objective is minimum cost for the entire system. These facilities might be machines, employees, plants, trucks, etc. We shall designate the facilities 1, 2, and 3. The jobs are designated *a*, *b*, and *c*. In order to solve the problem we must know the cost for *each* facility to do *each* job. This cost matrix is given in Figure 8–3.1, where the entries in the matrix are these costs, measured in

		Job		
		a	*b*	*c*
	1	8	4	7
Facility	2	5	2	4
	3	4	1	5

Fig. 8–3.1. Cost matrix.

time or money. That is, facility 1 can perform job *a* in 8 hours, or at a cost of 8 dollars, 800 dollars, or eight of some other measure of cost. Clearly, each facility is most efficient doing job *b*, but only one facility can be assigned to job *b*.

With a small problem such as this, the solution can be found by enumeration, as shown in Table 8–3.1. The result of the analysis of Table 8–3.1 is the single-column decision matrix of Figure 8–3.2. The optimal

TABLE 8–3.1

To jobs *a*, *b*, *c*, we can assign facilities in the following ways A_i	The payoffs or costs of these courses of action E_i
1–2–3	$8 + 2 + 5 = 15$
1–3–2	$8 + 1 + 4 = 13$
2–1–3	$5 + 4 + 5 = 14$
2–3–1	$5 + 1 + 7 = 13$
3–1–2	$4 + 4 + 4 = 12^*$
3–2–1	$4 + 2 + 7 = 13$

Source: Figure 8–3.1.

course of action is indicated by the asterisk. The result is, that by selecting A_5 (assignment 3–1–2) the total cost is 12, and this cost is lower than that associated with any other of the six possible assignments. The problem is solved.

A_i	E_i
A_1	15
A_2	13
A_3	14
A_4	13
A_5	12*
A_6	13

Fig. 8–3.2. Single-column decision matrix for assignment problem.

In any problem of this sort, there are $n!$ possible courses of action (configurations of assignments). In this case, with $n = 3$, there are $3! = 6$ possible courses of action. This is because each *permutation* represents a separate and distinct course of action (see Section 4–12, above). If there were four facilities and 4 jobs, there would be $4! = 24$ courses of action, A_i, and for $n = 5$, there would be $5! = 120$ different A_i. Obviously, the number of A_i increases rapidly as n increases, and, if n becomes much larger, the problem cannot be solved by enumeration, even with a computer. For example, if $n = 15$, the number of enumerations is 1.3×10^{12}. This number is so large, that, even with a computer which could evaluate alternatives at the rate of 1,000 per second or 3,600,000 per hour, it would take 3.6×10^5 hours or about 9,000 8-hour days or more than 8 years of around-the-clock operation. For $n = 25$ or even 20, the time required becomes astronomical numbers of centuries. Clearly, if problems such as these are to be solved, another method must be available.

It is exciting to bear in mind that the solution methods which we are about to examine are, in the history of ideas, very new. The methods of this chapter and of many of the succeeding chapters could not have been studied by our fathers, because these methods did not exist a generation ago. Indeed, many of these methods are younger than 25 years, and some of them date back only a decade. While the problems which we shall discuss: the assignment problem, the transportation problem, linear programming, certain scheduling and queueing problems, were recognized as problems, they could not be solved in the past. In this part of this volume we are chronologically close to the forefront of knowledge, as compared with some of the other mathematical methods, such as, for example, calculus, which was developed almost three centuries ago, and certain of the statistical methods, which are more than a hundred years old.

8–4. Direct Solution. Assignment problems may be solved directly by using the fact that, if a constant number is subtracted from *all of the entries in any row or any column*, each of the $n!$ possible assignments is reduced in cost by exactly the amount of that constant. For example, if we subtract the number 4 from all entries in the top row of the matrix of

Figure 8–3.1, the result is a revised matrix with associated costs as shown in Table 8–4.1. If the costs shown in Table 8–4.1 are compared with those of Table 8–3.1, it will be observed that each E_i is lower by 4 in Table

TABLE 8–4.1

Original Matrix		Revised Matrix
$\begin{bmatrix} 8 & 4 & 7 \\ 5 & 2 & 4 \\ 4 & 1 & 5 \end{bmatrix}$	Subtract 4 from Top Row $\longrightarrow$	$\begin{bmatrix} 4 & 0 & 3 \\ 5 & 2 & 4 \\ 4 & 1 & 5 \end{bmatrix}$

A_i Assignments	E_i Costs (Revised Matrix)
1–2–3	$\mathit{4} + 2 + 5 = 11$
1–3–2	$\mathit{4} + 1 + 4 = 9$
2–1–3	$5 + \mathit{0} + 5 = 10$
2–3–1	$5 + 1 + \mathit{3} = 9$
3–1–2	$4 + \mathit{0} + 4 = 8^*$
3–2–1	$4 + 2 + \mathit{3} = 9$

8–4.1. This follows from the fact that the top-row elements appear once and only once in each configuration, as seen by the *italicized* numbers in Table 8–4.1. These are the numbers which come from the top row, and there is exactly one of these in each configuration. Obviously, the same result would occur if a constant were subtracted from a *column* instead of a row.

The general theorem, then, is that, *if a constant number is subtracted from all of the entries in any row or column, the cost of each of the $n!$ possible assignment configurations is reduced by the amount of that constant number.*

From this theorem, we can derive a simple procedure for solving assignment problems. Since all of the $n!$ possible assignment configurations are reduced by the same amount, their relative positions or ranks remain the same. In other words, the optimal or lowest remains the lowest as constants are subtracted from rows or columns. The procedure then, is to subtract constants from rows and columns until at least one assignment configuration is reduced to zero cost. The assignment configuration (A_i) which reduces first to zero is the A_i which was lowest in the original cost matrix.

The steps for application of this procedure are:

1. Subtract the lowest number in each row (or column) from all of the numbers in that row (or column).
2. Repeat this for each column (or row).
3. Solution: pick zeros so that there is exactly *one* in each column and row.

TABLE 8–4.2

$$\begin{bmatrix} 8 & 4 & 7 \\ 5 & 2 & 4 \\ 4 & 1 & 5 \end{bmatrix} \xrightarrow{\text{Step 1}} \begin{bmatrix} 4 & 0 & 3 \\ 3 & 0 & 2 \\ 3 & 0 & 4 \end{bmatrix} \xrightarrow{\text{Step 2}} \begin{bmatrix} 1 & \checkmark 0 & 1 \\ 0 & 0 & \checkmark 0 \\ \checkmark 0 & 0 & 2 \end{bmatrix}$$

Solution

These rules are applied in Table 8–4.2. The checked zeros in the final matrix indicate the optimal solution, which is 3–1–2, or A_5 of Figure 8–3.2, just as was obtained by complete enumeration. The only remaining question is how the checked zeros were selected. Since one and only one zero is required for each row and column, and since the top row and last column contain only one zero each, those positions must be selected, and then, the zero at the bottom of the first column must be selected to fulfill the requirement of step 3. One could verify the result and reasoning by evaluating each of the six assignment configurations of the final matrix of Table 8–4.2, and one would find that configuration 3–1–2 has zero cost, and all other configurations have higher costs. Thus this configuration was the first to be reduced to zero and, therefore, it is the lowest, or optimal, in the original cost matrix.

8–5. The Fourth Step. In some cases, the procedure outlined above does not lead to a solution, because it does not reduce even the optimal configuration all the way to zero cost. Then another step is required to complete the reduction. In Table 8–5.1, the original matrix is similar to

TABLE 8–5.1

$$\begin{bmatrix} 8 & 4 & 7 \\ 5 & 3 & 4 \\ 4 & 1 & 5 \end{bmatrix} \xrightarrow{1} \begin{bmatrix} 4 & 0 & 3 \\ 2 & 0 & 1 \\ 3 & 0 & 4 \end{bmatrix} \xrightarrow{2} \begin{bmatrix} 2 & 0 & 2 \\ 0 & 0 & 0 \\ 1 & 0 & 3 \end{bmatrix}$$

No solution!

that of Figure 8–3.1, except that cell 2b is 3 instead of 2 as in the original case. In the final matrix in Table 8–5.1, there is no way to select exactly one zero in each column and row. This means that there is no assignment configuration with zero cost. The reader may verify this.

An important difference between the final matrices of Table 8–4.2 (where there is a solution) and Table 8–5.1 (where there is not a solution) is that it is possible to cover all of the zeros in the latter case (no solution) with only *two* straight horizontal or vertical lines. In the final matrix of Table 8–4.2, which is a solution, *three* lines are required, as seen in Figure 8–5.1. These lines may be drawn differently (i.e., all horizontal, or all

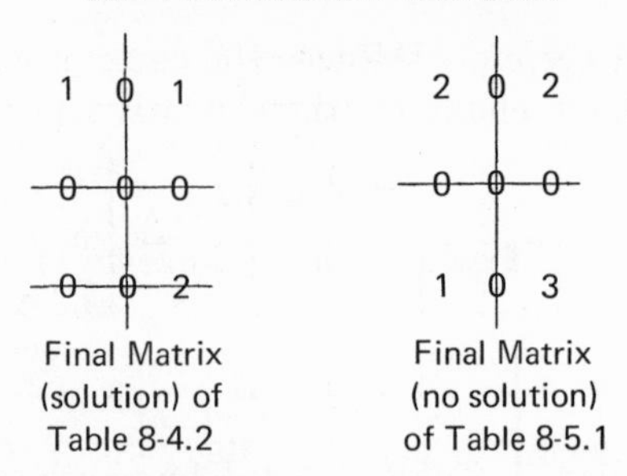

Fig. 8–5.1. It requires n straight horizontal or vertical lines to cover all of the zeros when there is a solution; but, when there is no solution, the zeros may all be covered with fewer than n lines.

vertical, etc.) in the left matrix of Figure 8–5.1, but the zeros cannot be covered by fewer than 3 lines. In the general case, when there is a solution, n lines are required to cover all of the zeros, and, if they can be covered by fewer than n lines, there is no solution yet, and step 4 must be performed. Indeed this is often a means of determining whether a solution is obtained or step 4 is necessary.

4. Draw the minimum number of lines that cover all of the zeros. (If the number of lines is n, a direct solution is possible. If it is fewer than n, continue with step 4.) Select the smallest element not covered by a line and subtract its value from all of the uncovered elements and add this value to the elements at the intersections of drawn lines.

Let us apply step 4 to the final matrix of Table 8–5.1. The procedure is shown in Table 8–5.2. The lowest uncovered element is 1, in cell 3a.

TABLE 8–5.2

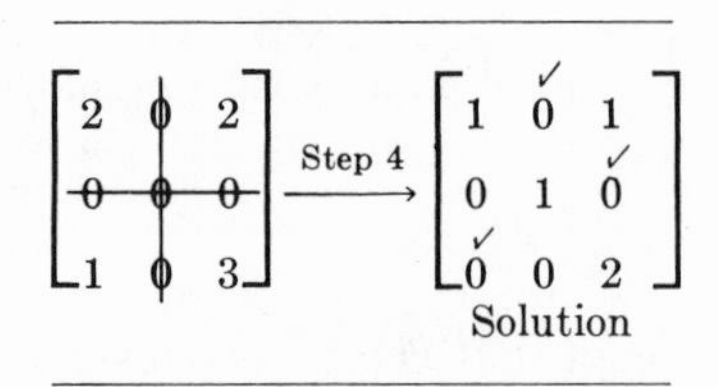

That this solution, 3–1–2, is the optimal, can be verified easily from the fact that, from Table 8–5.1, the cost of this assignment configuration is $4 + 4 + 4 = 12$. This was the same A_i and cost as the optimal solution to the matrix of Figure 8–3.1. Since the difference between these two original matrices is only that some of the allocations of Table 8–5.1 have *higher* costs than those of Figure 8–3.1, the optimal solution is the same.

A brief explanation will indicate why step 4 works. It can be shown that step 4 has the same effect as subtracting and adding a constant to rows and/or columns and therefore reduces the costs of all of the assignment configurations, without changing their relative positions. Table 8–5.3

TABLE 8–5.3

Explanation of Step 4

$$\begin{bmatrix}2&0&2\\0&0&0\\1&0&3\end{bmatrix}\rightarrow\begin{bmatrix}1&-1&1\\0&0&0\\0&-1&2\end{bmatrix}\rightarrow\begin{bmatrix}1&\overset{\checkmark}{0}&1\\0&1&\overset{\checkmark}{0}\\\overset{\checkmark}{0}&0&2\end{bmatrix}$$

Solution

shows a series of legitimate subtractions and additions which have the same effect as step 4. In the first matrix in Table 8–5.3, the lowest uncovered element is 1. Subtract this value from the top and bottom rows to produce the second matrix. We have generated two negative numbers, and, since this can yield negative cost configurations, it is inconsistent with our purpose, which is to reduce the lowest cost configuration to exactly zero cost. We can eliminate these negative numbers by adding 1 to the middle column, yielding the same final matrix as was obtained by step 4. A little contemplation of this result by the reader will indicate that step 4 always has a similar effect.

8–6. Maximization Problems. The assignment method as we have seen it serves only to find the *minimum* cost assignment. It cannot find the *maximum*. However, sometimes the data may be in the form of profit or some other function which should be maximized. In order to find the maximum assignment configuration by this method, it is necessary to convert the matrix entries to new entries with *reversed magnitudes*. The easiest way to do this is to subtract each entry from some constant, and the arithmetic is simplest if the largest element in the matrix is selected for this purpose. Then the solution is obtained in the usual way with the resulting matrix. In Table 8–6.1 the matrix of Figure 8–3.1 is solved for

TABLE 8–6.1

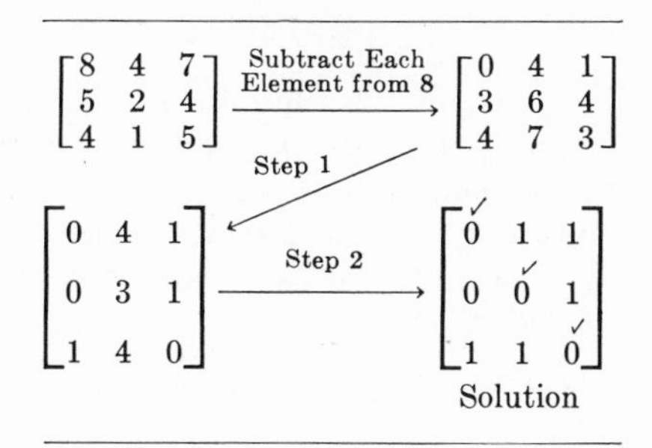

the maximum assignment as would be required if the entries therein were profits instead of costs. The solution is 1–2–3, which has a "profit" of 15. That this is indeed the maximum may be verified in Table 8–3.1.

A final point is that sometimes a solution may be found, but there may be more than one way to select the zeros to meet the requirements of step 3. This merely means that there is more than one optimal solution, or, in other words, that the minimum cost may be obtained by more than one possible assignment configuration.

Although it is essential in the assignment model that the number of tasks be equal to the number of facilities, it is possible to solve real-world problems in which this is not the case. The matrix can be made square by adding a "dummy" row or column. For example, if there were, say, five jobs to be assigned to six facilities, we could solve the problem by adding a dummy sixth job, entitled, for example, "idleness." Then "idleness," with its cost of zero or whatever it may properly be found to be for each facility, will be assigned to one of the facilities and the total cost over the entire system will be minimized. Conversely, if there are five facilities and six jobs, a dummy facility, "deferred" or "job not done," may be created, and then one of the jobs will be automatically selected by the assignment technique to be eliminated from this particular assignment schedule.

We shall later see that the assignment problem, like the transportation model which follows, solves problems which are a special subset of the problems which are solvable by the general methods of linear programming, and we shall see later how the general linear programming techniques may be used to solve these problems. However, in general, the problems which can be solved by the assignment or transportation techniques are most easily solved by these special techniques rather than by the general linear programming techniques.

SUGGESTIONS FOR FURTHER READING

See suggested readings for Chapter 13.

EXERCISES

8–1. The Lojor Sports Car Company, with six plants (Albany, Boston, Cleveland, Dallas, Denver, and Detroit) has just received orders for six of its special hand-made super sports racers. These orders are from individual customers in six different cities (Chicago, Hartford, Kansas City, Miami, Philadelphia, and Tulsa) and they require such rapid delivery that the only course of action open to the Company is to make one car in each plant. Manufacturing costs are identical in all plants, the company absorbs all transportation costs, and the allocation of the individual orders to the respective plants is to be made solely on the basis of transportation costs as given in the transportation cost matrix shown below. Which plant should ship to which customer? How much will transportation cost?

Transportation Costs ($) per Car

From	*To:* Chicago	Hartford	Kansas City	Miami	Philadelphia	Tulsa
Albany	110	20	180	200	30	220
Boston	130	10	200	200	40	240
Cleveland	40	70	150	180	60	150
Dallas	130	230	70	180	210	30
Denver	150	270	90	280	250	80
Detroit	40	100	100	200	100	140

8–2. We have planned ahead our gifts for special occasions that will occur this year. It is now January 1, and as we look ahead, we see the following requirements for gifts for the coming year.

A. Archie's birthday party is on February 1 (one month from now).

B. Bianca's wedding is on March 1.

C. Cecilia's coming-out party is May 1.

D. Dinah's quilting party is on June 1.

E. Evelina's homecoming party is on September 1.

F. Frankie's going-away party is on December 1.

For the occasions, we have acquired the following six gifts, to which we have taken title *today*.

1. A ten-pound angel cake.
2. A five-pound fruit cake.
3. A cask of Amontillado.
4. A ten-pound Cheshire cheese.
5. A Baskerville hound (live dog).
6. A side of beef weighing 200 lb.

We are indifferent as to who gets which present, and we want to parcel out the six gifts in a way such as to avoid spoilage and minimize the cost of storage. The storage costs are as follows:

Cake is stored in our freezer at a cost of 10¢ per pound per month. Fruit cake can last indefinitely, but angel cake deteriorates after *two* months and is then not suitable as a gift.

Cheese is stored in a hotel refrigerator at a cost of $1.00 per month for the 10-lb. wheel. It must age *at least three* months before it is suitable as a gift.

Amontillado is stored in a special cellar under an increasing rate. The rate is $2.00 for the first month, $4.00 for the second month, $6.00 for the third month, etc., the rate increasing $2.00 per month. (Thus, storage cost for three months is $\$12.00 = 2 + 4 + 6$.) Note that the Amontillado goes bad after *six* months and is not suitable as a gift.

"Sherlock" (the hound) is kept in a kennel where the charge is a flat $50.00 for the first three months or portion thereof, and $10.00 per month thereafter.

Beef is stored in our freezer locker where the rental charge is $5.00 per month, plus an initial charge of 10¢ per pound for freezing.

Who gets which gift? What is the total storage cost?

9

The Transportation Method

9–1. The Transportation Problem. The transportation method is a framework or technique for analyzing and solving certain kinds of problems. It is called the transportation technique or the transportation method, because, of the problems solved by this technique, the most obvious involve transportation or traffic management. However, as we shall see, the transportation technique is applicable to other kinds of problems having nothing to do with transportation. As pointed out at the end of the last chapter, the transportation technique, like the assignment technique, solves problems that are a subset of the problems which are solvable by the use of general linear programming techniques. We shall say more about this in Chapter 11.

The Siro Paper Company has two plants, located in Dallas and Memphis, and producing respectively 20 and 30 units (rolls of paper) per month. This month's production has been ordered by two customers located in Topeka and Chicago, requiring 10 and 40 units, respectively. The transportation costs per unit are as shown in the Figure 9–1.1, and the allocation is as shown in Figure 9–1.2. The total transportation cost is the sum of the products of the unit cost, (c_{ij}), times the number of items

Unit Transportation Cost

From:	To: Topeka	Chicago
Dallas	5	12
Memphis	10	8

Fig. 9–1.1. Transportation-cost matrix. Siro Paper Co. Entries are dollars per unit shipped from the origins to the destinations shown, c_{ij}.

Transportation Allocation

From:	To:	Topeka	Chicago	Units Available
	Dallas	10	10	20
	Memphis		30	30
	Units Required	10	40	50

Fig. 9–1.2. Transportation allocation. Siro Paper Co. Entries are units to be shipped from the origins to destinations shown, x_{ij}.

shipped, (x_{ij}), over each route:

$$\text{Total Cost} = \Sigma c_{ij}x_{ij} \tag{9–1.1}$$

$$= (5)(10) + (12)(10) + (10)(0) + (8)(30)$$

$$= 50 + 120 + 240 = \$410$$

For reasons which we shall examine later, this particular allocation is indeed the most economical way to ship the 50 units from the two plants to the two customers.

Suppose now that the patterns of shipment and the costs given above are planned and about to be implemented, when the traffic manager at the home office receives two emergency messages, one from the Topeka customer and one from the Memphis plant, saying, respectively,

1. REQUIRE ADDITIONAL UNIT MAKING NEW TOTAL REQUIREMENT ELEVEN—TOPEKA.
2. EXTRA UNIT ON HAND MAKING NEW TOTAL AVAILABILITY THIRTY-ONE. SEND SHIPPING INSTRUCTIONS—MEMPHIS.

The traffic manager might be inclined to consider these offsetting messages a happy coincidence, and instruct Memphis to ship the additional unit directly to Topeka. If he does this, the new transportation allocation is as shown in Figure 9–1.3, and the total cost is now \$420, since now one additional unit is shipped from Memphis to Topeka at a cost of \$10.

New Transportation Allocation – Direct

From:	To:	Topeka	Chicago	Availabilities
	Dallas	10	10	20
	Memphis	1	30	31
	Requirements	11	40	51

Fig. 9–1.3. Siro Paper Co. New transportation allocation of 51 units with the additional unit shipped *directly* from Memphis to Topeka.

However logical and simple this solution to the problem posed by the two messages may be, it is wrong! The traffic manager should not settle for this easy solution. But what alternative solution is available? Instead of shipping *directly* from Memphis to Topeka, he could ship *indirectly* from Memphis to Topeka by shipping

One more from Memphis to Chicago
One fewer from Dallas to Chicago
One more from Dallas to Topeka

This alternative allocation pattern will have the desired net effect, namely, one more shipped to Topeka and one more shipped from Memphis. However, the *cost* of this *indirect* shipment from Memphis to Topeka may be quite different from the cost of the direct shipment, i.e., $10.

The cost of indirect shipment, from Figure 9–1.1, is:

one more, Memphis to Chicago	$ 8
one fewer, Dallas to Chicago	−12
one more, Dallas to Topeka	5
	$ 1

The cost of *indirect* shipment is $1, thus he can save $9 by using the indirect pattern shown above. This is verified in Figure 9–1.4, which

New Transportation Allocation – Indirect

From:	To:	Topeka	Chicago	a_i
	Dallas	11	9	20
	Memphis		31	31
	b_j	11	40	51

Fig. 9–1.4. Siro Paper Co. New transportation allocation of 51 units with the additional unit shipped *indirectly* from Memphis to Topeka.

shows the entire new allocation of the 51 units to be shipped. Note that the availabilities are designated a_i, and the requirements b_j. The total cost of this allocation is

$$\begin{aligned}\text{Total Cost} &= \Sigma c_{ij}x_{ij}\\ &= (5)(11) + (12)(9) + (8)(31)\\ &= 55 + 108 + 248 = \$411\end{aligned}$$

This is, as we have already shown, $9 less than the $420 cost of shipping *directly* as shown in Figure 9–1.3. The reader will note that in the above equation we did not include, in the addition, the cells with no allocations, which would make zero contribution to the total cost. We shall continue this simplification practice, and in summing to arrive at total cost, we shall ignore the unoccupied cells.

Another conclusion from this analysis is that cell 21 (Memphis–Topeka, i.e., *second* row, *first* column) which is unoccupied, should remain unoccupied. That is, no shipments should be made from Memphis to Topeka. In fact, in a 2-by-2 matrix such as this, there must be at least one cell empty. Clearly, if it were economical to ship a unit directly from Memphis to Topeka, it would be economical to ship as many as possible, and the filling of this cell would be carried on until some other cell, in this case cell 11, was depleted. Thus, there will, in the optimal solution, always be at least one empty cell. There could conceivably be two empty cells, if, say, the number available at Dallas equalled the number required at St. Louis, and the number available at Memphis equalled the number required at Chicago, and if the costs in cells 11 and 22 were such that these were the lowest cost cells. Such a solution, where there are m rows and n columns in the matrix, and where the number of occupied cells is fewer than $(m + n - 1)$, is called a "degenerate" solution. In this case, with a 2-by-2 matrix, $(m + n - 1)$ yields 3 cells to be filled in a "basic" (nondegenerate) solution.

We shall find that the principles which we have seen above in this simple problem are the fundamental principles for the solution of all problems by the transportation technique. That is, some cells should be occupied and some should be empty, and the criterion for deciding whether a cell should be occupied or empty is the relationship between the costs of the *direct* and the *indirect* shipments between the origin and destination which define that cell.

9–2. The Transportation Model. The transportation model is the representation appropriate to a class of problems of which the classical illustration consists of finding the minimum transportation cost for shipping some number of units from m origins, with various availabilities, to n destinations, with various requirements.

Clearly, the assignment problem is a special case of the transportation problem in which

1. $m = n$
2. All origins and all destinations have requirements and availabilities, respectively, of 1.

In the transportation problem, each of the m origins has an availability of a_i units, and each of the n destinations has a requirement of b_j units; but

$$\Sigma a_i = \Sigma b_j \tag{9–2.1}$$

That is, the total requirements at all of the destinations must be exactly equal to the total availability at all of the origins. If, in some actual problem, this happens not to be the case, an additional step is required. This will be discussed later.

Also, there are mn costs (c_{ij}) of shipping one item from the ith origin to the jth destination. The problem is to empty the origins and fill the destinations by the minimum cost allocation. Stated another way, if x_{ij} is the amount shipped from the ith origin to the jth destination, our purpose is to find the x_{ij} (the allocations) that minimize

$$\text{Total Cost} = \Sigma c_{ij} x_{ij}$$

The technique for solving this kind of problem is an iteration technique, in which

1. A first "feasible" solution is found. *Feasible* here means that all of the a_i and b_j are satisfied.
2. The first feasible solution is examined to find whether it is optimal. If it is optimal, i.e., if there are no empty cells which should be occupied because their direct costs are lower than their indirect costs, the problem is solved.
3. If there is one or more empty cells which should be occupied because the direct cost is lower than the indirect cost, that cell which provides the greatest unit saving should be occupied, emptying another (now-occupied) cell and providing the next system solution for evaluation.

Steps 2 and 3 are repeated until the optimal solution is obtained.

We shall now examine this procedure in detail.

9–3. The First Feasible Solution. The Waymar Manufacturing Co. has four plants, in Cleveland, Dallas, Omaha, and Seattle, and it must ship finished production units to its warehouses in Atlanta, Chicago, Denver, New York, and Oakland. The unit shipping costs, availabilities at the factories, and requirements at the warehouses are shown in Figure 9–3.1.

There are several methods available for finding a first feasible solution or schedule. Obviously, the better the first solution (in terms of cost), the fewer the number of iterations that will be required. We shall examine two methods. The first is the *northwest-corner* method, which is simple to use but is seldom economical and usually requires several iterations to arrive at the optimal solution. The *northwest-corner* method is useful when the analysis is to be performed by electronic computer, but, for manual operation such as we shall illustrate here, there are more efficient computational procedures as we shall see below. Here we shall introduce and illustrate the northwest-corner method in order to see just what a feasible schedule and a basic-feasible schedule are.

Waymar Manufacturing Company
Unit Transportation Costs

From Origins (Factories)	To Destinations (Warehouses):	Atlanta	Chicago	Denver	New York	Oakland	Factory Availabilities a_i
	Cleveland	6	3	12	4	22	25
	Dallas	7	8	7	14	15	60
	Omaha	8	4	5	12	14	70
	Seattle	22	17	10	24	7	45
	Warehouse Requirements b_j	10	50	20	80	40	200

Fig. 9–3.1. Transportation problem. Entries in a_i column are availabilities at respective origins. Entries in b_j row are requirements at respective destinations. All other entries are the unit transportation costs between origin and destination indicated.

The northwest-corner method involves starting at the northwest corner (the reason for starting at this corner instead of one of the other three corners is nothing more than that that is the way we read a page) and allocating as many units as possible into each cell as we move to the east and south.

We can illustrate this procedure by examining Figure 9–3.2. The first step is to construct the matrix, with the cells empty, but with all of the

	ATL	CHI	DEN	NYC	OAK	a_i
CLE	10	15				25
DAL		35	20	5		60
OMA				70		70
SEA				5	40	45
b_j	10	50	20	80	40	200

Fig. 9–3.2. Waymar Mfg. Co. Transportation technique. First feasible solution by northwest-corner method.

a_i and b_j entered. Then starting in the "northwest" cell, i.e., Cleveland–Atlanta, enter the largest number of units feasible. This is, in this case, 10, which satisfies the Atlanta requirements. This completes the first column, and we move to the right and enter 15 in the Cleveland–Chicago cell. This exhausts the availability at Cleveland and completes the first row. We move down to Dallas–Chicago, which can take 35 units, completing the second-column requirement, and we move to the right. We continue this process, moving down and to the right, to complete the first feasible solution shown in Figure 9–3.2.

The total transportation cost of this first feasible solution is, from Figures 9–3.1 and 9–3.2,

$$\begin{aligned}\text{Total Cost} &= \Sigma c_{ij}x_{ij}\\ &= (6)(10) + (3)(15) + (8)(35) + (7)(20) + (14)(5)\\ &\qquad + (12)(70) + (24)(5) + (7)(40)\\ &= 60 + 45 + 280 + 140 + 70 + 840 + 120 + 280 = \$1{,}835\end{aligned}$$

This solution is *feasible* in that it satisfies all of the requirements and availabilities, but it may be a very-high-cost solution. We constructed this first feasible allocation schedule by the northwest-corner method, in which the cells to be occupied are selected on the basis of their *position* in the matrix and not on the basis of their *costs*. Therefore there is no reason to expect that this schedule is a low-cost solution. However, this first feasible schedule is a starting point from which we can proceed by iteration to the optimal solution. We shall examine the iteration procedure in detail later, but for the present, suffice it to recall that the iteration procedure consists of evaluating all of the empty cells to ascertain whether their "indirect costs" are lower than their "direct costs." If the indirect costs are lower, the cells should remain empty. If one or more empty cells have lower direct than indirect costs, the solution should be modified to take advantage of this fact, and then the evaluation and modification procedure must be repeated until all empty cells should, according to the above criterion, remain empty. The solution is then optimal.

If we use the northwest-corner method to obtain the first feasible solution, a large number of iterations may be required to arrive at the optimal schedule. This may be burdensome if the analysis is done by hand. If it is done on a computer, this is no problem, and the iteration procedure may proceed from the northwest-corner solution shown in Figure 9–3.2.

However, if the analysis is to be done with pencil and paper, it is preferable to spend a bit more time and effort to obtain a lower-cost first feasible solution, thereby decreasing the number of iterations required to arrive at the optimal solution.

Intuitively, we might be tempted to select the cells according to a *minimum*-cost criterion. That is, we can select the minimum-cost cell, allocate as many as possible to it, then select the next until the entire schedule is completed. We shall later see a superior procedure for arriving at the first feasible solution, but this minimum-cost procedure is easy to perform, and it does give a cost-based result. We start with the complete

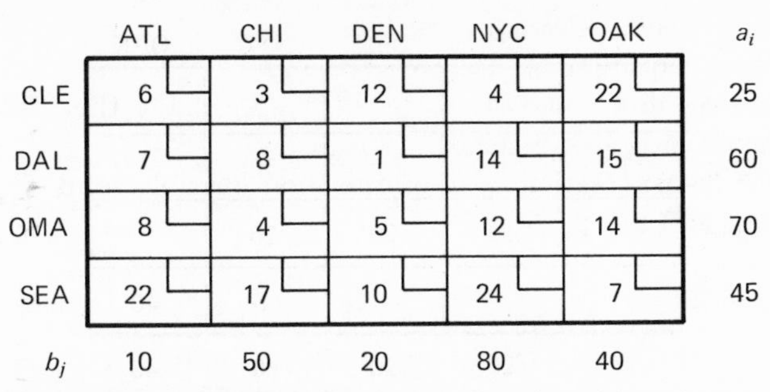

	ATL	CHI	DEN	NYC	OAK	a_i
CLE	6	3	12	4	22	25
DAL	7	8	1	14	15	60
OMA	8	4	5	12	14	70
SEA	22	17	10	24	7	45
b_j	10	50	20	80	40	

Fig. 9–3.3. Worksheet for finding first feasible solution.

information statement of Figure 9–3.3, which is identical with that of Figure 9–3.1 but has separate boxes drawn in the upper right corner of all of the cells. The allocated numbers of units will be entered in these boxes. The lowest cell cost is \$3 for cell 12 (CLE–CHI). That cell should then be allocated as many units as possible. Therefore 25 units are allocated to that cell, exhausting the capacity of the Cleveland Plant. Thus 25 is entered in the box in cell 12, zero is entered in all of the other boxes in that row, a horizontal line is then drawn through the cost figures in that CLE row, and the number 50 at the foot of the CHI column is crossed out and replaced by the number 25, indicating that, after this allocation, CHI still requires 25 units. Now the minimum cell cost is \$4 in cell 32. This cell receives an allocation of 25 units, completing the requirements of CHI and leaving OMA with a residual availability of 45. The appropriate entries are made in the boxes of the CHI column and a vertical line is drawn through the cost figures and the requirement figure of that column. Now, the lowest cost cell is cell 33 with \$5. The procedure is continued until the worksheet is completed as shown in Figure 9–3.4. The solution

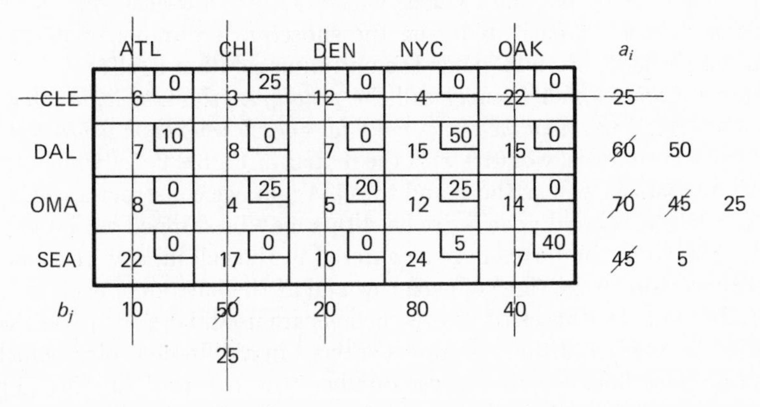

	ATL	CHI	DEN	NYC	OAK	a_i
CLE	6 [0]	3 [25]	12 [0]	4 [0]	22 [0]	25
DAL	7 [10]	8 [0]	7 [0]	15 [50]	15 [0]	~~60~~ 50
OMA	8 [0]	4 [25]	5 [20]	12 [25]	14 [0]	~~70~~ ~~45~~ 25
SEA	22 [0]	17 [0]	10 [0]	24 [5]	7 [40]	~~45~~ 5
b_j	10	~~50~~ 25	20	80	40	

Fig. 9–3.4. Completed worksheet for first feasible solution by minimum-cell-cost procedure.

	ATL	CHI	DEN	NYC	OAK	
CLE		25				25
DAL	10			50		60
OMA		25	20	25		70
SEA				5	40	45
	10	50	20	80	40	

Fig. 9–3.5. First feasible solution obtained by the minimum-cell-cost method.

schedule as copied from the boxes is shown in Figure 9–3.5. The total shipping cost of this first feasible solution is

$$TC = \Sigma c_{ij}x_{ij}$$
$$= (3)(25) + (7)(10) + (14)(50) + (4)(25) + (5)(20) + (12)(25) + (24)(5) + (7)(40)$$
$$= 75 + 70 + 700 + 100 + 100 + 300 + 120 + 280 = \$1{,}745$$

This cost is lower than the solution arrived at by the northwest-corner method, but a moment's reflection will indicate that there is still a better way to arrive at the first feasible solution. For example, in choosing the cell with the minimum cost of $3 in which to make the first allocation, we were later forced to choose a cell with costs of $24, while if we had made the allocation to the next highest cell cost in that row, $4, we might have been able to avoid the $24 cell, and allocate instead to one whose costs are $10. The first allocation, with a saving of $1, necessitated later allocation with a loss of $14.

We shall now consider a technique which does take this sensitivity factor into account, and which yields a very-low-cost first feasible solution, thereby greatly reducing the subsequent number of iterations required. Indeed, often it yields the optimum solution itself!

This method, which we may call the *penalty* method, specifies that we *select those cells such that the cost penalty for not selecting them is greatest.* To perform the analysis, we start with the matrix of Figure 9–3.1 which shows all of the costs as well as the a_i and the b_j. Again, we construct a small box in each cell (if colored pencils are used this may be skipped, and numbers to be entered in the boxes may be entered in the cell in, say, red pencil). Finally we add to the right of each row and at the bottom of each column a number in parentheses (if colored pencils are used, here the parentheses may be omitted, and these numbers entered in a different color) which is the difference between the lowest number (cost) in that row or column and the next lowest. It is the *penalty* for not selecting the lowest number. This construction is shown in Figure 9–3.6. Examination of Figure 9–3.6

	ATL	CHI	DEN	NYC	OAK	a_i	
CLE	6	3	12	4	22	25	(1)
DAL	7	8	7	14	15	60	(0)
OMA	8	4	5	12	14	70	(1)
SEA	22	17	10	24	7	45	(3)
b_j	10	50	20	80	40	200	
	(1)	(1)	(2)	(8)*	(7)		

Fig. 9–3.6. The transportation method. Worksheet for penalty method of finding a first feasible solution.

indicates that the largest of the penalty values is $8, and it is associated with cell 14, CLE–NYC. This value means that, if this cell is not used, the next best cell in that column will cost $8 more per unit. Therefore, we decide to use that cell for as many units as possible. This is 25 units, since that is the availability at CLE. We enter 25 in the box in that cell and zero in the box for each cell in the same row, since CLE is now satisfied. We draw a line through the CLE row and change the b_4 for NYC from 80 to 55, since NYC has received 25 units from CLE. We recompute penalty numbers as necessary, and we are ready to repeat the procedure. Figure 9–3.7 shows the state of the worksheet at this point. The highest penalty,

	ATL	CHI	DEN	NYC	OAK	a_i	
~~CLE~~	~~6~~ 0	~~3~~ 0	~~12~~ 0	~~4~~ 25	~~22~~ 0	~~25~~	~~(1)~~
DAL	7	8	7	14	15	60	(0)
OMA	8	4	5	12	14	70	(1)
SEA	22	17	10	24	7	45	(3)
b_j	10	50	20	~~80~~ 55	40	200	
	(1)	~~(1)~~	(2)	~~(8)~~*	(7)*		
		(4)		(2)			

Fig. 9–3.7. The transportation method. Worksheet, after first allocation, at intermediate stage, in finding first feasible solution by penalty method.

now is $7, associated with cell 45, SEA–OAK. This cell may take 40 units, satisfying the requirements of OAK, and completing the column. The proper adjustments are made, and the result is shown in Figure 9–3.8. The highest penalty on the worksheet now is again $7, associated with cell 43,

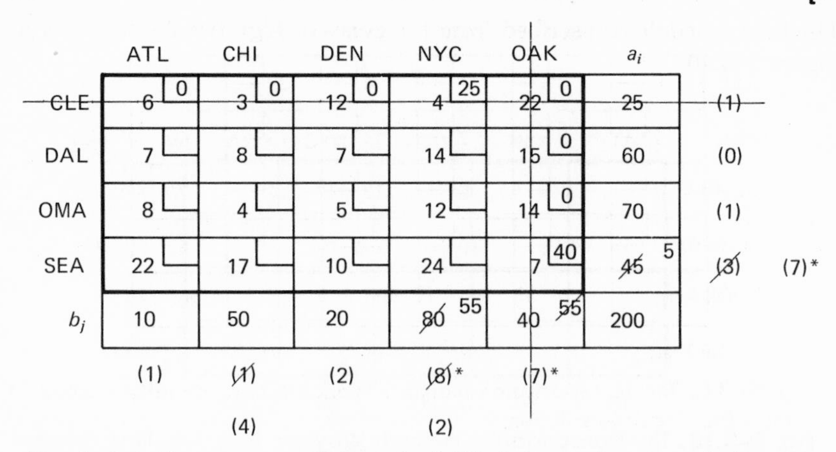

	ATL	CHI	DEN	NYC	OAK	a_i		
CLE	6 [0]	3 [0]	12 [0]	4 [25]	22 [0]	25	(1)	
DAL	7	8	7	14	15 [0]	60	(0)	
OMA	8	4	5	12	14 [0]	70	(1)	
SEA	22	17	10	24	7 [40]	45 5	(3)	(7)*
b_j	10	50	20	80 55	40 55	200		
	(1)	(1)	(2)	(8)*	(7)*			
		(4)		(2)				

Fig. 9–3.8. The transportation method. Worksheet after second allocation, at intermediate stage, in finding first feasible solution by penalty method.

SEA–DEN. This cell may take 5 units since 40 units of SEA's total availability of 45 have already been allocated to OAK. The adjustments are made and the process repeated until the worksheet is completed in the final stage shown in Figure 9–3.9. The sequence to the final stage is:

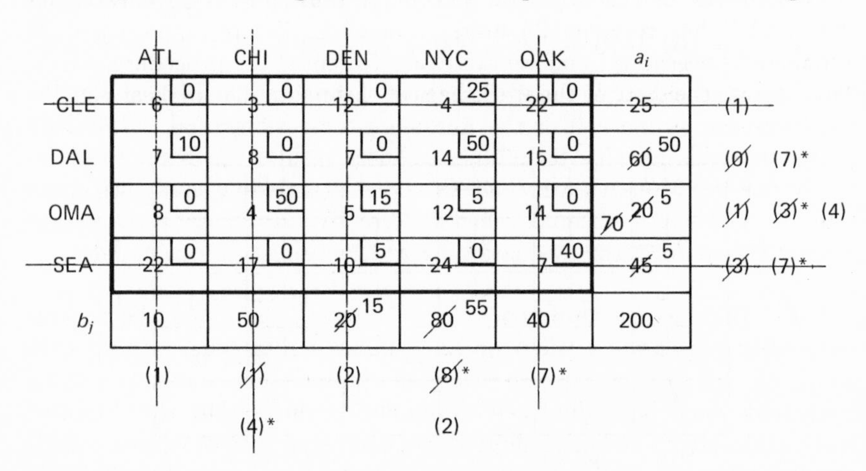

	ATL	CHI	DEN	NYC	OAK	a_i			
CLE	6 [0]	3 [0]	12 [0]	4 [25]	22 [0]	25	(1)		
DAL	7 [10]	8 [0]	7 [0]	14 [50]	15 [0]	60 50	(0)	(7)*	
OMA	8 [0]	4 [50]	5 [15]	12 [5]	14 [0]	70 20 5	(1)	(3)*	(4)
SEA	22 [0]	17 [0]	10 [5]	24 [0]	7 [40]	45 5	(3)	(7)*	
b_j	10	50	20 15	80 55	40	200			
	(1)	(1)	(2)	(8)*	(7)*				
		(4)*		(2)					

Fig. 9–3.9. The transportation method. Waymar Mfg. Co. Completed worksheet for penalty method of deriving first feasible solution.

OMA–CHI, with a penalty of $4, receives 50 units, completing the CHI column; OMA–DEN, with a penalty of $3, receives 15 units, completing the DEN column; DAL–ATL, with a penalty of $7, receives 10 units, completing the ATL column. Finally, with only the NYC column not completed, the two cells DAL–NYC and OMA–NYC receive 50 and 5 units, respectively, to complete the worksheet as shown in Figure 9–3.9.

The final schedule transcribed from the boxes of Figure 9–3.9 is shown in Figure 9–3.10.

	ATL	CHI	DEN	NYC	OAK	
CLE				25		25
DAL	10			50		60
OMA		50	15	5		70
SEA			5		40	45
	10	50	20	80	40	

Fig. 9–3.10. The transportation method. Waymar Mfg. Co. First feasible solution derived by penalty method.

The total transportation cost of this schedule is,

$$\begin{aligned}\text{Total Cost} &= \Sigma c_{ij}x_{ij}\\ &= (4)(25) + (7)(10) + (14)(50) + (4)(50) + (5)(15)\\ &\qquad + (12)(5) + (10)(5) + (7)(40)\\ &= 100 + 70 + 700 + 200 + 75 + 60 + 50 + 280 = \$1{,}535\end{aligned}$$

This cost is considerably lower than those of the schedules obtained by the northwest-corner method or the minimum-cell-cost method. Experience shows that this penalty technique produces results which require relatively few iterations to arrive at the optimal schedule, and that quite often it yields the optimal schedule directly. However, it is always essential to perform the evaluation procedure to test for optimality.

9–4. The Test for Optimality. As we have seen above, the test for optimality consists of evaluating each of the empty cells, i.e., the cells which are not utilized directly in the specific solution or schedule being evaluated. Such individual cell evaluation requires that the "indirect cost" of the empty cell be computed and compared with the direct cost. If the direct cost, i.e., the cost given in Figure 9–3.1, is lower, the cell should be occupied rather than empty, and if any of the empty cells show this result, the schedule being evaluated is not optimal.

The only complication in this procedure is the computation of the indirect cost for each cell. In order to be able to complete this computation for each cell in the matrix, there must be exactly $(m + n - 1)$ occupied cells. In the case of the matrix of Figure 9–3.10, which is a 4-by-5 matrix, $m + n - 1 = 8$, and the solution shown in Figure 9–3.10 does have exactly eight occupied cells. A feasible solution such as this, which has exactly $(m + n - 1)$ occupied cells, is called a *basic-feasible solution.* Indeed, any of the three procedures which we have seen will yield a basic-feasible solution, except where a particular allocation completes the availability of its row *and* the requirement of its column *at the same time.* Each time this happens, the number of occupied cells is reduced by 1. For example, in the northwest-corner solution of Figure 9–3.2, if NYC had required 75 (instead of 80) and OAK had required 45 (instead of 40), then, after entering the 70 in the OMA–NYC cell, *both* the OMA row and the NYC column would be completed, and the final entry of 45 into the southeast cell would complete the matrix which would then have only seven occupied cells. Schedules such as that, with fewer than $(m + n - 1)$ occupied cells are called *degenerate,* and for reasons which we shall explore in a moment, their evaluation requires a simple additional step.

Looking at the basic-feasible solution of Figure 9–3.10, we find that we can evaluate each of the empty cells in turn by the device of finding a *closed path, consisting of horizontal and vertical lines, leading from each empty cell back to itself, turning 90 degrees at occupied cells.* However, as we shall see, the closed path does not turn at *every* occupied cell through which it passes. It turns as necessary to create the closed path. Finding the closed path requires a bit of ingenuity in some cases, but the student will become quite adept at it very quickly. Let us see what these closed paths look like. Figure 9–4.1 shows such closed paths for three selected

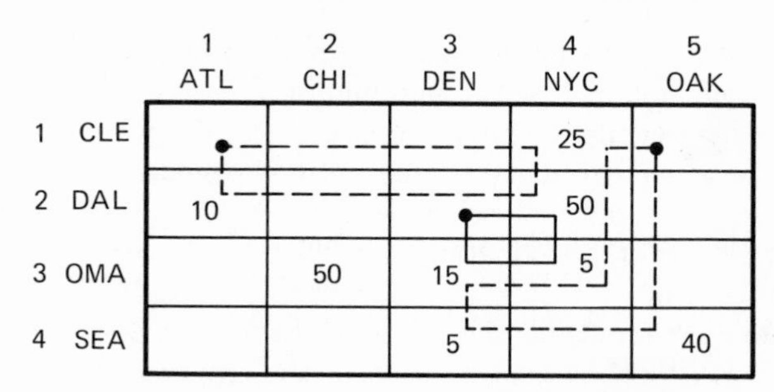

Fig. 9–4.1. Closed paths for cell evaluation for cells 23, 11, and 15.

cells. For cell 23, DAL–DEN, the closed path is a small square with the three adjacent occupied cells as shown by the solid fine line. For cell 11, the closed path is a rectangle as shown by the dashed line. For cell 15, the closed path is a more complex shape as shown by the dashed line.

The method for finding these paths has been called the *stepping-stones* method, from an analogy with walking on a path of stones half submerged in water. The numerical entries are called *stones,* and the cells which are occupied by these numerical entries are called *stone cells.* The unoccupied cells are called *water cells.* Then the path is found by moving from the selected water cell back to itself by horizontal and vertical movements.

The path may pass through any number of stone cells or water cells, but it may turn only on stone cells. This analogy may be helpful to the reader.

A similar closed path may be found for every unoccupied cell, provided that there are $(m + n - 1)$ *independent* cells occupied. The use of the word *independent* here is a new use; *occupied cells in a rectangular matrix are in independent positions, if it is not possible to find a closed path, as defined above, leading from any occupied cell back to itself.* The shipping schedule shown in Figure 9–4.1 does consist of $(m + n - 1)$ independent entries. The procedures which we have used for finding a first feasible solution will automatically yield entries in independent positions (unless an error is made).

The reader should try to describe the closed paths for each of the other 9 unoccupied cells. For checking, the correct paths are shown in Table 9–4.1.

TABLE 9–4.1

For Cell	Closed Path as Described by Corner Cell Designations
12	32–34–14
13	33–34–14
22	24–34–32
25	45–43–33–34–24
31	21–24–34
35	45–43–33
41	21–24–34–33–43
42	32–33–43
44	43–33–34

The fact that every unoccupied cell has a closed path back to itself proves that $(m + n - 1)$ *is the maximum number of independent positions.* That is, if $(m + n - 1)$ independent positions are occupied, no additional independent positions exist.

Let us now proceed with the evaluation of unoccupied cells, starting with cell 11. The "indirect" shipment of a unit from CLE to ATL, as defined in Section 9–1, would be achieved by changing the allocation in each of the corner cells as follows.

One unit more	CLE–NYC, costing \$ 4
One unit fewer	DAL–NYC, saving \$14
One unit more	DAL–ATL, costing \$ 7

The net effect of this would be to send one unit from CLE and receive one unit at ATL, at a net cost of $4 - 14 + 7 = \$-3$. This compares favorably with the direct cost of \$6, indicating that this cell, (11), which is unoccupied, should remain unoccupied, thus continuing to avoid the direct cost of \$6, which has a disadvantage of \$9 as compared with the indirect cost of \$−3.

Similarly we can evaluate cell 23, as shown in Figure 9–4.1. The direct cost is \$7 as given in Figure 9–3.1, and the indirect cost is $14 - 12 + 5 =$ \$7. For this cell, the direct and indirect costs are exactly equal. This means that cell 23 could be used with no penalty, but it also indicates that the non-use of this cell is also perfectly satisfactory.

In like manner we can evaluate all of the empty cells of Figure 9–4.1. If each of the unoccupied cells has its direct cost greater than indirect cost, the solution is optimal. That is, if we define Δ_{ij} (the capital Greek letter Delta with row and column subscript numbers to identify individual cells) as the difference between the direct cost c_{ij}, and the indirect cost I_{ij}, then

$$\Delta_{ij} = c_{ij} - I_{ij} \tag{9–4.1}$$

and $\Delta_{ij} > 0$ for all cells in the optimal solution.

If there are any cells in which Δ_{ij} is negative, i.e., which have direct cost less than indirect cost, the shipping schedule must be altered and then re-evaluated. Since the process of altering a nonoptimal shipping schedule involves selecting that empty cell with the *greatest* negative value of Δ_{ij}, it is clearly necessary to evaluate all empty cells. This procedure, which may be burdensome for manual computation, may be shortened and made more efficient. Therefore, before examining the process of altering and improving a nonoptimal schedule, let us first examine a more efficient procedure for evaluating the empty cells in a given basic-feasible solution.

9–5. Efficient Computational Procedure. Instead of evaluating each empty cell individually, it is possible to evaluate all of the empty cells simultaneously by the following procedure, known as the MODI (modified distribution) method. We shall illustrate this procedure by applying it to the first feasible shipping schedule obtained by the penalty method and shown in Figure 9–3.10.

1. Draw four blank matrices. In this case, they are 4-by-5 matrices, as in Figure 9–5.1.
2. In the first matrix place a large dash in the cells corresponding to the *unoccupied* cells of the solution being evaluated (Figure 9–3.10). In the other three matrices place a large dash in the cells corresponding to the *occupied* cells of the solution being evaluated.
3. In the first and third matrices enter the direct unit costs (as given in Figure 9–3.1) into the cells without dashes. Each cost figure is entered *once*.
4. To the first and second matrix add an additional column, labeled u_i, and row, labeled v_j. The values for u_i and v_j are computed in the first matrix and then transferred to the second matrix. The u_i and v_j are computed in the first matrix as follows. Select one

of the u_i or v_j to be zero. Actually, it does not matter which is selected, but the arithmetic is minimized by selection of a row or column with many entries. In Figure 9–5.1, column 4 is selected

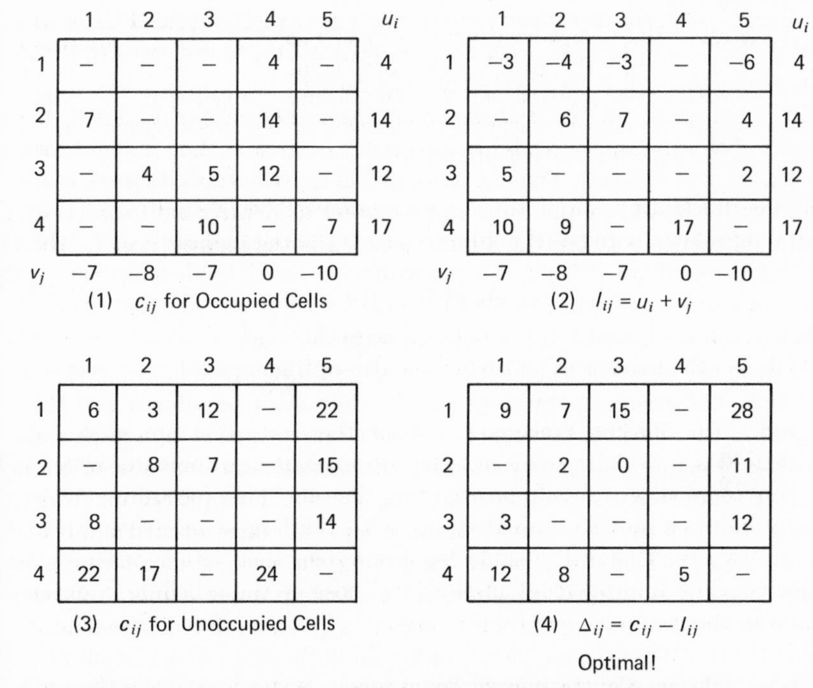

(1) c_{ij} for Occupied Cells

	1	2	3	4	5	u_i
1	–	–	–	4	–	4
2	7	–	–	14	–	14
3	–	4	5	12	–	12
4	–	–	10	–	7	17
v_j	−7	−8	−7	0	−10	

(2) $I_{ij} = u_i + v_j$

	1	2	3	4	5	u_i
1	−3	−4	−3	–	−6	4
2	–	6	7	–	4	14
3	5	–	–	–	2	12
4	10	9	–	17	–	17
v_j	−7	−8	−7	0	−10	

(3) c_{ij} for Unoccupied Cells

	1	2	3	4	5
1	6	3	12	–	22
2	–	8	7	–	15
3	8	–	–	–	14
4	22	17	–	24	–

(4) $\Delta_{ij} = c_{ij} - I_{ij}$

	1	2	3	4	5
1	9	7	15	–	28
2	–	2	0	–	11
3	3	–	–	–	12
4	12	8	–	5	–

Optimal!

Fig. 9–5.1. Waymar Mfg. Co. Worksheet for MODI method for evaluation of shipping schedule of Figure 9–3.10. Note: By using colored pencils or by subdividing cells, this may be done with fewer matrices.

to have its v_j equal to zero; i.e., $v_4 = 0$. Now complete the computation of all of the u_i and v_j, using the rule that, in this *first* matrix,

$$c_{ij} = u_i + v_j \tag{9–5.1}$$

Thus, with $v_4 = 0$, $u_1 = 4$, since $c_{14} = 4$. Similarly, $u_2 = 14$, and $u_3 = 12$. Now, since $u_2 = 14$, v_1 must equal -7, so that $c_{21} = 14 - 7 = 7$. Similarly $v_2 = -8$, and $v_3 = -7$. Now, with $v_3 = -7$, u_4 must equal 17, and then v_5 must equal -10.

5. Transfer the u_i and v_j values to the second matrix, and compute the indirect costs of the unoccupied cells, using the rule in the *second* matrix that

$$u_i + v_j = I_{ij} \tag{9–5.2}$$

The indirect costs generated in this way are exactly the same as those derived for individual cells in the last section.

6. Compute Δ_{ij} for each cell by subtracting the value in the second matrix from the corresponding value in the third matrix, following the rule

$$\Delta_{ij} = c_{ij} - I_{ij} \tag{9–5.3}$$

7. If all of the Δ_{ij} are positive or zero, the solution being evaluated is optimal, and the problem is completed. If one or more Δ_{ij} are negative, the solution is not optimal, and the cell with the largest negative value is selected as the cell to become occupied in the next step, the shifting procedure.

In this illustration, all of the Δ_{ij} were nonnegative, indicating that the shipping schedule given in Figure 9–3.10 is the optimal solution. That is, we were fortunate in that the procedure we used to develop the first feasible solution actually yielded the optimal solution. The fact that one of the Δ_{ij}, namely Δ_{23}, is equal to 0 indicates that there is another schedule which has the same cost and which is also optimal.

9–6. The Shifting Procedure. When the evaluation procedure indicates that a particular solution is not optimal, it also indicates which of the unoccupied cells should be occupied. The shifting procedure moves as many units as possible into that cell with the largest negative value of Δ_{ij}. If two cells have the same highest value, then either one may be selected. The improvement in the total cost of the schedule is exactly equal to the Δ_{ij} multiplied by the number of units shifted. That is, if the highest negative Δ_{ij} is, say, \$−4, and if 20 units may be shifted into that cell, the total cost of the new shipping schedule will be \$80 less than that of the previous solution.

Before performing the shifting, we must consult the current nonoptimal schedule in order to ascertain the closed path over which the shifting must take place. In our illustration, we shall use the solution obtained by the minimum-cell-cost method shown in Figure 9–3.5. We know that that schedule is not optimal, because its cost is \$1,745, which is higher than the \$1,535 of the solution obtained by the penalty method and which has been shown to be the optimal. However, we must evaluate this nonoptimal solution, if only to determine which unoccupied cell is to become occupied. Figure 9–6.1 shows the evaluation procedure for this basic-feasible schedule. The presence of the negative values in the Δ_{ij} matrix indicates that the solution is not optimal. The cell which we must select to become an occupied cell is the cell with the largest negative number; but, in this case, there are two cells with the same value, −7. We shall arbitrarily select cell 43, but we could just as correctly have selected cell 14.

Looking at Figure 9–6.2, we see that the closed path for cell 43 is such that, for every unit entered into cell 43, one must be removed from cell 33, one must be added to cell 34, and one must be removed from cell 44. This

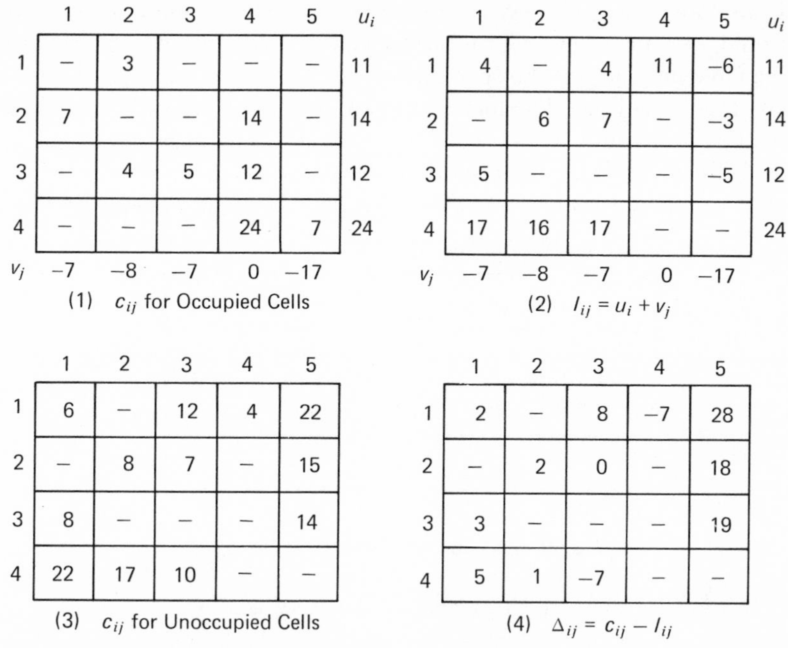

	1	2	3	4	5	u_i
1	–	3	–	–	–	11
2	7	–	–	14	–	14
3	–	4	5	12	–	12
4	–	–	–	24	7	24
v_j	−7	−8	−7	0	−17	

(1) c_{ij} for Occupied Cells

	1	2	3	4	5	u_i
1	4	–	4	11	−6	11
2	–	6	7	–	−3	14
3	5	–	–	–	−5	12
4	17	16	17	–	–	24
v_j	−7	−8	−7	0	−17	

(2) $I_{ij} = u_i + v_j$

	1	2	3	4	5
1	6	–	12	4	22
2	–	8	7	–	15
3	8	–	–	–	14
4	22	17	10	–	–

(3) c_{ij} for Unoccupied Cells

	1	2	3	4	5
1	2	–	8	−7	28
2	–	2	0	–	18
3	3	–	–	–	19
4	5	1	−7	–	–

(4) $\Delta_{ij} = c_{ij} - I_{ij}$

Fig. 9–6.1. Worksheet for evaluation of first feasible solution derived by minimum-cell-cost method as shown in Figure 9–3.5.

	1	2	3	4	5
1		25			
2	10			50	
3		25	20 ⊖	25 ⊕	
4			⊕	5 ⊖	40

Fig. 9–6.2. Nonoptimal first basic-feasible solution obtained by minimum-cell-cost method. Closed path for shifting into cell 43 shown.

procedure maintains the correct row and column totals, thus insuring that the new schedule will also be feasible. It is useful to follow the procedure shown in Figure 9–6.2; that is, to start at the new cell to become occupied and proceed around the closed path, entering alternately a minus sign and a plus sign in the successive *corner* cells, until the path is completed back to the new cell with its plus sign. This has been done for cell 43 in Figure 9–6.2.

The maximum number of units which may be shifted along the closed path is determined by the smallest number in the cells with minus signs.

In this case, five units may be shifted into cell 43 and out of cells 33 and 44 (and, of course, *into* cell 34, but this does not constitute a restriction). When five units have been thus shifted, cell 44 will be empty, and no more units may be shifted. The final result is that cell 43 will then be occupied with five units, and cell 44 will be unoccupied. The number of occupied cells is the same as before, the row and column totals are unchanged, and the new schedule is a basic-feasible solution. The result is shown in Figure

	1	2	3	4	5	
1		25				25
2	10			50		60
3		25	15	30		70
4			5		40	45
	10	50	20	80	40	

Fig. 9–6.3. Solution after first iteration.

9–6.3, which is the resulting schedule. Its total cost is

$$\begin{aligned} TC &= \Sigma c_{ij}x_{ij} \\ &= (3)(25) + (7)(10) + (14)(50) + (4)(25) + (5)(15) + (12)(30) \\ &\qquad + (10)(5) + (7)(40) \\ &= 75 + 70 + 700 + 100 + 75 + 360 + 50 + 280 = \$1{,}710 \end{aligned}$$

We now test this solution for optimality in Figure 9–6.4. The presence of the negative entry in the Δ_{ij} matrix again indicates that this solution is not optimal, and that the shifting process must be performed again.

It may seem that, since the -7 appearing in cell 14 was there in the previous cycle, we could have performed both shifting procedures, i.e., cell 43 and cell 14, after the first evaluation. This would not be sound procedure. The Δ_{ij} depends upon the indirect cost of the unoccupied cell, and this in turn depends upon the pattern of occupied cells. A comparison of Figure 9–6.4 with Figure 9–6.1 shows that several of the I_{ij} and, consequently, the Δ_{ij} have changed as a result of the first shifting step. Some of the Δ_{ij} are higher in Figure 9–6.1, and others are higher in Figure 9–6.4. Some changes may eliminate previous negative Δ's, and others may create new negative Δ's. It may be possible to try to predict these, but the best and safest method is to proceed as outlined here, shifting into only *one* cell in each iteration cycle.

The closed path for cell 14 is shown in Figure 9–6.5. The maximum number that may be shifted into cell 14 is twenty-five. This will empty cell 12. Twenty-five units will also be removed from cell 34 and added to cell 32. The new schedule is shown in Figure 9–6.6. This is the optimal

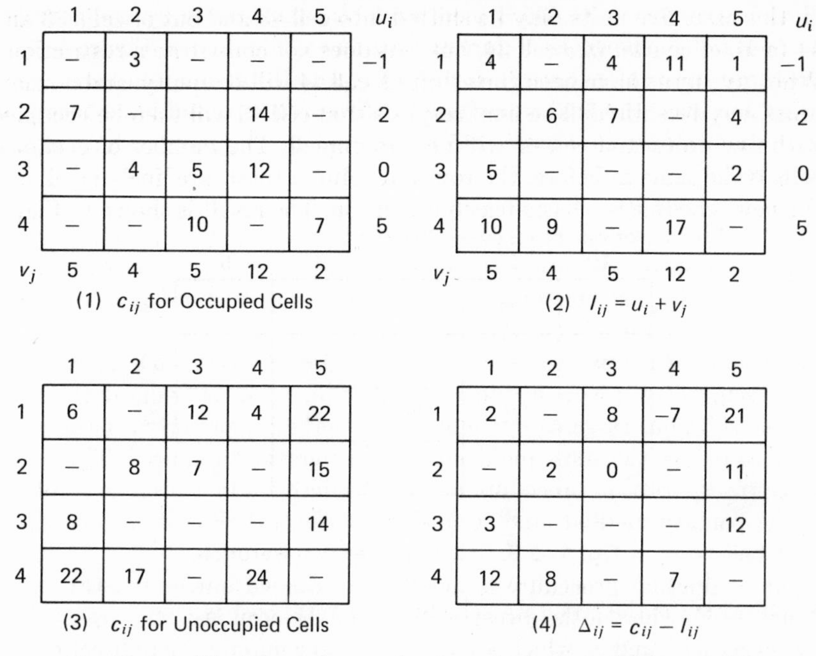

	1	2	3	4	5	u_i
1	–	3	–	–	–	–1
2	7	–	–	14	–	2
3	–	4	5	12	–	0
4	–	–	10	–	7	5
v_j	5	4	5	12	2	

(1) c_{ij} for Occupied Cells

	1	2	3	4	5	u_i
1	4	–	4	11	1	–1
2	–	6	7	–	4	2
3	5	–	–	–	2	0
4	10	9	–	17	–	5
v_j	5	4	5	12	2	

(2) $I_{ij} = u_i + v_j$

	1	2	3	4	5
1	6	–	12	4	22
2	–	8	7	–	15
3	8	–	–	–	14
4	22	17	–	24	–

(3) c_{ij} for Unoccupied Cells

	1	2	3	4	5
1	2	–	8	–7	21
2	–	2	0	–	11
3	3	–	–	–	12
4	12	8	–	7	–

(4) $\Delta_{ij} = c_{ij} - I_{ij}$

Fig. 9–6.4. Worksheet for evaluation of solution of Figure 9–6.3.

	1	2	3	4	5
1		25 ⊖		⊕	
2	10			50	
3		25 ⊕	15	30 ⊖	
4			5		40

Fig. 9–6.5. Nonoptimal solution resulting from first iteration. Closed path for shifting into cell 14 shown.

	1	2	3	4	5	
1				25		25
2	10			50		60
3		50	15	5		70
4			5		40	45
	10	50	20	80	40	

Fig. 9–6.6. Waymar Mfg Co. Solution after second iteration. Optimal!

solution with TC = \$1,535, which was obtained directly by the penalty method and is shown in Figure 9–3.10 and evaluated in Figure 9–5.1. Therefore it is not necessary for us to repeat the evaluation here. Normally, however, the final stage in the entire process would have been the evaluation shown in Figure 9–5.1, wherein no negative values of Δ_{ij} appeared.

9–7. The Iteration Procedure Reviewed. The entire iteration procedure consists of evaluation, followed by shifting, followed by evaluation, followed by shifting, etc., until the evaluation procedure indicates that the optimal solution has been reached.

Of course, it is first necessary to have a solution to evaluate, and, as we have seen, there are many possible procedures for arriving at the first feasible solution. In general, the penalty method is preferred, because it tends to reduce the subsequent number of iterations required. Thus, the entire transportation procedure is, first, to derive a first feasible solution by the penalty method, and second, to perform the iteration process as described here.

The evaluation procedure is most easily carried out as illustrated in Figure 9–5.1, wherein the direct costs, c_{ij}, of the occupied cells are used to compute the u_i and v_j, which are then used to compute the indirect costs, I_{ij}, of the unoccupied cells; and from these, the Δ_{ij}, the differences between the direct and indirect costs of the unoccupied cells, are computed. If all of the Δ_{ij} are nonnegative, the evaluated solution is optimal.

If the evaluated solution is not optimal, the cell with the largest negative Δ_{ij} is selected as the unoccupied cell to become occupied by the shifting of units into it. A closed path must be constructed from this cell back to itself, turning on corners which are occupied cells. Some of the cells at the corners will lose units (those in the same row and column as the new cell will lose units; there may or may not be others, depending on the circuity of the path), and others will gain units, with the losing and gaining corners alternating.

The number of units to be shifted is the smallest number in an occupied *losing* corner cell. After the shift, this cell will be unoccupied.

After this shift has been completed, the resulting new schedule must be evaluated; and the process is repeated. No matter how many unoccupied cells had negative Δ_{ij} in the evaluation procedure, only *one* is selected to become occupied; the shift is made into that cell, and the evaluation procedure is repeated.

9–8. Degenerate Solutions. If, at any stage in the iteration procedure, either at the outset or after a shift which emptied two (or more) cells simultaneously, the number of occupied cells is fewer than $(m + n - 1)$, where m is the number of rows and n is the number of columns, that solution is said to be *degenerate*, and the evaluation procedure cannot be continued without a new step. This is because, with a degenerate solution, a closed path cannot be constructed for each unoccupied cell; and for the same reason, the u_i and v_j cannot all be computed.

The situation is easily remedied by selecting an additional cell (or two or more, if necessary) to be treated as if it were occupied. That is, if the number of occupied cells is $(m + n - 2)$, then the solution is deficient by one occupied cell. Select an unoccupied cell which, if occupied, would create, with the already occupied cells, $(m + n - 1)$ *independent* cells. There may be more than one such position available before one has been selected, but once one has been selected, there will be no *additional* independent positions.

Enter ϵ, the lower-case Greek letter epsilon, into this cell. The ϵ is treated as an extremely small number of units. It can be shifted if necessary and treated just like any number, except that, where a is any number,

$$a + \epsilon = a$$

so that, if the ϵ cell receives a units, the resulting entry in that cell is a. Also, in computing the total cost of a schedule, of course the ϵ units incur no cost.

If, in shifting, the ϵ cell *loses* units, then the maximum number of units which can be shifted is ϵ, and the result is merely the shifting of the ϵ entry from its present position to the cell selected to receive units. This shift, of course, causes no change in the total cost. When this happens, it merely means that the ϵ was in a relatively-high-cost cell. Since the evaluation procedure evaluates only the *costs* of the occupied and unoccupied cells, it treats the ϵ cell as an occupied cell, and, if it is a high-cost cell, the procedure will shift the ϵ to a lower-cost cell, so that the final result will be the best cost configuration for all occupied cells, including the ϵ cell (or cells). Therefore, in selecting a position for entering ϵ, it is efficient to select a low-cost cell, if possible, thereby possibly reducing the number of subsequent iterations which may be required. (Of course, if the cell entries are profits rather than costs, as discussed in the next section, then one would seek a *high* profit cell.)

In some cases, two or even more ϵ's may be required to bring the number of "occupied" cells up to $(m + n - 1)$. This is not a complication. Entering the ϵ's as described and following the iteration procedure will lead to the optimal solution.

9–9. Maxima vs. Minima.

In some problems, the entries in the cells are not costs, but rather are profits, and the purpose is to find the maximum rather than the minimum. This often occurs with problems which use the *transportation model* but do not deal with transportation, i.e., the movement of persons or goods. In such cases, the procedure can be carried through with no formal modification. The analyst need only remember that it is a maximization problem. Then, in finding the first feasible solution, he selects the largest penalty between the *highest* and *second highest* profit in each row and column. And, in the evaluation procedure, he wishes the direct profit of the unoccupied cells to be *smaller* than their indirect profit. Clearly, then, the Δ_{ij} should all be negative or zero at the optimal.

9–10. Unequal Requirements and Availabilities. It has been emphasized above that, in order for the transportation procedure to be performed, the total availabilities at the origins must be equal to the total requirements of the destinations ($\Sigma a_i = \Sigma b_j$). This condition *must* be met, or the procedure cannot be used. However, often in real situations this is not the case, and there is excess capacity or shortage in the system. Then in order to perform the analysis it is merely necessary to add an additional "dummy" row or column, labeled "excess capacity" or "shortage," balancing Σa_i and Σb_j.

For example, in the matrix of Figure 9–3.1, if New York were to require 100 instead of 80, a new row, labeled "shortage" would be added below Seattle, with "availability" of 20 and shipping costs of zero. Then the procedure would allocate the system shortage of 20 units to the various destinations in a way that will minimize total system transportation cost. Conversely, if, say, Dallas had 75 to ship instead of 60, a new column, labeled "excess capacity" or "carry-over inventory" would be added to the right of Oakland. It would have a "requirement" of 15 units and zero shipping costs. The transportation procedure then would allocate this system overage to the various origins in a way that will minimize total system shipping costs.

In pricing a "dummy" origin or destination, it does not matter what price is used, as long as the same price is used for all entries in that dummy column or row. The transportation method will yield the same allocation in any case, since, with the cost of the dummy allocations thus fixed, the system will optimize the remainder of the allocation, and that "remainder" is, of course, the original allocation to be optimized.

9–11. An Illustration. In the following illustration, we shall see three matters which have been referred to above. First, it is a transportation model, but it has nothing to do with transportation; second, the requirements and availabilities are not equal; and third, the first feasible solution is degenerate.

The Vibrin Manufacturing Company purchases raw wool and spins it into yarn. The annual sales of the company are 12,000 pounds of wool yarn, with the manufacturing and sales distributed throughout the four calendar quarters of the year as shown in Table 9–11.1. Table 9–11.1 also

TABLE 9–11.1

Vibrin Manufacturing Company Production, Sales, Purchase and Price Data

Calendar Quarter	Production (lb.)	Sales of Yarn (lb.)	Raw Wool Purchase Price (per lb.)
1	2,000	2,000	$ .40
2	3,000	3,000	.60
3	3,000	3,000	.75
4	4,000	4,000	1.00

shows the price of raw wool, which is the only raw material that the Vibrin Company purchases. The price varies seasonally as shown in the table.

Since the company is a going concern, operating continuously for many years, it seeks to develop a pattern of raw-wool purchases which will minimize its costs for purchasing, manufacturing, and storage. The manufacturing and storage costs are given in Table 9–11.2. In analyzing

TABLE 9–11.2

Vibrin Manufacturing Company Cost Data

Purchase Date	Processing and Storage Cost per lb.
Same quarter as processing	$ .50
One quarter earlier	.60
Two quarters earlier	.80
Three quarters earlier	1.00
Four or more quarters earlier	Prohibitive

this problem, we can assume that raw wool is delivered to Vibrin on the first day of the quarter in which it is purchased. Wool purchased at any time may be processed in that same quarter, or it may be kept in the raw wool inventory for processing in a subsequent quarter. The finished yarn is processed as it is sold, so that the sales and processing figures in Table 9–11.1 are identical. The sales price for Vibrin's yarn is constant at $2.00 per pound, and the only restriction on the purchasing pattern is that the company cannot purchase more than 5,000 pounds of raw wool per quarter.

This problem may be treated as a transportation problem in which the "sources" are the quarters of the year in which the raw wool is purchased, and the "destinations" are the quarters in which the wool is processed into yarn and sold. Since the company has the capability to purchase up to

5,000 pounds in each quarter, one of the outputs of the analysis will be a quarter-by-quarter allocation of "unpurchased capability."

Thus, of the 5,000 pounds of raw wool *which may be purchased* in each quarter, some may be allocated to production in the first quarter, some in the second quarter, some in the third quarter, and some in the fourth quarter, and some will not be purchased. In Figure 9–11.1, each cost is the sum of the purchase cost from Table 9–11.1 and the processing and storage

		Quarter Processed and Sold				Not	
		1	2	3	4	Purchased	a_i
Quarter Purchased	1	0.90	1.00	1.20	1.40	0	5,000
	2	1.60	1.10	1.20	1.40	0	5,000
	3	1.55	1.75	1.25	1.35	0	5,000
	4	1.60	1.80	2.00	1.50	0	5,000
	b_j	2,000	3,000	3,000	4,000	8,000	20,000

Fig. 9–11.1. The Vibrin Company problem. Cost matrix with a_i and b_j shown.

cost of Table 9–11.2. For example, cell 11 represents the cost of raw wool purchased in the first quarter ($0.40) and processed in the same quarter in which it was purchased ($0.50). Similarly cell 23 represents cost of raw wool purchased in the second quarter ($0.60) and processed in the next quarter ($0.60). Cell 21 represents raw wool purchased in the second quarter ($0.60) and processed in the first quarter of the next calendar year, which is three quarters later ($1.00). In this way the costs shown in the body of the matrix of Figure 9–11.1 have been computed. Note that there is an additional column in that matrix and that it is headed "Not Purchased." This is a so-called *dummy* column which is added to equalize the availabilities and capacities. It takes up the slack in the purchase capability, and, since it represents raw wool that is not purchased, the costs in that column are zero. The a_i are shown as 5,000 lb. per quarter, and the b_j are the amounts to be processed and sold in each quarter. Obviously, there will be an unpurchased capability of 8,000 lb. each year. The analysis will determine how this will be allocated to the four calendar quarters.

The first feasible solution, as found by the penalty method, is shown in Figure 9–11.2. The reader should verify this result (see Exercise 9–1).

The allocation matrix shown in Figure 9–11.2 has seven real entries. Since $(m + n - 1)$ is equal to 8, this solution is degenerate, as defined in Section 9–8. It has also been pointed out that it is not possible to evaluate an allocation matrix unless it has exactly $(m + n - 1)$ occupied cells. Therefore, an ϵ, *epsilon*, has been entered in cell 15. This position is only one of several possible cells into which the ϵ could have been entered. The

Quarter Processed and Sold

Quarter Purchased	1	2	3	4	Not Purchased
1	2,000	3,000			ϵ
2			3,000	2,000	
3				2,000	3,000
4					5,000

Fig. 9–11.2. The Vibrin Company. First feasible solution by the penalty method. Degenerate solution. For evaluation, ϵ is entered in cell 15.

only restriction here is that the ϵ must be entered in an *independent* position. That is, after it is entered, there must be no closed loops as defined in Section 9–4, especially in Figure 9–4.1, from any occupied cell (including the ϵ cell) back to itself. Clearly, cells 25, 33, and 44 would *not* have been eligible. The solution is now evaluated in the usual way. The only difference, with one or more ϵ's in the system, is that, if the ϵ is to be shifted, it is moved to the indicated cell, but the other cells, which are occupied by real numbers, are unchanged; i.e., ϵ is so small that adding or subtracting ϵ does not change any real number. The evaluation in Figure 9–11.3 shows that this solution is not optimal and that cell 25 should be

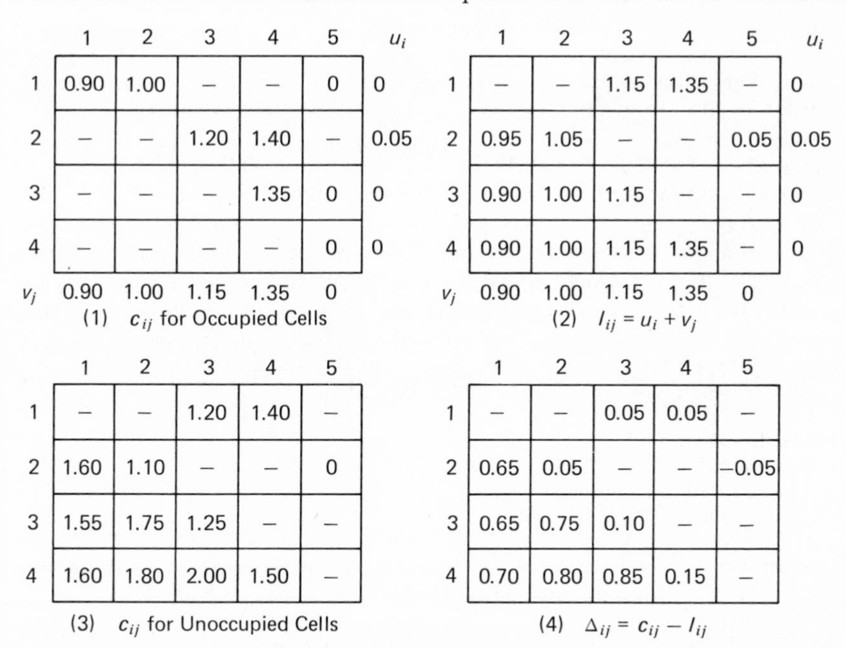

	1	2	3	4	5	u_i
1	0.90	1.00	–	–	0	0
2	–	–	1.20	1.40	–	0.05
3	–	–	–	1.35	0	0
4	–	–	–	–	0	0
v_j	0.90	1.00	1.15	1.35	0	

(1) c_{ij} for Occupied Cells

	1	2	3	4	5	u_i
1	–	–	1.15	1.35	–	0
2	0.95	1.05	–	–	0.05	0.05
3	0.90	1.00	1.15	–	–	0
4	0.90	1.00	1.15	1.35	–	0
v_j	0.90	1.00	1.15	1.35	0	

(2) $I_{ij} = u_i + v_j$

	1	2	3	4	5
1	–	–	1.20	1.40	–
2	1.60	1.10	–	–	0
3	1.55	1.75	1.25	–	–
4	1.60	1.80	2.00	1.50	–

(3) c_{ij} for Unoccupied Cells

	1	2	3	4	5
1	–	–	0.05	0.05	–
2	0.65	0.05	–	–	–0.05
3	0.65	0.75	0.10	–	–
4	0.70	0.80	0.85	0.15	–

(4) $\Delta_{ij} = c_{ij} - I_{ij}$

Fig. 9–11.3. Vibrin Company. Worksheet for MODI method for solution evaluation. Solution not optimal—negative entry in cell 25.

occupied. Examination of Figure 9–11.2 shows that the closed path for shifting into cell 25 is the small path involving cells 24, 34, and 35, and that 2,000 pounds can be shifted. The next feasible solution, after this shift has been made is shown in Figure 9–11.4. This is the optimal

		Quarter Processed and Sold				
		1	2	3	4	Not Purchased
Quarter Purchased	1	2,000	3,000			ϵ
	2			3,000		2,000
	3				4,000	1,000
	4					5,000

Fig. 9–11.4. Vibrin Company. Optimal solution.

solution. The reader should evaluate this solution to verify that it is optimal (see Exercise 9–2).

SUGGESTIONS FOR FURTHER READING

See suggested readings for Chapter 13.

EXERCISES

9–1. Verify the solution given in Figure 9–11.2 by finding the first feasible solution to the Vibrin Company problem using the penalty method.

9–2. Evaluate the solution to the Vibrin Company problem as given in Figure 9-11.4. Show that it is optimal. What are the costs to the Company? What is the Company's annual profit from the spinning operation?

9–3. Starting with the degenerate solution to the Vibrin Company problem as given in Figure 9–11.2, enter ϵ in some other place and find the optimal solution.

9–4. The Henrei Garment Manufacturing Company manufactures ladies' skirts, jackets, and coats. For the purposes of this analysis, we shall assume that all garments require exactly the same amount of fabric, namely, precisely 3 yd. of fabric per garment. These garments may be made from any of the following four fabrics, of which the amount on hand is given below:

Wool, 120 yd. on hand
Dacron and cotton, 90 yd. on hand
Orlon, 75 yd. on hand
Acetate blend, 60 yd. on hand

The company must manufacture this week exactly 30 of each type of garment (i.e., 30 skirts, 30 jackets, and 30 coats) from the fabric on hand. These may be made of any of the four fabrics in any proportions, but each individual garment is made wholly of one of the four fabrics, and no additional fabrics of any kind are available in the present planning period. The accounting department reports the expected profit per garment to be as given in the following table:

Fabric	Skirt	Jacket	Coat
Wool	$10	$18	$20
Dacron–Cotton	8	15	18
Orlon	6	10	15
Acetate blend	5	8	10

a) How many of each type of garment should be made of each fabric for maximum profit?

b) How much profit will be earned?

9–5. The Lojor Sports Car Company production manager is scheduling the production and shipping of orders for the coming month. The numbers of cars to be delivered at the end of the coming month are:

To Be Delivered In	Number of Cars
Chicago	28
Hartford	18
Kansas City	7
Miami	15
Philadelphia	10
Tulsa	12

The monthly production capacity of each of the Company's plants is:

Plant	Monthly Capacity (Cars)
Albany	10
Boston	20
Cleveland	15
Dallas	15
Denver	10
Detroit	30

Using the transportation costs provided in Exercise 8–1, what is the minimum cost schedule for shipping the cars from the plants to their destinations? What is the minimum cost of shipping the cars?

9–6. What is the best production scheduling program for the Lojor Sports Car Company (Exercise 9–5) to follow in order to minimize manufacturing and transportation costs, if the company continues to absorb transportation costs, and if the manufacturing costs are not the same in all plants but rather are as given below?

Do not complete the iteration procedure to arrive at the optimal program. The student is here asked only to derive the first feasible solution by the penalty method. The complete manual working out of the iteration procedure for this problem is very long and tedious, and the major instructional purpose of the exercise is achieved by setting up the problem and finding the first feasible solution. However, for those who wish to pursue this problem to its completion, the questions given below will be of interest.

Plant	Unit Manufacturing Costs
Albany	$4,500
Boston	4,700
Cleveland	4,850
Dallas	4,350
Denver	4,000
Detroit	4,000

What is the total cost of the optimal program? Compare your result with the total cost (including manufacturing cost) of the program, which you obtained in the previous question, in which only the transportation costs were considered in making the allocation.

10

Introduction to Linear Programming

10–1. The Basic Statement of the Problem. The basic problem which can be solved by linear programming is that of maximizing (or minimizing) some linear objective function subject to one or more linear constraints. Let us try to understand this last statement by analyzing it piece by piece and illustrating it in terms of a graphic analysis of a specific problem.

The objective to be achieved in this illustrative problem is to determine how the Everich Air Cargo Company should load a cargo airplane for a single flight in order to maximize the revenue from that flight. There are two kinds of cargo. Cargo type A is delicate cargo, e.g., live chicks, which must be carried in the pressurized portion of the aircraft; and cargo of type B is ordinary cargo, e.g., machinery and clothing, which may be carried in the unpressurized hold of the aircraft. The revenue for the trip is $3,000 per ton for cargo of type A, and $1,000 per ton for cargo of type B. There is available more of both kinds of cargo than can be carried in this flight, and therefore the problem is merely to load the aircraft for maximum revenue.

The aircraft has two holds: a pressurized cabin hold and a larger unpressurized main hold. Since there is no shortage of cargo of either type, cargo type A will be put into the cabin hold, and cargo type B will be put into the main hold. The variables in the problem, then, are:

x_1, the number of tons of cargo carried in the main hold
x_2, the number of tons of cargo carried in the cabin hold

The total revenue, E ("effectiveness"), from the flight, in thousands of dollars, is

$$E = x_1 + 3x_2 \tag{10–1.1}$$

This is the *linear objective function.* The purpose of the problem is to select x_1 and x_2 in the way which will maximize E. The linearity of this function is seen in Figure 10–1.1. In order to plot the function, it is

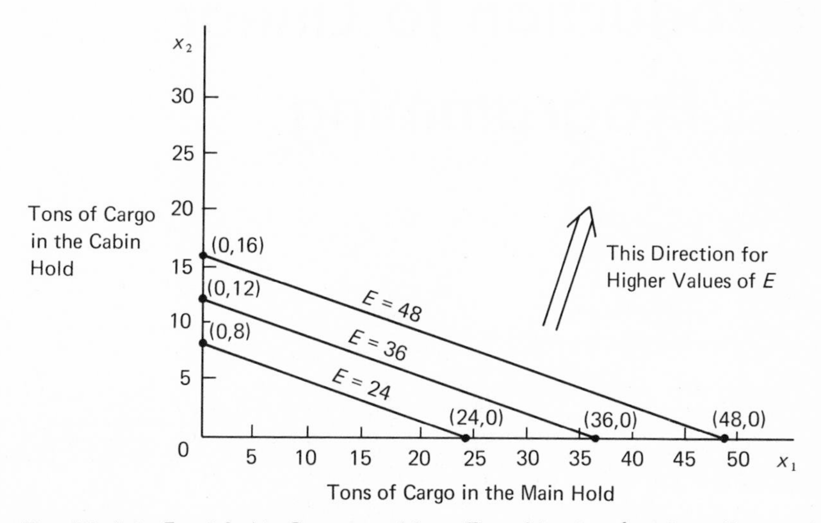

Fig. 10–1.1. Everich Air Cargo problem. The objective function: $E = x_1 + 3x_2$, for $E = 24$, $E = 36$, and $E = 48$.

necessary to select, arbitrarily, some value of E, and the line then represents all combinations of values of x_1 and x_2 which will yield that specified value of E. For example, let us select $E = 24$ thousand dollars. Then the equation is

$$24 = x_1 + 3x_2 \tag{10–1.2}$$

In order to plot this straight line, we must identify any two points and connect them.

Clearly, if $x_1 = 0$, then $x_2 = 8$; also, if $x_2 = 0$, then $x_1 = 24$.

Thus the points (0,8) and (24,0) satisfy the equation. This is the line plotted in Figure 10–1.1 and identified as $E = 24$. Similarly, for $E = 36$, two points would be: (0,12) and (36,0). In Figure 10–1.1, this line, $E = 36$, is plotted, as is also the line for $E = 48$.

Clearly, the objective function may be viewed as a family of straight parallel lines, each line representing a different value of that objective function. In this problem, where the purpose is to achieve the maximum value of the objective function, clearly, if there were no constraints on the amount of cargo that could be carried, then the purpose would be achieved by making x_1 and x_2 indefinitely large. That is, if there were no constraints, we could choose any point in the space shown on Figure 10–1.1 and any point at higher values of x_1 and x_2 even extending beyond the page. For example, the point (40,30) would yield a revenue of

$$E = 40 + (3)(30) = 130 \text{ thousand dollars}$$

However, why stop there? We could pick points at higher values of x_1 and x_2 and realize even greater revenues. Clearly, in any real situation this is impossible. There are restrictions in this problem as in any problem of this sort. In this particular case, the restrictions have to do with the capacities of the aircraft. There are four restrictions.

1. The main hold can take no more than 20 tons of cargo.
2. The cabin hold can take no more than 10 tons of cargo.
3. For balance, the cabin hold can take no more than 1 ton more than $\frac{2}{3}$ the load in the main hold.
4. The aircraft can carry no more than 28 tons of cargo.

These four restrictions are *linear inequalities*. A linear inequality is an *inequation*, which, for our purposes, is an expression in which the symbol, ($\geq$) or ($\leq$) occurs in place of the equality sign,[1] and which, if the symbol had been an equal sign, would be a *linear* equation. The four restrictions given above may be written in symbolic form:

1. $$x_1 \leq 20 \qquad (10\text{–}1.3)$$
2. $$x_2 \leq 10 \qquad (10\text{–}1.4)$$
3. $$x_2 \leq 1 + \tfrac{2}{3}x_1 \qquad (10\text{–}1.5)$$
4. $$x_1 + x_2 \leq 28 \qquad (10\text{–}1.6)$$

Thus, the restrictions are restrictions on the values which the variables may take in the objective function. We can see immediately that the point (40,30), which was discussed in connection with Figure 10–1.1, does not represent a possible (feasible) load for the aircraft, since it violates every one of the four restrictions.

We can now repeat the statement made at the beginning of this section, and it should now be quite meaningful. The basic problem of linear programming is that of maximizing, or minimizing, some linear objective function, subject to one or more linear constraints. Stated in those terms,

[1] It would also be an inequation if the symbol were ($>$) or ($<$) or ($\neq$), but these other forms are not of interest here.

the Everich Air Cargo problem is:

$$\text{Maximize:} \quad E = x_1 + 3x_2 \tag{10–1.7}$$

$$\text{subject to:} \quad x_1 \leq 20 \tag{10–1.8}$$

$$x_2 \leq 10 \tag{10–1.9}$$

$$-\tfrac{2}{3}x_1 + x_2 \leq 1 \tag{10–1.10}$$

$$x_1 + x_2 \leq 28 \tag{10–1.11}$$

This is the specific statement of this air-cargo problem. It corresponds to the general statement for linear programming problems, which, in general terms is:

$$\text{Maximize:} \quad E = c_1x_1 + c_2x_2 + c_3x_3 + \cdots + c_nx_n \tag{10–1.12}$$

$$\text{subject to:} \quad a_{11}x_1 + a_{12}x_2 + \cdots + a_{1n}x_n \leq b_1 \tag{10–1.13}$$

$$a_{21}x_1 + a_{22}x_2 + \cdots + a_{2n}x_n \leq b_2 \tag{10–1.14}$$

$$\vdots \qquad \vdots \qquad \vdots$$

$$a_{m1}x_1 + a_{m2}x_2 + \cdots + a_{mn}x_n \leq b_m \tag{10–1.15}$$

where: n = the number of variables, and m = the number of restrictions

In even more general terms:

$$\text{Maximize:} \quad E = \sum_{j=1}^{n} c_jx_j$$

$$\text{subject to:} \quad \sum_{j=1}^{n} a_{ij}x_j \leq b_i$$

where there are m such restrictions, and i takes values from $i = 1$ for the first restriction to $i = m$ for the mth

In the Everich Air Cargo case, of course, $n = 2$, and, for this reason, as we shall see, the problem can be represented and solved on a two-dimensional graph. When n is larger than 2, the problem cannot be solved graphically in the way which we shall illustrate in the next Section. If $n = 3$, it may sometimes be solved graphically by one skillful in three-dimensional drafting, but for $n \geq 4$, even that is not possible.

One last condition is the nonnegativity requirement. That is,

$$x_i \geq 0 \qquad \text{for all } i \tag{10–1.16}$$

This states that none of the variables may be negative. Clearly, in this aircraft problem, x_1 or x_2 cannot be negative; i.e., a hold cannot take a negative amount of cargo. This nonnegativity requirement applies to, and is an essential part of, all linear programming problems.

10–2. The Graphical Solution. Linear inequations such as those of Equations (10–1.8) to (10–1.11) may be expressed graphically. The points which satisfy such a linear inequation are all of the points which lie on the line for the corresponding *linear equation,* plus all of the points in the entire half-plane lying on one side of that line.

Consider the first inequation of the four:

$$x_1 \leq 20 \qquad (10\text{–}1.8)$$

The corresponding equation is $x_1 = 20$. The graph of that equation would be the vertical line at $x_1 = 20$, as seen on Figure 10–2.1. However, the

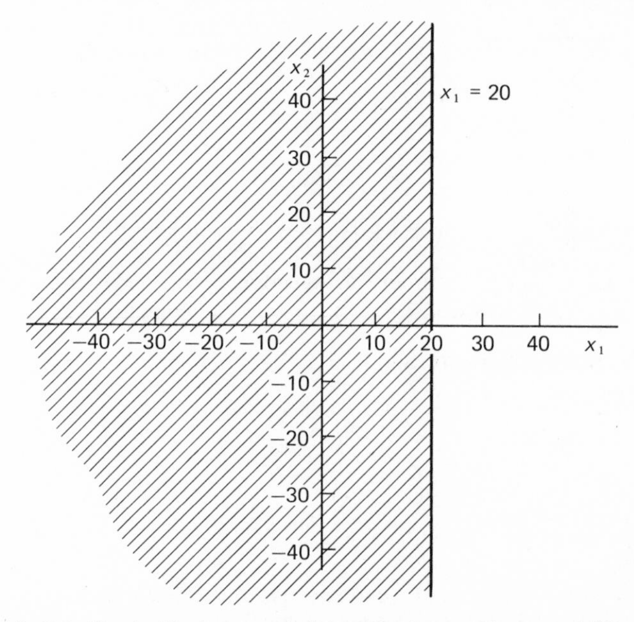

Fig. 10–2.1. The half-plane satisfying the inequation, $x_1 \leq 20$.

inequation is satisfied not only by all of the points *on* that line, but *also* by all of the points lying to the left of the line, i.e., the entire half-plane. That is, if we think of an entire plane (e.g., the plane of this page) extending to infinity in all directions, then any straight line cuts it into two half-planes. In the case of a linear inequality characterized by the symbol ($\geq$) or ($\leq$), one of the two half-planes (as well as the line) satisfies the inequality.

Similarly, for the second inequation,

$$x_2 \leq 10 \qquad (10\text{–}1.9)$$

The half-plane is shown in Figure 10–2.2. Similarly, for the other two inequations,

$$-\tfrac{2}{3}x_1 + x_2 \leq 1 \qquad (10\text{–}1.10)$$

$$x_1 + x_2 \leq 28 \qquad (10\text{–}1.11)$$

The corresponding half–planes are shown in Figures 10–2.3 and 10–2.4.

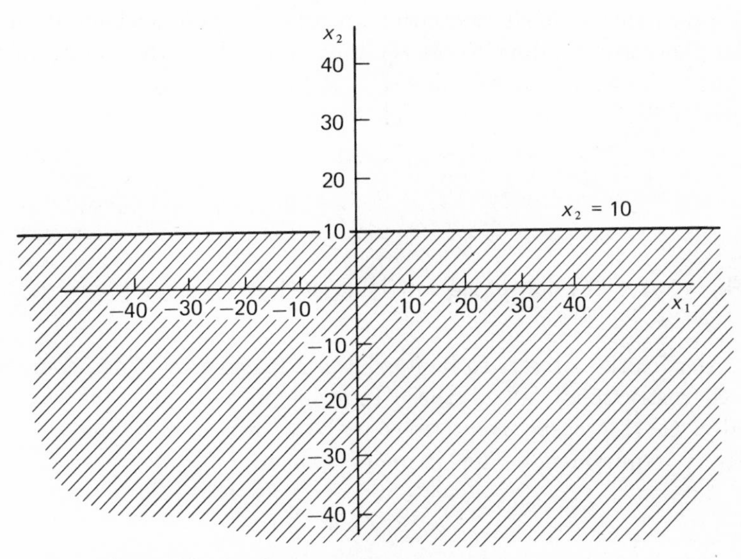

Fig. 10–2.2. The half-plane satisfying the inequation, $x_2 \leq 10$.

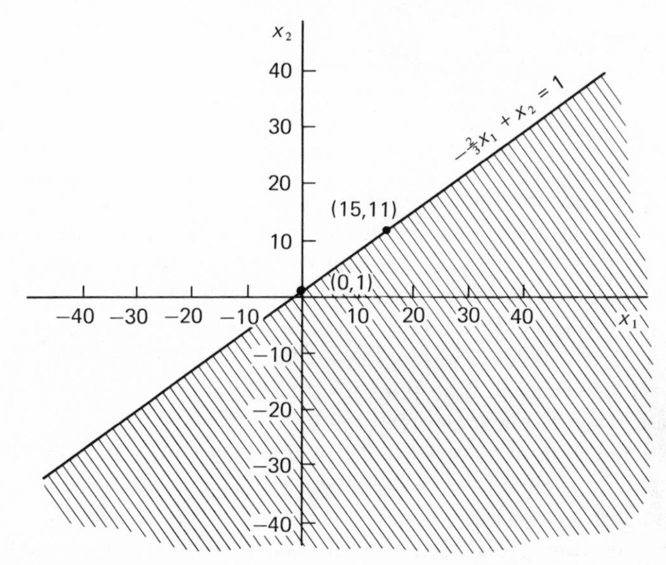

Fig. 10–2.3. The half-plane satisfying the inequation $-\frac{2}{3}x_1 + x_2 \leq 1$.

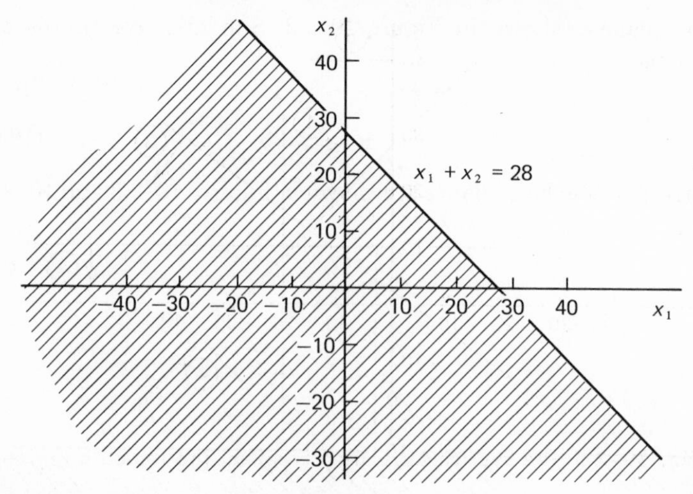

Fig. 10–2.4. The half-plane satisfying the inequation $x_1 + x_2 \leq 28$.

In order for the aircraft to be loaded in a feasible way (i.e., consistent with all restrictions), all of these four inequations must be satisfied. Actually, there are six inequations to be satisfied, including the nonnegativity requirements. The six inequations are:

1. $$x_1 \leq 20 \qquad (10\text{–}1.8)$$
2. $$x_2 \leq 10 \qquad (10\text{–}1.9)$$
3. $$-\tfrac{2}{3}x_1 + x_2 \leq 1 \qquad (10\text{–}1.10)$$
4. $$x_1 + x_2 \leq 28 \qquad (10\text{–}1.11)$$
5. $$x_1 \geq 0 \qquad (10\text{–}2.1)$$
6. $$x_2 \geq 0 \qquad (10\text{–}2.2)$$

The half-planes for the last two inequations, the nonnegativity restrictions, are, respectively, the x_2 (vertical) axis and the area lying to the right of it, and the x_1 (horizontal) axis and the area lying above it.

The area which is satisfied by all six equations is shown in Figure 10–2.5. In the figure, the arrow affixed to each line indicates the direction of the half-plane that satisfies the inequation for which the line represents the corresponding *equation*. The lines are numbered to correspond with the numbers of the inequations given above.

The shaded area in Figure 10–2.5 is the area which satisfies all of the restrictions. It is called the *feasible* region. Only points which lie in that region (including the boundaries) satisfy *all* of the restrictions and are, therefore, feasible. Note that the successive application of each of the inequations has decreased the size of the area within which solutions may

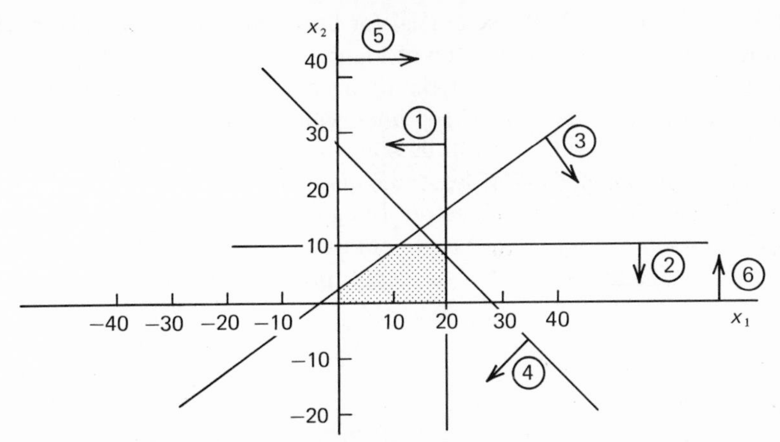

Fig. 10–2.5. The Everich Air Cargo problem. The feasible region.

be sought. That is, the *solutions* space has been reduced, from the entire (x_1,x_2) plane, to the feasible region depicted in Figure 10–2.5.

The fundamental theory of linear programming is based on the characteristics of a feasible region which is delineated in this way, i.e., by a set of linear inequalities. The shape that is thus delineated is called a *convex polygon*, or a *convex set*. A convex polygon or set is a region (in two- or three- or higher multi-dimensional space—although it is difficult to imagine a region in multi-dimensional space) such that, for any two points in the set, the straight line connecting those two points lies wholly within the set. This can be seen to be true for the feasible region shown in Figure 10–2.5, and it can be seen to be true for any shape which is created by a series of linear inequalities. (In the case of three dimensions, each inequality would be represented by a plane, and in more dimensions, by a *hyperplane*.)

Figure 10–2.6 indicates, for the two-dimensional case, the basic difference between convex sets and shapes which are not convex sets. This

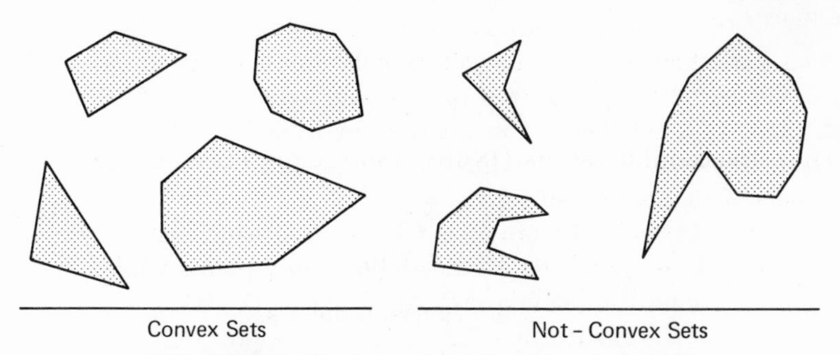

Fig. 10–2.6. Convex sets and not-convex sets.

difference is, as we shall see, crucial for linear programming. The reader will note, upon brief examination of Figure 10–2.6, that the shapes which are drawn on the right side of the figure could not result from a set of linear inequalities. That is, if the lines which delineate their perimeters are drawn and extended, it will be seen that there is some of the area of the shape on *both* sides of at least one of the lines.

If we superimpose the objective function of Figure 10–1.1 upon the feasible region of Figure 10–2.5, we obtain Figure 10–2.7, and, on Figure 10–2.7, the solution to the air cargo problem becomes immediately

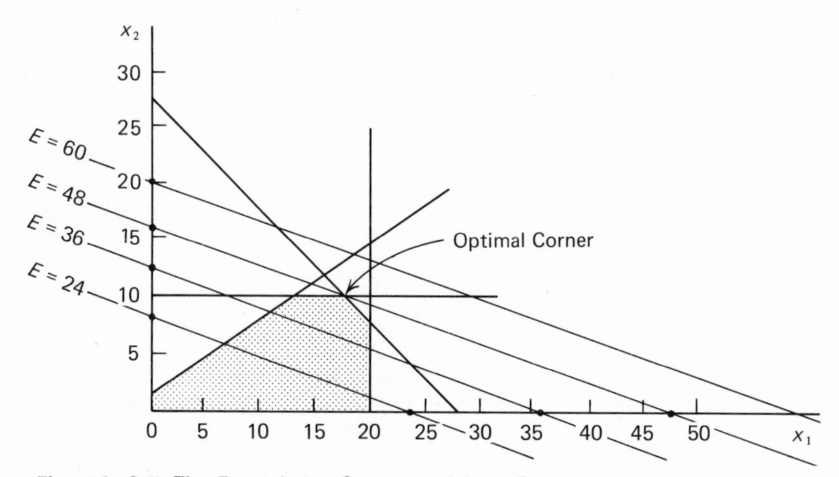

Fig. 10–2.7. The Everich Air Cargo problem. Complete analysis. At optimal, $E = 48$, $x_1 = 18$, $x_2 = 10$.

apparent. Clearly, the line $E = 48$ is the line for the highest value of E such that the line includes any points in the feasible region. As shown in the figure, that line just touches the feasible region at one point, i.e., the corner of the feasible region where $x_2 = 10$ and $x_1 = 18$. We can compute the coordinates of this point easily, because it is at the intersection of the lines

$$x_2 = 10$$

$$x_1 + x_2 = 28$$

Thus, the coordinates are (18,10). And the total revenue is:

$$\begin{aligned} E &= x_1 + 3x_2 \qquad (10\text{–}1.1) \\ &= 18 + (3)(10) \\ &= 48 \text{ thousand dollars} \end{aligned}$$

The solution, then is to carry 10 tons of cargo type A in the pressurized cabin hold and 18 tons of cargo type B in the main hold, and the revenue for the flight will be 48 thousand dollars. There is no way, subject to the restrictions, to load the aircraft for greater revenue!

The crucial general conclusion to be drawn from this problem is that *the optimum solution always must lie at a corner of the feasible region.* This can be seen from the diagram of Figure 10–2.7. The line for $E = 60$ lies outside of the feasible region, and the line for $E = 36$ lies partly within the feasible region. Thus, 36 can be achieved but 60 cannot. Also, examination of the diagram indicates that more than 36 can be obtained, and it indicates that the optimum value must occur at the corner (18,10). For any linear convex set, a linear objective function has its optimum value, be it maximum or minimum, at a corner of the set.

This is illustrated in Figure 10–2.8, using the convex sets of Figure 10–2.6. In Figure 10–2.8, let us assume that the objective function

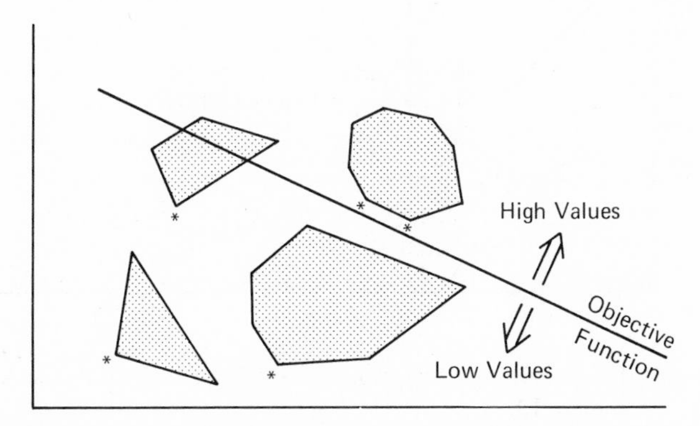

Fig. 10–2.8. Illustration that optimality occurs at the corners of convex sets.

depicted is costs and that we wish to minimize costs. Clearly, the minimum for the three lower sets would be at the points indicated by asterisks. However, the objective function is exactly parallel to the lowest side of the uppermost set. In that case, *both* corners on that side are optimal, as of course must be every point on the line connecting those corners.

The conclusion from this consideration of linear objective functions and convex sets is that, although there is an infinite number of points which satisfy the restrictions, the optimum solution must occur at one of a finite number of points, i.e., the corners of the set defined by the restrictions.

The general rule, then, is that *the optimum value always occurs at a corner of the set.* It may occur at more than one corner, and then there are many optimal solutions, but it is not possible for the optimal solution not to occur at some corner of the set. This last statement leads to an alternative procedure for solving the problem. We need only evaluate each corner of the set and select the best. From Figure 10–2.5, moving clockwise from the origin, the corners are:

Corner	Revenue ($)	
(0,0)	0	
(0,1)	3,000	
$(13\frac{1}{2},10)$	43,500	
(18,10)	48,000	Optimal
(20,8)	44,000	

The optimal corner is seen to be (18,10). We know this is the optimal point in the entire feasible region, because it is not possible for some non-corner point to be superior to all corner points.

This method of solution is not convenient when there are many corner points, because then the task of evaluating each of the many corners is too arduous. There are better ways.

10–3. The General Applicability of the Model. Before proceeding to examine the more general techniques for solution, let us look at some of the seemingly different kinds of problems, all of which are linear programming problems. The linear programming model is an excellent illustration of what has been referred to above where it was noted that certain mathematical structures tend to recur in a wide variety of real-world situations. The problems at the end of this chapter suggest the breadth of problem areas which have been described and analyzed by the linear programming model. These areas include: media selection in advertising, the blending of diets for animals and people, petroleum blending in refineries, production scheduling in offices and factories, the scheduling of lecturers and other activities in teaching and training situations, and the allocation of department store space among departments and products, and many, many more.

10–4. An Algebraic Solution. Thus far, we have examined the basic structure of linear programming problems, and we have solved a simple example by graphical methods. However, graphical solution is only the first step in explaining linear programming. Not only is it a fairly cumbersome procedure, but it suffers severe limitations in that it is limited to two-dimensional problems; i.e., it can solve only problems with two variables. Now we shall introduce nongraphical, mathematical techniques for solving linear programming problems. These are not limited with respect to dimensions and are fully capable of handling problems with large numbers of variables and restrictions.

We shall look first at an algebraic approach to the problem. This method, or *algorithm*, is more general than the graph, but it is not the most efficient method. It is introduced here only for pedagogical purposes, for it is a bridge which leads us into the procedure known as the *simplex method,* which is the easiest and quickest method for arriving at optimum solutions.

In Section 10–2, it was demonstrated that the optimum solution to a linear programming problem must always occur at a corner of the feasible region. We shall now use this result to solve the Everich Air Cargo problem, and we shall do this by manipulation of the restriction inequations. A linear programming problem involves m inequations in n variables. In the Everich problem $m = 4$ and $n = 2$. Using x_1 to designate the number of tons of cargo in the main hold and x_2 to designate the number of tons of cargo in the cabin hold, the restrictions are, as before:

1. $x_1 \leq 20$ (10–1.3)
2. $x_2 \leq 10$ (10–1.4)
3. $x_2 \leq 1 + \frac{2}{3}x_1$ (10–1.5)
4. $x_1 + x_2 \leq 28$ (10–1.6)

We begin by modifying the restriction *inequations.* We convert these to *equations* by adding "slack variables." *There is one slack variable added for each of the inequations, except the nonnegativity restrictions.* Thus, there will be m slack variables. In this case there are four slack variables, which we shall designate: q, r, s, t. In any given problem, the slack variables may or may not have a physical interpretation. In the present case they do. For the air cargo problem, after we add one slack variable *to the small side* of each inequation, the new *equations* and the slack variable interpretations are:

11.	$x_1 + q = 20$	q = unused main hold capacity	(10–4.1)
12.	$x_2 + r = 10$	r = unused cabin hold capacity	(10–4.2)
13.	$x_2 + s = \frac{2}{3}x_1 + 1$	s = unused cabin hold balance capacity	(10–4.3)
14.	$x_1 + x_2 + t = 28$	t = unused aircraft lift capacity	(10–4.4)

Note that these equations are itemized as 11 to 14, corresponding to numbers 1–4 in the previous set. We shall assign numbers 21–24, 31–34, etc. to subsequent corresponding sets of equations, always retaining the sequence, 1–4. Thus the first restriction equation in the several steps will be: 11, 21, 31, etc., and the second will be 12, 22, 32, etc.

Like x_1 and x_2, the slack variables must also be nonnegative. Negative unused capacity in some hold would mean that the particular compartment is loaded beyond full capacity, which is impossible.

Figure 10–4.1 shows that the feasible region is a six-sided convex poly-

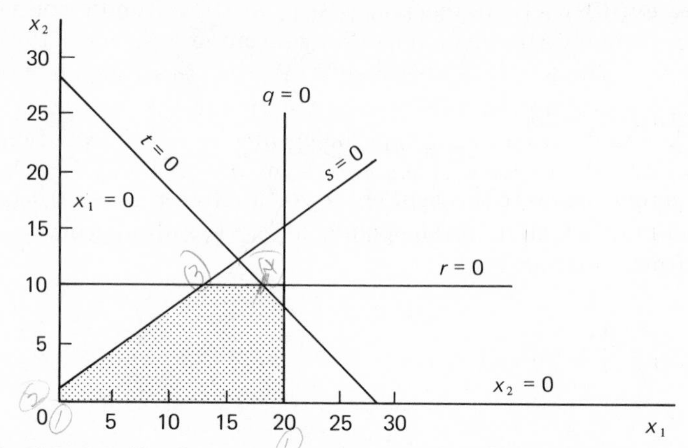

Fig. 10–4.1. The Everich Air Cargo problem. The feasible region.

gon, such that, on each of the sides, one of the following inequations is an equation.

$$x_1 \geq 0 \tag{10–4.5}$$

$$x_2 \geq 0 \tag{10–4.6}$$

$$q \geq 0 \tag{10–4.7}$$

$$r \geq 0 \tag{10–4.8}$$

$$s \geq 0 \tag{10–4.9}$$

$$t \geq 0 \tag{10–4.10}$$

Clearly, then, at a *corner* of the set, *two* of the variables must be zero. Indeed, this is a crucial characteristic of a corner of the set. The four restriction equations, (10–4.1), (10–4.2), (10–4.3), and (10–4.4), which for convenience we have numbered 11, 12, 13, and 14, respectively, have six unknown variables. Therefore, with six variables in only four equations, there are many values of the six variables which satisfy the four equations. However, if two of the variables are zero, the other four must take unique values, because then the four equations have four unknowns, and the system has only one solution. *Thus, at each corner of the feasible region, two of the variables are equal to zero, and the other four have unique values.* The two variables which are equal to zero are called the "zero variables," and the other four are called the "basic variables."

Also, in the feasible region (including the boundaries) all of the variables are nonnegative. Consider the point on the x_1-axis (20,0). At that point,

$x_1 = 20$; therefore, from Equation (10–4.1), $q = 0$. This may be seen on the graph. To the right of that point, q is negative. For example, at the point (25,0), q is equal to -5. This may be seen from Equation (10–4.1), which we shall refer to also as equation 11:

$$\text{11.} \qquad x_1 + q = 20 \qquad (10\text{–}4.1)$$

Substituting $x_1 = 25$,

$$q = 20 - 25 = -5$$

Clearly, as one moves to the right of the vertical line at $x_1 = 20$, q becomes more and more negative. At the point (30,0), t has also become negative, as seen from equation 14:

$$\text{14.} \qquad x_1 + x_2 + t = 28 \qquad (10\text{–}4.4)$$

Substituting $x_1 = 30$ and $x_2 = 0$,

$$t = 28 - 30 = -2$$

Thus, above and to the right of the line labeled $t = 0$, t is negative. Also, above the horizontal line at $x_2 = 10$, r is negative, and above and to the left of the line labeled $s = 0$, s is negative. Therefore, only in the feasible region as shown (including, of course, the boundaries) are all of the variables nonnegative. Indeed, that is the essential characteristic of the feasible region.

Thus, any point which is the intersection of two of these lines has two of the variables equal to zero, but it is not necessarily a corner of the feasible region. *Only if all of the other variables are nonnegative is that point a corner of the feasible region.*

Consider, for example, the point at which $s = 0$, and $t = 0$. The coordinates of that point, as may be computed from equations 13 and 14, are (16.2,11.8). The graph tells us that this point is not in the feasible region, and it tells us that the point is not feasible, because r is negative, indicating that inequation 2:

$$\text{2.} \qquad x_2 \leq 10 \qquad (10\text{–}1.4)$$

is violated. The value of r at that point may be computed:

$$\text{12.} \qquad x_2 + r = 10 \qquad (10\text{–}4.2)$$

and substituting $x_2 = 11.8$,

$$r = 10 - 11.8 = -1.8$$

Therefore, a corner of the feasible region is a point at which all of the variables are nonnegative, and at least two of them are zero. We can see from the graph of Figure 10–4.1 that, at the corners of the set in this problem, *exactly* two of the slack variables are zero. However, it is possible that more than two may be zero. For example, if three lines were to meet at a point, then three variables would be zero at this point. Such a situation is characterized as "degenerate." We shall discuss this in a later section. Strictly speaking, then, we must say that *at least* two of the variables are zero at a corner of the set.

In the algebraic method which follows, and in the simplex method which we shall examine subsequently, we shall identify a corner of the feasible region by these two characteristics:

n zero variables (in the Everich problem, $n = 2$).
No negative variables.

If these two conditions are met, the point is a corner of the feasible region.

At this stage, let us pause a moment, and gather up the threads of our argument so far. We know that the optimal solution lies in the convex set bounded by these six lines. We know, further, that the optimal solution lies at one of the corners of the set. Our procedure is, therefore, to find a feasible corner, see if it is optimal, and, if it is not, move from that corner to another one in such a way as to increase the objective function. In other words, if the corner under consideration is not optimal, we want to move from that corner to another corner which lies closer to, or is, the corner at which the objective function is optimum.

To start the procedure, we must first find a corner of the polygon; and whenever possible, the easiest one to start with is the point of origin. At that point, $x_1 = 0$, and $x_2 = 0$. Thus it is a corner. Also, at the origin corner, $q = 20$, $r = 10$, $s = 1$, and $t = 28$. Thus, since all other variables, the basic variables, are nonnegative, we know that the origin is a *feasible* corner.

Let us rewrite equations 11, 12, 13, and 14, and the objective function, in terms of the nonzero variables. That is, the zero variables are placed on the right side of the equations, and only the four basic variables are on the left side. We can do this for any corner, because there will be two zero variables and four basic variables at each corner. The set of equations representing the origin is:

20. $$E = x_1 + 3x_2 \quad (10\text{–}1.1)$$

21. $$q = 20 - x_1 \quad (10\text{–}4.11)$$

22. $$r = 10 - x_2 \quad (10\text{–}4.12)$$

23. $$s = 1 + \tfrac{2}{3}x_1 - x_2 \quad (10\text{–}4.13)$$

24. $$t = 28 - x_1 - x_2 \quad (10\text{–}4.14)$$

Using the convention that the variables to the right of the equal sign are zero, we can say that the set of equations 20–24 represents the origin.

The first equation is the objective function, and the others are the restriction equations. The numbers just to the right of the equal sign, the *constants*, represent the values of the nonzero or "basic" variables, since the other terms on the right side of all of the equations are zero. Here, at the origin, also, $E = 0$. From equation 20,

$$E = 0 + (3)(0) = 0$$

We must now have an iteration procedure which will:

a. Determine whether this corner is optimal and, if it is not optimal,
b. Indicate the direction in which to move, and
c. Indicate how far to move.

The procedure is quite simple and direct.

a. The corner represented by the set of equations is not optimal if one or more of the zero variables in the objective function have positive coefficients. The reasoning behind this is that, if a zero variable in the objective function has a positive coefficient, then if we increase that variable from zero to some positive value, we will increase the objective function.
b. Since we wish to maximize the objective function, we will not want to leave that variable at its zero value but will move around the perimeter of the feasible region in a direction which will increase the value of that variable whose coefficient is positive. If more than one variable has a positive coefficient, we will select that with the largest coefficient. In this case, in equations 20–24, both x_1 and x_2 have positive coefficients in the objective function, i.e., 1 and 3, respectively. We select x_2 because its coefficient is larger.
c. The variable which is to be increased will be increased as much as possible, subject to the restrictions defining the feasible region. That is, until some other variable is reduced to zero and becomes a zero variable. This will occur, of course, at a corner of the set, and that is as far as we can go because, if the increasing variable is increased further, that new zero variable would become negative, which is not permitted.

This process, then, causes us to move from one corner to another corner. Thus, it creates a new basic variable from one of the zero variables and, at the same time, transforms one of the basic variables into a zero variable and increases the objective function. We always follow the procedure of *increasing* the objective function. If, as is the case in some problems, the objective function is to be *minimized*, we merely multiply that objective function through by -1 and then follow this *maximization* procedure. We then, in effect, *minimize* the cost by *maximizing its negative*. This is a perfectly sound and consistent procedure.

Returning to the Everich Air Cargo problem, we wish to increase x_2, but by *how much* can we increase x_2? Looking at restriction equations 21–24, equation 21 indicates that increasing x_2 has no effect on q. Equation 22 indicates that x_2 can increase to take a value of 10 before r becomes negative; i.e., at $x_2 = 10$, $r = 0$. Similarly, equation 23 indicates that x_2 can increase to 1 before s becomes negative, and equation 24 indicates that x_2 can increase to 28 before t becomes negative. Thus, the limiting values of x_2 are, from equations 21–24,

Equation	Limit for x_2
21	∞
22	10
23*	1
24	28

An asterisk is placed at equation 23, because that equation is the limiting restriction for this iteration. After x_2 is increased to 1, s will be zero.

The procedure for obtaining the next set of equations; i.e., for moving to the next corner, is merely to rearrange the limiting equation (equation 23) to conform to the convention that the new basic variable (here, x_2) shall be to the left of the equal sign. From equation 23, Equation (10–4.13), we obtain

$$33. \qquad x_2 = 1 + \tfrac{2}{3}x_1 - s$$

which we identify as equation 33, and we proceed to substitute this expression throughout the set of equations 20–24. For identification, we shall number the new equations 30–34.

From equation 20,

$$E = x_1 + 3(1 + \tfrac{2}{3}x_1 - s)$$

$$30. \qquad E = 3 + 3x_1 - 3s$$

Equation 21 is unchanged, since x_2 does not appear in it, and therefore equation 31 will be identical with equation 21.

From equation 22,

$$r = 10 - (1 + \tfrac{2}{3}x_1 - s)$$

$$32. \qquad r = 9 - \tfrac{2}{3}x_1 + s$$

Equation 33 has already been derived. It was the limiting restriction.

From equation 24,

$$t = 28 - x_1 - (1 + \tfrac{2}{3}x_1 - s)$$

$$34. \qquad t = 27 - 1\tfrac{2}{3}x_1 + s$$

The new set of equations is:

30. $E = 3 + 3x_1 - 3s$ (10–4.15)

31. $q = 20 - x_1$ (10–4.16)

32. $r = 9 - \frac{2}{3}x_1 + s$ (10–4.17)

33. $x_2 = 1 + \frac{2}{3}x_1 - s$ (10–4.18)

34. $t = 27 - 1\frac{2}{3}x_1 + s$ (10–4.19)

Examination of these equations tells us:

a. They represent the point (0,1). (x_1 is on the right side of the equations, and is, therefore, a zero variable; x_2 is, in equation 33, on the left side, and is therefore a basic variable, whose value is the constant on the right side, since everything else on the right side is equal to zero.)
b. It is a feasible point. (All of the basic variables are nonnegative; i.e., the constants are all nonnegative. It should be noted that the constants in the equations are the values of the basic variables, because everything else on the right side of the equations is equal to zero.)
c. The value of the objective function is 3. (In equation 30, on the right side, all but the constant is equal to zero. This also means that the aircraft can be loaded with 1 ton in the cabin hold and nothing in the main hold, and the revenue will be $3,000.)
d. It is not optimal. (In equation 30, the coefficient of x_1 is positive; thus, x_1 can be increased with desirable results.)
e. The next step is to increase x_1.

How far can x_1 be increased? The limiting values for x_1 from each of the restriction equations are:

Equation	Limit for x_1
31	20
32*	$13\frac{1}{2}$
33	∞ (since the coefficient of x_1 is positive)
34	$16\frac{1}{5}$

Equation 32, then, is the limiting restriction. When x_1 increases to become $13\frac{1}{2}$, r will become zero. Then x_1 will be the new basic variable, and r will be the new zero variable. Therefore, now equation 32 is rearranged to implement these changes and to form equation 42:

42. $x_1 = 13\frac{1}{2} - 1\frac{1}{2}r + 1\frac{1}{2}s$

Substituting equation 42 into equations 30–34 yields:

40. $E = 3 + 3(13\frac{1}{2} - 1\frac{1}{2}r + 1\frac{1}{2}s) - 3s = 43\frac{1}{2} - 4\frac{1}{2}r + 1\frac{1}{2}s$

41. $q = 20 - (13\frac{1}{2} - 1\frac{1}{2}r + 1\frac{1}{2}s) = 6\frac{1}{2} + 1\frac{1}{2}r - 1\frac{1}{2}s$

42. $x_1 = 13\frac{1}{2} - 1\frac{1}{2}r + 1\frac{1}{2}s$

43. $x_2 = 1 + \frac{2}{3}(13\frac{1}{2} - 1\frac{1}{2}r + 1\frac{1}{2}s) - s = 10 - r$

44. $t = 27 - 1\frac{2}{3}(13\frac{1}{2} - 1\frac{1}{2}r + 1\frac{1}{2}s) + s = 4\frac{1}{2} + 2\frac{1}{2}r - 1\frac{1}{2}s$

The new system of equations is:

40. $$E = 43\frac{1}{2} - 4\frac{1}{2}r + 1\frac{1}{2}s \qquad (10\text{–}4.20)$$

41. $$q = 6\frac{1}{2} + 1\frac{1}{2}r - 1\frac{1}{2}s \qquad (10\text{–}4.21)$$

42. $$x_1 = 13\frac{1}{2} - 1\frac{1}{2}r + 1\frac{1}{2}s \qquad (10\text{–}4.22)$$

43. $$x_2 = 10 - r \qquad (10\text{–}4.23)$$

44. $$t = 4\frac{1}{2} + 2\frac{1}{2}r - 1\frac{1}{2}s \qquad (10\text{–}4.24)$$

Examination of these equations tells us:

a. They represent the point $(13\frac{1}{2},10)$.
b. It is a feasible point.
c. The value of the objective function is $43\frac{1}{2}$ ($43,500).
d. It is not optimal.
e. The next step is to increase s.

How far can s be increased? The limiting values for s, from each of the restriction equations are:

Equation	Limit for s
41	$4\frac{1}{3}$
42	∞
43	∞
44*	3

Thus, the limiting restriction is equation 44. At $s = 3$, $t = 0$. Therefore, equation 44 must be expressed in terms of s to yield equation 54:

$$1\frac{1}{2}s = 4\frac{1}{2} + 2\frac{1}{2}r - t$$

54. $$s = 3 + 1\frac{2}{3}r - \frac{2}{3}t$$

Substituting equation 54 into equations 40–44 yields

50. $$E = 43\frac{1}{2} - 4\frac{1}{2}r + 1\frac{1}{2}(3 + 1\frac{2}{3}r - \frac{2}{3}t)$$

51. $$q = 6\frac{1}{2} + 1\frac{1}{2}r - 1\frac{1}{2}(3 + 1\frac{2}{3}r - \frac{2}{3}t)$$

52. $x_1 = 13\frac{1}{2} - 1\frac{1}{2}r + 1\frac{1}{2}(3 + 1\frac{2}{3}r - \frac{2}{3}t)$

53. $x_2 = 10 - r$

54. $s = 3 + 1\frac{2}{3}r - \frac{2}{3}t$

Simplifying, the new system of equations is:

50. $$E = 48 - 2r - t \quad (10\text{–}4.25)$$

51. $$q = 2 - r + t \quad (10\text{–}4.26)$$

52. $$x_1 = 18 + r - t \quad (10\text{–}4.27)$$

53. $$x_2 = 10 - r \quad (10\text{–}4.28)$$

54. $$s = 3 + 1\tfrac{2}{3}r - \tfrac{2}{3}t \quad (10\text{–}4.29)$$

Examination of these equations tells us:

a. They represent the point (18,10).
b. It is a feasible point.
c. The value of the objective function is 48 ($48,000).
d. It is optimal, since the coefficients of r and t in equation 50 are negative.

The optimal solution, then, is to load 18 tons of cargo type B into the main hold and 10 tons of cargo type A into the pressurized cabin hold. The total revenue for the flight will be $48,000, and there is no way to load the aircraft which will yield greater revenue.

Although the algebraic method did not require recourse to the graph, it is instructive to follow on the graph the path traced out by this method. Looking at the graph of Figure 10–4.1, the origin (0,0) was the starting point. The next step increased x_2, thus movement was along the x_2-axis until stopped by the line labeled $s = 0$. This was point (0,1), with revenue $3,000. The next step increased x_1 by moving to the right along the line labeled $s = 0$. This also increased x_2 at the same time. Movement in this direction was stopped by the horizontal line at $x_2 = 10$, labeled $r = 0$. This was point ($13\frac{1}{2}$,10) with revenue $43,500. The next step increased s by moving horizontally to the right along the line $r = 0$, increasing x_1 at the same time, until stopped by the line $t = 0$, at the point (18,10), which, with revenue of $48,000, was optimal. Notice that, at each corner, movement was stopped by a line, because crossing that line would make some variable negative, which is not permitted. In this sense, the lines may be regarded as walls, which cannot be crossed, but along which we may proceed. We always know which line to move along, because in every one of these transformations, or *pivots*, one of the zero variables remains a zero variable while the other increases to become a basic variable. We move along the line which corresponds to zero value for the zero variable which remains zero.

Note also that, at the optimal point, $q = 2$ and $s = 3$, indicating that there is unused capacity of 2 tons in the main hold, and there is unused balance capacity of 3 tons in the cabin hold. Of course, neither of these unused capacities can be used under the optimal solution, because the airplane lift capacity is being fully utilized.

We have now seen an algebraic solution, an *algorithm*, which yielded exactly the same result as the graphic method. The algebraic method does not require the graph, and therefore need not be limited to two-dimensional problems. However, this algorithm is inefficient. We shall see in the next chapter that one can obtain the same result more quickly and easily by the use of the *simplex* algorithm.

SUGGESTIONS FOR FURTHER READING

See suggested readings for Chapter 13.

EXERCISES

10–1. The Marstar Aviation Company's cargo airplane is to be loaded in a way such as to maximize the revenue from a single flight. The airplane has four holds: a main hold, two wing holds, and a cabin hold, each of which can carry a different kind of cargo at a different rate. (Actually, for this flight, there are only three different kinds of cargo and three different rates, since the two wing holds will carry the same kind of cargo and earn the same rate.) There is plenty of each kind of cargo available for the flight, and the only objective of this decision is to maximize the revenue, given the rates of $1,000 per ton in the *main* hold, $2,000 per ton in the *left wing* hold, $2,000 per ton in the *right wing* hold, and $3,000 per ton in the pressurized *cabin* hold. The load is to be *exactly* 50 tons, and the loading must be such that the wing holds are exactly balanced and the load in the main hold must be at least as great as the total wing-hold load plus twice the load in the cabin hold. Solve graphically to find the optimal allocation of cargo. (Hint: Eliminate the main hold by substituting for its equivalent, i.e., 50 tons less the cargo allocated to the other holds, and plot the cargo allocated to the cabin hold and wing holds as the two axes.)

10–2. Abrash's Department Store has 100,000 square feet of space on the main floor and is in the process of redesigning its allocation of space among the three users of the main floor: (1) Cosmetics, (2) Mens' Wear, (3) Special Sales Items. Good taste requires that Cosmetics occupy no more than 50% of the main floor. Existing commitments require that Special Sales Items and Cosmetics, together, must not exceed Mens' Wear by more than 30,000 square feet. Solve graphically to find how the space should be allocated for maximum profitability. What is the value of the maximum profitability?

The annual profitability for these items is:

(1) Cosmetics,	$1,000 per square foot
(2) Mens' Wear,	600 per square foot
(3) Special Sales Items,	800 per square foot

(Hint: Eliminate men's wear by substituting for its equivalent, i.e., the total floor space less that allocated to the other departments. Then plot the floor space allocated to the other two departments as the two axes.)

10–3. The Vanchar Oriental Carpet Company must allocate its local annual advertising budget of $200,000 for the metropolitan area. They can purchase local radio spots at $100 per spot, local TV spots at $500 per spot, or local newspaper advertising at $200 per insertion.

Legal contractual requirements specify that they must spend at least $30,000 in TV. Their general corporate advertising policy prohibits annual local newspaper expenditures in excess of $50,000 or in excess of 50% of the TV expenditures, whichever is smaller.

The payoff from each advertising medium is a function of its audience size and audience characteristics. The general feeling in the firm and in the agency is that the values of insertions and spots in terms of an arbitrary unit, known in the company as "audience points," are as given below:

Radio, 30 audience points per spot
TV, 150 audience points per spot
Newspapers, 270 audience points per insertion

Solve the problem graphically to find the optimal allocation of expenditures to these three media under the assumption that all relationships are linear.

10–4. The finishing division of the Eligin Hardware Manufacturing Company is scheduling its work for the next day. There are three possible products which can be made. The following table lists the profit on each and the time required in each of the three processes being scheduled.

Product	Profit per Unit	Hours Required per Unit in		
		Machining	Plating	Polishing
Axles	$10	1	1	1
Bearings	$20	3	1	2
Channels	$30	2	3	2

During the next day, the machining operation will work for 2 shifts (up to 16 hr), the plating operation will work for $1\frac{1}{2}$ shifts (up to 12 hr), and polishing will work for only up to 6 hr.

Determine graphically the number of each of the products to be produced during the next day for maximum profit. The number of axles produced must be exactly the same as the number of bearings produced. Do not be concerned about the order in which the three operations are performed, since the hours operated will be staggered as necessary. What is the total profit?

11

Simplex Procedure

11–1. The Simplex Algorithm. The simplex procedure is an iterative method for solving linear programming problems by finding successive basic-feasible solutions and testing them for optimality. Although the language of the simplex method is new, we shall see that in fact the simplex method, or *algorithm*, may be regarded as a systematic and efficient procedure for doing precisely what was done in the algebraic solution described in the final section of the preceding chapter. That is, it is a procedure for moving from one corner of the feasible region to another, always improving the objective function until it can be improved no further, in which case, the solution is optimal.

A linear programming problem may be described as the maximization of a linear objective function in n variables, subject to m linear restrictions, which are expressed as linear inequalities or *inequations* involving the n variables. In the Everich Air Cargo problem of the last chapter, the statement of the problem is:

Maximize: $$E = x_1 + 3x_2 \qquad (10\text{–}1.7)$$

subject to: $$x_1 \leq 20 \qquad (10\text{–}1.8)$$

$$x_2 \leq 10 \qquad (10\text{–}1.9)$$

$$-\tfrac{2}{3}x_1 + x_2 \leq 1 \qquad (10\text{–}1.10)$$

$$x_1 + x_2 \leq 28 \qquad (10\text{–}1.11)$$

The first step is to convert the m linear *inequations* to m linear *equations* by adding a *slack variable* to the smaller side of each inequation. This requires m slack variables, one for each restriction, and the number of variables in the problem becomes $m + n$: n *real* variables, and m *slack* variables. Here we shall designate the slack variables x_3, x_4, x_5, x_6, in place of q, r, s, t as in the preceding chapter. This nomenclature follows the standard practice whereby the real variables are designated $x_1, x_2, \ldots, x_n$, and the slack variables are $x_{n+1}, x_{n+2}, \ldots, x_{n+m}$. The restriction equations with the slack variables added are

$$x_1 + x_3 = 20 \tag{11–1.1}$$

$$x_2 + x_4 = 10 \tag{11–1.2}$$

$$-\tfrac{2}{3}x_1 + x_2 + x_5 = 1 \tag{11–1.3}$$

$$x_1 + x_2 + x_6 = 28 \tag{11–1.4}$$

Here we have four equations with six unknowns. If two of these unknown variables are zero, the system has a unique solution, and, as we have seen, any basic-feasible solution is one in which two of the variables are zero. *The algorithm serves the purpose of finding which two of the variables are zero at the optimal point.* In general terms, there are m equations and $m + n$ variables, so that n of the variables (in the Everich Air Cargo problem, $n = 2$) will be zero for any solution. The other m variables are called *basic* variables. In the Everich problem, there are four *basic* variables and two *zero* variables at each solution, i.e., each corner of the feasible region.

The simplex algorithm, then, is an orderly iterative process for determining which variables must be *basic* (i.e., "in the basis") and which must be zero at the optimal.

The second step is to rewrite the equations with the basic variables on the left and the constants and zero variables on the right. As a *first solution*, we write the equations with the slack variables in the basis and the real variables as the zero variables.

$$E = x_1 + 3x_2 \tag{11–1.5}$$

$$x_3 = 20 - x_1 \tag{11–1.6}$$

$$x_4 = 10 - x_2 \tag{11–1.7}$$

$$x_5 = 1 + \tfrac{2}{3}x_1 - x_2 \tag{11–1.8}$$

$$x_6 = 28 - x_1 - x_2 \tag{11–1.9}$$

When the equations are expressed in this form, they indicate a point, i.e., that point at which $x_1 = 0$ and $x_2 = 0$. Also, since all terms on the right side of the equations (except the constants) are equal to zero, the basic variables have the values of the constants. Equations (11–1.6) to (11–1.9) represent the origin, where the real variables are zero, and the slack variables are the basic variables, which have, at the origin, the values of the constants; i.e., with the n real variables equal to zero, all capacities are unused.

The constants are all nonnegative, indicating that the solution is *feasible,* i.e., that the origin lies in the feasible region. The value of the objective function is zero. The positive coefficients to the zero variables in the objective function, Equation (11–1.5) tell us that the indicated solution is not optimal. Our purpose then is to move to a better solution.

Finally, this first solution is not only feasible, but it is *basic.* That is, all of the basic variables are not only nonnegative, but they are *positive.* If any of them were negative, the indicated solution would not be feasible; if one or more were zero, the solution could be feasible, but then it would not be basic and would be identified as *degenerate,* as we shall see later.

In any event, this first solution is basic and feasible and we are now ready to proceed to the orderly procedure—the algorithm—that will enable us to move by successive iterative steps from this first solution to the optimal solution.

11–2. The Simplex Tableau. Equations (11–1.5) to (11–1.9) may be expressed as a 5-by-3 matrix, as shown in Figure 11–2.1.

		x_1	x_2
E	0	1	3
x_3	20	−1	0
x_4	10	0	−1
x_5	1	2/3	−1
x_6	28	−1	−1

Fig. 11–2.1. The Everich Air Cargo problem. Simplex tableau for first solution: the origin.

This matrix, or *simplex tableau,* is constructed to consist of $m + 1$ rows and $n + 1$ columns, not including the identifying column and row outside the ruled rectangle. The number of rows must be $m + 1$, because there must be one row for each of the m restrictions, plus one for the objective function. The number of columns must be $n + 1$, because there must be one for each of the n zero variables and one for the constants. The numbers in the first column are the constants, and the numbers in the other columns are the coefficients of the respective zero variables indicated at the top of the columns. Note that zeros are entered in the matrix in the appropriate locations as coefficients for variables which do not appear in the various equations.

The variables identified at the top of the matrix, x_1 and x_2, are the zero variables. The fact that these variables are zero tells that the indicated point is the origin. The constants in the first column are the values of the basic variables, which, in this first tableau, are the slack variables.

The matrix of Figure 11–2.1 is nothing more than an alternative formal representation of the set of Equations (11–1.5) to (11–1.9). However, as we shall see, this is a very useful form, since it lends itself very conveniently to the kind of manipulation which is necessary for moving from one corner of the feasible region to another.

In order to represent a different corner of the feasible region, the matrix need only be changed so that one of the zero variables becomes a basic variable, one of the basic variables becomes a zero variable, and the various constants and coefficients are changed correspondingly. This may be done by a manipulation of the matrix known as *pivoting*.

The matrix is pivoted about a point, i.e., one of the matrix elements, known as the *pivot element*. The pivot element is the element at the intersection of the row corresponding to the basic variable about to become zero and the column corresponding to the zero variable about to become basic.

The first step, then, in pivoting the matrix, is to find the pivot element. The procedure here corresponds exactly to the procedure in the algebraic method described in the final section of the preceding chapter.

11–3. The Pivot Element. *The column.* The zero variable which should be made basic (i.e., "brought into the basis") is that one which looks like it will make the optimum contribution to the objective function. That is the zero variable with the largest positive coefficient in the objective function. The rule then is that the column for the pivot element is:

The column with the largest positive element in the top row.

The row. The basic variable to become zero is that basic variable which will become zero *first* as the selected zero variable increases. It is this reduction of a basic variable which limits the amount by which the zero variable can increase. Therefore, the row of the pivot element is the row corresponding to the restriction equation which is, in this sense, the most restrictive.

To find the pivot row, look down the pivot column and consider only negative elements. This is because positive elements provide no restriction; i.e., if the coefficient of the zero variable is positive, the zero variable in the pivot column may be increased without limit, as far as that row is concerned. The negative elements in the column indicate, respectively, the amount by which the basic variable in that row will be decreased for each unit increase in the zero variable in the column. Also, the constant, the entry in the first column, indicates the present value of the basic variable and, therefore, the amount by which the value of the basic variable may decrease before it becomes zero. It should be noted that this is exactly what we did in the algebraic method of the preceding chapter in a more roundabout way.

Therefore, for each row with a negative element in the pivot column, we examine the ratio of the constant (first column) in that row to that negative element and choose the row with the smallest absolute value of the ratio. The selected row, then is:

The row with the smallest absolute value of the ratio of the constant to the negative element in the pivot column (i.e., the smallest "row ratio").

Applying this procedure to the tableau of Figure 11–2.1, the pivot column must be the x_2 column, since the top row has its highest positive entry, 3, in that column. The pivot row is found by examining the row ratios for rows x_4, x_5, and x_6. These row ratios are found to be 10, 1, and 28, respectively. The x_5 row, with the smallest ratio value (1), must be selected as the pivot row. The pivot element, then, is the entry in the x_5 row and the x_2 column, as seen in Figure 11–3.1. The pivoting process,

		x_1	x_2
E	0	1	3
x_3	20	−1	0
x_4	10	0	−1
x_5	1	2/3	(−1)
x_6	28	−1	−1

Fig. 11–3.1. Simplex tableau with pivot element identified.

then, will interchange x_5 and x_2. The present basic variable x_5 will become zero, and the present zero variable x_2 will become basic. In the course of the pivoting, the constants and coefficients in the matrix will automatically be changed as necessary.

11–4. Pivoting the Matrix. The arithmetic required for pivoting the matrix calls for four distinct procedures, one for the pivot element, one for the other elements in the pivot column, one for the other elements in the pivot row, and the last for all of the other elements. The rules are:

1. Pivot element—*Change to reciprocal.* It is negative, and it remains negative.
2. Other pivot row elements—*Divide by absolute value of pivot element.* Their signs are unchanged since the pivot element's minus sign is ignored.

3. Other pivot column elements—*Divide by pivot element.* Their signs all change since the pivot element is negative.
4. All other elements—For each element, consider the element to be changed, the pivot element and the two corner elements, one in the same row and in the pivot column and one in the same column and in the pivot row. These four elements form a rectangle, with the element to be changed and the pivot element at the ends of a diagonal. To change the element, *subtract from it the product of the two corner elements divided by the pivot element.* In equation form:

$$\text{New element} = \text{Present element} - \frac{\text{Product of corner elements}}{\text{Pivot element}}$$

   This fourth rule is further illustrated below after the introduction of the necessary symbols.

These rules may be stated quite simply in algebraic form. Let P represent the pivot element:

i, j, p (subscripts)	represent the ith row, the jth column, and the *pivot* row or column, respectively
* (asterisk)	represents a new element; absence of asterisk indicates an old element
Y_{ij}	represents an element; the element in the ith row and j^{th} column
Y_{ip}	represents the element in the ith row and pivot column
Y_{pj}	represents the element in the pivot row and j^{th} column

Then

1. $P^* = \dfrac{1}{P}$ for pivot element
2. $Y^*_{pj} = \dfrac{Y_{pj}}{|P|}$ for pivot row
3. $Y^*_{ip} = \dfrac{Y_{ip}}{P}$ for pivot column
4. $Y^*_{ij} = Y_{ij} - \dfrac{Y_{ip}Y_{pj}}{P}$ for all other elements

This fourth rule is illustrated in Figure 11-4.1. In that figure, the element Y_{ij} is an element which is not in the pivot row or column. The figure represents the matrix to be pivoted, and the element P is the pivot element. As we shall see below, it is customary to identify the pivot element by enclosing it in a circle. The reader will find it easy to understand rule 4 by relating it to the figure.

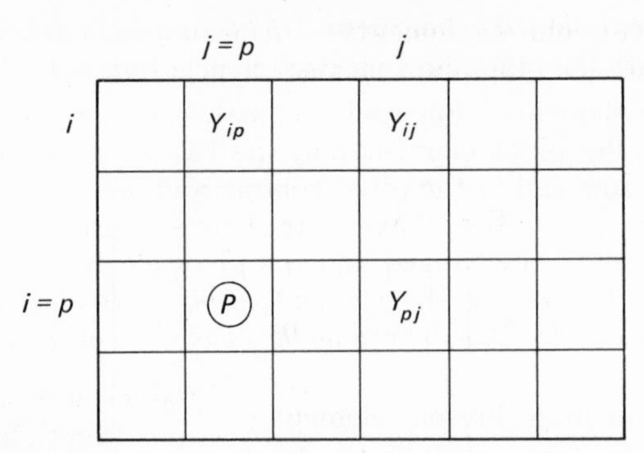

Fig. 11–4.1. Illustration for the fourth rule for pivoting.

These rules for pivoting the matrix will yield precisely the same results as were obtained by the algebraic method of the preceding chapter. Let us examine the reasoning behind this in order to understand why these rules will produce the desired results.

1. The pivot element. If we consider Equation (11–1.8), representing the pivot row of the matrix, we can see that, in the pivoted matrix, x_2 will be expressed in terms of x_5 instead of the contrary, so the new coefficient of x_5 will be the reciprocal of the old coefficient of x_2. (Actually, since the coefficient in this specific illustration is -1, the new and old coefficients are the same.)
2. Other pivot row elements. The rule given above is oversimplified, as we shall see. Actually, it should read, "Change the sign of the element and divide by the pivot element." This row represents the equation which is being rearranged. Each "other" element now has its sign changed as it moves to the other side of the equation and it must be divided by the old (negative) coefficient of the variable chosen to become basic, since that variable must now have a coefficient of $+1$. This old coefficient of the chosen variable is, of course, the pivot element, and, in the pivoting of the matrix, the double change of sign is accomplished by using the absolute value of the pivot element.
3. Other pivot column elements. Since the new value for the new basic variables, expressed in terms of the zero variables, is now to be substituted into each of the other equations, the new coefficient of the new zero variable is the old coefficient of the former zero variable multiplied by the reciprocal of the old coefficient of the new zero variable.
4. All other elements. This is too complex to describe in a sentence or two. The student can trace this through the equations of the last chapter to verify the procedure.

11–5. Completing the Iterations. Pivoting from the first basic solution, which, with the pivot element encircled, is Figure 11–5.1 (identical to

		x_1	x_2
E	0	1	3
x_3	20	−1	0
x_4	10	0	−1
x_5	1	2/3	(−1)
x_6	28	−1	−1

Fig. 11–5.1. Tableau for first solution: the origin.

Figure 11–3.1), the second solution is given by the tableau of Figure 11–5.2. This second tableau or matrix was derived as follows from the pivoting procedure. First, the pivot element, which was at the intersection

		x_1	x_5
E	3	3	−3
x_3	20	−1	0
x_4	9	−2/3	1
x_2	1	2/3	−1
x_6	27	−5/3	1

Fig. 11–5.2. Tableau for second solution: x_1 = 0, x_2 = 1, revenue = $3,000.

of x_5 and x_2, was -1. The reciprocal also is -1. Now, for the pivot *row,* we divide by $|-1|$. This yields the pivot row unchanged as seen in Figure 11–5.3. Next, the pivot *column* is divided by the pivot element, but the *sign is not ignored.* Therefore, this division by a negative quantity insures

		x_1	x_5
E			−3
x_3			0
x_4			1
x_2	1	2/3	−1
x_6			1

Fig. 11–5.3. Pivot row and column of second solution.

that the *sign does change*. This yields the pivot column shown in Figure 11–5.3. For all other elements, the rule is:

$$\text{New element} = \text{Present element} - \frac{\text{Product of corner elements}}{\text{Pivot element}}$$

For illustrative purposes, in this paragraph, let us designate the hitherto unnamed first column as k, for "constant." Then the designation (E,k) represents the element in the E row and k column, etc. The remaining new elements are computed as follows:

$$(E,k) = 0 - \frac{(1)(3)}{-1} = 3 \qquad (E,x_1) = 1 - \frac{(\frac{2}{3})(3)}{-1} = 3$$

$$(x_3,k) = 20 - \frac{(1)(0)}{-1} = 20 \qquad (x_3,x_1) = -1 - \frac{(\frac{2}{3})(0)}{-1} = -1$$

$$(x_4,k) = 10 - \frac{(1)(-1)}{-1} = 9 \qquad (x_4,x_1) = 0 - \frac{(\frac{2}{3})(-1)}{-1} = -\frac{2}{3}$$

$$(x_6,k) = 28 - \frac{(1)(-1)}{-1} = 27 \qquad (x_6,x_1) = -1 - \frac{(\frac{2}{3})(-1)}{-1} = -\frac{5}{3}$$

Note that the entire x_3 row is unchanged. This follows from the fact that there is a zero in that row in the pivot column, and as the calculations above indicate, the product of the corners for all elements in that row will be zero, leaving the old elements unchanged. Thus, as a general rule, whenever there is a zero in the pivot column, all other elements in the row with that zero will be unchanged in pivoting; and, similarly, whenever there is a zero in the pivot row, all other elements in the column with that zero will be unchanged in pivoting.

In the matrix of Figure 11–5.4, we see that, since there is a positive entry in the top row (in other than the constant column), the indicated solution is not optimal. Element (E,x_1) is positive, so that x_1 designates

		x_1	x_5
E	3	3	−3
x_3	20	−1	0
x_4	9	(−2/3)	1
x_2	1	2/3	−1
x_6	27	−5/3	1

Fig. 11–5.4. Tableau for second solution with pivot element encircled.

the pivot column. To determine the pivot row, the ratios are:

Row	Ratio
x_3	20
x_4	$13\frac{1}{2}$*
x_5	$16\frac{1}{5}$

Thus, the pivot row is designated by x_4. The matrix to be pivoted, with the pivot element encircled, is shown in Figure 11–5.4. Pivoting, as before, yields the new tableau shown in Figure 11–5.5. In this tableau, which

		x_4	x_5
E	$43\frac{1}{2}$	$-9/2$	$3/2$
x_3	$6\frac{1}{2}$	$3/2$	$-3/2$
x_1	$13\frac{1}{2}$	$-3/2$	$3/2$
x_2	10	-1	0
x_6	$4\frac{1}{2}$	$5/2$	$-3/2$

Fig. 11–5.5. Tableau for third solution: ($13\frac{1}{2}$,10). Revenue = \$43,500. Not optimal. Pivot element circled.

represents the point ($13\frac{1}{2}$,10), the element (E,x_5) is positive, and the indicated solution is not optimal. The row ratios are $\frac{13}{3}$ for the x_3 row, and 3 for the x_6 row. Thus the pivot element is (x_6,x_5). The iteration procedure gives us the new tableau shown in Figure 11–5.6. Since both coefficients in the top row are negative, the indicated solution is optimal.

		x_4	x_6
E	48	-2	-1
x_3	2	-1	1
x_1	18	1	-1
x_2	10	-1	0
x_5	3	$5/3$	$-2/3$

Fig. 11–5.6. Tableau for fourth solution: (18,10). Revenue = \$48,000. Optimal!

The solution, then, is to load 18 tons into the main hold and 10 tons into the cabin hold. This will yield revenue of \$48,000, and there is no way to load the aircraft, subject to the restrictions, which will yield greater revenue.

The student should compare this solution and the succession of tableaux with the sets of equations of the algebraic algorithm of the previous chapter and with the geometric points in the graphic solution of that chapter. The three methods of solution are, of course, completely equivalent.

The values of the other variables indicate that, since x_4 and x_6 are zero, the cabin hold capacity is fully utilized and the lift capacity of the aircraft is completely utilized. The value of 2 for x_3 indicates that there are 2 tons of unused capacity in the main hold, and $x_5 = 3$ indicates 3 tons of unused balance capacity in the cabin hold. It is not possible to utilize these unused capacities, since, among other things, the lift capacity of the aircraft is exhausted by the indicated solution.

11–6. Concluding Comments. The simplex algorithm has been illustrated here in the solution of a *maximization* problem. Obviously, one may be faced with minimization problems as well. These are handled by maximizing the negative; that is, multiply the entire objective function by -1, and then maximize in the usual way. For example, if the objective is to minimize costs, and the objective function to be *minimized* is, where C = cost,

$$C = 150 + 35x_1 - 18x_2 \tag{11–6.1}$$

The problem would be handled in the usual way, but we would maximize:

$$-C = -150 - 35x_1 + 18x_2 \tag{11–6.2}$$

Clearly, the maximum value of the quantity $-C$ will correspond to the minimum value of the quantity C.

The simplex method requires no graphical representation. The graphical method of the previous chapter could be applied only to two-dimensional problems, or possibly to three-dimensional problems, by those who like to draw three-dimensional graphs. For four variables, there is no graphic solution. The simplex method is not bound by this geometric requirement, and linear programming problems can be solved with any number of variables, even hundreds, with no conceptual difficulty.

For large problems, the pivoting process is usually performed on electronic computers; computer programs are available which require only that the objective function and the restrictions be stated in a form acceptable to the computer, and the computations are then performed at very high speeds.

SUGGESTIONS FOR FURTHER READING

See suggested readings for Chapter 13.

EXERCISES

11–1. The Erikis Data Processing Company has four kinds of data processing activities it is performing: payrolls, inventories, software development, and astronomical computations. Each of these kinds of jobs may be broken down into "job units," for which the time requirements and profit are given below. "Job units" may be further subdivided as necessary with no difficulty.

Job	Profit per Unit ($)	Time Requirements (Minutes per Unit)		
		Key Punching	Computations	Output (Printer)
Payrolls	200	1,100	30	200
Inventories	150	1,200	20	40
Software development	400	500	50	200
Astronomical compuations	80	10	110	10
Machine availability (minutes)		(12,000)	(300)	(1,000)

Since output printing is all done off-line on a separate small computer, each job may be thought of as moving serially from one machine to the next. Jobs may be interspersed as they move from machine to machine, but any job or part of a job which starts today in key punching must finish today in printing. Although the installation on which Erikis rents time works 24 hours per day, the amount of time available today for these jobs is limited.

Today's machine availability for these four kinds of jobs is given in the last line of the table above. This time may be scheduled at any time Erikis selects.

How many units of each type of job should be scheduled for today for maximum profit?

11–2. Solve Eligin Hardware Manufacturing Company problem (Exercise 10–4) of Chapter 10 using the simplex method.

11–3. The Roshay Bank has a large amount of cash to invest this month. There are five possible investment opportunities available.

	Current Yield
Amalgamated Trust	4% per year
Brand X Corporation	5% per year
Consolidated Fund	8% per year
Diversified Fund	6% per year
Earnmore Corporation	3% per year

On the assumption that the current yields will persist, the Bank wishes to invest for maximum yield. How should the Bank distribute its money among these five opportunities, and what is its actual realized yield? Legal regulations require that the investment in Consolidated cannot exceed the total investment in Amalgamated, Brand X, and Earnmore, combined. Also, the Bank's directors require that the amount invested in Amalgamated be at least as large as that in Consolidated and Diversified, combined.

12

Other Topics in Linear Programming

12–1. Unconformities. In the last chapter we dealt with the solution of linear programming problems by the simplex procedure. The problem which was used for illustration was one in which no difficulties arose, and we were able to proceed directly and easily to the optimal solution. Often problems arise which do not conform to the ideal pattern. We shall examine six types of such failure to conform. Some involve error in analyzing and defining the problem, and others arise from irregularities inherent in the problem. The examination of these uncomformities will serve two purposes for the student. First, it will teach the student to recognize them and deal with them if and when they arise. Second, and more important, the tracing of the implications of these situations through graphical and simplex analyses will give the student a deeper and surer understanding of the concept of linear programming.

The first four which we shall examine are of the latter type. They represent irregularities which may, and often do, occur and which may be recognized and handled quite easily. These are identified as: *origin not feasible*, *degeneracy*, *exact restrictions*, and *multiple solutions*. The last two, which result from errors in analysis or formulation of the problem, are identified as *contradictory restrictions*, and *unbounded feasible region.*

12–2. Origin Not Feasible. If there is a minimum restriction on one or more of the real variables in the problem, then the origin (where all of the real variables are zero) is not in the feasible region. Clearly, if this is the case, the device which we used in the last chapter, i.e., the use of the origin as the first feasible corner, is not correct. Then, we must, as our first task, find some other first feasible corner.

In illustrating this unconformity as well as all of the others, we shall use the Everich Air Cargo problem from Chapters 10 and 11, with modifications. That is, in each case we shall introduce a modification into the description of the Everich problem, and that modification will change the problem from its original all-conforming configuration to an illustration of the particular unconformity being discussed.

Let us suppose that the Everich Air Cargo Company had previously contracted to take 5 tons of ordinary cargo in the main hold. This means that, in addition to the maximum restrictions of 20 tons for the main hold, 10 tons for the cabin hold, 28 tons for the aircraft, and the balance maximum for the cabin hold of one ton more than $\frac{2}{3}$ of the main-hold load, there is also a minimum restriction of 5 tons in the main hold. The tariff, as before, is \$1,000 per ton for main-hold cargo and \$3,000 per ton for cabin-hold cargo. The problem, with E measured in thousands of dollars, then is as follows.

Maximize: $$E = x_1 + 3x_2 \tag{10–1.1}$$

subject to:
$$x_1 \leq 20 \tag{10–1.3}$$
$$x_2 \leq 10 \tag{10–1.4}$$
$$x_2 \leq 1 + \tfrac{2}{3}x_1 \tag{10–1.5}$$
$$x_1 + x_2 \leq 28 \tag{10–1.6}$$
$$x_1 \geq 5 \tag{12–2.1}$$

In graphical analysis, this problem presents no difficulty at all. In Figure 12–2.1, the fact that the origin is not in the feasible region is clear, but it does not affect the optimal solution, which again is seen to be at the point (18,10), with total revenue of \$48,000.

In the simplex procedure, this unconformity requires a new device, called the *artificial variable*. If we follow the usual practice of adding a slack variable to the smaller side of each of the inequations and then putting the slack variables alone on the left sides of the resulting equations, the resulting set of equations is:

$$x_3 = 20 - x_1 \tag{11–1.6}$$
$$x_4 = 10 - x_2 \tag{11–1.7}$$
$$x_5 = 1 + \tfrac{2}{3}x_1 - x_2 \tag{11–1.8}$$
$$x_6 = 28 - x_1 - x_2 \tag{11–1.9}$$
$$x_7 = -5 + x_1 \tag{12–2.2}$$

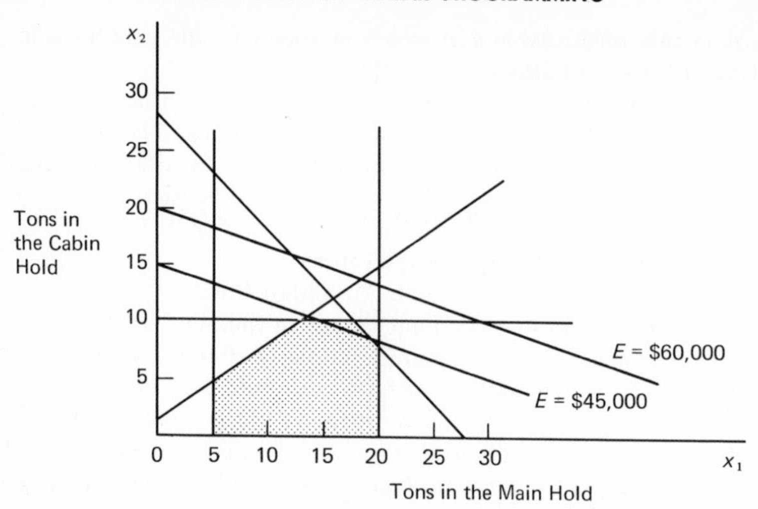

Fig. 12–2.1. Everich Air Cargo problem modified so that origin is not in the feasible region.

The first four equations as their equation numbers indicate are identical with those derived and used in the last chapter. The last equation (12–2.2) is derived by adding the slack variable numbered sequentially x_7, to the smaller side of the inequation (12–2.1) thereby converting it into an equation:

$$x_1 \geq 5 \tag{12–2.1}$$

$$x_1 = 5 + x_7 \tag{12–2.3}$$

and then solving for x_7:

$$x_7 = -5 + x_1 \tag{12–2.2}$$

This equation, with its negative constant, indicates that the slack variable x_7 is negative and therefore the origin is not in the feasible region. It actually tells us that, if $x_1 = 0$, the minimum restriction for the main hold is violated by 5 tons.

It will be recalled that, in order to use the simplex algorithm, the constants must be nonnegative. Therefore we must do something about the negative constant in Equation (12–2.2). The standard technique is to introduce an *artificial variable,* which we may designate x_a (in large programs this might be designated by the next number in sequence, i.e., x_8, but here, for clarity, we shall use x_a for "artificial"). This artificial variable is defined to be less than or equal to the appropriate slack variable. That is

$$x_a \leq x_7 \tag{12–2.4}$$

and therefore

$$x_7 - x_a \geq 0 \tag{12–2.5}$$

Then, it is this term, $(x_7 - x_a)$, which is added to the smaller side of Equation (12–2.1) as follows:

$$x_1 \geq 5 \qquad (12\text{–}2.1)$$

$$x_1 = 5 + x_7 - x_a \qquad (12\text{–}2.6)$$

Solving then for x_a yields an equation which has a positive constant:

$$x_a = 5 - x_1 + x_7 \qquad (12\text{–}2.7)$$

and which can be used in the first simplex tableau; the equation system then is:

Maximize: $\quad E = x_1 + 3x_2 \qquad (10\text{–}1.1)$

subject to: $\quad x_3 = 20 - x_1 \qquad (11\text{–}1.6)$

$$x_4 = 10 - x_2 \qquad (11\text{–}1.7)$$

$$x_5 = 1 + \tfrac{2}{3}x_1 - x_2 \qquad (11\text{–}1.8)$$

$$x_6 = 28 - x_1 - x_2 \qquad (11\text{–}1.9)$$

$$x_a = 5 - x_1 + x_7 \qquad (12\text{–}2.7)$$

The corresponding simplex tableau, which is shown in Figure 12–2.2, has an additional column headed x_7. All of the constants are positive, so the

		x_1	x_2	x_7
E	0	1	3	0
x_3	20	−1	0	0
x_4	10	0	−1	0
x_5	1	2/3	−1	0
x_6	28	−1	−1	0
x_a	5	−1	0	1

Fig. 12–2.2

solution which it represents seems to be feasible. Actually, as we know, it is not feasible, and no solution with x_a in the basis is feasible. However, if we pivot in order to remove x_a from the basis, and if then none of the constants is negative, we then have a feasible solution, and we can proceed with the normal iteration procedure. In this illustration, that device works readily, and a feasible corner is arrived at in one step.

Let us illustrate by pivoting to eliminate x_a from the basis. The only negative element (the pivot element must be negative, it will be recalled) in the x_a row is in the x_1 column. Therefore we must ignore the general rule that we select as pivot column the column with the largest positive coefficient in the objective function and must pivot in the x_1 column, since *our purpose here is not yet to increase* E but rather *first to arrive at a feasible solution.* Pivoting on that column yields the tableau of Figure 12–2.3. In

		x_a	x_2	x_7
E	5	−1	3	1
x_3	15	1	0	−1
x_4	10	0	−1	0
x_5	13/3	−2/3	−1	2/3
x_6	23	1	−1	−1
x_1	5	−1	0	1

Fig. 12–2.3

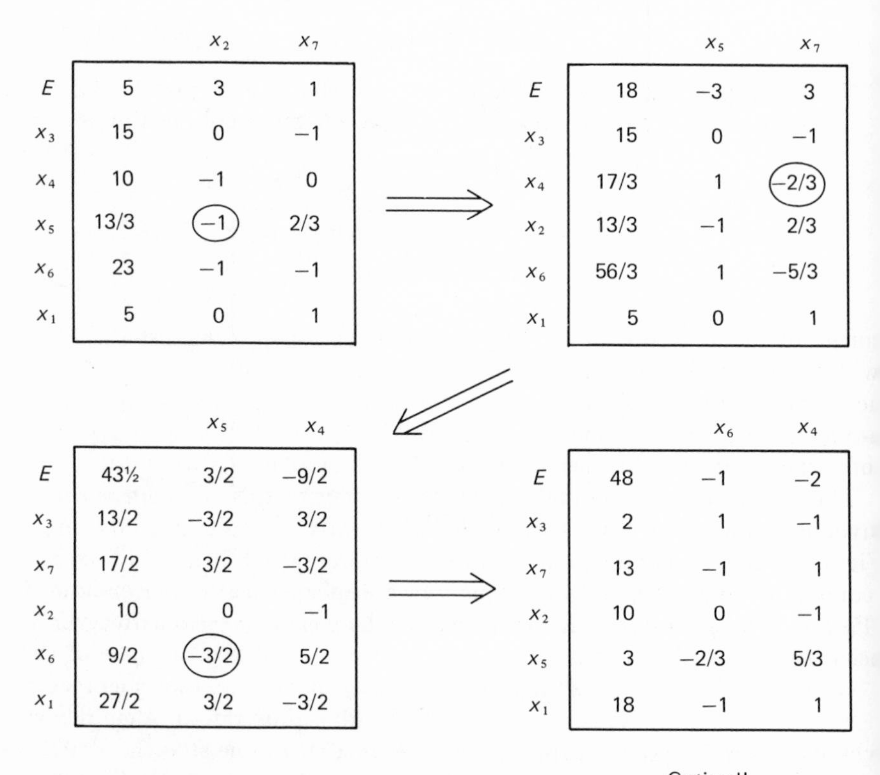

		x_2	x_7
E	5	3	1
x_3	15	0	−1
x_4	10	−1	0
x_5	13/3	(−1)	2/3
x_6	23	−1	−1
x_1	5	0	1

⟹

		x_5	x_7
E	18	−3	3
x_3	15	0	−1
x_4	17/3	1	(−2/3)
x_2	13/3	−1	2/3
x_6	56/3	1	−5/3
x_1	5	0	1

		x_5	x_4
E	43½	3/2	−9/2
x_3	13/2	−3/2	3/2
x_7	17/2	3/2	−3/2
x_2	10	0	−1
x_6	9/2	(−3/2)	5/2
x_1	27/2	3/2	−3/2

⟹

		x_6	x_4
E	48	−1	−2
x_3	2	1	−1
x_7	13	−1	1
x_2	10	0	−1
x_5	3	−2/3	5/3
x_1	18	−1	1

Optimal!

Fig. 12–2.4

Figure 12–2.3, the constants are all positive, and x_a is not in the basis. Therefore it represents a corner of the feasible region, namely point (5,0). Therefore, since x_a is now equal to zero, we no longer need it; we can eliminate it and its entire column, reducing the tableau to the first tableau of Figure 12.2–4, from which we can iterate to the optimal in the usual way as shown in Figure 12–2.4.

The procedure which we have used here, wherein we introduced an artificial variable into the restriction equation, pivoted to make the artificial variable a zero variable, and then eliminated the artificial variable and its entire column, is a procedure which cannot be depended upon to yield a feasible solution after one pivot or even after several. For example, even in two dimensions, if the feasible region looks like that of Figure 12–2.5, there is no way to proceed from the origin to a feasible

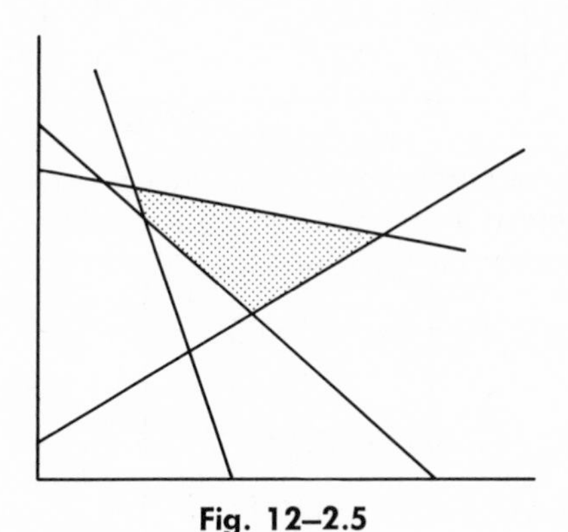

Fig. 12–2.5

corner in one pivot operation. Thus, after the first pivot operation, there will still be one or more negative constants in the tableau, and there will be no clear indication of the correct direction in which to proceed. In n-dimensions, it is even more difficult. In effect, there is a feasible region somewhere out in n-dimensional space, and the problem is to find it.

There is a very simple and ingenious solution to this problem which involves doing exactly what we have done to arrive at the first tableau, Figure 12–2.2, and the equations which it represents, but in addition it requires a simple modification of the objective function, Equation (10–1.1). The objective function is modified to include a term with x_a. It becomes

$$E = x_1 + 3x_2 - Lx_a \tag{12–2.8}$$

where L is a *very large* number. It is so large that this device has the effect of automatically insuring that x_a will be a zero variable, since, if x_a is not zero, the objective function will be small and therefore not optimum.

The modified Everich Air Cargo problem then becomes:

Maximize: $E = x_1 + 3x_2 - Lx_a$ (12–2.8

subject to: $x_3 = 20 - x_1$ (11–1.6

$x_4 = 10 - x_2$ (11–1.7

$x_5 = 1 + \frac{2}{3}x_1 - x_2$ (11–1.8

$x_6 = 28 - x_1 - x_2$ (11–1.9

$x_a = 5 - x_1 + x_7$ (12–2.7

This is called a *feasibility program*, and since it is "feasible" (i.e., havin no negative constants), it can be solved in the usual way for its optimal and its optimal will, for reasons we have seen, be the optimal solution fo the desired linear programming problem. This is illustrated in Figur 12–2.6, where we have arbitrarily let $L = 100$ (we could just as well hav chosen any large number or even have retained the letter L). Then,

$$E = x_1 + 3x_2 - 100x_a$$

Now, according to our rules, a simplex tableau cannot have x_a, a *basi* variable, in the objective function, so we substitute it out by means o the appropriate restriction equation (12–2.7):

$$E = x_1 + 3x_2 - 100(5 - x_1 + x_7)$$
$$= x_1 + 3x_2 - 500 + 100x_1 - 100x_7$$
$$E = -500 + 101x_1 + 3x_2 - 100x_7 \quad (12\text{–}2.9$$

This last equation, (12–2.9), then, is the objective equation used in plac of Equation (12–2.8) in the first tableau. Note that, in this problem, afte the first iteration, a large negative number remains as the coefficient in th top line in the x_a column. *This automatically has the effect of keeping x_a as zero variable*, and therefore the x_a column could have been eliminated fron the second and all succeeding tableaux of Figure 12–2.6. In the future, w shall eliminate artificial variables and their entire columns from tableau as soon as they become zero variables, since, when they become equal t zero, they have served their purpose, and they are of no further use.

This procedure may be used with any number of artificial variable One artificial variable must be added for each negative constant, i.e., fo each minimum restriction on a real variable, and one new term must b added to the objective function, i.e., $-Lx_a - Lx_b - Lx_c$, etc., for eac artificial variable. The procedure is then automatic, and a person or com puter can proceed to the optimal solution via the usual rules for iteratior

12–3. Degeneracy. It has been pointed out that at a corner of th feasible region there are always n zero variables and m basic variables, an also that sometimes one or more of the basic variables may have a value c zero. It was for this reason that the term *nonzero* is not used, and the terr

		x_1	x_2	x_7
E	−500	101	3	−100
x_3	20	−1	0	0
x_4	10	0	−1	0
x_5	1	2/3	−1	0
x_6	28	−1	−1	0
x_a	5	(−1)	0	1

⇒

		x_a	x_2	x_7
E	5	−101	3	1
x_3	15	1	0	−1
x_4	10	0	−1	0
x_5	13/3	−2/3	(−1)	2/3
x_6	23	1	−1	−1
x_1	5	−1	0	1

⇙

		x_a	x_5	x_7
E	18	−103	−3	3
x_3	15	1	0	−1
x_4	17/3	2/3	1	(−2/3)
x_2	13/3	−2/3	−1	2/3
x_6	56/3	5/3	1	−5/3
x_1	5	−1	0	1

⇒

		x_a	x_5	x_4
E	43½	−100	3/2	−9/2
x_3	13/2	0	−3/2	3/2
x_7	17/2	1	3/2	−3/2
x_2	10	0	0	−1
x_6	9/2	0	(−3/2)	5/2
x_1	27/2	0	3/2	−3/2

⇙

		x_a	x_6	x_4
E	48	−100	−1	−2
x_3	2	0	1	−1
x_7	13	1	−1	1
x_2	10	0	0	−1
x_5	3	0	−2/3	5/3
x_1	18	0	−1	1

Optimal!

Fig. 12–2.6

asic is used to identify these variables. Whenever one or more of the basic ariables has a value of zero, that solution is said to be *degenerate*.

If the Everich Air Cargo problem had been:

Maximize: $$E = x_1 + 3x_2 \qquad (10\text{–}1.1)$$

subject to: $$x_1 \leq 20 \qquad (10\text{–}1.3)$$

$$x_2 \leq 10 \qquad (10\text{–}1.4)$$

$$x_2 \leq 1 + \tfrac{2}{3}x_1 \qquad (10\text{–}1.5)$$

$$x_1 + x_2 \leq 23\tfrac{1}{2} \qquad (12\text{–}3.1)$$

the problem would, because of the changed fourth restriction, involve degeneracy.

The graphic solution to the problem is again quite simple, as seen in Figure 12–3.1. Three lines meet in a point at $(13\frac{1}{2},10)$. The slope of the

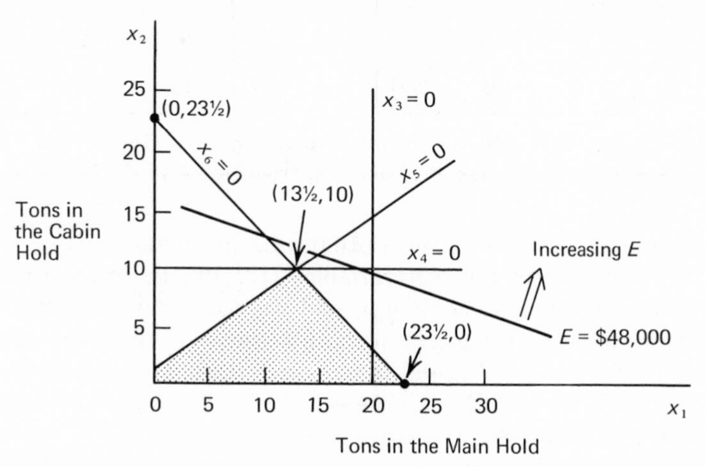

Fig. 12–3.1. Everich Air Cargo problem modified so that degeneracy occurs.

revenue line indicates quite clearly that the optimal solution occurs at that point, and that the optimal value of the revenue is therefore \$43,500.

In the simplex algorithm, the degeneracy is indicated by the fact that, at that corner, three variables (x_4,x_5,x_6) are all equal to zero. Since there can be only two zero variables, one of the basic variables must be zero. In Figure 12–3.2, after the first iteration, the selection of the next pivot

		x_1	x_2
E	0	1	3
x_3	20	−1	0
x_4	10	0	−1
x_5	1	2/3	(−1)
x_6	23½	−1	−1

⟹

		x_1	x_5
E	3	3	−3
x_3	20	−1	0
x_4	9	(−2/3)	1
x_2	1	2/3	−1
x_6	22½	(−5/3)	1

Fig. 12–3.2

element indicates that the following corner will represent a degenerate solution. There are two equal candidates for the next pivot element. Both have a ratio of $13\frac{1}{2}$, and both are circled. If we pivot on either one, the constant in the other row will also become zero. In Figure 12–3.3, the left tableau is the result of pivoting in the x_4 row, and the right tableau is the

		x_4	x_5
E	43½	−9/2	3/2
x_3	6½	3/2	−3/2
x_1	13½	−3/2	3/2
x_2	10	−1	0
x_6	0	5/2	(−3/2)

		x_6	x_5
E	43½	−9/2	−6/5
x_3	6½	3/5	−3/5
x_4	0	2/5	3/5
x_2	10	−2/5	−3/5
x_1	13½	−3/5	3/5

Fig. 12–3.3. Left tableau: result of pivoting from Figure 12–3.2 on (x_4,x_1) element. Right tableau: result of pivoting from Figure 12–3.2 on (x_6,x_1) element.

result of pivoting in the x_6 row. Both results are identical in that they have the same values of the real variables $(13\frac{1}{2},10)$, the same value of the nonzero basic variable ($x_3 = 6\frac{1}{2}$), and the same value for the revenue. However, in one case x_6 is a basic variable, while in the other, x_4 is a basic variable ("in the basis"), and in one case, the left, the positive value in the top row in the x_5 column is the standard indication that the solution is not optimal. However, the zero tells us to pivot on the x_6 row, and also that pivoting will not increase x_5 from zero or change the first column. However, the rule instructs that pivoting should continue. Figure 12–3.4

		x_4	x_6
E	43½	−2	−1
x_3	6½	−1	1
x_1	13½	1	−1
x_2	10	−1	0
x_5	0	5/3	−2/3

Fig. 12–3.4

shows the result of pivoting again. The values for the real variables, the revenue, and the nonzero basic variable have not changed. Now the top row tells us that this solution is optimal. The two final tableaux, the tableau of Figure 12–3.4 and the right tableau of Figure 12–3.3, can be converted one into the other by pivoting on the *positive* element in the (x_4,x_5) or (x_5,x_4) position.

If the degenerate corner is not optimal, then it is necessary to pivot *from* that corner. Sometimes this can be done easily by following the familiar rules, and sometimes it is necessary to use other devices such as shifting one or more of the lines by a very small amount, thus eliminating the degeneracy.

12–4. Equality Restrictions. Sometimes one or more of the restrictions may be equations rather than inequations. In a graphical solution of a two-dimensional problem, this unconformity not only may be handled easily, but it makes the problem extremely simple.

If the Everich Air Cargo problem had been:

Maximize: $$E = x_1 + 3x_2 \tag{10–1.1}$$

subject to: $$x_1 \leq 20 \tag{10–1.3}$$

$$x_2 \leq 10 \tag{10–1.4}$$

$$x_2 = 1 + \tfrac{2}{3}x_1 \tag{12–4.1}$$

$$x_1 + x_2 \leq 28 \tag{10–1.6}$$

the problem would involve an *equality* or an *exact restriction,* Equation (12–4.1). The graphical solution is shown in Figure 12–4.1, where the

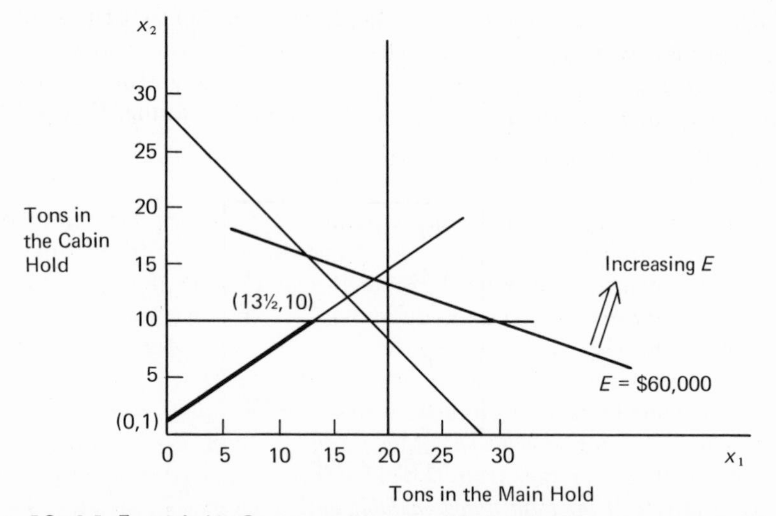

Fig. 12–4.1. Everich Air Cargo problem modified to involve an exact restriction. Feasible region is the line segment from point (0,1) to point (13½,10).

entire feasible region is merely the line segment from point (0,1) to point (13½,10) which is drawn as a heavy line. The optimum value must occur at an end of the line. In this case it is obviously at point (13½,10) with revenue, E = $43,500.

In the simplex algorithm, this unconformity may often be handled easily by substituting for the equality restriction algebraically throughout the set of inequalities, thereby reducing the number of restrictions by one, and reducing the number of dimensions by one. The restriction inequations become, with $1 + \frac{2}{3}x_1$ substituted for x_2 in the first, second, and fourth equations.

$$\left\{\begin{aligned} x_1 &\leq 20 \\ 1 + \tfrac{2}{3}x_1 &\leq 10 \\ x_1 + 1 + \tfrac{2}{3}x_1 &\leq 28 \end{aligned}\right\} \Rightarrow \left\{\begin{aligned} x_1 &\leq 20 \\ \tfrac{2}{3}x_1 &\leq \ \ 9 \\ \tfrac{5}{3}x_1 &\leq 27 \end{aligned}\right\}$$

This set of equations could be solved by simplex, but in this case that is unnecessary, since only one variable is involved. The entire problem becomes, with the substitution made in the objective function also:

Maximize:

$$E = x_1 + 3(1 + \tfrac{2}{3}x_1) = x_1 + 3 + 2x_1 = 3 + 3x_1 \qquad (12\text{–}4.2)$$

subject to:

$$x_1 \leq 20 \qquad (10\text{–}1.3)$$

$$x_1 \leq 13\tfrac{1}{2} \qquad (12\text{–}4.3)$$

$$x_1 \leq 16\tfrac{1}{5} \qquad (12\text{–}4.4)$$

Clearly, Equation (12–4.2) indicates that E is increased as x_1 is increased and therefore x_1 should be as large as possible. Of the three remaining restriction equations, Equation (12–4.3) is the limiting equation. Therefore the optimal value of x_1 is $13\frac{1}{2}$, E = \$43,500, and x_2 may be computed to be equal to 10, from the equality restriction, Equation (12–4.1).

In more complex problems, equality restrictions, by reducing the number of dimensions, often make it possible to solve three-dimensional or four-dimensional problems graphically or to solve manually problems which otherwise might be too difficult.

Unfortunately, this simple method of substitution does not always lead to the correct answer in the simplex algorithm. It is easy to see why this is so. When one variable is eliminated by substitution of its equality, we can be assured, of course, that the equality relationship will be satisfied in the solution which emerges from the algorithm, but *we cannot be sure that the nonnegativity of the eliminated variable will be preserved.* This follows from the fact that, having eliminated that variable from the entire analysis, we have no way to enforce its nonnegativity, and therefore the simplex algorithm may produce an "optimal" solution which later proves to be not feasible, if the eliminated variable, when evaluated, is found to be negative.

A better method of operation is to treat one of the variables in the equality restriction as a slack variable rather than to eliminate it from the restrictions. Since that selected variable will now appear in the first basis, it should be eliminated (by substitution) from the objective function (if it appears there) and from any other restriction expressions in which it appears.

Using this method with the system of equations (10–1.1), (10–1.3), (10–1.4), (12–4.1), and (10–1.6), given at the beginning of this section, selecting x_2 as the "slack" variable, and eliminating x_2 by substitution elsewhere, yields, first, a set of equations which resemble those of the original problem, except that x_5 does not appear. Then, substitution of the equality in the objective function and the *other* restrictions yields a system

$$\begin{pmatrix} E = x_1 + 3x_2 \\ x_3 = 20 - x_1 \\ x_4 = 10 - x_2 \\ x_2 = 1 + \frac{2}{3}x_1 \\ x_6 = 28 - x_1 - x_2 \end{pmatrix} \Rightarrow \begin{pmatrix} E = 3 + 3x_1 \\ x_3 = 20 - x_1 \\ x_4 = 9 - \frac{2}{3}x_1 \\ x_2 = 1 + \frac{2}{3}x_1 \\ x_6 = 27 - \frac{5}{3}x_1 \end{pmatrix}$$

which can be handled by the simplex algorithm. This problem is solved in this way in Figure 12–4.2.

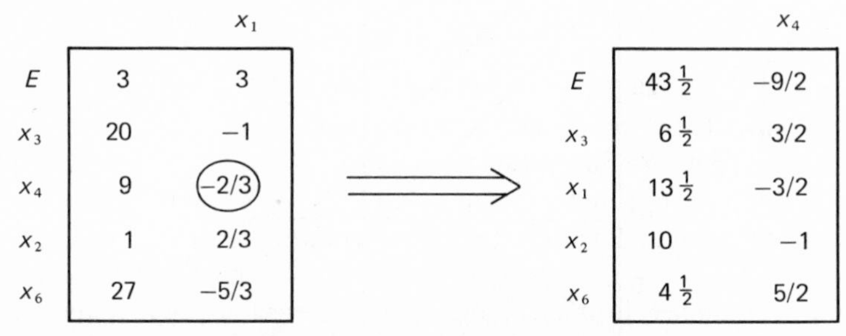

Fig. 12–4.2. Simplex solution with equality restriction. Solution by treating one of the variables in the equality restriction as a slack variable.

It is also possible to solve linear programming problems with equality restrictions by adding an artificial variable to each equality restriction. Then, by also adding these artificial variables to the objective function with large negative coefficients ($-L$), the artificial variables will be forced to be equal to zero at the optimal solution, assuring that the equality restrictions are fulfilled. This method always works perfectly, but it is, in most cases, unnecessarily cumbersome.

12–5. Multiple Solutions. When the objective function is parallel to a side of the feasible region, the two corners which terminate that side both have the same value of the objective function, as does every point on the line segment joining those two corners. In three dimensions the side is a plane, and if the plane is parallel to the plane which is the objective function, then every point on that plane has the same value of the objective function. In more than three dimensions, there is no geometrical representation, but, as we shall see, the simplex procedure handles this unconformity with no difficulty.

If the Everich Air Cargo problem had been:

Maximize: $$E = x_1 + x_2 \tag{12–5.1}$$

subject to: $$x_1 \le 20 \tag{10–1.3}$$

$$x_2 \le 10 \tag{10–1.4}$$

$$x_2 \le 1 + \tfrac{2}{3}x_1 \tag{10–1.5}$$

$$x_1 + x_2 \le 28 \tag{10–1.6}$$

the objective function, Equation (12–5.1), is parallel to the aircraft lift restriction, Equation (10–1.6). Figure 12–5.1 shows that the optimal

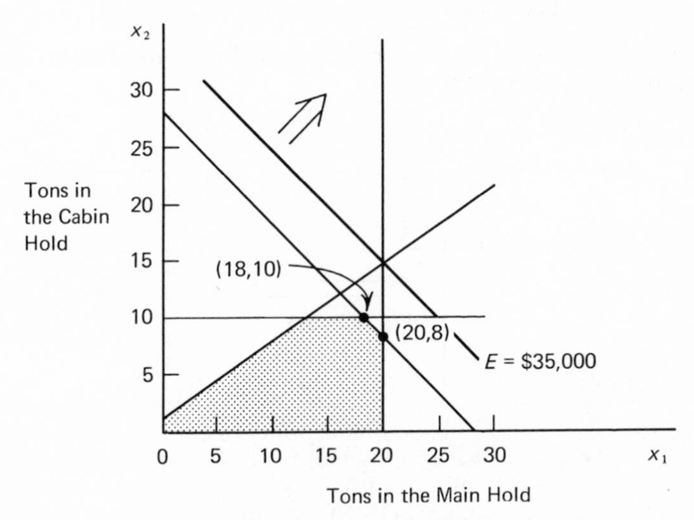

Fig. 12–5.1. **Everich Air Cargo problem modified so that there are multiple solutions.**

solution is at the corner points (18,10) and (20,8) and also at every point on the line segment connecting those points. The revenue is $28,000 at every point on that line segment.

In the simplex algorithm, the equations are first modified by the addition of the slack variables. The problem then is:

Maximize: $$E = x_1 + x_2$$

subject to:

$$\begin{Bmatrix} x_1 + x_3 = 20 \\ x_2 + x_4 = 10 \\ x_2 + x_5 = 1 + \tfrac{2}{3}x_1 \\ x_1 + x_2 + x_6 = 28 \end{Bmatrix} \Rightarrow \begin{Bmatrix} x_3 = 20 - x_1 \\ x_4 = 10 - x_2 \\ x_5 = 1 + \tfrac{2}{3}x_1 - x_2 \\ x_6 = 28 - x_1 - x_2 \end{Bmatrix}$$

and this problem is solved in Figure 12–5.2.

		x_1	x_2
E	0	1	1
x_3	20	−1	0
x_4	10	0	−1
x_5	1	2/3	(−1)
x_6	28	−1	−1

⟹

		x_1	x_5
E	1	5/3	−1
x_3	20	−1	0
x_4	9	(−2/3)	1
x_2	1	2/3	−1
x_6	27	−5/3	1

⟹

		x_4	x_5
E	23½	−5/2	3/2
x_3	13/2	3/2	−3/2
x_1	27/2	−3/2	3/2
x_2	10	−1	0
x_6	9/2	5/2	(−3/2)

⟹

		x_4	x_6
E	28	0	−1
x_3	2	−1	1
x_1	18	1	−1
x_2	10	−1	0
x_5	3	5/3	−2/3

Optimal!

Fig. 12–5.2

The final tableau in Figure 12–5.2 is optimal in that there are no positive coefficients in the top row. This means that pivoting will not increase the value of the objective function. However, there is a zero in the top row. This zero coefficient tells us that pivoting in that column will move the solution from its present point, (18,10) to some other point; but the zero in that column in the top row tells us that, as a consequence of the pivoting rules, pivoting will not change the top row. Therefore the value of the objective function must be unchanged, and the top row must still indicate optimality. The result of pivoting on the (x_3,x_4) element is shown in Figure 12–5.3. The solution has moved from corner point (18,10) to corner point (20,8), but the revenue remains $28,000.

		x_3	x_6
E	28	0	−1
x_4	2	−1	1
x_1	20	1	0
x_2	8	−1	−1
x_5	6⅓	−5/3	1

Fig. 12–5.3

Whenever there is more than one basic solution with the same value of the objective function, there exists an infinite number of solutions with the same value; but they are not all basic. Here, only these two corner points are basic (i.e., two zero variables). There is an infinite number of points on the line segment connecting these two corner points, and they are all equally optimal, with revenue equal to $28,000; but they are not basic. They have only one zero variable, namely, x_6.

12–6. Contradictory Restrictions. The four unconformities which we have discussed above: origin not feasible, degeneracy, exact restrictions, and multiple solutions, are all irregularities which can and do arise in the normal and correct application of linear programming to real-world problems. Now we shall look at two situations *which represent errors* in the definition or formulation of the problem. They are included here because they can and do occur, and it is well to understand how they may be recognized in the graphical method and particularly in the simplex algorithm.

When there are contradictory restrictions, there is *no feasible region;* i.e., every point violates one or more of the restrictions. This kind of situation arises when one or more of the restrictions is incorrectly stated.

If the Everich Air Cargo problem had been:

Maximize: $$E = x_1 + 3x_2 \qquad (10\text{–}1.1)$$

subject to: $$x_1 \geq 20 \qquad (12\text{–}6.1)$$

$$x_2 \leq 10 \qquad (10\text{–}1.4)$$

$$x_2 \geq 1 + \tfrac{2}{3}x_1 \qquad (12\text{–}6.2)$$

$$x_1 + x_2 \leq 28 \qquad (10\text{–}1.6)$$

the altered restrictions (12–6.1) and (12–6.2) would then have the effect of contradicting the others, with the result that, as seen in Figure 12–6.1, there would be no feasible region.

In the simplex procedure, the first step is to add the four slack variables and two artificial variables, as necessary, to the two minimum restrictions. The two artificial variables are then entered into the objective function with large (L) negative coefficients. This is to assure that the artificial variables will be zero variables at the optimum. The problem then may be stated:

Maximize: $$E = x_1 + 3x_2 - L_a x_a - L_b x_b \qquad (12\text{–}6.3)$$

subject to: $$x_a = 20 - x_1 + x_3 \qquad (12\text{–}6.4)$$

$$x_4 = 10 - x_2 \qquad (11\text{–}1.7)$$

$$x_b = 1 + \tfrac{2}{3}x_1 - x_2 + x_5 \qquad (12\text{–}6.5)$$

$$x_6 = 28 - x_1 - x_2 \qquad (11\text{–}1.9)$$

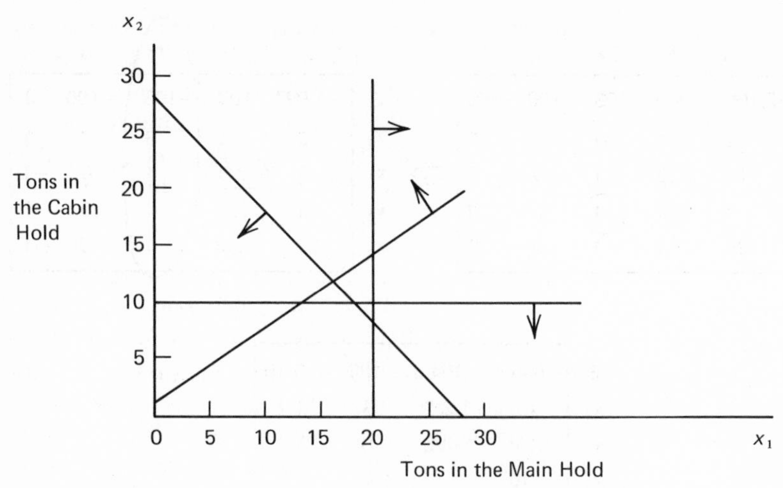

Fig. 12–6.1. Everich Air Cargo problem modified so that there is no feasible region.

The objective function must be modified by substitution from Equations (12–6.4) and (12–6.5) to remove the x_a and x_b, since these artificial variables are, in this first tableau, in the basis. If we arbitrarily let $L_a = L_b = 100$, Equation (12–6.3) becomes

$$E = x_1 + 3x_2 - 100(20 - x_1 + x_3) - 100(1 + \tfrac{2}{3}x_1 - x_2 + x_5)$$

$$= x_1 + 3x_2 - 2{,}000 + 100x_1 - 100x_3 - 100 - 66\tfrac{2}{3}x_1 + 100x_2 - 100x_5$$

$$E = -2{,}100 + 34\tfrac{1}{3}x_1 + 103x_2 - 100x_3 - 100x_5 \tag{12–6.6}$$

The simplex algorithm is shown in Figure 12–6.2, where the last tableau seems to signal that the optimal solution has been reached because all of the coefficients in the objective function are negative. However, an artificial variable remains in the basis. There is no way to pivot it out, since there are no negative elements in the row. If we try to pivot on one of the positive elements in that row, a negative constant will be generated. That is, of course, not an admissible procedure in our algorithm, but we mention this to emphasize that there is no way to remove the artificial variable from the basis and achieve a feasible solution. (To see why this would generate a negative constant, see the explanation of the pivoting rules given in Section 11–4.)

This inability to achieve a feasible solution indicates that an error has been made in formulating the problem and that the restrictions are inconsistent.

Thus, any errors of this type which may be introduced in the formulation of the problem will be detected by the algorithm. In a computer

		x_1	x_2	x_3	x_5
E	−2,100	34⅓	103	−100	−100
x_a	20	−1	0	1	0
x_4	10	0	−1	0	0
x_b	1	2/3	(−1)	0	1
x_6	28	−1	−1	0	0

⇒

		x_1	x_b	x_3	x_5
E	−1,997	103	−103	−100	3
x_a	20	−1	0	1	0
x_4	9	(−2/3)	1	0	−1
x_2	1	2/3	−1	0	1
x_6	27	−5/3	1	0	−1

⇙

		x_4	x_3	x_5
E	−606.5	−154.5	−100	−151.5
x_a	6½	3/2	1	3/2
x_1	13½	−3/2	0	−3/2
x_2	10	−1	0	0
x_6	4½	5/2	0	3/2

Fig. 12–6.2. Simplex algorithm for Everich Air Cargo problem modified so that there is no feasible region. That the artificial variable remains in the basis with no way to pivot it out indicates that there is no feasible region. The loop around the x_b column in the second matrix indicates that that artificial variable and its entire column will be eliminated from the analysis since it has served its purpose and is no longer needed.

program, of course, the generation of any negative constant will be recognized as an unacceptable result, and the operator will be so notified by the computer output.

12–7. Unbounded Feasible Region. If the Everich Air Cargo problem had been:

Maximize: $$E = x_1 + 3x_2 \tag{10–1.1}$$

subject to: $$x_1 \geq 20 \tag{12–7.1}$$

$$x_2 \leq 10 \tag{10–1.4}$$

$$x_2 \leq 1 + \tfrac{2}{3}x_1 \tag{10–1.5}$$

restriction inequation (12–7.1) is a minimum restriction, and as Figure 12–7.1 indicates, there is no boundary to the feasible region in the optimizing direction. Thus, the optimum value of E is infinitely large, since there is no upper limit to x_1. Clearly, in formulating this problem, some one or more restrictions have erroneously been omitted or mis-stated.

In the simplex procedure, the first step is to add the three slack variables and the artificial variable as necessary to the minimum restriction. The artificial variable is also added to the objective function with a large (L)

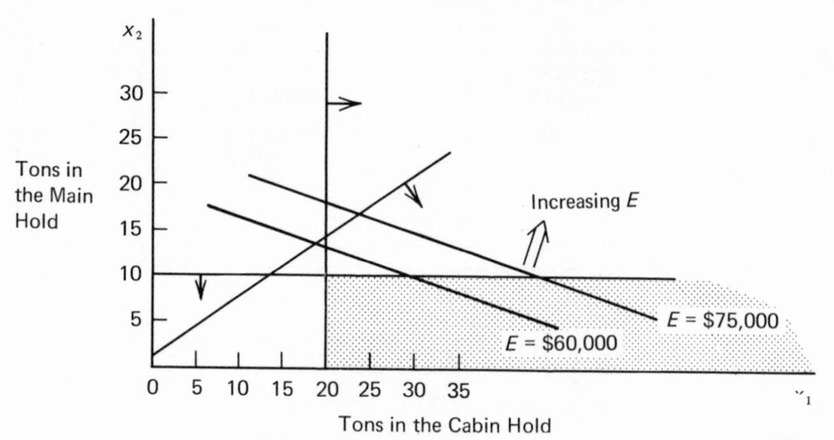

Fig. 12–7.1. Everich Air Cargo problem modified so that there is no right boundary to the feasible region.

negative coefficient. The problem may then be stated

Maximize:	$E = x_1 + 3x_2 - Lx_a$	(12–7.1)
subject to:	$x_a = 20 - x_1 + x_3$	(12–7.2)
	$x_4 = 10 - x_2$	(11–1.7)
	$x_5 = 1 + \frac{2}{3}x_1 - x_2$	(11–1.8)

The objective function must be modified by substitution from Equation (12–7.2) to remove x_a from the objective function, since x_a is, in this first tableau, in the basis. If we arbitrarily let $L = 100$, Equation (12–7.1) becomes

$$\begin{aligned} E &= x_1 + 3x_2 - 100(20 - x_1 + x_3) \\ &= x_1 + 3x_2 - 2{,}000 + 100x_1 - 100x_3 \\ E &= -2{,}000 + 101x_1 + 3x_2 - 100x_3 \end{aligned} \tag{12–7.3}$$

The simplex algorithm is shown in Figure 12–7.2, where it is seen that, in the last tableau, there is no negative element in the x_3 column, indicating that x_3 can increase without limit. Thus, it is impossible to find a pivot element in the column which has the largest (in this case, the only) positive coefficient in the objective function. This automatically indicates that the feasible region is unbounded *in the optimizing direction.*

In a computer program, this inability to find a negative element in the column with the largest positive coefficient in the objective function will be recognized as an error, and the computer output will so indicate.

It is not always an error for the feasible region to be unbounded. For example, if the diagram of Figure 12–7.1 represented a problem in which a *minimum* value of E were sought, the correct solution, namely point (20,0), with E = \$20,000, would be found by either the graphical or the

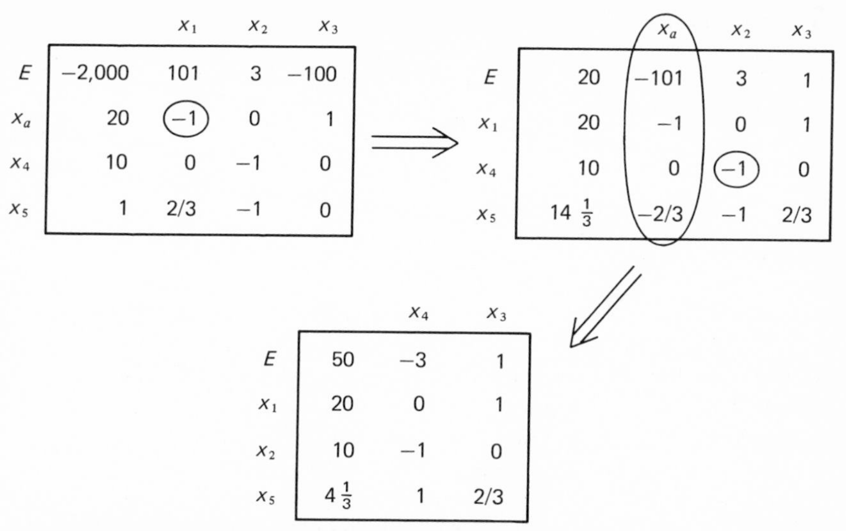

		x_4	x_3
E	50	−3	1
x_1	20	0	1
x_2	10	−1	0
x_5	$4\frac{1}{3}$	1	2/3

Fig. 12–7.2. Simplex algorithm for Everich Air Cargo problem modified so that the feasible region is unbounded in the optimizing direction. This is indicated by there being no negative elements in the column with the highest positive coefficient in the objective function.

simplex method. Indeed, in blending problems, as we shall see in Section 12–10, the feasible region is often unbounded upwards, but a minimum cost solution is desired, so that there is no difficulty arriving at an optimal solution in the normal way. An unbounded feasible region is an unconformity, indeed an error, only when it is unbounded in the direction of optimality.

12–8. The Transportation Problem as Linear Programming. The type of problem which was discussed in Chapter 9, *The Transportation Method*, is a linear programming problem, and it can be solved by the methods of linear programming. The transportation method, however, is much simpler and should be used whenever the transportation model adequately describes the phenomenon. However, we can, as a matter of interest, show that the problem can be solved by the simplex algorithm in the usual way.

It will be recalled that, in the transportation model, there are:

m origins, designated $i = 1, 2, 3, \ldots, m$

n destinations, designated $j = 1, 2, 3, \ldots, n$

a_i units available at the ith origin

b_j units required at the jth destination

mn transportation costs c_{ij}

mn quantities shipped x_{ij} (many of which are zero)

The problem is

Minimize: $$\sum c_{ij}x_{ij} \quad \text{over all } ij \tag{12–8.1}$$

subject to: $$\sum_{j=1}^{n} x_{ij} = a_i \tag{12–8.2}$$

$$\sum_{i=1}^{m} x_{ij} = b_j \tag{12–8.3}$$

Since $\sum_{i=1}^{m} a_i = \sum_{j=1}^{n} b_j$, the $m + n$ restriction equations (12–8.2) and (12–8.3) are not all independent, but rather any one of them may be derived from all of the others. This means that there are $(m + n - 1)$ independent restrictions and that, therefore, although there are mn unknowns (x_{ij}) to be determined, a basic solution will have $(m + n - 1)$ nonzero variables (i.e., values of x_{ij}), and the rest will be equal to zero.

We can demonstrate the procedure by applying it to the very simple Siro Paper Company problem of Chapter 9, Section 9–1. The problem is shown in Figure 12–8.1. It was noted in Chapter 9, that this problem may

Siro Paper Company
Unit Transportation Costs

From Origins (Plants):	To Destinations (Customers): Topeka	Chicago	Units Available a_i
Dallas	5	12	20
Memphis	10	8	30
Units Required b_j	10	40	50

Fig. 12–8.1. Transportation problem. Entries in a_i column are availabilities at the respective origins. Entries in b_j row are requirements at the respective destinations. All other entries are the unit transportation costs between the origin and destination indicated.

be solved very easily by the transportation method. In linear programming form, the problem is:

Minimize: $$TC = 5x_{11} + 12x_{12} + 10x_{21} + 8x_{22} \tag{12–8.4}$$

subject to: $$x_{11} + x_{12} = 20 \tag{12–8.5}$$

$$x_{21} + x_{22} = 30 \tag{12–8.6}$$

$$x_{11} + x_{21} = 10 \tag{12–8.7}$$

(The obvious fourth equation would be redundant. There are only three *independent* equations.)

This total-cost equation (12–8.4) is to be *minimized*. Thus, since we have established our rules for the simplex algorithm so that we *maximize* the objective function, we shall multiply through by -1 to arrive at a function to be *maximized*. Clearly, the *maximum* of the *negative* is the same as the *minimum* of the *original* cost function. The objective function to be maximized, then, is

$$-TC = -5x_{11} - 12x_{12} - 10x_{21} - 8x_{22} \qquad (12\text{–}8.8)$$

We now add three artificial variables (x_a, x_b, x_c), one to each of the three restriction equations (12–8.5), (12–8.6), and (12–8.7), and we also add the same artificial variables, with large (L) negative coefficients, to the objective function. The statement of the problem becomes

Maximize:

$$-TC = -5x_{11} - 12x_{12} - 10x_{21} - 8x_{22} - L_a x_a - L_b x_b - L_c x_c \qquad (12\text{–}8.9)$$

subject to:

$$x_a = 20 - x_{11} - x_{12} \qquad (12\text{–}8.10)$$

$$x_b = 30 - x_{21} - x_{22} \qquad (12\text{–}8.11)$$

$$x_c = 10 - x_{11} - x_{21} \qquad (12\text{–}8.12)$$

All that remains is to remove the artificial variables from the objective function, Equation (12–8.9), by substitution of the restriction equations (12–8.10), (12–8.11), and (12–8.12). Arbitrarily letting $L_a = L_b = L_c = 100$,

$$\begin{aligned} -TC &= -5x_{11} - 12x_{12} - 10x_{21} - 8x_{22} - 100(20 - x_{11} - x_{12}) \\ &\qquad - 100(30 - x_{21} - x_{22}) - 100(10 - x_{11} - x_{21}) \\ &= -5x_{11} - 12x_{12} - 10x_{21} - 8x_{22} - 2{,}000 + 100x_{11} + 100x_{12} \\ &\qquad - 3{,}000 + 100x_{21} + 100x_{22} - 1{,}000 + 100x_{11} + 100x_{21} \end{aligned}$$

$$-TC = -6{,}000 + 195x_{11} + 88x_{12} + 190x_{21} + 92x_{22} \qquad (12\text{–}8.13)$$

The simplex algorithm is shown in Figure 12–8.2, where the solution is: $x_{11} = 10$, $x_{12} = 10$, $x_{22} = 30$, and $TC = \$410$; i.e., $-TC = -410$. This solution is precisely the same as the optimum arrived at by the transportation method in Section 9–1.

This method is cumbersome and seldom used. For example, even the relatively simple 4-by-5 Waymar Manufacturing Company problem of Figure 9–3.1, if handled in this way, would require eight equations and, therefore, eight artificial variables and eight iterations of a 9-by-21 matrix to remove these one by one from the basis. That particular problem was much more easily solved in Chapter 9 by using the transportation method, i.e., the penalty method, to arrive at a first feasible solution, which, upon evaluation, proved to be optimal.

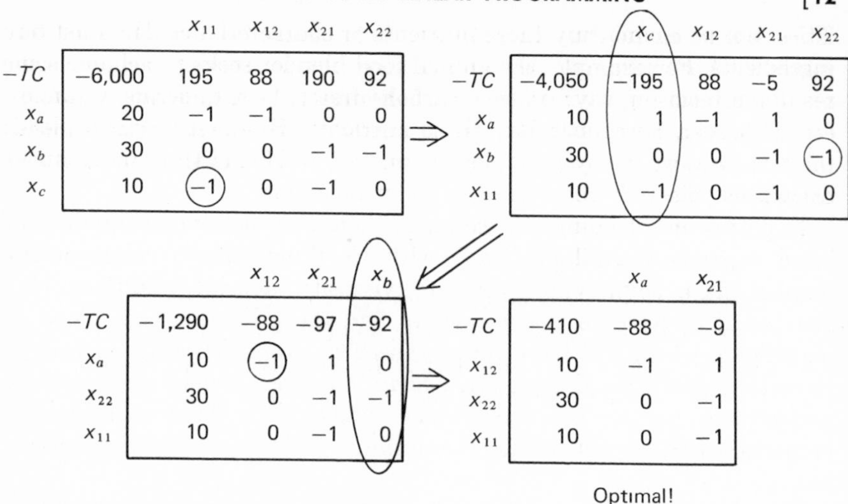

Fig. 12–8.2. Siro Paper Co. Solution of transportation problem by simplex algorithm.

There are also other ways in which a transportation problem may be formulated for application of the simplex algorithm, but none can be expected to yield the optimum solution as quickly and as easily as the transportation method.

12–9. The Assignment Problem as Linear Programming. The assignment problem which was discussed in Chapter 8, is a special case of the transportation problem in which $m = n$, all $a_i = 1$, all $b_j = 1$, and all x_{ij} are equal to either 1 or 0. Thus, the solution of an assignment problem via the simplex algorithm is possible. However, it is made particularly bothersome by the fact that the solution is always degenerate. That is, in a solution to the assignment problem, there are exactly m values of x_{ij} which are equal to 1, while the rest are 0. Since the number of nonzero variables in a *basic* solution is $2m - 1$, a solution to the assignment problem is always degenerate. Thus, because the simplex solution is difficult and the method given in Chapter 8 is so simple and efficient, the simplex method is not used for problems of this type.

12–10. Blending or Diet Problems. Blending or mixing problems, often called *diet* problems are among the most important and widely used applications of linear programming in the world today. They are extremely important in the petroleum industry and in the animal feed industry. In these problems, the purpose is typically to find the minimum cost blend of the available *ingredients* which meets some set of minimum standards with respect to specified *nutrients* or *characteristics*. That is, the decision maker wishes to achieve some result in terms of nutrients or characteristics, but he cannot buy these nutrients or characteristics. He must buy ingredients. For example, the animal food blender seeks to achieve some results in terms of, say: protein, carbohydrates, fats, minerals, vitamins, etc. However, he cannot buy these nutrients. He must buy and blend: meat, milk powder, soy bean meal, corn, etc., and blend these in a manner calculated to satisfy requirements about nutrients.

In petroleum blending, for example, there may be several fractions or basic *ingredients* available, each with its ("nutrients") color, octane number, flash point, vapor pressure, viscosity, density, additives, etc., *and cost.* The purpose is typically to find the minimum cost blend of ingredients which will have certain specified properties with respect to these characteristics. On the other hand, however, it may sometimes be preferable to find the optimum octane number for a blend with specified properties with respect to the other criteria, *including specified maximum cost.*

This illustrates a very important aspect of most linear programming problems. That is that there may be several objectives to be achieved. One of these must be selected to be optimized, while the others are introduced as restrictions. For example, even in the Everich Air Cargo problem, we could have defined the objective as to find the minimum amount of cabin-hold cargo which we could load subject to the restrictions given, and the additional restriction that revenue be at least $40,000. This would be a perfectly reasonable linear programming problem—but a different one! Indeed, in real-world situations it may be difficult to decide which of several objectives shall be the objective function, and which objectives shall be stated as restrictions.

Let us consider the problem of the Gipon City Zoo. It has just acquired a new tiger cub whose daily dietary requirements include at least 12 lb. of lean meat and 6 lb. of meat fat. There are two foods (ingredients) available from which to select the diet. The zoo keeper may purchase either one or both of the following foods, and his objective is to minimize the cost of a diet which meets the two (nutrient) restrictions, one for lean and one for fat. The essential characteristics of the two ingredients are given in the following table.

	Nutrient Analysis		
Ingredient	% Lean	% Fat	Cost per lb.
Horsemeat	80	20	$.50
Pork Residue	50	50	.40

Using the familiar approach to linear programming, the problem may be stated as follows, where x_1 and x_2 are the number of pounds purchased of horsemeat and pork residue, respectively:

Minimize: $$TC = 0.50x_1 + 0.40x_2 \tag{12–10.1}$$

subject to: $$0.80x_1 + 0.50x_2 \geq 12 \tag{12–10.2}$$

$$0.20x_1 + 0.50x_2 \geq 6 \tag{12–10.3}$$

The objective function is the total cost at \$.50 per lb. for horsemeat and \$.40 per lb. for pork residue. The first restriction equation says that the total amount of lean (80% of the horsemeat and 50% of the pork residue) must be at least 12 lb. *Exactly* 12 lb. would require 15 lb. of horsemeat alone, point (15,0) on Figure 12–10.1, or 24 lb. of pork alone, point (0,24), or any combination represented by a point on the straight line connecting these two points.

The second equation says that the total amount of fat (20% of the horsemeat and 50% of the pork residue) must be at least 6 lb. *Exactly* 6 lb. would require 30 lb. of horsemeat alone, point (30,0), or 12 lb. of pork alone, point (0,12), or any combination represented by a point on the straight line connecting these two points. The graphical analysis is shown in Figure 12–10.1. The feasible region is unbounded upward and to the

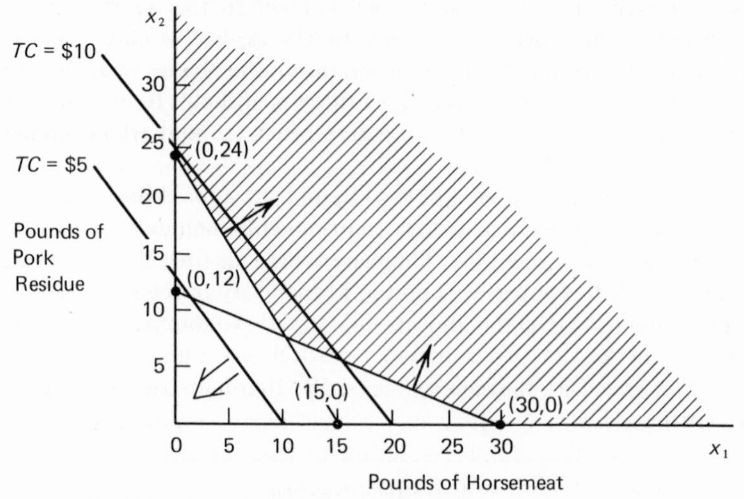

Fig. 12–10.1. Gipon City Zoo problem. A diet problem.

right, but this creates no difficulty since it *is* bounded in the direction of optimality. The optimal diet must be at one of the three corners: (0,24), which meets exactly the lean restriction, (30,0), which meets exactly the fat restriction, or the intersection, which meets exactly both nutrient restrictions. The slope of the objective function indicates that the optimal diet is at the intersection, which, by simultaneous solution of the two restrictions, written as *equations*, is

$$\begin{aligned} 0.8x_1 + 0.5x_2 &= 12 \\ 0.2x_1 + 0.5x_2 &= \ \ 6 \\ \hline 0.6x_1 \qquad\quad &= \ \ 6 \end{aligned}$$

$$x_1 = 10$$

$$x_2 = 8$$

$$TC = (0.5)(10) + (0.4)(8) = 5.0 + 3.2 = \$8.20$$

It is instructive to examine all three corner points:

Corner	Lb. Lean	Lb. Fat	Cost
(0,24)	12	12	$9.60
(10,8)	12	6	8.20
(30,0)	24	6	15.00

At corner (0,24), which lies on the line of the lean restriction, the diet yields exactly 12 lb. of lean, but purchases excess fat; whereas at corner (30,0), which lies on the line of the fat restriction, the diet yields exactly 6 lb. of fat, but purchases excess lean. At corner (10,8), both restrictions are met exactly, and there is no excess of either lean or fat. Also, this corner is the optimal. However the reason it is optimal is not because there is no excess (waste), but rather because the configuration of prices makes it so. If pork residue had been cheaper, say $.25 per lb., then corner (0,24) would be optimal. That is, it would pay to buy all pork residue and accept the fact that there was excess fat, because the price would then favor that course of action. Note that there is no maximum restriction on either nutrient. That is, there is no indication that excess fat or lean is undesirable. If that were the case, it would have to be stated in the formulation of the problem. As the problem is stated here, all three corners are equally good nutritively, and the sole criterion for discrimination among them is cost.

Diet problems with large numbers of ingredients and nutrients are solved by the hundreds every day on electronic computers in a wide number of areas. The simplex solution to this problem is quite simple (see Exercise 12–1 at the end of this chapter).

12–11. Requirements Space. Whenever a linear programming problem has two real variables, it may be graphed, as we have seen above. Thus far, we have graphed in what may be called *solutions space*. That is, the space in which the graph is constructed consists of points which represent various combinations of the two *controllable* variables; i.e., the axes are the two controllable variables. This was true of both the Everich Air Cargo problem and the Gipon City Zoo problem.

It is also possible to construct a graph in which each *restriction* is represented by an axis. Such a space is called *requirements space*, for obvious reasons. We shall illustrate this concept with the problem of the last section. That diet problem had two controllable variables (ingredients) and two restrictions, one for each of two nutrients. If there had been more restrictions for more nutrients, the problem could still have been solved graphically in solutions space. That is, for example, if the weight of vitamin B per lb. were given for each ingredient, and if a minimum requirement for vitamin B in the diet were specified, this would merely involve another line in Figure 12–10.1. On the other hand, if more ingredients were available, a graphical solution in two-dimensional solutions space would be impossible. However, it could be plotted in *requirements space*, as can any linear programming problem with only *two restrictions*, regardless of the number of controllable variables.

In the Gipon City Zoo problem of the previous section, the two requirements were for lean and fat. Therefore we shall label the axes *lean* and *fat*, respectively. Then, the lines for the restrictions are simply a vertical line at 12 lb. of lean and a horizontal line at 6 lb. of fat, as seen in Figure 12–11.1, where the feasible region is shaded.

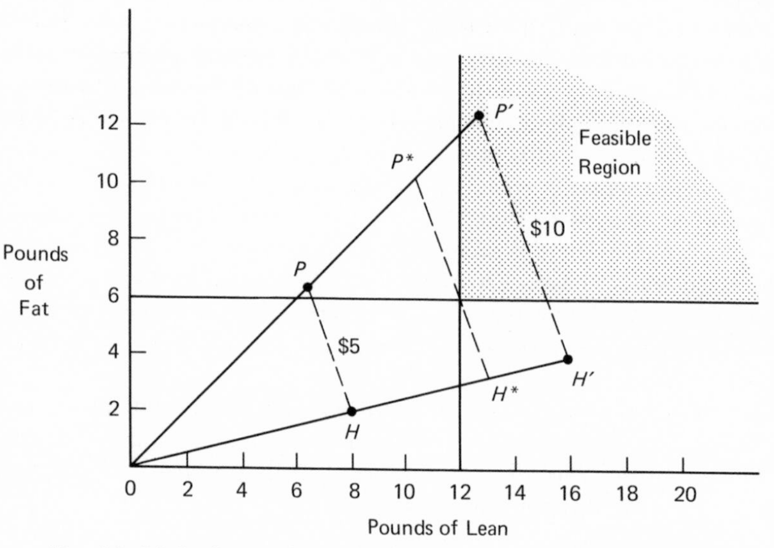

Fig. 12–11.1. Gipon City Zoo problem in requirements space.

Points H and P are plotted to represent the amount of lean and fat obtained for \$5 worth of horsemeat or pork residue, respectively. That is, if \$5 had been spent for horsemeat alone, it would purchase 10 lb. of horsemeat, which would yield 8 lb. of lean and 2 lb. of fat. That is point H, (8,2). Similarly, point P represents the results of spending \$5 on pork residue, purchasing 12.5 lb. of pork, yielding 6.25 lb. of lean and 6.25 lb. of fat. That is point P (6.25,6.25). The choice of \$5 is purely arbitrary. All that is required is that the *same* amount of money be spent for each ingredient. Points H' and P' represent the results of purchasing \$10 worth of horsemeat or pork, respectively. Notice that H' and P' are twice as far from the origin as H and P, and that the origin, H, and H' form a straight line. Such a line emanating from the origin is called a *ray*, and any purchase of horsemeat alone will yield a combination of lean and fat which will lie on this same ray. Similarly, any purchase of pork alone will lie on the OPP' ray.

The dashed line connecting H and P represents the yield of lean and fat for all combinations of horsemeat and pork costing exactly \$5. This varies from (8,2) at H for pure horsemeat to (6.25,6.25) at P for pure pork. Similarly, the line connecting H' and P' represents the yield of lean and fat for all combinations of horsemeat and pork costing exactly \$10. Clearly the lines PH and $P'H'$ must be parallel to each other.

Examination of Figure 12–11.1 suggests that there is a line parallel to PH which just touches the feasible region at the corner of the feasible region (12,6), and that the diet at that point is the least-cost-feasible diet. That is, a lower-cost line would not touch the feasible region, and a higher-cost line would serve no purpose. That line is P^*H^*. The optimal amounts of horsemeat and pork and the minimum cost may be computed easily, since now we know that, at the optimal point, the yield is exactly 12 lb. of lean and 6 lb. of fat, and thus 18 lb. are purchased.

Again, letting x_1 and x_2 represent the pounds of horsemeat and pork purchased,

$$\begin{aligned} 0.8x_1 + 0.5(18 - x_1) &= 12 \\ 0.8x_1 + 9 - 0.5x_1 &= 12 \\ 0.3x_1 &= 3 \\ x_1 &= 10 \\ x_2 &= 8 \\ TC &= (0.5)(10) + (0.4)(8) = \$8.20 \end{aligned}$$

Let us now suppose that, instead of two ingredients, the Gipon City Zoo keeper has five foods from which to select. These foods are given below.

Ingredient	Symbol	Nutrient Analysis % Lean	% Fat	Cost per lb.
Horsemeat	x_1	80	20	\$.50
Pork residue	x_2	50	50	.40
Lamb residue	x_3	55	45	.38
Veal residue	x_4	76	24	.60
Beef residue	x_5	45	55	.25

This five-ingredient problem cannot be solved graphically in solutions space, but, since there are still only two restrictions, the problem may be solved graphically in requirements space. For the graphic solution, each food adds one additional point to the requirements space diagram. For a fixed outlay of $5 on each food individually, the nutrient yields would be:

		Lean	Fat
x_1	Horsemeat	(5/0.50)(0.80) = 8.00	(5/0.50)(0.20) = 2.00
x_2	Pork	(5/0.40)(0.50) = 6.25	(5/0.40)(0.50) = 6.25
x_3	Lamb	(5/0.38)(0.55) = 7.23	(5/0.38)(0.45) = 5.93
x_4	Veal	(5/0.60)(0.76) = 6.33	(5/0.60)(0.24) = 2.00
x_5	Beef	(5/0.25)(0.45) = 9.00	(5/0.25)(0.55) = 11.00

These nutrient yields are the coordinates of the five points shown in Figure 12–11.2. In the figure, rays have been drawn to all five points, and

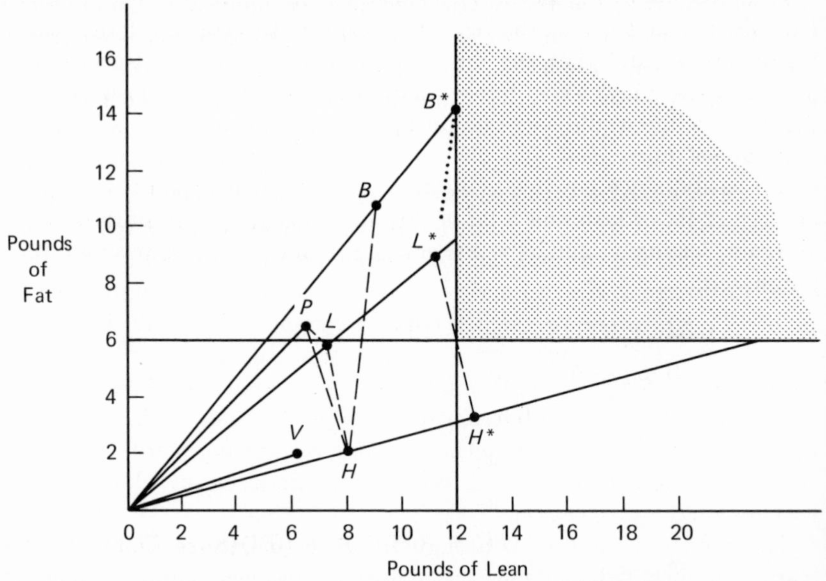

Fig. 12–11.2. Gipon City Zoo problem with five ingredients in requirements space.

the rays through the points for beef (B), lamb (L), and horsemeat (H) have been extended to the feasible region. From these lines it is clear that, as the expenditure is increased from $5, the points will move away from the origin, along their respective rays, at speeds proportional to their distance from the origin, and the first point to enter the feasible region will be point B^*. The line from B^* to the corresponding point on the ray through H, which will be parallel to BH, will be such that point B^* will touch the feasible region before any other point on that (dotted) line. This tells us that the use of only one food, beef residue, will be the lowest-cost way of meeting the nutritional requirements. From the graph, it can be seen that at B^*, exactly 12 lb. of lean meat are obtained. Since the beef is 45% lean, this means that $\frac{12}{0.45} = 26.67$ lb. of beef are needed. At \$.25 per lb., this diet costs \$6.67. Of course, this diet yields 14.67 lb. of fat, which is far in excess of the requirement of 6 lb., but it is nevertheless the most economical diet.

The graph illustrates a very important characteristic of linear programming, namely that, when there are m restrictions, there are *at most* m foods used in the optimal solution. If there are two restrictions, for example, then, at most, two foods are used. Clearly, then, when $m = 1$, only one food is used, i.e., the one for which the particular required nutrient is cheapest. With the two restrictions as stated, and a choice of five foods, beef will satisfy all of the restrictions most economically. The line from the origin through point B shows that the feasible region is entered by meeting the lean restriction, the fat restriction having been met at an earlier stage. Thus, the critical nutrient is "lean." Using beef alone, we need $26\frac{2}{3}$ lb. to supply the minimum requirement of 12 lb. of lean. This costs \$6.67.

As a final exercise, let us suppose that beef is eliminated as a source of the required nutrients. The only foods available are represented by points P, L, V, and H. Since now all of the lines connecting the points slope downward to the right, the optimal point will lie on some line connecting two points. It will not lie on the line connecting points P and H, because for every point on that line there is a point on one of the other lines (PL or LH) which has more of both nutrients at the same cost. This statement holds also for all lines connecting point V with points P, L, and H. The optimal point lies, then, on either the line connecting point P with L or the one connecting H with L. Which it is, depends on which line first touches the feasible region.

The ray from the origin through the point of intersection of the two restriction lines (which define the requirements space) passes through the line joining points L and H, so that the optimal point lies on that line. The optimal mixture will thus contain horsemeat and lamb.

In the familiar notation, our problem is stated as follows (no beef):

$$\text{Minimize:}\quad TC = 0.50x_1 + 0.40x_2 + 0.38x_3 + 0.60x_4$$

$$\text{subject to:}\quad 0.80x_1 + 0.50x_2 + 0.55x_3 + 0.76x_4 \geq 12$$

$$0.20x_1 + 0.50x_2 + 0.45x_3 + 0.24x_4 \geq 6$$

Now, from the graph we have derived two additional pieces of information.

1. The optimal diet occurs in the feasible region in requirements space at the intersection of the restriction lines; therefore, at the optimal, they are both equations.
2. The optimal diet uses only x_1 and x_3 as foods.

The problem is thus greatly simplified to two equations, which are solved simultaneously.

$$(1) \qquad 0.80x_1 + 0.55x_3 = 12$$

$$(2) \qquad 0.20x_1 + 0.45x_3 = 6$$

Multiply (2) by 4:

$$(3) \qquad 0.80x_1 + 1.80x_3 = 24$$

Subtract (1) from (3):

$$1.25x_3 = 12$$

$$x_3 = 9.6$$

$$x_1 = 8.4$$

	Lean, lb.	Fat, lb.	Cost, $
8.4 lb. horsemeat yields	6.72	1.68	4.20
9.6 lb. lamb yields	5.28	4.32	3.65
Total diet yields	12.00	6.00	7.85

Therefore, with the beef not available, the optimum cost is increased to $7.85, but it is still more economical than the cost when only horsemeat and pork were available. The results graphically obtained above may be obtained by the simplex algorithm (see Exercise 12–1 at the end of this chapter).

Finally, as noted before, it can be seen from the graph that, in this problem, with *two restrictions*, the greatest number of ingredients which will be utilized (basic variables) is *two*. This confirms our previous conclusion that the maximum number of basic variables is m, the number of restrictions. There may be fewer, in which case the solution is degenerate, as in the five-variable case above, wherein only one ingredient (beef) was utilized by the optimal diet.

In graphically solving a linear programming problem in requirements space, the feasible region is, of course, the region defined by the restrictions, but this feasibility criterion does not take into account the feasibility requirement that all variables must be nonnegative. Solutions space does this automatically, since it uses the variables as its axes, and feasibility occurs only in the positive quadrant. Requirements space does not take this into account, and therefore it is possible that what may seem to be an optimal solution may turn out, upon examination, to be not feasible, because one or more of the variables may be negative. Therefore, one must be sure to check for nonnegativity of the variables in the solution.

12–12. The Linearity Requirement. In this chapter and in the two preceding chapters we have dealt with *linear* programming, and we have defined this as requiring that *all* of the functions, both the restrictions and the objective function, be straight line functions. If these linear conditions are not met, the techniques of linear programming cannot be depended upon to yield the optimal result.

Let us examine for a moment the implications of nonlinearity in either the restrictions or the objective function.

If the objective function is nonlinear, either concave or convex, as seen in Figure 12–12.1, then, even though the restrictions are linear and the

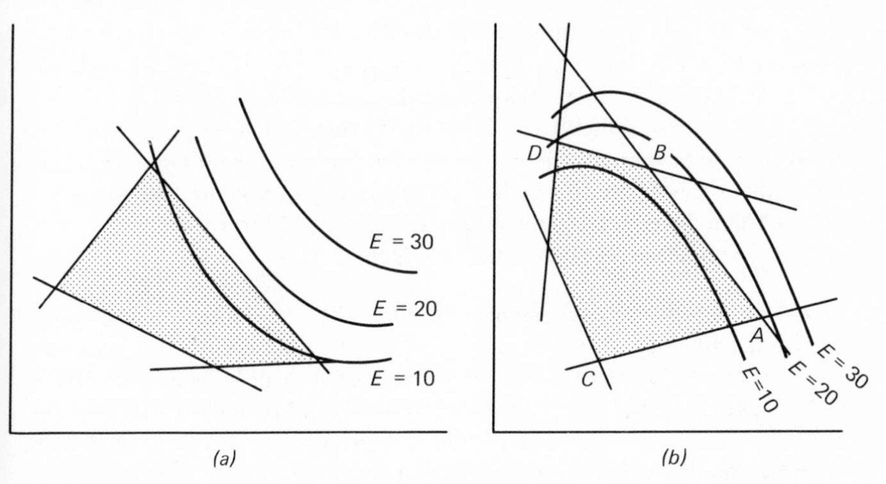

Fig. 12–12.1. Nonlinear objective functions. Maximization desired.

feasible region a convex set, nevertheless, serious problems may arise. In Figure 12–12.1(a), the optimal is not at a corner of the set, and the simplex algorithm may yield the best corner, but that will not be the optimal solution to the problem. In Figure 12–12.1(b), although the optimal is still at a corner, the simplex algorithm might erroneously conclude that corner point A is the optimal, since it is more favorable than adjacent points B and C; whereas, actually corner point D is the optimal.

Similar difficulties may arise when one or more of the restriction inequations are nonlinear. That is, a convex, nonlinear restriction may create an optimal point that is not at a corner as in Figure 12–12.2(a), and in Figure 12–12.2(b) the simplex might conclude that corner point A is optimal, although the adjacent corner point B is actually optimal. This could happen, because *in the vicinity of* A, moving toward B decreases E.

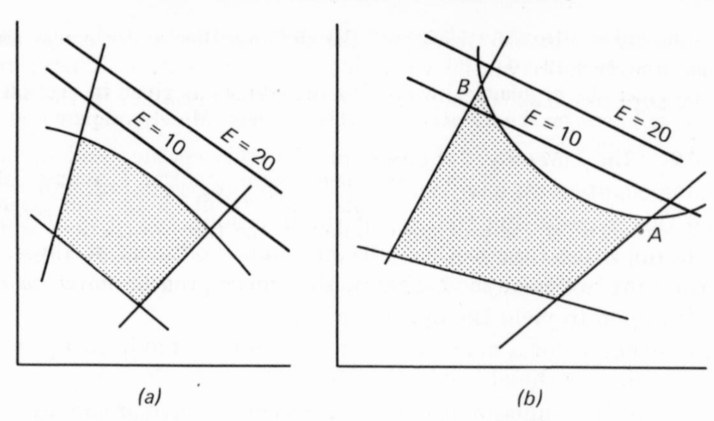

Fig. 12–12.2. Nonlinear restriction. Maximization desired.

Clearly, if curvilinear functions defined *both* the feasible region and the objective function, the difficulties involved in seeking the optimal solution via the traditional simplex algorithm may well be compounded.

In spite of these difficulties, there are mathematical methods available and still others constantly being developed for dealing with specific kinds of nonlinearities in mathematical programming problems. We shall not discuss them here, but there is already a large literature dealing with varieties of *nonlinear programming* problems.

12–13. Integer Requirements. Often the variables being allocated must be applied in integral units. In the Gipon City Zoo problem, we were not troubled by the need to purchase 8.4 lb. of horsemeat or 9.6 lb. of lamb per day. However, if we had to order and receive each day's diet every day, and if we were constrained to purchase in 1- or 2- or even 5-lb. cans, our result might be quite different.

While it is true that, in most cases requiring integers as answers, a thoroughly satisfactory result may be obtained by solving the problem in the usual way and rounding; nevertheless, there are some situations in which such a procedure is clearly non-optimal. In those cases, the methods of *integer programming* may be applied to arrive at the optimal integral solution. Detailed discussions of integer programming may be found in the Suggestions for Further Reading, e.g., Baumol (1965).

SUGGESTIONS FOR FURTHER READING

See suggested readings for Chapter 13.

EXERCISES

12–1. Solve the Gipon City Zoo problem of Section 12–10 and 12–11 by the simplex method and verify the results given in the text.

a) Consider the problem with just the two ingredients: horsemeat and pork as in Section 12–10.

b) Consider the problem with the five ingredients as given in Section 12–11. Do not perform the iterations for this problem. Merely prepare and present the first tableau.

12–2. *a*) Solve the Abrash Department Store problem (Exercise 10–2) of Chapter 10 graphically in requirements space. (Hint: If the hint given in the original statement of the problem is followed, the three restrictions will be reduced to two because one is redundant with respect to one of the others. When the redundant restriction is eliminated, the problem can be solved in requirements space.)

b) Solve the problem by the simplex method.

12–3. Solve the Vanchar Oriental Carpet Company problem (Exercise 10–3) of Chapter 10 using the simplex method.

12–4. A five-day development program is being prepared for salesmen of the Maran Manufacturing Company. The program for these salesmen will include some combination of four activities: a guest speaker, a work leader, case conferences, and a management game. The planning of the program is to be based on information the Conference Chairman has about the cost per day for each activity and the expected additional annual sales to the Company as a consequence of each day of the training.

Activity	Cost per Day ($)	Expected Additional Annual Sales per Day of Activity (Thousands of Units)
Speaker	400	800
Laboratory work	200	500
Case conferences	0	100
Management game	100	500

The Conference Chairman must choose among these four activities for the five-day meeting. The meeting will take exactly 5 days. There are no restrictions on the number of days which any of the activities are available to the Chairman. He may use as little or as much of each activity as he wishes. No two activities may take place simultaneously, but partial days may be allocated to any of the activities, if he so desires. If partial days are used, the cost and gains are linearly proportionally divisible, and no time is lost shifting between activities.

The Chairman has decided that he wants to have, in total, nor more than 3 days of student active participation in discussion or laboratory activity, and no more than 3 days of student's passive listening to presentations. The various activities are divided percentagewise between active and passive as follows (in your work, please use the following symbols):

Activity	Symbol	Active Time	Passive Time
Speaker	S	10	90
Laboratory	L	40	60
Case	C	100	0
Game	G	60	40

Net profit is $.50 per unit sold (this is net after all costs *except* this conference). What is the optimum expected net profit allocation of the five days (taking into account the costs of this conference)? Solve the problem (a) graphically and (b) by simplex.

12–5. *a*) Solve the Marstar Aviation Company problem (Exercise 10–1) of Chapter 10 graphically in requirements space. (Hint: Use as axes, *balance*, which must be greater than or equal to 0 when defined as the load in the main hold less the load in the wing holds plus twice the load in the cabin hold, i.e., balance $= M - 2W - 2C \geq 0$; and *total*, which, of course, must be exactly equal to 50, making the feasible region a line segment.)

b) Solve the problem by the simplex method.

12–6. In the Erikis Data Processing Company problem (Exercise 11–1), if the keypunching operation is omitted, the problem can be solved graphically in two dimensions. Solve graphically for the optimal (maximum profit) scheduling of the other two operations, with the keypunching omitted.

13

The Dual in Linear Programming

13–1. Introduction. We shall, in Section 13–2, describe a transformation process which can be applied to any linear programming problem to produce its *dual.* Since, as we have seen, every linear programming problem can be expressed in a standard form, every linear programming problem can be equally well subjected to this same turning-about procedure to produce its dual. This is a purely mechanical or mathematical transformation, and its existence is hardly more surprising than the fact that any fraction can be inverted to produce its reciprocal or that any multidigit number can be rewritten with its digits reversed. What is surprising about the dual is the set of properties which it turns out to have.

The transformation process which produces the dual from the original linear programming problem, the *primal,* is *symmetrical.* That is, like the reciprocal of a fraction or the reverse of a multidigit number, the process, if applied to the dual, produces the original primal back again. Therefore, if problem B is the dual of problem A, then it is equally true that problem A is the dual of problem B. From this it follows that, given a problem and its dual, it does not matter which is called the *primal* and which the *dual.* For convenience we usually consider the problem as first stated to be the primal.

As we shall soon see, the surprising and immensely valuable property of the dual is that *the solution to the primal and the solution to the dual are closely related and easily transformed, one into the other.*

13–2. The Transformation Process. The original or primal statement of a linear programming problem may be expressed in the standard form:

Maximize:

$$E = c_1x_1 + c_2x_2 + \cdots + c_nx_n$$

subject to:

$$\begin{array}{l} a_{11}x_1 + a_{12}x_2 + \cdots + a_{1n}x_n \leq b_1 \\ a_{21}x_1 + a_{22}x_2 + \cdots + a_{2n}x_n \leq b_2 \\ \quad \vdots \\ a_{m1}x_1 + a_{m2}x_2 + \cdots + a_{mn}x_n \leq b_m \end{array}$$

The dual problem is obtained by: reversing the direction of optimization, i.e., if the primal's objective function is to be maximized, the dual's is to be minimized, and vice versa; transforming the a_{ij} so that the rows become columns and vice versa; interchanging the c_j and b_i; reversing the directions of the inequalities; and finally, replacing the x_j with a complete new set of variables which we shall designate y_i. The statement of the dual problem then, is

Minimize:

$$E' = b_1y_1 + b_2y_2 + \cdots + b_my_m$$

subject to:

$$\begin{array}{l} a_{11}y_1 + a_{21}y_2 + \cdots + a_{m1}y_m \geq c_1 \\ a_{12}y_1 + a_{22}y_2 + \cdots + a_{m2}y_m \geq c_2 \\ \quad \vdots \\ a_{1n}y_1 + a_{2n}y_2 + \cdots + a_{mn}y_m \geq c_n \end{array}$$

The relationship between the primal and the dual may be understood by the examination of the equations for both statements, noting:

1. If the primal system's objective function is to be *maximized*, the dual system's objective function is to be *minimized*.
2. The values of the a_{ij} are the same, but the *rows and columns are interchanged;* i.e., each a_{ij} moves to the a_{ji} position.
3. If the primal system has n variables and m restrictions, the dual system has m variables and n restrictions.
4. If the primal restrictions read $\leq$, the dual restrictions read $\geq$, and vice versa.

5. The b_i and c_j are interchanged.
6. A new set of variables (y_i) is introduced.
7. The nonnegativity restrictions are *not* changed; i.e., for all y, $y_i \geq 0$.

From the systematic nature of the rearrangement process, it must be evident that, in any statement of a problem, the inequality restrictions must all be pointed in the same direction. That is, the primal must be either a maximization problem subject to maximum restrictions or a minimization problem subject to minimum restrictions. The primal is one of these, and the dual is the other. If, in the original formulation of the problem, one or more of the restrictions have their inequalities pointed in the other direction, these must be reversed. This is easily done by multiplying through by -1.

13-3. A Diet Problem. Eric, a young bachelor with limited income, is forced to live frugally and does all his own cooking to stretch his food budget to the end of the month. One day he decides to make a beef and potato stew for himself and three colleagues whom he has, in a rash moment of generosity, invited for dinner. Knowing something about dietary requirements, he stipulates that the stew must yield at least 4,000 calories and at least 200 grams of protein. His decision problem is to find that combination of beef and potatoes which he must buy to yield his minimum food requirements at minimum cost. He knows that beef will yield 1,200 calories and 125 grams of protein per pound, and also that it costs $1.00 per pound. Potatoes cost only 25¢ a pound, and yield 400 calories and 12 grams of protein per lb.

From this information, he can easily set up his primal linear programming problem. Letting x_1 and x_2, respectively, be the number of pounds of beef and potatoes purchased, and measuring E, the cost, in cents instead of dollars for ease of computation,

Minimize:

$$E = 100x_1 + 25x_2 \text{ (in cents)} \tag{13-3.1}$$

subject to:

1. $$1{,}200x_1 + 400x_2 \geq 4{,}000 \text{ (calorie restriction)} \tag{13-3.2}$$

2. $$125x_1 + 12x_2 \geq 200 \text{ (protein restriction)} \tag{13-3.3}$$

This problem can be solved graphically, as shown in Figure 13-3.1. From restriction 1 we obtain line 1; if $x_1 = 0$, $x_2 = 10$, and if $x_2 = 0$, $x_1 = 3\frac{1}{3}$. Similarly, from restriction 2, if $x_1 = 0$, $x_2 = 16\frac{2}{3}$, and if $x_2 = 0$, $x_1 = 1\frac{3}{5}$. These two points permit the plotting of line 2. Price lines are drawn for arbitrarily selected amounts; e.g., spending $3 yields 3 lb. of all beef or 12 lb. of all potatoes or any point on the line connecting these two points. Similarly, the price line for $2 may be drawn.

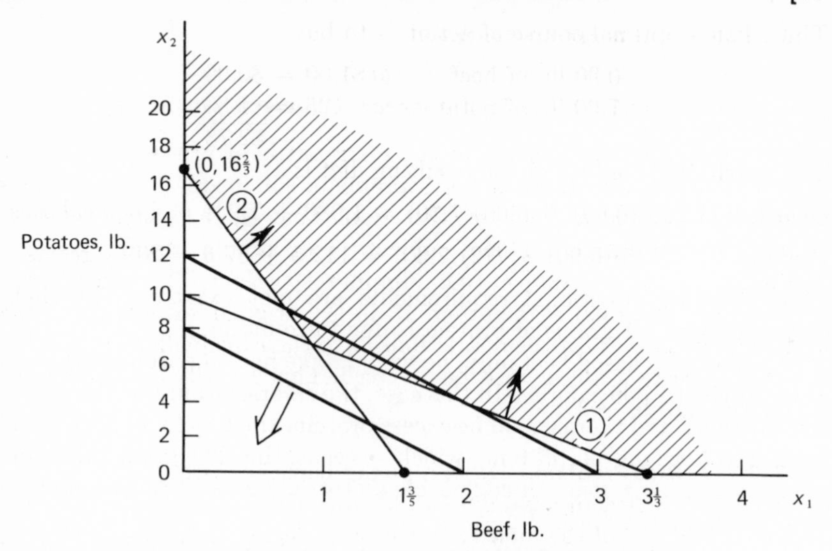

Fig. 13–3.1. Linear programming problem. Eric's diet.

It is thus clear that the optimal solution, i.e., the minimum cost solution, lies at the intersection of the two restriction lines. At this point the lowest price line just touches the corner of the feasible region. (Note that, since the restrictions are minimum restrictions, the feasible region lies to the *right* of and *above* the lines; and since the objective function is a *minimizing* one, the optimum solution is that corner which meets the *lowest* price line.)

Since the optimal solution lies at the intersection of the two restriction lines and therefore on both lines, both *inequations* are *equations* at that point, and the coordinates of that point may be found by simultaneous solution of those two equations:

1. $$1{,}200x_1 + 400x_2 = 4{,}000$$

2. $$125x_1 + 12x_2 = 200$$

Equation 1 may be multiplied by $\frac{3}{100}$ to yield

3. $$36x_1 + 12x_2 = 120$$

Subtracting equation 3 from equation 2 yields

$$89x_1 = 80$$

$$x_1 = 0.90 \text{ lb.}$$

Then, from equation 1, divided by 100,

$$(12)(0.90) + 4x_2 = 40$$

$$x_2 = 10 - 2.70 = 7.30 \text{ lb.}$$

Thus, Eric's optimal course of action is to buy

0.90 lb. of beef	@$1.00	=	$0.90
7.30 lb. of potatoes	@ .25	=	1.83
			$2.73

The nutritional content of the resulting diet is

Calories: $(1{,}200)(0.90) + (400)(7.30) = 1{,}080 + 2{,}920 = 4{,}000$ calories

Protein: $(125)(0.90) + (12)(7.30) = 112.5 + 87.6 = 200.1$ grams

Thus the two nutritional requirements are met exactly. (The slight discrepancy of 0.1 grams of protein is due to rounding.)

If he had purchased beef only, he would have had to purchase $3\frac{1}{3}$ lb. in order to yield 4,000 calories. In this case, the calories would be the expensive nutrient, and there would be excess protein, since $3\frac{1}{3}$ lb. of beef would yield 416.7 grams of protein, which exceeds the 200 gram minimum requirement. This nonoptimal feasible diet would cost $3.33 as compared with $2.73 for the optimal diet.

If he had purchased potatoes only, he would have had to purchase $16\frac{2}{3}$ lb. at a cost of $4.17 in order to yield the required 200 grams of protein. In that nonoptimal case, the protein would be the expensive nutrient, and there would be excess calories; actually 6,666.7 calories as against the minimum requirement of 4,000 calories.

We have noted these characteristics of these two nonoptimal solutions, and we shall have occasion to refer to them after we have examined the dual problem.

13–4. The Dual of the Diet Problem. Using the transformation procedure described in Section 13–2, the dual for Eric's diet problem is:

Maximize:

$$E' = 4{,}000y_1 + 200y_2 \text{ (also in cents)} \tag{13–4.1}$$

subject to:

$$1{,}200y_1 + 125y_2 \leq 100 \text{ (beef restriction)} \tag{13–4.2}$$

$$400y_1 + 12y_2 \leq 25 \text{ (potato restriction)} \tag{13–4.3}$$

This problem also is capable of solution by means of a graph, and this is done in Figure 13–4.1. From restriction equation (13–4.2), when $y_2 = 0$, $y_1 = 0.0833$; and when $y_1 = 0$, $y_2 = 0.80$. From restriction equation (13–4.3), when $y_2 = 0$, $y_1 = 0.0625$; and when $y_1 = 0$, $y_2 = 2.083$. Lines can be drawn for selected values of E'. For example, when $E' = 200$; if $y_1 = 0, y_2 = 1$, and if $y_2 = 0, y_1 = 0.05$; similarly, if $E' = 300$, for $y_2 = 0$, $y_1 = 0.075$ and for $y_1 = 0, y_2 = 1.5$. It will be seen from the graph that the optimum solution is at the point of intersection of the two restriction lines, and that therefore we can solve for y_1 and y_2 by simultaneous solution of the two equations.

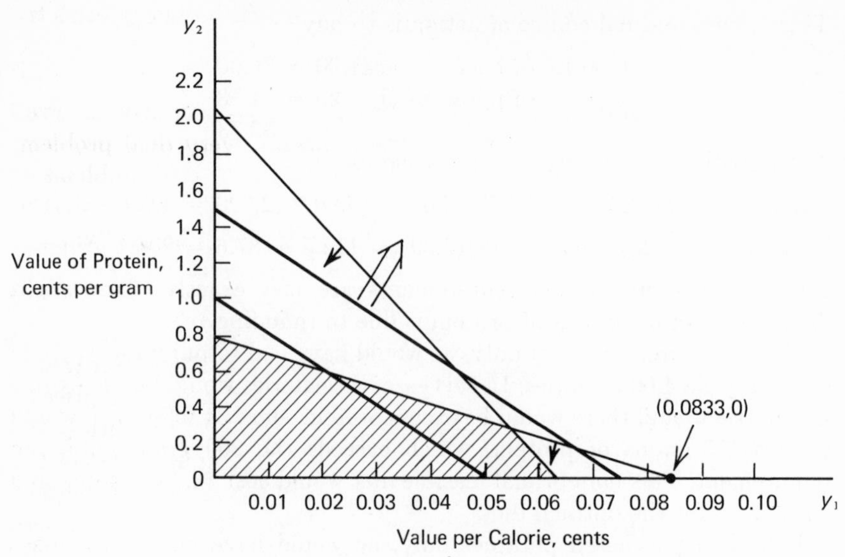

Fig. 13–4.1. Dual of Eric's diet problem.

1. $$1{,}200y_1 + 125y_2 = 100$$

2. $$400y_1 + 12y_2 = 25$$

Multiplying equation 2 by 3 yields

3. $$1{,}200y_1 + 36y_2 = 75$$

Subtracting equation 3 from equation 1 yields

$$89y_2 = 25$$
$$y_2 = 0.281$$

Substituting in equation 1 yields

$$1{,}200y_1 + (125)(0.281) = 100$$
$$1{,}200y_1 = 100 - 35.1 = 64.9$$
$$y_1 = 0.0541$$

Then

$$\begin{aligned} E' &= (4{,}000)(0.0541) + (200)(0.281) \\ &= 216.4 + 56.2 = 272.6 \text{ cents} \\ &= \$2.73 \end{aligned}$$

The optimum value of E' for the dual is identical with the optimum value of E for the primal.

Now that we have constructed and solved the dual problem, let us try to interpret it.

13–5. Interpretation of the Dual. While it is not easy or even possible to find a simple verbal interpretation for every dual problem, such an explanation does exist for diet problems and related problems as well as for many others.

To interpret the dual for Eric's diet problem, let the y_i be the "values" of the nutrients; calories and grams of protein, respectively. "Value" as used here means the *economic value of the nutrient* in the sense that it is the imputed price of the nutrient. It is, in effect, the amount he has to pay to acquire the marginal unit of the nutrient. We shall see later that if there is an excess of any nutrient in a particular diet, the imputed price to that diet of that nutrient is zero. In the restriction inequalities, the requirements which are stipulated are that the total imputed cost of the nutrients in a unit of an ingredient can not exceed the actual unit market price, or cost, of the ingredient. At the limit of the restriction, i.e., where the inequation is an equation, the sum of the imputed values of the nutrients in that ingredient, in terms of the amounts and imputed prices (or "*shadow prices*") of the nutrients is exactly equal to the cost of that ingredient.

Looking first at the beef restriction in the dual,

$$1{,}200y_1 + 125y_2 \leq 100 \text{ (beef restriction)} \qquad (13\text{–}4.2)$$

y_1 is the unit value of a calorie and y_2 is the unit value of a gram of protein. Since there are 1,200 of the former and 125 of the latter in each pound of beef, the left side of Equation (13–4.2) is the total value of nutrients in a pound of beef. The right side is the price (in cents). Therefore, that restriction inequation says that the total value (or price which he is required to pay) of the nutrients in a pound of beef cannot be more than the actual unit price of the beef. Equation (13–4.3) may be interpreted in exactly the same way for potatoes.

The objective function:

Maximize:

$$E' = 4{,}000y_1 + 200y_2 \text{ (also in cents)} \qquad (13\text{–}4.1)$$

indicates that Eric's purpose is to maximize the value which he derives from his 4,000 calories and 200 grams of protein. He is to do this subject to the restrictions that the values of the nutrients contained in a unit of an ingredient cannot exceed the unit cost of that ingredient.

On the graph of Figure 13–4.1, the axes are y_1 and y_2, the values (prices) of the nutrients, calories and grams of protein, respectively; and the solution assigns such values to them that the optimal diet has a maximum value, subject to the restriction that, for each ingredient, the sums of the nutrient values of that ingredient do not exceed its market price.

Thus, in the optimal diet, calories have a value (y_1) of 0.0541 cents per calorie, and protein has a value (y_2) of 0.281 cents per gram. At that optimum point, the diet contains exactly enough of each nutrient to meet the restrictions, and the value is:

$$\begin{aligned} &\text{4,000 calories at } 0.0541¢ \text{ per calorie} &= 216.4¢ \\ &\text{200 grams of protein at } 0.281¢ \text{ per gram} &= \underline{56.2} \\ & &272.6¢ = \$2.73 \end{aligned}$$

As we have seen, the solutions of the dual and the primal are identical. This fact enables us to determine the solution of one, given the solution to the other.

If Eric had elected a diet at one of the other corners of the feasible region, the value (imputed price) of one of the nutrients would be zero. For example, at the corner ($3\frac{1}{3}$,0) in the primal (Figure 13–3.1), Eric purchases beef only. He buys $3\frac{1}{3}$ pounds of beef at $1.00 per pound and pays $3.33. This is feasible, but its cost exceeds the optimal cost of $2.73. This amount of beef yields 4,000 calories, which is exactly the required amount, but it yields 416.7 grams of protein, which is in excess of the 200 required.

In the dual, Figure 13–4.1, this corresponds to the corner (0.0625,0) where y_1, the unit value of calories, is 0.0625, and protein has no value at all. This is not surprising. Since this diet contains excess protein, the amount which Eric pays to acquire the marginal unit of protein is zero. The total "value" of this feasible nonoptimal solution is the sum of these imputed or "shadow" prices.

$$\begin{aligned} E' &= 4{,}000y_1 + 200y_2 = (4{,}000)(0.0625) + (200)(0) \\ &= 250¢ = \$2.50 \end{aligned}$$

which is less than the optimum value of $2.73.

At the optimal point, it will be recalled, he spends $2.73 and obtains a value of $2.73. At this nonoptimal point, he spends $3.33 and obtains a value in terms of these imputed prices of only $2.50. This suggests an important general rule. At the optimal point, the costs and returns are equal, but at nonoptimal points, costs are higher and returns are lower.

If we introduce the symbol R to represent "return," i.e., that which is to be maximized, and the symbol C to represent "cost," i.e., that which is to be minimized, we may restate this rule:

$$R \leq C \tag{13–5.1}$$

and, at the optimal, $R = C$.

13–6. Simplex Solution to Primal and Dual. The simplex solution to Eric's diet problem, using C for cost and R for return, in place of E and E':

a. The Primal

Minimize:

$$C = 100x_1 + 25x_2$$

subject to:

1. $$1{,}200x_1 + 400x_2 \geq 4{,}000$$

2. $$125x_1 + 12x_2 \geq 200$$

We add a slack variable to the small side of each inequation:

11. $$1{,}200x_1 + 400x_2 = 4{,}000 + x_3$$

where x_3 = excess calories purchased

12. $$125x_1 + 12x_2 = 200 + x_4$$

where x_4 = excess grams of protein purchased

Now, since the slack variables are positive on the same side of the equation as the positive constant, if we set up a tableau with slack variables as the nonzero, basic, variables; the constants are negative, and the solution is not feasible. This means that the origin is not in the feasible region (see Figure 13–3.1). We must add two artificial variables. We shall use x_5 and x_6:

21. $$1{,}200x_1 + 400x_2 - x_3 + x_5 = 4{,}000$$

22. $$125x_1 + 12x_2 - x_4 + x_6 = 200$$

Rearranging for simplex application,

31. $$x_5 = 4{,}000 - 1{,}200x_1 - 400x_2 + x_3$$

32. $$x_6 = 200 - 125x_1 - 12x_2 + x_4$$

The objective function must be modified to assure that the artificial variables are zero variables in the optimal solution. The objective function, to be *minimized* is

$$C = 100x_1 + 25x_2$$

but we wish to use the simplex rules for maximization. Therefore, we multiply by -1 and we maximize:

$$-C = -100x_1 - 25x_2$$

In order to insure that x_5 and x_6, the artificial variables, are zero variables in the optimal, we add them to the objective function with very large

(L) negative coefficients. The objective function then is

$$-C = -100x_1 - 25x_2 - Lx_5 - Lx_6$$

but, from equations 31 and 32,

$$\begin{aligned} -C &= -100x_1 - 25x_2 - L(4{,}000 - 1{,}200x_1 - 400x_2 + x_3) \\ &\qquad - L(200 - 125x_1 - 12x_2 + x_4) \\ &= -100x_1 - 25x_2 - 4{,}000L + 1{,}200Lx_1 + 400Lx_2 - Lx_3 \\ &\qquad - 200L + 125Lx_1 + 12Lx_2 - Lx_4 \\ &= -4{,}200L + (1{,}325L - 100)x_1 + (412L - 25)x_2 - Lx_3 - Lx_4 \end{aligned}$$

The problem then is to maximize this function subject to the restrictions as given in equations 31 and 32 above. The resulting first simplex tableau and the tableaux which emerge from the pivoting operations as indicated are shown in Figure 13–6.1. The final tableau therein is the optimal solution, and, since the artificial variables are both equal to zero, the

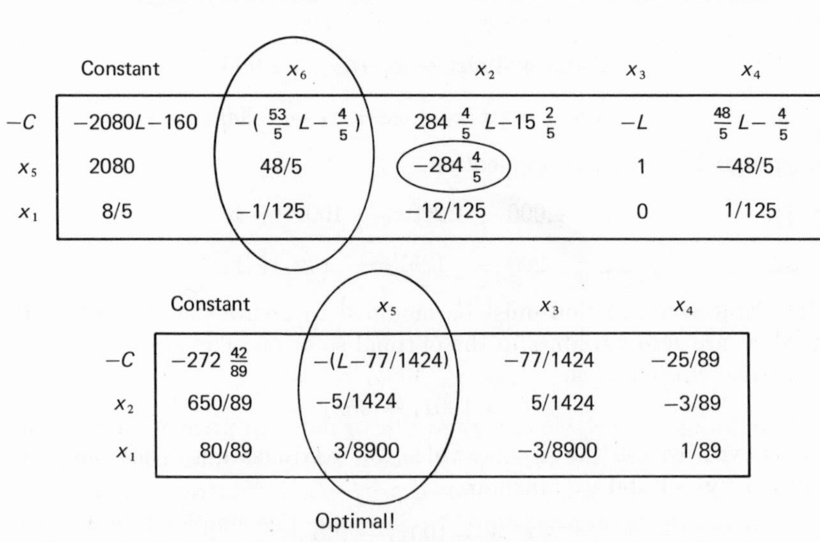

	Constant	x_1	x_2	x_3	x_4
$-C$	$-4200L$	$(1325L-100)$	$(412L-25)$	$-L$	$-L$
x_5	4000	-1200	-400	1	0
x_6	200	-125 (circled)	-12	0	1

	Constant	x_6	x_2	x_3	x_4
$-C$	$-2080L-160$	$-(\frac{53}{5}L-\frac{4}{5})$	$284\frac{4}{5}L-15\frac{2}{5}$	$-L$	$\frac{48}{5}L-\frac{4}{5}$
x_5	2080	48/5	$-284\frac{4}{5}$ (circled)	1	$-48/5$
x_1	8/5	$-1/125$	$-12/125$	0	1/125

	Constant	x_5	x_3	x_4
$-C$	$-272\frac{42}{89}$	$-(L-77/1424)$	$-77/1424$	$-25/89$
x_2	650/89	$-5/1424$	5/1424	$-3/89$
x_1	80/89	3/8900	$-3/8900$	1/89

Fig. 13–6.1. Eric's diet problem. Simplex solution to the primal. This illustrates the alternative technique whereby L is not given a specific numerical value, but is allowed to stand for "some very large number."

optimal tableau may be rewritten with the artificial variables and their columns omitted, as is shown in Figure 13–6.2, where the rows have been

		x_3	x_4
$-C$	$272\frac{42}{89}$	$-77/1424$	$-25/89$
x_1	$80/89$	$-3/8900$	$1/89$
x_2	$650/89$	$5/1424$	$-3/89$

Fig. 13–6.2. Eric's diet problem. Optimal solution to the primal.

interchanged in order to arrange all subscripts in ascending order. The results are (with slight rounding error in the value of C) the same as those obtained by the graphical method:

$$C = 272\tfrac{42}{89} = 272.47 \text{ cents} = \$2.72$$

$$x_1 = \tfrac{80}{89} = 0.90 \text{ pounds of beef}$$

$$x_2 = \tfrac{650}{89} = 7.30 \text{ pounds of potatoes}$$

b. The Dual

Maximize:

$$R = 4{,}000y_1 + 200y_2$$

subject to:

1. $$1{,}200y_1 + 125y_2 \leq 100$$

2. $$400y_1 + 12y_2 \leq 25$$

We add a slack variable to the small side of each inequation.

11. $$1{,}200y_1 + 125y_2 + y_3 = 100$$

12. $$400y_1 + 12y_2 + y_4 = 25$$

Rearranging for simplex application,

21. $$y_3 = 100 - 1{,}200y_1 - 125y_2$$

22. $$y_4 = 25 - 400y_1 - 12y_2$$

Here, the slack variable y_3 is the value or imputed price of nutrients in beef other than calories and protein which make the total price equal to 100 cents. Similarly, y_4 is the imputed price of other nutrients in potatoes which make the total price equal to 25 cents. The simplex tableaux are shown in Figure 13–6.3. The final, optimal, tableau is rewritten to array the subscripts and the resulting optimal tableau is shown in Figure 13–6.4, and the results are (with slight rounding error in the value of R) the same

		y_1	y_2
R	0	4000	200
y_3	100	−1200	−125
y_4	25	(−400)	−12

		y_4	y_2
R	250	−10	80
y_3	25	3	(−89)
y_1	1/16	−1/400	−3/100

		y_4	y_3
R	$272\frac{42}{89}$	$-7\frac{27}{89}$	−80/89
y_2	25/89	3/89	−1/89
y_1	77/1424	−5/1424	3/8900

Optimal!

Fig. 13–6.3. Eric's diet problem. Simplex solution to the dual.

		y_3	y_4
R	$-272\frac{42}{89}$	−80/89	−650/89
y_1	77/1424	3/8900	−5/1424
y_2	25/89	−1/89	3/89

Fig. 13–6.4. Eric's diet problem. Optimal solution to the dual.

as those obtained by the graphical method:

$$R = 272\tfrac{42}{89} = 272.47 \text{ cents} = \$2.72$$

$$y_1 = \tfrac{77}{1424} = 0.0541 \text{ cents per calorie}$$

$$y_2 = \tfrac{25}{89} = 0.281 \text{ cents per gram of protein}$$

13–7. The Relationship Between the Primal and Dual Solutions. The most interesting aspect of the solutions shown in Figures 13–6.2 and 13–6.4 is not that each yields the same result as we obtained earlier for each corresponding problem. Rather, the surprising result is the relationship between these two solutions. Examination of these two optimal tableaux indicates that, for either tableau, if the signs are changed throughout, and if the rows and columns are interchanged, the result is the other tableau.

Since this is always the case, it is clear that one may solve *either* the primal or the dual and thereby obtain the solution to both. Clearly, then, if the solution to the dual is simpler to obtain than the direct solution to the primal, it is efficient to convert the primal to the dual, solve the dual, and convert the dual solution to the primal solution. In Eric's diet problem the primal was difficult to solve because the origin was not in the feasible region and therefore artificial variables were required. In this case, it would have been far easier to solve the original primal problem by converting to the dual and solving the dual.

13–8. Symmetry of the Subscripts. In comparing the optimal solutions to the primal and dual as shown in Figures 13–6.2 and 13–6.4, respectively, it is clear that the symmetry within the matrix of numbers is not shared by the subscripts of the variables identifying the rows and columns. That is, the subscripts identifying the rows are 1 and 2, while those identifying the columns are 3 and 4 in both solutions. For purposes of symmetry, it is often desirable to select the subscripts for the y_i of the dual in a way that will assure that the row subscripts in the optimal solution to the primal will be the column subscripts in the optimal solution to the dual, and vice versa.

The method for doing this is simple enough, but before describing it, let us take a moment to try to derive it. We shall, in the following explanation, assume that there is no degeneracy. Clearly, if in the optimal solution to the primal any particular slack variable is zero and therefore not in the basis, the corresponding restriction inequation is an *equation* at that solution, and there is no excess nutrient (in a diet problem) or excess capacity (of a scarce resource being allocated). In that case, the real variable, i.e., the "shadow price" of the allocated resource, has a positive value in the optimal solution to the dual. Thus, if the first slack variable in the primal turns out to be zero, the first real variable in the dual has a positive value. Similarly, if the second slack variable in the primal *is* in the basis, the second real variable in the dual has zero value, since that resource is not fully utilized (i.e., in a diet problem, there is an excess of that nutrient), and it is not in the basis for the optimal solution to the dual.

Therefore, if a slack variable *is* in the basis in the primal, the corresponding real variable is *not* in the basis in the dual, and vice versa. In the optimal solution to the primal of Eric's diet problem, the two slack variables representing excess calories and excess protein are not in the basis for the optimal solution of the primal. Therefore, the values of these nutrients (the real variables in the dual) *are* in the basis for the optimal solution to the dual; i.e., they have positive values. Thus, the same subscripts appear in both solutions *in the same place.*

This can be avoided by assigning subscripts in the dual so that the subscripts of the n *real* variables in the *primal* are the same as the subscripts of the n *slack* variables in the dual, and the subscripts of the m *slack* variables in the *primal* correspond to the subscripts of the m *real* variables in the *dual.* The system for doing this is quite simple. The primal is numbered as before, but the dual is numbered differently as follows:

Primal Subscripts
n real variables $1, 2, 3, \ldots, n$.
m slack variables $(n+1), (n+2), (n+3), \ldots, (n+m)$.
Dual Subscripts
m real variables $(n+1), (n+2), (n+3), \ldots, (n+m)$.
n slack variables $1, 2, 3, \ldots, n$.

We shall use this system in solving the dual of the Everich Air Cargo problem.

13–9. The Dual of the Everich Air Cargo Problem. This problem which has been discussed in detail in Chapters 10 and 11, is an illustration of another classical form of linear programming problem, i.e., the maximization of profit (or some other measure of return) subject to limitations (maximum restrictions) on scarce resources. In that problem the scarce resources were the capacities of the various holds and of the aircraft itself.

That problem, it will be recalled, sought the maximum revenue load for an aircraft with two holds. The cargo revenue was $1,000 per ton in the main hold and $3,000 per ton in the (pressurized) cabin hold. This primal problem is restated along with the dual in Table 13–9.1.

TABLE 13–9.1

Everich Air Cargo Problem

Primal	Dual
Maximize:	Minimize:
$E = x_1 + 3x_2$	$E' = 20y_3 + 10y_4 + y_5 + 28y_6$
Subject to:	Subject to:
$x_1 + 0 \leq 20$	$y_3 + 0 - \frac{2}{3}y_5 + y_6 \geq 1$
$0 + x_2 \leq 10$	$0 + y_4 + y_5 + y_6 \geq 3$
$-\frac{2}{3}x_1 + x_2 \leq 1$	
$x_1 + x_2 \leq 28$	

In the primal problem, the variables x_1 and x_2 were the capacities of the main and cabin holds, respectively, and the objective function to be maximized was the revenue. In the dual problem, the y_i are the economic values of the scarce resources. It must be noted that, although there are only *two* holds, there are *four* scarce resources, one for each restriction in the primal. The four scarce resources are, respectively: (1) capacity of the main hold, (2) capacity of the cabin hold, (3) balance capacity in the cabin hold, and (4) total lift capacity of the airplane. The y_i in the dual are the imputed unit values of these four scarce resources.

In setting up the dual we have assigned subscripts as described above, and have assigned to the real variables in the dual the same numbers as will be assigned to the slack variables in the primal.

Before adding the slack variables, let us dwell a moment on the interpretation of the dual. In the first inequality of the dual, the right-side constant, 1 (which it will be recalled, is in thousands of dollars), is the unit revenue from cargo in the main hold. The coefficients of the y_i in this inequation are the *amounts* of each of the scarce resources which are required to produce for sale a unit of capacity in the main hold. Then the total on the left side of that inequation is the combined value (amounts times unit values) of the scarce resources which are required to produce a unit of output (i.e., a ton of capacity in the main hold). Each unit of this output yields \$1,000 of revenue to the company. Thus the first inequality merely stipulates that the total imputed value of the scarce resources consumed to produce a unit of main hold capacity must be at least equal to the revenue derived from this unit. In other words, in this inequation the revenue from the main hold cargo is allocated to the four scarce resources, and it is allocated in such a way that the sum of the allocations must be at least equal to the revenue. If, in the optimal solution, the left side is larger than the right, that suggests that the revenue from a unit of main hold capacity does not fully return the imputed values of the resources which have gone into producing it, and that within the framework of the restrictions of this problem, it is best for Everich not to try to remedy this.

The second restriction inequation makes a comparable statement for the cabin hold.

The objective function in the dual stipulates that the purpose of the problem is to find the smallest imputed value for the total of the scarce resources given up, and it is subject to the restrictions that this total value of the scarce resources which go into each output must be at least equal to the revenue derived from these two outputs, respectively.

The dual of the Everich Air Cargo problem cannot be represented graphically in solutions space, since it has four real variables. It can, however, be graphed in requirements space, since there are only two restrictions. The solution in requirements space is shown in Figure 13–9.1, where the axes represent, respectively, the main hold value restriction and the cabin hold value restriction. Table 13–9.2 provides the data which are plotted in the figure. The number 28,000 for E' was selected arbitrarily to minimize the arithmetic of dividing by 28. The first column in the table is derived by computing the value of each y_i, in turn, necessary to yield \$28,000, if no other scarce resource but the selected y_i is used. The computation, of course, is done in the objective function equation for the dual as given in Table 13–9.1. This equation, it will be recalled, is in thousands of dollars:

$$E' = 20y_3 + 10y_4 + y_5 + 28y_6 \qquad (13\text{–}9.1)$$

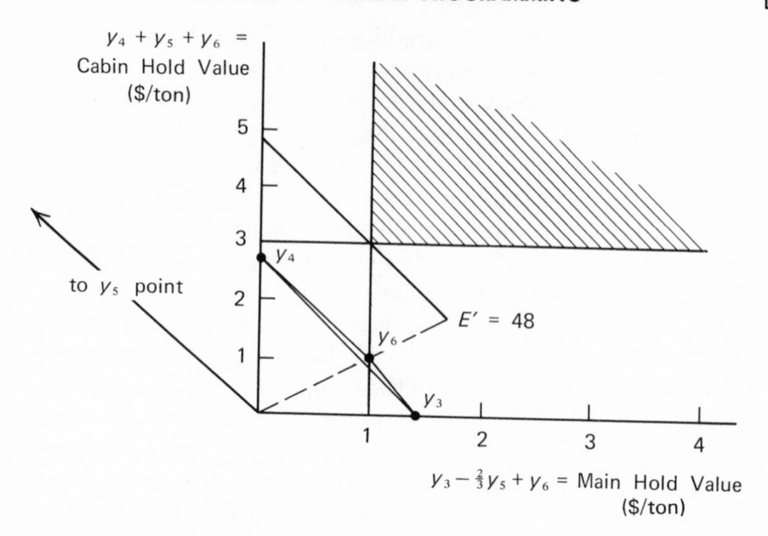

Fig. 13–9.1. Solution to dual of Everich Air Cargo problem in requirements space.

TABLE 13–9.2

Data for Graph of Figure 13–9.1

(all data in thousands of dollars)

For $E' = 28$ thousand dollars, with only one y_i (1)	Unit Value of Main Hold Capacity (2)	Unit Value of Cabin Hold Capacity (3)
$y_3 = 1.4$	1.4	0
$y_4 = 2.8$	0	2.8
$y_5 = 28$	$-18\frac{2}{3}$	28
$y_6 = 1$	1	1

Substituting the arbitrary value, $E' = 28$,

$$28 = 20y_3 + 10y_4 + y_5 + 28y_6 \tag{13–9.2}$$

This equation is solved for each y_i in turn (letting all of the other y_i be zero) to obtain the data in column (1).

Columns (2) and (3) are obtained by computing the value of the left side of the respective restriction inequations:

$$y_3 + 0 - \tfrac{2}{3}y_5 + y_6 \geq 1 \qquad \text{(main hold)} \tag{13–9.3}$$

$$0 + y_4 + y_5 + y_6 \geq 3 \qquad \text{(cabin hold)} \tag{13–9.4}$$

with only the single indicated y_i used. That is, each y_i is substituted into these two equations in turn (letting all of the other y_i be zero) to obtain the data in columns (2) and (3) which is the resulting value of the left side of the equation.

The plotted points indicate that the optimal solution will consist of y_4 and y_6, and that at the optimal, both restrictions are just met. Thus, at the optimal, $y_3 = y_5 = 0$, and from Equations (13–9.3) and (13–9.4).

$$y_6 = 1$$

$$y_4 + y_6 = 3$$

$$y_4 = 2$$

and

$$E' = (10)(2) + (28)(1) = 48$$

This result tells us that, at the optimum, the value of the resources used is $48,000, and since both y_3 and y_5 are equal to zero, the value of main hold capacity is zero and the value of cabin hold balance capacity is zero, indicating that there is an excess, unused, amount of each of these resources. This result is completely consistent with the solution to the primal which we have seen in Chapters 10 and 11.

13–10. Simplex Solution to Everich Air Cargo Dual. We shall solve the dual of this problem by the simplex method. The dual problem with slack variables, y_1 and y_2, and artificial variables, y_7 and y_8, is

Maximize:

$$-C = -20y_3 - 10y_4 - y_5 - 28y_6 - Ly_7 - Ly_8 \quad (13\text{–}10.1)$$

subject to:

$$y_7 = 1 + y_1 - y_3 + 0 + \tfrac{2}{3}y_5 - y_6 \quad (13\text{–}10.2)$$

$$y_8 = 3 + y_2 + 0 - y_4 - y_5 - y_6 \quad (13\text{–}10.3)$$

Letting L be 100, the objective function becomes

$$-C = -400 - 100y_1 - 100y_2 + 80y_3 + 90y_4 + 32\tfrac{1}{3}y_5 + 172y_6$$

In solving this problem we have used C for cost in place of E', its equivalent, to help us remember that this objective function is to be minimized. Also, since we wish to use the simplex rules for maximization, we have multiplied the objective function by -1, so that we can proceed to maximize $-C$.

The tableaux are shown in Figure 13–10.1. If we rearrange the columns and rows of the final optimal tableau of that figure to array the subscripts in ascending order as we have done before, we obtain the final tableau on the left side of Figure 13–10.2. On the right side is the solution to the primal, as given in Figure 11–5.6. Here the symmetry is complete. Inter-

		y_1	y_2	y_3	y_4	y_5	y_6
$-C$	−400	−100	−100	80	90	$32\frac{1}{3}$	172
y_7	1	1	0	−1	0	2/3	(−1)
y_8	3	0	1	0	−1	−1	−1

		y_1	y_2	y_3	y_4	y_5	y_7
$-C$	−228	72	−100	−92	90	147	−172
y_6	1	1	0	−1	0	2/3	−1
y_8	2	−1	1	1	−1	(−5/3)	1

		y_1	y_2	y_3	y_4	y_8
$-C$	$-51\frac{3}{5}$	$-16\frac{1}{5}$	$-11\frac{4}{5}$	$-3\frac{4}{5}$	9/5	$-88\frac{1}{5}$
y_6	9/5	3/5	2/5	−3/5	−2/5	2/5
y_5	6/5	−3/5	3/5	3/5	(−3/5)	3/5

		y_1	y_2	y_3	y_5
$-C$	−48	−18	−10	−2	−3
y_6	1	1	0	−1	2/3
y_4	2	−1	1	1	−5/3

Optimal!

Fig. 13–10.1. Simplex solution to Everich Air Cargo dual problem.

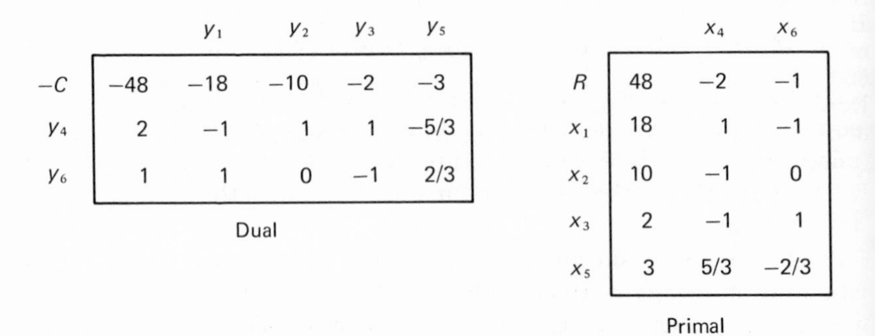

		y_1	y_2	y_3	y_5
$-C$	−48	−18	−10	−2	−3
y_4	2	−1	1	1	−5/3
y_6	1	1	0	−1	2/3

Dual

		x_4	x_6
R	48	−2	−1
x_1	18	1	−1
x_2	10	−1	0
x_3	2	−1	1
x_5	3	5/3	−2/3

Primal

Fig. 13–10.2. Optimal solution to primal and dual of Everich Air Cargo problem.

changing the rows and columns, including the subscripts, and changing the signs of all elements in the matrix, transforms one solution to the other. (The fact that, in Figure 11–5.6, the rows are in slightly different order is of no consequence here.)

Any linear programming problem may be solved either as stated or as its dual. Often, one form is easier to solve than the other, and efficiency dictates that, if this is the case, the easier method should be used.

In Chapter 18 below, in our study of game theory, we shall see another application of the dual.

SUGGESTIONS FOR FURTHER READING

ARNOFF, E. L., and S. S. SENGUPTA. "Mathematical Programming," in *Progress in Operations Research*, Vol. 1 (R. L. Ackoff, ed.). New York: John Wiley & Sons, Inc., 1961.

BAUMOL, W. J. *Economic Theory and Operations Analysis* (2d ed.). Englewood Cliffs, N.J.: Prentice-Hall, Inc., 1965.

BOULDING, K. E., and W. A. SPIVEY. *Linear Programming and the Theory of the Firm.* New York: The Macmillan Co., Publishers, 1960.

CHARNES, A., and W. W. COOPER. *Management Models and Industrial Applications of Linear Programming* (2 vols.). New York: John Wiley & Sons, Inc., 1963.

DORFMAN, R., P. A. SAMUELSON, and R. M. SOLOW. *Linear Programming and Economic Analysis.* New York: McGraw-Hill Book Co., Inc., 1958.

GASS, S. I. *Linear Programming: Methods and Applications.* New York: McGraw-Hill Book Co., Inc., 1959.

EXERCISES

13–1. State and solve graphically the dual of the Abrash Department Store problem (Exercise 10–2) of Chapter 10. (Hint: First simplify the problem by following the hint given in the original statement of the problem.) Interpret your results.

13–2. Mr. S. Hokeson, director of the Management Educators Lecturing Team, is setting up a 20-day lecture series in which it is providing the expert lectures for an inplant course for executives of the Melan Woolen Corporation. He will assign some combination of lecturers, Charles, Ernest, Kirby, Roger, of its staff. For this project, he will earn a profit of $100 per day on Charles, $200 per day on Ernest, $300 per day on Kirby, and $400 per day on Roger. However, he cannot use Roger for more days than double the sum of the number of days assigned to the two lecturers, Ernest and Kirby.

How many days should be assigned to each of the four lecturers in order to maximize Hokeson's profit? Each works an assigned number of whole or partial days, and only one man works at a time.

a) Solve the problem by the simplex method.
b) Solve the dual problem graphically.
c) Solve the primal graphically.

13–3. The Gebrad Hardware Company store seeks to allocate its 5,000 square feet of floor space on the basis of estimated annual net revenue per square foot. Estimated annual net revenue per square foot is $10 for paint, $15 for hardware items, and \$8 for housewares, and these relationships are linear within the ranges considered here. Cooperative advertising contracts require that at least 500 square feet be allocated to paint, but the store's lease limits its paint display to a maximum of 2,000 square feet. The store's image as more than a simple hardware store requires that hardware be limited to a maximum of 3,500 square feet and that hardware and paint be limited to a combined total of 4,500 square feet. How should the space be allocated for maximum annual net revenue?

Solve the primal and the dual by graph and by simplex. (Note: See last paragraph of Section 12–11.)

Part IV

STOCHASTIC MODELS

14

Queueing Theory

14–1. The Queueing Model. One of the most useful and widely applicable models in Operations Research is the queueing or *waiting line* model. In its simplest form it may be represented by the diagram of Figure 14–1.1. In that diagram, each arrow represents an element. These

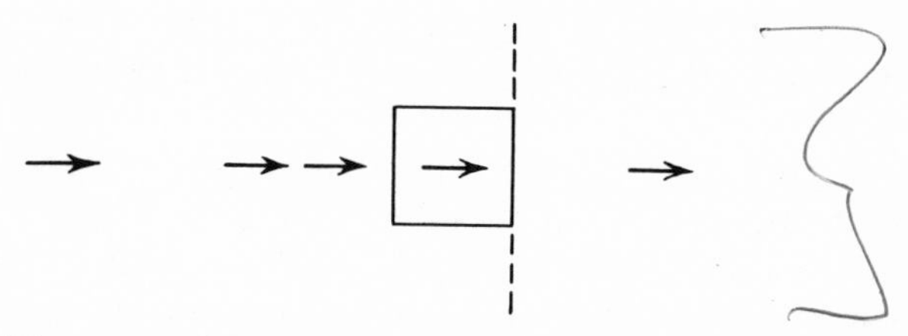

Fig. 14–1.1. Diagrammatic representation of a single-channel queue.

elements arrive at the service facility, wait in line if necessary, receive the desired service and leave the system. Note that the *number in the system* is defined as *including the number in the queue plus the number being serviced;* i.e., the system includes all elements to the left of the dashed line in the diagram. In the diagram, the system includes three elements; one has just left, and another is about to enter the system.

This model can be applied to a wide range of different kinds of phenomena, including: cars at toll booths; individuals at the bank, barber shop, or post office; individuals or equipment waiting for repairs at a repair facility, or waiting for the service facility to come to them; delivery or receipt of parcels; documents waiting for processing; testing or inspection of all kinds; steps in manufacturing processes; aircraft in airport landing procedures; checkout counters at supermarkets; loading and unloading ships or other vehicles; and a multitude of others.

In the model, elements arrive at the facility for service, wait until the facility is free, are serviced, and leave the system. The theory and mathematical models are used to describe the behavior of the system in terms of such parameters as the rate of arrivals, the time required for servicing, and the number of service stations or *channels*. This analysis may then be used to adjust the controllable variables for the best cost–performance balance.

The basic inputs of a queueing model are four in number: (1) the probability distribution of arrival times, (2) the probability distribution of service times, (3) the number of channels or service stations, and (4) the queue discipline. This last item is the decision rule or policy which governs the entry into service from the line or queue. This may be FIFO (first-in, first-out), LIFO (last-in, first-out), random selection, VIP's first, or some other system of priority. In addition, as we shall see, some queues are characterized by truncation, i.e., some limit to the number of units which will wait for service. The measures of effectiveness of the system are usually cost, queue length, and some measure of waiting time.

To illustrate briefly, let us imagine a service station on a highway. Cars arrive from time to time for gasoline. The arrival rate will presumably depend on the flow of traffic at the time. The service station's capacity to handle customers will depend on the number of pumps. The service time will depend on the quantity of gasoline and other services required or requested, as well as the delivery rate of the pumps and the efficiency of the employees. The length of time that a car is in the system, i.e., in the station, will depend on the service time, as well as the number of cars ahead of it, and the number of pumps. The concept of truncation, which will be discussed in detail later, may be illustrated by the fact that drivers may not be willing to wait for service if the queue ahead of them is longer than some given length. This limit may be a function of the drivers' impatience, which is likely to vary among individuals, in which case the truncation limit is stochastic or variable. If, however, the rules of the highway do not allow cars waiting to be serviced to remain on the roadway, then the queue has an absolute size limit, namely the number of cars that can fit from the pumps to the edge of the road.

The theory seeks to find optimal service procedures, numbers of channels, and queue disciplines in order to control the length of queue and the waiting time of the units to be serviced.

To analyse the various factors that influence the objective functions (queue length and waiting times) we set up a formal mathematical model, which takes into account the parameters listed above. Let us examine each of these in turn.

Before proceeding to derive the mathematical model for a single channel system, it should be noted that it is not necessary for the student to be able to derive the model in order to use it. Those readers who are not interested in the mathematical and logical reasoning on which the model is based may omit any or all of Sections 14–2 through 14–8 and proceed directly to Section 14–9, where the complete model is presented and applied. Some readers who are interested in the derivation may wish to look ahead at Section 14–9 before working through the detailed development of the model. In any event, the reader is urged to spend some time and effort on Sections 14–2 through 14–8 so that he will understand the reasoning and assumptions which underlie the model.

14–2. Arrivals. The pattern of arrivals at the service facility may be *regular*, as in an assembly line, or it may be *variable*, as is usually the case in the kinds of problem in which we are interested. The particular pattern of arrivals which we shall deal with primarily here is that which is known as *completely random arrivals*, and which is described by the familiar Poisson distribution.

Here, as elsewhere in probability theory, the word "random" has a very special well-defined meaning. Here, we mean by "random arrivals" that, in any fixed time interval, one or more items may or may not arrive for service, and that this is governed by the play of chance. Therefore, certain probability relationships may apply.

Consider a very short time interval Δt. The probability of one arrival in this interval is p and the interval is so small that the probability of more than one arrival in the interval is negligible. Now let us take a much larger time interval t that may be viewed as being composed of a very large number (N) of these very short intervals Δt. Then,

$$t = N\,\Delta t$$

As we have fixed the probability of an arrival in the very short time interval Δt at a constant, p, we know that the probability of x arrivals in the relatively long time interval t is governed by the familiar binomial distribution for x successes in N trials since the long time interval t contains N of the very short (Δt) time intervals, each of which may or may not contain an arrival:

$$P(x) = \frac{N!}{x!\,(N-x)!}\,p^x(1-p)^{N-x} \tag{14–2.1}$$

Let λ (Greek letter "lambda," lower case) represent the average rate of arrivals in elements per unit time. Then λt is the average *number* of arrivals in the time interval t. But this average number of arrivals in the time interval t is also the mean of the binomial distribution Np. Therefore,

$$\lambda t = Np \tag{14–2.2}$$

and

$$p = \frac{\lambda t}{N} \tag{14–2.3}$$

but

$$\Delta t = \frac{t}{N} \tag{14–2.4}$$

thus

$$p = \lambda \Delta t \tag{14–2.5}$$

Substituting this into Equation (14–2.1) yields

$$P(x) = \frac{N!}{x!\,(N-x)!}(\lambda \Delta t)^x (1 - \lambda \Delta t)^{N-x} \tag{14–2.6}$$

However, since Δt is very small, $\lambda \Delta t$ is also very small. We shall show that under these conditions we can approximate the binomial distribution by the Poisson distribution. This has been shown in Section 4–20, but its relevance here is so great that we repeat it in terms of the queueing theory symbols.

Substituting Equation (14–2.4) into Equation (14–2.6),

$$P(x) = \frac{N!}{x!\,(N-x)!}\left(\frac{\lambda t}{N}\right)^x \left(1 - \frac{\lambda t}{N}\right)^{N-x} \tag{14–2.7}$$

$$P(x) = \frac{N!}{x!\,(N-x)!}\left(\frac{\lambda t}{N}\right)^x \left(1 - \frac{\lambda t}{N}\right)^{N} \left(1 - \frac{\lambda t}{N}\right)^{-x} \tag{14–2.8}$$

but

$$\frac{N!}{x!\,(N-x)!} = \frac{N(N-1)(N-2)\cdots(N-x+1)}{x!} \tag{14–2.9}$$

and, since N is very large,

$$N \cong N-1 \cong N-2 \cong \cdots \cong N-x+1$$

thus

$$N(N-1)(N-2)\cdots(N-x+1) \cong N^x$$

Therefore

$$P(x) \cong \frac{N^x}{x!}\left(\frac{\lambda t}{N}\right)^x \left(1 - \frac{\lambda t}{N}\right)^{N} \left(1 - \frac{\lambda t}{N}\right)^{-x} \tag{14–2.10}$$

$$P(x) \cong \frac{1}{x!}(\lambda t)^x \left(1 - \frac{\lambda t}{N}\right)^{N} \left(1 - \frac{\lambda t}{N}\right)^{-x} \tag{14–2.11}$$

also, since N is very large (and x is not),

$$\left(1 - \frac{\lambda t}{N}\right)^{-x} \cong (1)^{-x} = 1$$

thus

$$P(x) = \frac{1}{x!}(\lambda t)^x \left(1 - \frac{\lambda t}{N}\right)^{N} \tag{14–2.12}$$

However, from Equation (2–9.2), the definition of e is

$$e = \lim_{x\to\infty}\left(1 - \frac{1}{x}\right)^{-x} = \lim_{x\to\infty}\left(1 + \frac{1}{x}\right)^{x}$$

Therefore

$$\lim_{N\to\infty}\left(1 - \frac{\lambda t}{N}\right)^{N} = \lim_{N\to\infty}\left[\left(1 - \frac{\lambda t}{N}\right)^{-N/\lambda t}\right]^{-\lambda t} = e^{-\lambda t}$$

Now

$$P(x) = \frac{(\lambda t)^x e^{-\lambda t}}{x!} \tag{14–2.13}$$

This is the familiar mathematical statement of the Poisson distribution with mean λt. We shall see that this probability distribution is extremely important in queueing theory.

Now we shall see that there is a very close relationship between the Poisson distribution and the familiar exponential distribution, which is also of great importance in queueing theory. Looking at Equation (14–2.13) for the Poisson distribution, we can see that the probability of zero arrivals in an interval t would be found by substituting $x = 0$ into Equation (14–2.13) (it will be recalled that $0! = 1$):

$$P(0) = e^{-\lambda t} \tag{14–2.14}$$

This may be viewed as a probability function; that is, it is the probability of zero arrivals in a time interval of length t, or any shorter interval between t and 0. Obviously, at zero time, we would have a zero probability of arrivals or a 1.0 probability of no arrivals, and as the time interval t lengthens, $P(0)$ decreases. This function is shown in Figure (14–2.1) for

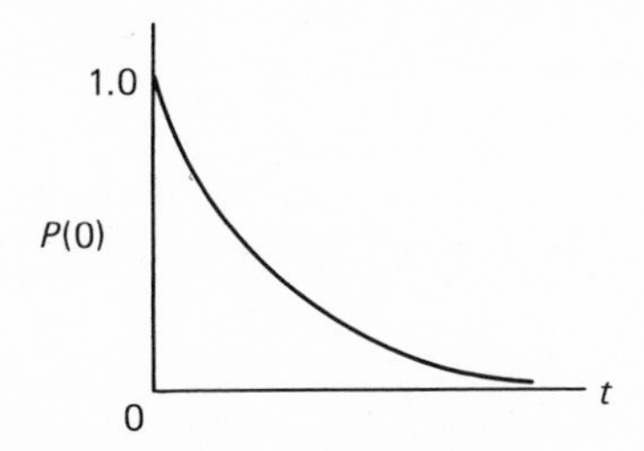

Fig. 14–2.1. Graph of the function $P(0) = e^{-\lambda t}$.

a constant λ. It is the probability that a time interval can be of length t *or shorter* with no arrival, when the average arrival rate is λ. Clearly, $P(0)$ is some function of t.

Now, the function

$$F(t) = 1 - e^{-\lambda t} \tag{14–2.15}$$

is a *cumulative distribution function* with all of the properties described in Section 6–2. That is, as t increases, $F(t)$ is monotonically nondecreasing, and it approaches 1.0 as its limit. This function is shown in Figure 14–2.2; $F(t)$ is $1 - P(0)$. Therefore it can be interpreted as the probability of one or more arrivals in the time interval t. It may also be viewed as the probability that the time interval between successive arrivals is *t or less*, and it approaches 1.0 as t becomes very large.

The slope of this curve is

$$\frac{d}{dt}F(t) = \frac{d}{dt}(1 - e^{-\lambda t}) = \lambda e^{-\lambda t} \qquad (14\text{–}2.16)$$

Thus the slope is λ at the origin where $t = 0$, and the slope approaches zero (horizontal) as t becomes very large. This confirms the shape of the curve as shown in Figure 14–2.2, and it also confirms the intuitive

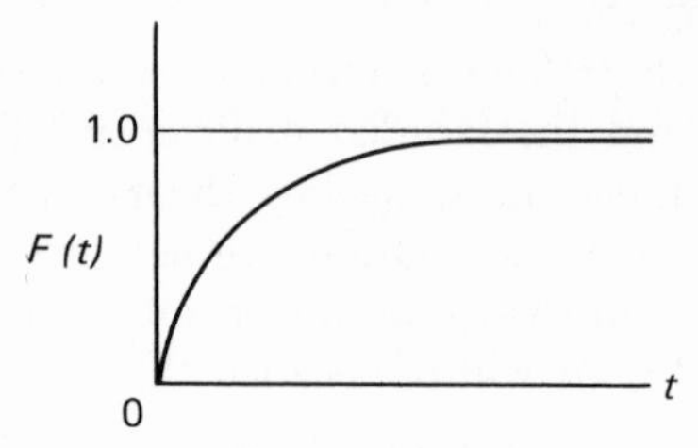

Fig. 14–2.2. Graph of the *cdf*, $F(t) = 1 - e^{-\lambda t}$.

expectation that the curve should rise more rapidly for large λ than for small λ.

The function given in Equation (14–2.15) is the cumulative distribution function for the familiar *exponential distribution* with parameter λ, and its derivative, given in Equation (14–2.16) is its density function (*pdf*):

$$f(t) = \frac{d}{dt}F(t) = \lambda e^{-\lambda t} \qquad (14\text{–}2.17)$$

The graph of this density function is given in Figure 14–2.3. This is the distribution of the random variable t, which is the "inter-arrival time."

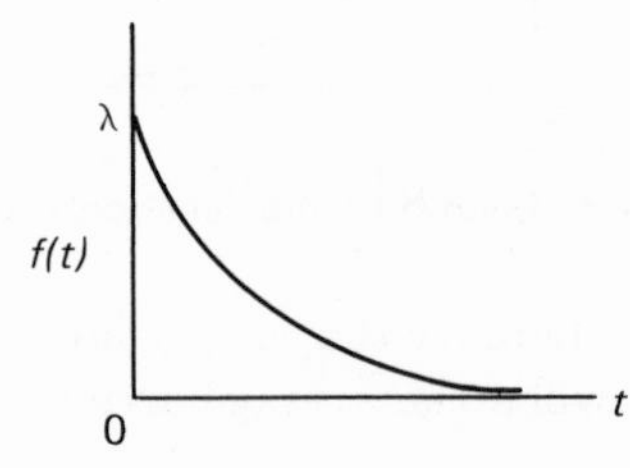

Fig. 14–2.3. Graph of the density function, $f(t) = \lambda e^{-\lambda t}$.

That is, as with any continuous density function, the probability of time intervals between any desired limits may be computed as the definite integral evaluated between those limits. Also, as a density function, the area under the curve must be equal to 1. Since t, the inter-arrival time, can take values between 0 and ∞, the definite integral between these limits must be 1. This is the case as seen below.

$$\int_0^\infty \lambda e^{-\lambda t} = -e^{-\lambda t}\Big|_0^\infty = 0 - (-1) = 1 \qquad (14\text{–}2.18)$$

Thus, that which we have described as "random arrivals" may be characterized by the discrete Poisson distribution or by the continuous exponential distribution, depending upon which aspects of the phenomenon we seek to describe. If we ask the probability of 0 or 1 or 2, etc., arrivals in some fixed time interval, that is given by the Poisson distribution. On the other hand, if we inquire into the probability of time intervals of various lengths between successive arrivals, that is given by the exponential distribution.

From the exponential distribution, if the arrival rate is λ, the average time interval between successive arrivals ($\bar{t}_a$) is $\frac{1}{\lambda}$ as derived below.

$$\bar{t}_a = \int_0^\infty tf(t)\,dt = \int_0^\infty t\lambda e^{-\lambda t}\,dt$$

Integrate by parts:

$$\int u\,dv = uv - \int v\,du \qquad (5\text{–}5.6)$$

let

$$u = t\lambda$$

and

$$dv = e^{-\lambda t}\,dt$$

then

$$du = \lambda\,dt$$

and

$$v = -\frac{1}{\lambda}e^{-\lambda t}$$

Then

$$\bar{t}_a = -te^{-\lambda t}\Big|_0^\infty - \int_0^\infty - e^{-\lambda t}\,dt$$

$$= -te^{-\lambda t}\Big|_0^\infty - \frac{1}{\lambda}e^{-\lambda t}\Big|_0^\infty$$

$$= 0 - 0 + 0 - \left(-\frac{1}{\lambda}\right)$$

$$= \frac{1}{\lambda}$$

For the Poisson distribution, the mean and variance, as shown in Section 4–21, are both equal to λt.

Finally, in order to identify the distribution of *arrivals*, let us use, in place of $f(t)$, the designation

$$a(t) = \lambda e^{-\lambda t} \tag{14–2.19}$$

14–3. Servicing. If the servicing time, like the arrival rate, is completely random, then the exponential distribution (but *not* the Poisson) for the individual service times holds exactly as described in the last section for arrival intervals.

There is a very important distinction between the arrival phenomenon and the servicing phenomenon, and because of this distinction, *the Poisson distribution is not applicable to servicing.* The crucial distinction is that, when there are no elements in the system, none can be serviced. The average service time, which we shall call μ (Greek letter "mu," lower case) is the average time taken for servicing *while servicing is going on.* Idle time is not counted. Thus, the distinction between arriving and servicing is that arriving is always going on, and time between arrivals is counted in computing the average arrival rate. Servicing, on the other hand, takes place only when one or more elements are in the system. Thus, the average service rate, μ, is the average number of elements serviced per unit time of continuous servicing.

For this reason, and since there usually is some idle time, we cannot apply the Poisson distribution to servicing and use it to describe the probability of turning out some number of units in a fixed time interval. (It would, of course, hold for a fixed time interval of *continuous servicing*, but we never know when or even *if* this will occur.)

However, the exponential distribution does describe the distribution of service times according to the following familiar formula, using $s(t)$ to represent the density function for *service* times.

$$s(t) = \mu e^{-\mu t} \tag{14–3.1}$$

and the average service time is

$$\bar{t}_s = \frac{1}{\mu} \tag{14–3.2}$$

For the reasons discussed above, we generally refer to a system characterized by random arrivals and random service times as described above, as a *Poisson-exponential* system, meaning that arrivals are characterized by the Poisson distribution and the service times by the exponential distribution. Clearly, we may, if we wish, describe both arrival and service by the exponential distribution, but the *Poisson-exponential* designation has become traditional, and we shall use it henceforth.

14–4. A Single-Channel System. We shall now construct a system model for the analysis of a single-channel queue. We shall start by computing the probability that there are n elements in the system where n may be 0, 1, 2, . . . , etc. Here we shall be dealing with the *steady state.* The system is operating. Items are arriving according to the Poisson distribution, and they are being serviced with simple queue discipline; i.e., first in, first out. The service times are distributed according to the exponential distribution as described above. The number in the system, the waiting line *plus* the one being serviced if there is one or more in the system, fluctuates as the chance processes of arrival and service continue to act; but, at the steady state, there is no long-term trend in the number in the system. That is, the probability that there are n in the system is constant over time.

At any time t there may be n elements in the system, and the probability that there are n elements in the system at time t is designated $P_t(n)$. We shall always use the symbol n to refer to the number of elements in the system.

Let us consider some time, $t + \Delta t$, a very short interval after time t, and let us evaluate $P_{t+\Delta t}(n)$, the probability of the event that there are n elements in the system at time $t + \Delta t$. There are many ways in which this event may occur as a consequence of the state of the system at time t, a very short time, Δt, earlier. However, of all of the ways in which this can happen, only the following three involve zero or one *event* (arrival or departure) in the very short time interval Δt.

a) There were n elements in the system at time t, and no elements arrived or were serviced in the very short time interval Δt.

b) There were $n + 1$ elements in the system at time t, and no elements arrived, but one was serviced and departed in the interval Δt.

c) There were $n - 1$ elements in the system at time t, and one element arrived and no elements were serviced in the interval Δt.

Since we define the time interval Δt as very short, the probability of more than one event in that interval is negligibly small. This can be illustrated numerically by computing the probability of one arrival in some arbitrarily selected relatively very short interval Δt.

If the average arrival rate is λ; that is, if, on the average, λ units arrive per unit time (day, hour, minute, etc.), that means that the *expected* number of arrivals in that time is λ. In any short time Δt the expected number of arrivals is $\lambda\Delta t$. That is the same as saying that the probability of an arrival in that very short interval is $\lambda\Delta t$.

For example, if the average number of customers arriving at a single-position airline ticket counter is 18 per hour, Poisson, then in any given second (i.e., letting $\Delta t = 1$ sec. for this illustration) the expected number of arrivals is $\lambda\Delta t = (18)(\frac{1}{3600}) = 0.005$. We may also describe this quantity by saying the probability of an arrival in any given second is 0.005.

Similarly, we could say that, if the service rate μ is 27 customers per hour, then the probability that a customer will be serviced and depart from the system in any given second is $\mu\Delta t = (27)(\frac{1}{3600}) = 0.0075$, *while servicing is taking place.* Again, this is equivalent to saying that the probability of a departure in any second (while servicing is taking place) is 0.0075.

The probability of *two* departures in any given second is 0.000056, the probability of two arrivals in one second is 0.000025, and the probability of one arrival and one departure in one second is 0.000038. These probabilities for *two movements* are so small compared to the probabilities for one movement that they may be safely ignored in our analysis. Actually, as we shall see, these "small" probabilities become in fact equal to zero when we take the limit as Δt approaches zero in the derivation which follows.

Therefore, if we consider only the possibilities of zero or one movement in a very short period Δt, then the above-listed three ways of arriving at n items in the system at time $t + \Delta t$ are the only possibilities. All others such as, for example, n items in the system at time t and one arrival and one departure, or $n - 2$ items in the system at time t, or $n + 2$ items in the system at time t, all involve two or more movements in the very short interval Δt.

Limiting our consideration to the three ways of arriving at n items in the system at time $t + \Delta t$, let us evaluate the probability of each of these. Then, since these are all mutually exclusive, the probability of n in the system at time $t + \Delta t$ is the sum of the probabilities of the three ways in which that can happen. The three events may be designated a, b, and c, as identified above.

We will make use of the following notation:

$$P(n \text{ elements in the system at time } t) = P_t(n)$$
$$P(1 \text{ arrival in time interval } \Delta t) = \lambda\Delta t$$
$$P(0 \text{ arrivals in time interval } \Delta t) = 1 - \lambda\Delta t$$
$$P(1 \text{ departure in time interval } \Delta t) = \mu\Delta t$$
$$P(0 \text{ departures in time interval } \Delta t) = 1 - \mu\Delta t$$
$$P(a) = P(n \text{ elements at time } t, 0 \text{ arrivals}, 0 \text{ departures})$$
$$P(b) = P(n + 1 \text{ elements at time } t, 0 \text{ arrivals}, 1 \text{ departure})$$
$$P(c) = P(n - 1 \text{ elements at time } t, 1 \text{ arrival}, 0 \text{ departures})$$

Since the elementary events are all independent,

$$P(a) = P_t(n)(1 - \lambda\Delta t)(1 - \mu\Delta t) = P_t(n) - P_t(n)\lambda\Delta t - P_t(n)\mu\Delta t + P_t(n)\lambda\mu(\Delta t)^2$$

$$P(b) = P_t(n + 1)(1 - \lambda\Delta t)\mu\Delta t = P_t(n + 1)\mu\Delta t - P_t(n + 1)\lambda\mu(\Delta t)^2$$

$$P(c) = P_t(n - 1)\lambda\Delta t(1 - \mu\Delta t) = P_t(n - 1)\lambda\Delta t - P_t(n - 1)\lambda\mu(\Delta t)^2$$

Since these events, a, b, and c, are mutually exclusive, and since we may safely ignore all terms with $(\Delta t)^2$ as being too small to consider (indeed, we could keep them in at this point, and they would drop out between Equations (14–4.1) and (14–4.3) as Δt goes to zero, but the equations are less messy if we drop them here),

$$P_{t+\Delta t}(n) = P(a \cup b \cup c) = P(a) + P(b) + P(c)$$

$$P_{t+\Delta t}(n) = P_t(n) - P_t(n)\lambda\Delta t - P_t(n)\mu\Delta t + P_t(n+1)\mu\Delta t + P_t(n-1)\lambda\Delta t$$

$$\frac{P_{t+\Delta t}(n) - P_t(n)}{\Delta t} = -P_t(n)(\lambda + \mu) + P_t(n+1)\mu + P_t(n-1)\lambda \tag{14–4.1}$$

From Equation (2–5.11),

$$\lim_{\Delta t \to 0} \frac{P_{t+\Delta t}(n) - P_t(n)}{\Delta t} = \frac{d}{dt}(P(n)) \tag{14–4.2}$$

$$\frac{d}{dt}(P(n)) = -P_t(n)(\lambda + \mu) + P_t(n+1)\mu + P_t(n-1)\lambda \qquad \text{for } n > 0 \tag{14–4.3}$$

Equation (14–4.3) holds for $n > 0$. If $n = 0$, the last term involving $P_t(n-1)$ is absent since $P(-1)$ is meaningless. If we were to derive the same expression for $P(0)$, we would find that events a and b are the only two ways of getting to zero in the system at time $t + \Delta t$, and that event a is simplified also, since the probability of no departures with zero in the system is 1. The result is

$$\frac{d}{dt}(P(0)) = -\lambda P_t(0) + \mu P_t(1) \tag{14–4.4}$$

At the steady state, $P(n)$ is not a function of t, and therefore

$$\frac{d}{dt}(P(n)) = 0 \qquad \text{at steady state for every } n \tag{14–4.5}$$

Also, since t is *any* point in time, the subscript t may be eliminated from Equations (14–4.3) and (14–4.4), which, after eliminating the subscript, setting the derivatives equal to zero, and solving for $\mu P(n+1)$ and $P(1)$, respectively, become

$$\mu P(n+1) = (\lambda + \mu)P(n) - \lambda P(n-1) \qquad \text{for } n > 0 \tag{14–4.6}$$

$$P(1) = \frac{\lambda}{\mu} P(0) \tag{14–4.7}$$

We shall now use Equations (14–4.6) and (14–4.7) to derive $P(2)$ and $P(3)$. Equation (14–4.6) may be rearranged to read

$$P(n+1) = \frac{\lambda}{\mu} P(n) + P(n) - \frac{\lambda}{\mu} P(n-1) \qquad \text{for } n > 0 \tag{14–4.8}$$

Now we can solve for $P(2)$ by letting $n = 1$ in Equation (14–4.8) and then using the expression for $P(1)$ given in Equation (14–4.7).

$$P(2) = \frac{\lambda}{\mu} P(1) + P(1) - \frac{\lambda}{\mu} P(0)$$

$$= \left(\frac{\lambda}{\mu}\right)^2 P(0) + \frac{\lambda}{\mu} P(0) - \frac{\lambda}{\mu} P(0)$$

$$P(2) = \left(\frac{\lambda}{\mu}\right)^2 P(0) \tag{14–4.9}$$

Similarly we can solve for $P(3)$ by letting $n = 2$:

$$P(3) = \frac{\lambda}{\mu} P(2) + P(2) - \frac{\lambda}{\mu} P(1)$$

and from Equations (14–4.9) and (14–4.7),

$$P(3) = \left(\frac{\lambda}{\mu}\right)^3 P(0) + \left(\frac{\lambda}{\mu}\right)^2 P(0) - \left(\frac{\lambda}{\mu}\right)^2 P(0)$$

$$P(3) = \left(\frac{\lambda}{\mu}\right)^3 P(0) \tag{14–4.10}$$

It is quite clear that this process may be continued, and that the general relationship is

$$P(n) = \left(\frac{\lambda}{\mu}\right)^n P(0) \tag{14–4.11}$$

Before continuing with the mathematics, let us examine Equation (14–4.11). It is clear that, if $\frac{\lambda}{\mu} > 1$, $P(n)$ is greater for greater n. This means that longer lines are more probable than shorter lines, or that the line grows and grows indefinitely. Even the case where $\frac{\lambda}{\mu} = 1$ leads to indefinitely long lines, since, according to the equation, *all possible* lengths of line are equally likely.

The last may be surprising in that one might be tempted to think that if $\lambda = \mu$, there would be a smooth functioning system with no idle facility time and no waiting in line. Unfortunately, this holds only for the *ideal* assembly line situation where arrival intervals are *absolutely regular* and service times are *absolutely constant.* Such a zero-variance situation is almost never realizable in practice. When there is variation in either arrival interval or service time or both, some idle facility time is created. This time is lost forever. It can never be made up, and the line is created. In random arrivals and random service times (Poisson-exponential), the variance of service times and inter-arrival times is such that, as is indicated by Equation (14–4.11), if $\lambda = \mu$, the line has no theoretical limit. We shall return to this point later.

The consequence of the information provided by Equation (14–4.11) is that *only cases where* $\frac{\lambda}{\mu} < 1$ *are feasible for analysis in a single-channel system.*

14–5. The Probability that the Facility Is Idle. Equation (14–4.11) can enable us to compute the average number in the system $\bar{n}$, since it tells us the probability of every possible n. However, in order to use it, we must know $P(0)$, the probability that there are no elements in the system. This is, of course, the probability that the service facility is idle.

In order to evaluate $P(0)$, we must use the simple expression for the sum of a geometric series starting with 1, and with constant multiplier whose absolute value is smaller than 1. This is a *convergent* series in that its sum approaches a limit as n increases. Let us see what that limit is. Let the sum of the series be S, and let a be the constant multiplier, where $0 < |a| < 1$. Then

$$S = 1 + a + a^2 + a^3 + a^4 + \cdots + a^{n-1} + a^n$$

$$aS = a + a^2 + a^3 + a^4 + a^5 + \cdots + a^n + a^{n+1}$$

Subtracting the second equation from the first,

$$S - aS = 1 - a^{n+1}$$

$$S = \frac{1}{1-a} - \frac{a^{n+1}}{1-a} \tag{14–5.1}$$

but, since $0 < |a| < 1$,

$$\lim_{n\to\infty} a^{n+1} = 0 \tag{14–5.2}$$

Thus, for an infinite geometric series, starting with 1, and where $0 < |a| < 1$,

$$S = \frac{1}{1-a} \tag{14–5.3}$$

Now, we can evaluate $P(0)$. By definition,

$$1 = \sum_{n=0}^{\infty} P(n) = P(0) + P(1) + P(2) + P(3) + \cdots + P(n) + \cdots$$

$$= P(0) + \frac{\lambda}{\mu}P(0) + \left(\frac{\lambda}{\mu}\right)^2 P(0) + \left(\frac{\lambda}{\mu}\right)^3 P(0) + \cdots + \left(\frac{\lambda}{\mu}\right)^n P(0) + \cdots$$

$$= P(0)\left[1 + \frac{\lambda}{\mu} + \left(\frac{\lambda}{\mu}\right)^2 + \left(\frac{\lambda}{\mu}\right)^3 + \cdots + \left(\frac{\lambda}{\mu}\right)^n + \cdots\right]$$

But, since the term in the brackets is the sum of an infinitely long geometric series starting with 1, and with constant multiplier $\frac{\lambda}{\mu}$ such that $0 < \frac{\lambda}{\mu} < 1$, from Equation (14–5.3),

$$1 = P(0)\left(\frac{1}{1 - \frac{\lambda}{\mu}}\right)$$

$$P(0) = 1 - \frac{\lambda}{\mu} \tag{14–5.4}$$

Thus, the probability that the facility is idle is $1 - \frac{\lambda}{\mu}$, indicating that as we have seen before, the amount of idle time becomes smaller as λ approaches μ.

In the illustration of the last section, the airline ticket counter with $\lambda = 18$ and $\mu = 27$ would be idle $\frac{1}{3}$ of the time:

$$P(0) = 1 - \frac{18}{27} = 0.333$$

From Equations (14–5.4) and (14–4.11), it follows that

$$P(n) = \left(\frac{\lambda}{\mu}\right)^n \left(1 - \frac{\lambda}{\mu}\right) \tag{14–5.5}$$

Equation (14–5.4) clearly indicates that, when the queue is finite, i.e., when $\frac{\lambda}{\mu} < 1$, *there must be some idle time.* That is, there must be some idle time if all arrivals do join the queue, and the queue is finite. If ever a situation occurs in which there is no idle time and the queue is nevertheless finite, this is a clear indication that the queue discipline is characterized by *truncation.*[1] That is, for some reason some elements do not join the queue. Usually the reason is that the line is considered too long, and the arriving elements, seeing this, prefer to change their plans and not join the queue, thereby avoiding what they consider to be too lengthy a wait.

In this and the succeeding sections we shall assume that there is no truncation, and that all arrivals do join the queue. Later, in Section 14–13, we shall consider truncated queues.

14–6. The Average Number in the System. Now, using the familiar formula for the expected value or arithmetic mean of a discrete probability distribution with an infinite number of possible values of the

[1] Of course, it might also indicate that the service times are controlled and manipulated to insure that the facility is never idle. However, we shall continue to treat service times as independent of n.

discrete random variable

$$E(x) = \sum_{i=1}^{\infty} x_i P(x_i)$$

the average number in the system, $\bar{n}$, is

$$\bar{n} = \sum_{n=0}^{\infty} nP(n) \tag{14–6.1}$$

$$= 0P(0) + 1P(1) + 2P(2) + 3P(3) + 4P(4) + \cdots$$

$$= 0 + \frac{\lambda}{\mu}P(0) + 2\left(\frac{\lambda}{\mu}\right)^2 P(0) + 3\left(\frac{\lambda}{\mu}\right)^3 P(0) + 4\left(\frac{\lambda}{\mu}\right)^4 P(0) + \cdots$$

$$\bar{n} = P(0)\left[\left(\frac{\lambda}{\mu}\right) + 2\left(\frac{\lambda}{\mu}\right)^2 + 3\left(\frac{\lambda}{\mu}\right)^3 + 4\left(\frac{\lambda}{\mu}\right)^4 + \cdots\right]$$

$$\left(\frac{\lambda}{\mu}\right)\bar{n} = P(0)\left[\left(\frac{\lambda}{\mu}\right)^2 + 2\left(\frac{\lambda}{\mu}\right)^3 + 3\left(\frac{\lambda}{\mu}\right)^4 + 4\left(\frac{\lambda}{\mu}\right)^5 + \cdots\right]$$

$$\bar{n} - \left(\frac{\lambda}{\mu}\right)\bar{n} = P(0)\left[\frac{\lambda}{\mu} + \left(\frac{\lambda}{\mu}\right)^2 + \left(\frac{\lambda}{\mu}\right)^3 + \left(\frac{\lambda}{\mu}\right)^4 + \cdots\right]$$

$$\bar{n}\left(1 - \frac{\lambda}{\mu}\right) = P(0)\left(\frac{\lambda}{\mu}\right)\left[1 + \frac{\lambda}{\mu} + \left(\frac{\lambda}{\mu}\right)^2 + \left(\frac{\lambda}{\mu}\right)^3 + \cdots\right]$$

but

$$P(0) = 1 - \frac{\lambda}{\mu} \tag{14–5.4}$$

and, from Equation (14–5.3), the term in the brackets is equal to

$$\frac{1}{1 - \frac{\lambda}{\mu}}$$

Therefore

$$\bar{n}\left(1 - \frac{\lambda}{\mu}\right) = \left(1 - \frac{\lambda}{\mu}\right)\left(\frac{\lambda}{\mu}\right)\frac{1}{1 - \frac{\lambda}{\mu}}$$

$$\bar{n} = \frac{\frac{\lambda}{\mu}}{1 - \frac{\lambda}{\mu}} \tag{14–6.2}$$

This is the average number of elements in the system. Again we see the importance of the fact that $\lambda < \mu$. In Equation (14–6.2), as λ approaches μ, $\bar{n}$ becomes extremely large. This is consistent with what we have seen above.

Finally we shall inquire how long these elements must wait in the system.

14–7. The Average Waiting Time. Let W be the *average time an element spends in the system.* If elements arrive at random at the average rate of λ elements per unit time, then, at the moment when an element is discharged from the system, there will be, on the average, λW units in the system behind it. But the average number in the system is $\bar{n}$, and, since discharge from the system is also at random, the average number at the moment of discharge must also be $\bar{n}$. Therefore

$$\lambda W = \bar{n}$$

$$W = \frac{\bar{n}}{\lambda} \tag{14–7.1}$$

but

$$\bar{n} = \frac{\frac{\lambda}{\mu}}{1 - \frac{\lambda}{\mu}} \tag{14–6.2}$$

Therefore

$$W = \frac{\frac{\lambda}{\mu}}{\lambda\left(1 - \frac{\lambda}{\mu}\right)} = \frac{\frac{1}{\mu}}{1 - \frac{\lambda}{\mu}}$$

$$W = \frac{1}{\mu - \lambda} \tag{14–7.2}$$

This is the average length of time spent in the system.

14–8. The Average Number and Time in the Queue. All of the quantities which we have computed thus far have dealt with the *entire system,* that is, the queue plus the one being serviced. For some purposes it is desirable to be able to compute the average number and time *in the queue, waiting for service,* $\bar{n}_q$ and W_q, respectively. From Equation (14–7.2), it is easy to compute W_q, *the average time in the queue waiting for service to begin.* Since the average service time is $\frac{1}{\mu}$,

$$W = W_q + \frac{1}{\mu} \tag{14–8.1}$$

$$W_q = \frac{1}{\mu - \lambda} - \frac{1}{\mu} = \frac{\mu - \mu + \lambda}{\mu(\mu - \lambda)}$$

$$W_q = \frac{\lambda}{\mu}\left(\frac{1}{\mu - \lambda}\right) = \frac{\lambda}{\mu} W \tag{14–8.2}$$

Also, we can reason that, at the moment an element enters service (i.e., completes its average wait of W_q in the queue), there will be $W_q\lambda$ elements behind it in the line. This is the average length of the queue $\bar{n}_q$:

$$\bar{n}_q = W_q\lambda = \left(\frac{\lambda}{\mu}\right)\left(\frac{1}{\mu - \lambda}\right)\lambda = \frac{\lambda^2}{\mu^2\left(1 - \frac{\lambda}{\mu}\right)}$$

$$\bar{n}_q = \frac{\left(\frac{\lambda}{\mu}\right)^2}{1 - \frac{\lambda}{\mu}} \tag{14–8.3}$$

$$\bar{n}_q = \frac{\lambda}{\mu}\bar{n} \tag{14–8.4}$$

Thus, in both cases, the length of the queue and the waiting time, the quantity for *the queue alone* may be derived by multiplying the corresponding quantity for *the system* by $\frac{\lambda}{\mu}$.

Since, from Equation (14–5.4),

$$\frac{\lambda}{\mu} = 1 - P(0) \tag{14–8.5}$$

Equations (14–8.2) and (14–8.4) may also be written

$$W_q = (1 - P(0))W \tag{14–8.6}$$

and

$$\bar{n}_q = (1 - P(0))\bar{n} \tag{14–8.7}$$

These equations indicate that the length of time in the queue and the average number in the queue are negatively related to the percentage of idle time. If the facility is idle much of the time, then, of course, the average number in the queue and the average waiting time in the queue will be relatively small.

14–9. Applications of the Model. The model which we have derived describes any single-channel system with random arrivals and service times, i.e., *Poisson arrivals and exponential service times.* Then, if λ is the average arrival rate and μ is the average service time, and if the queue discipline is simple, i.e., first-in first-out, the model is the following set of equations.

The probability that there are no elements in the system; i.e., that the facility is idle:

$$P(0) = 1 - \frac{\lambda}{\mu} \tag{14–5.4}$$

The probability that there are n elements in the system (including the element being serviced):

$$P(n) = \left(\frac{\lambda}{\mu}\right)^n\left(1 - \frac{\lambda}{\mu}\right) \tag{14–5.5}$$

The average number in the system (including the element being serviced):

$$\bar{n} = \frac{\frac{\lambda}{\mu}}{1 - \frac{\lambda}{\mu}} \tag{14–6.2}$$

The average time spent in the system (including service time):

$$W = \frac{1}{\mu - \lambda} \tag{14–7.2}$$

The average waiting time in the queue (before service begins):

$$W_q = \frac{\lambda}{\mu} W \tag{14–8.2}$$

The average number in the queue (waiting for service):

$$\bar{n}_q = \frac{\lambda}{\mu} \bar{n} \tag{14–8.4}$$

It is quite obvious that the term $\frac{\lambda}{\mu}$ is extremely important in queueing theory. It is sometimes referred to as the *utilization factor* of the service facility. Some authors prefer to use a separate symbol for it, $\left(\rho = \frac{\lambda}{\mu}\right)$, in the various equations. It is expressed in units of "Erlangs" in honor of the Danish queueing theory pioneer, A. K. Erlang. In this volume we shall not use the additional symbol, but we shall continue to use $\frac{\lambda}{\mu}$.

We can illustrate the broad applicability of this model by selecting some seemingly widely divergent kinds of situations and applying the model to them. Let us consider four situations.

1. The Riten County Airport, under instrument conditions, can land 12 aircraft per hour on the average. Aircraft arrive into the landing pattern at the average rate of 9 per hour.
2. The toll bridge to Rusta Island has a toll booth which can collect automobile tolls at the average rate of 400 cars per hour. Cars cross the bridge and arrive at the toll booth at the average rate of 360 per hour.
3. The Pamac Power Company receives customer complaints about power outages at the average rate of 2 per hour. The company has a continuously cruising radio-controlled repair truck which can service, on the average, 3 calls per hour.
4. The Charste Oil Refinery receives crude oil from the Middle East at the average rate of one tanker per day. The unloading facilities,

which operate 24 hours per day, can handle only one tanker at a time, but can unload tankers at the average rate of two per day.

We can use the model given above to describe each of these four situations on the assumption that the arrival and service patterns may be adequately characterized as Poisson-exponential. Table 14–9.1 shows many of the results which the model can produce. The percentage of time with 0, 1, or 2 elements in the system is computed. Obviously it is a simple matter to compute the probability that the number in the system exceeds any desired value; i.e., from the data on the table, for the Rusta Island Toll Bridge,

$$P(n > 2) = 1 - (0.100 + 0.090 + 0.081) = 0.729$$

while for the Charste Oil Refinery,

$$P(n > 2) = 1 - (0.500 + 0.250 + 0.125) = 0.125$$

Clearly, if the management in both cases had determined that $n \geq 3$ is a state to be avoided, these two situations are quite different!

An illuminating implication of the model is the rapid increase in $\bar{n}$ and W as λ approaches μ. Table 14–9.1 indicates that, if $\lambda = 0.5\mu$, then $\bar{n}$ is only 1 element. However, when $\lambda = 0.9\mu$, then $\bar{n} = 9$ elements. If $\lambda = 0.95\mu$, then $\bar{n}$ becomes 19 elements. The relationship between $\bar{n}$ and the ratio $\frac{\lambda}{\mu}$ is shown in Figure 14–9.1. The steepness of the curve for the high values of

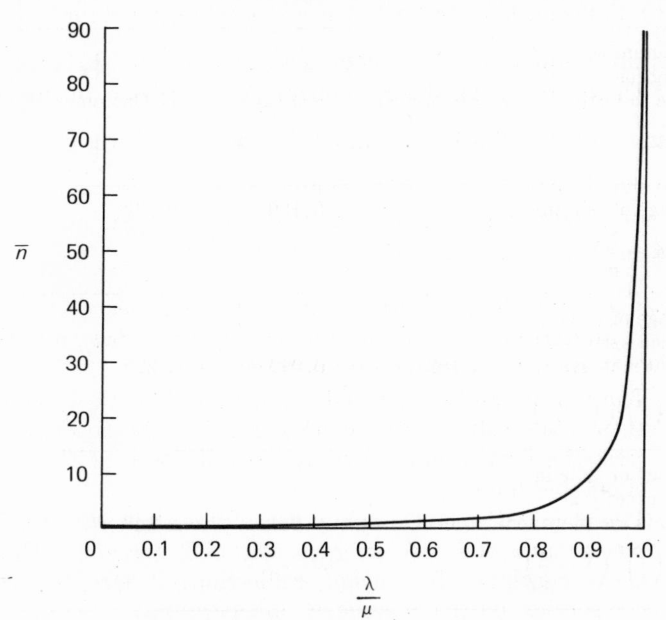

Fig. 14–9.1. Relationship between n and λ/μ for a single-channel Poisson-exponential system.

TABLE 14–9.1

Application of the Single-Channel Model to Four Situations

	Riten County Airport $\lambda = 9/\text{hr.}$ $\mu = 12/\text{hr.}$ $\frac{\lambda}{\mu} = 0.75$	Rusta Island Toll Bridge $\lambda = 360/\text{hr.}$ $\mu = 400/\text{hr.}$ $\frac{\lambda}{\mu} = 0.90$	Pamac Power Company $\lambda = 2/\text{hr.}$ $\mu = 3/\text{hr.}$ $\frac{\lambda}{\mu} = 0.67$	Charste Oil Refinery $\lambda = 1/\text{day}$ $\mu = 2/\text{day}$ $\frac{\lambda}{\mu} = 0.50$
Average number in the system $\bar{n} = \frac{\frac{\lambda}{\mu}}{1 - \frac{\lambda}{\mu}}$	3 Aircraft	9 Cars	2 Customers	1 Tanker
Average time spent in the system $W = \frac{1}{\mu - \lambda}$	$\frac{1}{3}$ hr. = 20 min.	$\frac{1}{40}$ hr. = 1.5 min.	1 hr.	1 day
Average wait before service begins $W_q = \frac{\lambda}{\mu} W$	15 min.	1.35 min.	40 min.	12 hr.
Average number waiting for service to begin $\bar{n}_q = \frac{\lambda}{\mu} \bar{n}$	$2\frac{1}{4}$ Aircraft	$8\frac{1}{10}$ Cars	$1\frac{1}{3}$ Customers	$\frac{1}{2}$ Tanker
Percentage of idle time $P(0) = 1 - \frac{\lambda}{\mu}$	0.250	0.100	0.333	0.500
Percentage of time in which exactly 1 element is in system $P(1) = \left(\frac{\lambda}{\mu}\right)\left(1 - \frac{\lambda}{\mu}\right)$	0.188	0.090	0.222	0.250
Percentage of time in which exactly 2 elements are in system $P(2) = \left(\frac{\lambda}{\mu}\right)^2\left(1 - \frac{\lambda}{\mu}\right)$	0.141	0.081	0.148	0.125

$\frac{\lambda}{\mu}$ indicates the extreme sensitivity of the system to small changes in λ or μ when λ is close to μ.

14–10. Poisson Arrivals—General Case. It has been shown that, for single-channel systems, when arrivals are characterized by the Poisson distribution, the expected number of elements in the system may be expressed by the following equation, *for any service pattern.*

$$\bar{n} = \frac{\lambda}{\mu} + \frac{\lambda^2 \sigma_s^2 + \left(\frac{\lambda}{\mu}\right)^2}{2\left(1 - \frac{\lambda}{\mu}\right)} \tag{14–10.1}$$

where σ_s^2 is the variance of the service times

According to Equation (14–10.1), if the service times are exponential, and, consequently, $\sigma_s^2 = \frac{1}{\mu^2}$,

$$\bar{n} = \frac{\lambda}{\mu} + \frac{\left(\frac{\lambda}{\mu}\right)^2 + \left(\frac{\lambda}{\mu}\right)^2}{2\left(1 - \frac{\lambda}{\mu}\right)} = \frac{\frac{\lambda}{\mu} - \left(\frac{\lambda}{\mu}\right)^2 + \left(\frac{\lambda}{\mu}\right)^2}{1 - \frac{\lambda}{\mu}}$$

$$\bar{n} = \frac{\frac{\lambda}{\mu}}{1 - \frac{\lambda}{\mu}} \tag{14–6.2}$$

This, as is to be expected, is the familiar equation for $\bar{n}$ in a Poisson-exponential system.

If the arrivals are Poisson, and the service times are constant as, for example, might be the case in an automatic car wash, then $\sigma_s^2 = 0$, and Equation (14–10.1) reduces to

$$\bar{n} = \frac{\lambda}{\mu} + \frac{\left(\frac{\lambda}{\mu}\right)^2}{2\left(1 - \frac{\lambda}{\mu}\right)} = \frac{\frac{\lambda}{\mu} - \left(\frac{\lambda}{\mu}\right)^2 + \frac{1}{2}\left(\frac{\lambda}{\mu}\right)^2}{1 - \frac{\lambda}{\mu}} = \frac{\frac{\lambda}{\mu}\left(1 - \frac{\lambda}{2\mu}\right)}{1 - \frac{\lambda}{\mu}}$$

$$\bar{n} = \frac{\frac{\lambda}{\mu}}{1 - \frac{\lambda}{\mu}}\left(1 - \frac{\lambda}{2\mu}\right) \tag{14–10.2}$$

Since, in all single-channel cases which we discuss, $0 < \frac{\lambda}{\mu} < 1$, it follows that, also

$$0 < \left(1 - \frac{\lambda}{2\mu}\right) < 1$$

Therefore with Poisson arrivals, the average length of line is shorter for the same average service time when service times are constant, than when they are exponentially distributed. Indeed, it is shorter than when there is any variability at all. This last generalization follows from the fact that, if $\sigma_s^2 = 0$, a positive term drops out of the general equation (14–10.1) thereby reducing $\bar{n}$ below what it would be for any (always positive, of course) values of σ_s^2.

In the Rusta Island Toll Bridge example of Table 14–9.1, if service time had been constant instead of exponential, the average number in the system would be reduced according to Equation (14–10.2) from nine cars to slightly less than five cars:

$$\bar{n} = 9\left(1 - \frac{360}{800}\right) = \frac{99}{20} = 4.95 \text{ cars}$$

Similarly, if the Riten County Airport landing system could bring in aircraft with constant service time, the average number of aircraft in the holding and landing pattern could be reduced from three aircraft to less than two:

$$\bar{n} = 3\left(1 - \frac{9}{24}\right) = \frac{15}{8} = 1.875$$

This little exercise serves as an illustration of the cost which society must pay as a consequence of the variability in real world phenomena, both natural and man made. If aircraft could arrive at regular intervals at the Riten County Airport, and if the service time were constant, keeping the same λ and μ of 9 and 12, respectively, the average number in the system would be 0.75 aircraft. That is, an aircraft would arrive every $6\frac{2}{3}$ minutes, it would be serviced in 5 minutes, and the facility would wait $1\frac{2}{3}$ minutes for the next aircraft.

However, if arrivals alone are randomly variable, the number in the system jumps to 1.875 aircraft, and, for random service times also, $\bar{n}$ is 3. Even more striking is the toll-bridge example with $\frac{\lambda}{\mu} = 0.9$. Then the three $\bar{n}$ values are 0.9, 4.95, and 9.0, respectively, for the regular-constant, Poisson-constant, and Poisson-exponential systems. Although the analysis of the relatively rare regular-exponential system (regular arrivals, exponential service times) is beyond the scope of this book, it can be shown[2] that, for $\frac{\lambda}{\mu} = 0.9$, $\bar{n}$ in that system is 4.7, indicating that in that case the cost of randomness is roughly the same, whether it occurs in the arrivals or in the service times.

[2] Morse, P. M., *Queues, Inventories and Maintenance* (New York: John Wiley & Sons, Inc., 1958), page 91.

Clearly, if λ is uncontrollable, any reduction of variability without decreasing μ or unduly increasing the cost is desirable, and if arrivals are controllable, any steps which contribute to regularity, without unduly increasing the costs, are worthy of consideration.

14–11. Erlang Distributions. In this volume we deal only with Poisson and regular arrivals and with exponential and constant service times. However, these are clearly not the only kinds of situations which occur and for which mathematical models are required.

A useful set of distributions is the Erlang distributions, which are gamma distributions with $a = r - 1$ and $b = r\mu$. Detailed consideration of these is beyond the scope of this book, but the general formula is presented below. The density function is in the form

$$f(t) = (r\mu t)^{r-1} \left[\frac{e^{-r\mu t}}{(r-1)!}\right] r\mu \tag{14–11.1}$$

As with the exponential distribution, the same form may be used to describe either arrivals or service times. The parameter r characterizes the distribution. The reader may easily verify that, if $r = 1$, Equation (14–11.1) becomes the *pdf* for the exponential distribution. Also, as r becomes very large, Equation (14–11.1) approaches the formula for regular arrivals (constant arrival intervals) or constant service times. For values of r such that $1 < r < \infty$, Equation (14–11.1) describes the Erlang family of distributions, which has been successfully applied in queueing applications. Figure 14–11.1 indicates roughly the general shape of some of the Erlang distributions and suggests the nature of the relation-

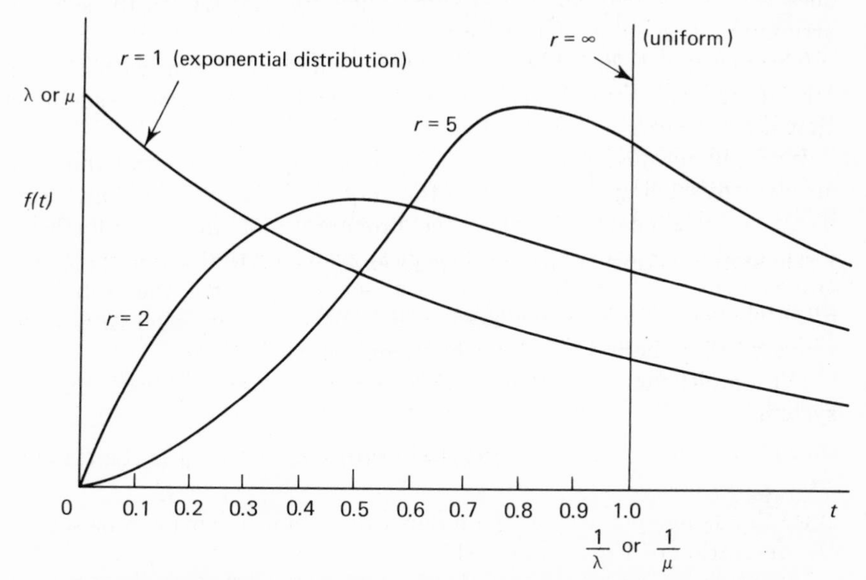

Fig. 14–11.1. Erlang distributions for arrivals or service times.

ship between the shape of the distribution and the parameter r. In practical applications, one would ascertain the value of r from direct observations of arrival intervals or service times. These distributions cannot be expected to fit all possible real-world distributions, but they do seem to have wide applicability. The most common, of course, is the limiting distribution with $r = 1$, the exponential distribution. However, one exact application of the Erlang distribution is when there are a series of r service stations through which each element must pass *in order* and for all of which the service time is exponential with mean $\frac{1}{r\mu}$. Then, for the system, the Erlang distribution is appropriate.

14–12. Multiple Channels. With many servicing facilities, such as bank tellers, supermarket checkout counters, retail clerks, barber shops, toll booths, and a wide variety of others, one of the important controllable variables is the number of *channels*, or parallel facilities. That is, management may adjust the queue lengths or waiting times by varying the number of channels in response to changes in arrival patterns.

While there are many possible queue disciplines in a multiple channel system, we shall consider only the discipline, by far the most common, in which the k channels are served from a single queue on a first-in, first-out, basis. This system describes most common situations, even the bank teller or supermarket situation, where although there may be long queues at each channel, individuals shift from one queue to another as they see an opportunity to reduce their waiting times. (While this channel shifting does have the same effect on system averages as does a single queue, it does not necessarily have the same effect on an arbitrarily selected arriving unit, such as you or me.)

The mathematical model for a multiple-channel system with Poisson arrivals and exponential service may be derived via the same reasoning as that used in Sections 14–4 to 14–8 above.

It will be recalled that, for a single-channel system, the probability of an element's being discharged in the very short interval Δt is $\mu\Delta t$. Similarly, for a 2–channel system, the probability of an element's being discharged in the short interval Δt is $2\mu\Delta t$, provided that there are at least two elements in the system. Also, for a k-channel system, the probability of an element's being discharged in the short time interval Δt is $k\mu\Delta t$, provided that there are at least k elements in the system.

For a multi-channel system, $P(1)$ is as given before for a single-channel system,

$$P(1) = \frac{\lambda}{\mu} P(0) \tag{14–4.7}$$

since this is independent of the number of channels. This can be seen in the derivation of Equation (14–4.7).

However $P(0)$ is quite different and complex. It is given here without proof:

$$P(0) = \frac{1}{\displaystyle\sum_{n=0}^{k-1} \frac{1}{n!}\left(\frac{\lambda}{\mu}\right)^n + \frac{1}{k!}\left(\frac{\lambda}{\mu}\right)^k \frac{k\mu}{k\mu - \lambda}} \qquad \text{for } k\mu > \lambda \quad (14\text{–}12.1)$$

The general formula for $P(n)$ consists of two parts, one for $n \leq k$ and one for $n > k$. The reason for this is that the probability of discharge from the system in a short interval Δt is $k\mu\Delta t$ if all channels are operating, i.e., if $n \geq k$; but it is $n\mu\Delta t$ if $n < k$ (actually, the two equations are the same for $n = k$):

$$P(n) = \frac{1}{k!\,k^{n-k}}\left(\frac{\lambda}{\mu}\right)^n P(0) \qquad \text{for } n > k \qquad (14\text{–}12.2)$$

$$P(n) = \frac{1}{n!}\left(\frac{\lambda}{\mu}\right)^n P(0) \qquad \text{for } n \leq k \qquad (14\text{–}12.3)$$

Although the general equations (14–12.2) and (14–12.3) are rather complex, the specific equations for a 2–channel system are relatively easy to derive. The derivation is left as an exercise for the reader (see Exercise 14–1 at the end of this chapter). It may also be shown that, for $k = 1$, Equations (14–12.1), (14–12.2), and (14–12.3) reduce to the familiar single-channel form (see Exercise 14–2 at the end of this chapter).

The average number $\bar{n}$ in a multiple-channel system is given by the following formula, which is here presented without proof:

$$\bar{n} = \frac{\lambda\mu\left(\frac{\lambda}{\mu}\right)^k}{(k-1)!\,(k\mu - \lambda)^2} P(0) + \frac{\lambda}{\mu} \qquad (14\text{–}12.4)$$

This equation also reduces to the familiar single-channel form when $k = 1$.

We can illustrate the use of these equations by considering the cosmetic counter at Royb's Department Store. Customers arrive at the rate of 10 per hour (Poisson), and they can be served by a single clerk at the rate of 12 per hour (exponential). The average number in the system is, from Equation (14–6.2),

$$\bar{n} = \frac{\frac{5}{6}}{1 - \frac{5}{6}} = 5$$

If a second clerk is added, then $k = 2$, and from Equation (14–12.1),

$$P(0) = \frac{1}{1 + \frac{5}{6} + \frac{1}{2}\left(\frac{5}{6}\right)^2\left(\frac{24}{14}\right)} = \frac{1}{\frac{11}{6} + \frac{(25)(24)}{(2)(36)(14)}} = \frac{1}{\frac{77}{42} + \frac{25}{42}}$$

$$= \frac{42}{102} = \frac{7}{17}$$

Then, from Equation (14–12.4),

$$\bar{n} = \frac{120\left(\frac{5}{6}\right)^2}{1!\,(14)^2}\left(\frac{7}{17}\right) + \frac{5}{6} = \frac{125}{714} + \frac{5}{6} = \frac{720}{714}$$
$$= 1.008$$

Increasing the number of clerks from one to two reduces the number of customers in the system by a factor of five! The actual benefit, if any, to the Royb Company depends upon its estimate of customer waiting costs. If, for example, the management assigns a cost of \$2.00 per hour for customer displeasure from waiting, then the customer waiting cost is reduced from \$10.00 per hour to \$2.02, a saving of \$7.98 per hour. Clearly, then, if the additional clerk costs less than \$7.98 per hour, the two-channel system is to be preferred.

14–13. Single-Channel Truncated Queues. As has been suggested in Section 14–5 above, often there is a maximum length to the queue, either because of *voluntary truncation*, where customers refuse to join the queue, or *involuntary truncation*, where the queue length is limited by physical waiting space as in some restaurants and filling stations or by management decision or legal requirement, as with certain amusements and exhibits. Of most interest to management is voluntary truncation, since when this occurs, profits may be dropping off the end of the queue without management's being aware of it.

The equations for $P(n)$ and $\bar{n}$ for Poisson-exponential single-channel systems with a *maximum number in the system of* a, are given here without proof. The number a is the number such that all elements which arrive will join the queue if $n < a$, but none will join if $n = a$. That is, a is the *truncation level:*

$$P(n) = \frac{1 - \frac{\lambda}{\mu}}{1 - \left(\frac{\lambda}{\mu}\right)^{a+1}}\left(\frac{\lambda}{\mu}\right)^n \qquad \text{for } 0 \le n \le a \qquad (14\text{–}13.1)$$

$$\bar{n} = \left(\frac{\lambda}{\mu}\right)\frac{1 - (a+1)\left(\frac{\lambda}{\mu}\right)^a + a\left(\frac{\lambda}{\mu}\right)^{a+1}}{\left(1 - \frac{\lambda}{\mu}\right)\left[1 - \left(\frac{\lambda}{\mu}\right)^{a+1}\right]} \qquad (14\text{–}13.2)$$

We can illustrate the use of these formulas with the following example. Ivar operates a nonautomatic car wash in which he personally washes cars at the rate (exponential) of 4 cars per hour. Cars arrive at the rate of 5 per hour (Poisson), but refuse to get in line if there are two cars in the establishment (one being washed and one waiting). What is the average number of cars in his establishment? What percentage of his time is idle? What percentage of his potential business does he lose?

$$\bar{n} = \left(\frac{5}{4}\right)\frac{1 - 3\left(\frac{5}{4}\right)^2 + 2\left(\frac{5}{4}\right)^3}{\left(1 - \frac{5}{4}\right)\left[1 - \left(\frac{5}{4}\right)^3\right]} = \left(\frac{5}{4}\right)\frac{1 - \frac{75}{16} + \frac{250}{64}}{\left(-\frac{1}{4}\right)\left(1 - \frac{125}{64}\right)}$$

$$= \left(\frac{5}{4}\right)\frac{64 - 300 + 250}{\left(-\frac{1}{4}\right)(64 - 125)} = \frac{(5)(14)}{61} = \frac{70}{61} = 1.15$$

$$P(n) = \frac{1 - \frac{5}{4}}{1 - \left(\frac{5}{4}\right)^3}\left(\frac{5}{4}\right)^n = \frac{-\frac{1}{4}}{-\frac{61}{64}}\left(\frac{5}{4}\right)^n = \frac{16}{61}\left(\frac{5}{4}\right)^n$$

$$= 0.262\left(\frac{5}{4}\right)^n$$

$$P(0) = 0.262\left(\frac{5}{4}\right)^0 = 0.262$$

$$P(1) = 0.262\left(\frac{5}{4}\right)^1 = 0.328$$

$$P(2) = 0.262\left(\frac{5}{4}\right)^2 = 0.410$$

Since, when $n = 2$, arriving customers will not enter the system, and since this is the case 41 per cent of the time, he loses 41 per cent of his potential business. His *effective arrival rate* is $\lambda[1 - P(2)]$, which is only $(5)(0.59) = 2.95$, instead of the true arrival rate (λ) of 5 cars per hour.

We shall not consider the multi-channel case with truncation level a where $a > k$. This is beyond the scope of this book, but it may be found in the literature. However, when $a = k$, the analysis is quite simple. That is the subject of the next section.

14-14. Absolute Truncation. In many multi-channel situations, such as, for example, hotels, parking lots, car rentals, and others, customers arrive and enter service as long as there is one or more idle channels. When all channels are occupied, customers do not wait. This is called *absolute truncation*. In such cases, at all times, $0 \le n \le k$, where k is the number of channels.

The equations for $P(n)$ and $\bar{n}$ for Poisson-exponential multi-channel systems with absolute truncation are given here without proof:

$$P(n) = \frac{\dfrac{\left(\dfrac{\lambda}{\mu}\right)^n}{n!}}{\displaystyle\sum_{n=0}^{k} \dfrac{\left(\dfrac{\lambda}{\mu}\right)^n}{n!}} \qquad (14\text{–}14.1)$$

$$\bar{n} = \left(\frac{\lambda}{\mu}\right) \frac{\displaystyle\sum_{n=0}^{k-1} \dfrac{\left(\dfrac{\lambda}{\mu}\right)^n}{n!}}{\displaystyle\sum_{n=0}^{k} \dfrac{\left(\dfrac{\lambda}{\mu}\right)^n}{n!}} \qquad (14\text{–}14.2)$$

These equations are extremely easy to use. It should be noted that, in any single problem, for all n, $P(n)$ has the same denominator, and this denominator is the sum of all possible numerators. Also, these same terms are the series used to compute $\bar{n}$, and in the equation for $\bar{n}$, there is, in the denominator, one term more than in the numerator, and the denominator is the same as for $P(n)$.

Let us illustrate this model with a simple illustration. The Freway tourist home (at the falls) has 4 rooms. Tourists arrive (Poisson) at the rate of 3 per day. If the rooms are all occupied, they leave and go to Josh's Motel, which always has space. If there is a room available at Freway, tourists stay (exponential) for an average period of 2 days. Thus $k = 4$, $\lambda = 3$, $\mu = \frac{1}{2}$. If the tariff is $10 per room per day, what is the average daily revenue? What percentage of Freway's potential business is lost because of shortage of space? The general formula is

$$\bar{n} = \left(\frac{\lambda}{\mu}\right) \frac{1 + \dfrac{\frac{\lambda}{\mu}}{1!} + \dfrac{\left(\frac{\lambda}{\mu}\right)^2}{2!} + \cdots + \dfrac{\left(\frac{\lambda}{\mu}\right)^{k-1}}{(k-1)!}}{1 + \dfrac{\frac{\lambda}{\mu}}{1!} + \dfrac{\left(\frac{\lambda}{\mu}\right)^2}{2!} + \cdots + \dfrac{\left(\frac{\lambda}{\mu}\right)^{k-1}}{(k-1)!} + \dfrac{\left(\frac{\lambda}{\mu}\right)^k}{k!}} \qquad (14\text{–}14.3)$$

Here, where $k = 4, \lambda = 3, \mu = \frac{1}{2}, \frac{\lambda}{\mu} = 6$,

$$\bar{n} = (6)\frac{1 + 6 + \frac{36}{2} + \frac{216}{6}}{1 + 6 + \frac{36}{2} + \frac{216}{6} + \frac{1296}{24}} = (6)\frac{1 + 6 + 18 + 36}{1 + 6 + 18 + 36 + 54} = (6)\frac{61}{115}$$

$$= \frac{366}{115} = 3.18$$

The average daily revenue is \$31.80.

$$P(0) = \frac{1}{115} = 0.01$$

$$P(1) = \frac{6}{115} = 0.05$$

$$P(2) = \frac{18}{115} = 0.16$$

$$P(3) = \frac{36}{115} = 0.31$$

$$P(4) = \frac{54}{115} = 0.47$$

$$\overline{1.00}$$

Thus, 47 per cent of Freway's potential business is lost. One could also compute the Freway average daily revenue from the fact that its *effective arrival rate* is (3)(1 − 0.47) and that it therefore services, on the average, 1.59 persons arriving per day, and, since the average stay is two days, they yield on the average \$20 per stay, giving Freway its average daily revenue of \$31.80 per day.

14–15. Simulation—Monte Carlo. In each of the queueing-theory problems which we have discussed in this chapter, we have built a mathematical model to describe the situation and then solved the model. It is not always necessary to do this. In many situations, especially those involving complex phenomena, it is easier to solve by simulation than by the use of a formal mathematical model.

Consider, for example, a traffic light at a busy intersection with cars coming from four directions. Cars in each of the four flow streams may elect any of three directions of exit from the intersection. That is, they may proceed straight through the intersection, or they may turn either left or right. Traffic authorities, seeking to select the optimal sequence of time intervals for green, yellow, and red lights, might well find that this can be done easily by computer simulation, whereas it might be very difficult to formulate a mathematical model to describe the situation. Moreover, if the traffic authorities are concerned with the light-changing patterns for the signals at a group of intersections, all related in that some of the outflows from each of the intersections constitute inflows to others, then a formal mathematical model may be impossibly difficult to build, but a simulation model might still provide the desired answers quickly and easily.

In order to construct such a simulation model, all that is required is a description of the relevant patterns of flow. These data may be obtained quite easily by observers stationed at the appropriate points with stop-watches. Once the patterns of arrival and exit from the various intersections are determined, the entire process may be programmed on a computer, using a so-called *Monte Carlo* system. That is, the probability distributions representing the various arrival patterns and turning patterns are stored in the computer, and then the computer can simulate these stochastic processes by selecting numbers from a table of random numbers which is either stored in the computer or generated by the computer as needed. This process of *simulation by random sampling* has been given the name *Monte Carlo.* The computer selects a random number, which may represent an arrival interval or an exit pattern or any of the other relevant activities in the system. The number is keyed in the computer's storage to some specific numerical measure of the activity, and the model then takes account of the implications of that specific occurrence, and then it selects another number, etc., performing all of these numerical manipulations at electronic speeds.

Thus, in the simulation model, cars arrive and turn and move from one intersection to the next at random according to the probability distributions which were observed in the real world for these phenomena. The operator may then try many different patterns of signal control and quickly acquire a long history of simulated experience, observing queue lengths, waiting times, etc., with each of these various patterns. The best of these can then be selected according to some criterion involving queue lengths, waiting times, and possibly other measures of congestion.

SUGGESTIONS FOR FURTHER READING

Feller, W. *An Introduction to Probability Theory and Its Applications* (2 vols.). New York: John Wiley & Sons, Inc., Vol. 1, 1957; Vol. 2 (2d ed.), 1966.

Morse, P. M. *Queues, Inventories, and Maintenance*. New York: John Wiley & Sons, Inc., 1958.

Saaty, T. L. *Elements of Queueing Theory with Applications*. New York: McGraw-Hill Book Co., Inc., 1961.

Stoller, D. S. *Operations Research: Process and Strategy*. Berkeley: University of California Press, 1964.

EXERCISES

14–1. Prove that, for a 2-channel Poisson-exponential system

$$P(3) = \frac{1}{4}\left(\frac{\lambda}{\mu}\right)^3 P(0) \qquad \text{for } n > 2$$

Hint: *a*) Follow the procedures of Section 14–4 to derive

$$P(n+1) = \frac{\lambda + 2\mu}{2\mu} P(n) - \frac{\lambda}{2\mu} P(n-1) \qquad \text{for } n \geq 2 \quad \text{(14–E1.1)}$$

remembering that the probability of discharging an element from the system when there are 2 channels working is $2\mu\Delta t$.

b) The above equation may be rewritten

$$P(n) = \frac{\lambda + 2\mu}{2\mu} P(n-1) - \frac{\lambda}{2\mu} P(n-2) \qquad \text{for } n \geq 3 \quad \text{(14–E1.2)}$$

then

$$P(3) = \frac{\lambda + 2\mu}{2\mu} P(2) - \frac{\lambda}{2\mu} P(1) \qquad \text{(14–E1.3)}$$

c) Now, use the procedure of Section 14–4 to show that

$$P(2) = \frac{\lambda + \mu}{2\mu} P(1) - \frac{\lambda}{2\mu} P(0) \qquad \text{(14–E1.4)}$$

d) Finally, substitute Equations (14–E1.4) and (14–4.7) into equation (14–E1.3).

14–2. Show that, for $k = 1$, Equations (14–12.1), (14–12.2), and (14–12.3) reduce to single-channel equations.

14–3. Show that, for $k = 1$, Equation (14–12.4) reduces to the single-channel form.

14–4. In Section 14–12, the Royb department store found that, if cosmetics clerks cost \$4.00 per hour (total cost, including all benefits, etc.), the cosmetic counter should have 2 clerks in preference to 1. What is the optimal number of clerks?

14–5. The Cargree gasoline station has a single curved driveway which, because of limited space, permits only two cars to be in the station at once. That is, at most, one car can be receiving gasoline and one can be waiting. There simply is not room for an additional car to get into the driveway.

The owner of the station, Mr. Cargree, has studied the various possibilities and has concluded that he has *two additional* alternatives. He can slightly enlarge the driveway and move the pump to permit a third car to enter (i.e., one in service and two waiting) or he can add another pump and attendant to permit servicing two cars at once but with no queue possible. That is, at most, two cars could be side-by-side being fueled, and no additional cars could enter the station. This would require an additional attendant on duty. Should he stay as he is, or should he adopt one of the alternatives? What is his expected profit under all three alternatives?

Cars arrive at the rate of 15 per hour (Poisson) and a pump can service them at the rate of 10 per hour (exponential). He earns a gross profit of \$1 per car.

The capital costs are $0.80 per hour for lengthening the driveway and moving the pump. The capital costs of the two-pump alternative are $0.20 per hour, and the additional attendant costs $2.00 per hour.

14–6. The Strata-Gem Jewelry Co. has a full-time credit analyst who must verify the account of each purchaser who makes a credit purchase. The standard procedure requires that the salesman, after making the sale, must telephone upstairs to the credit analyst, who consults his records and approves the new credit extension (only, of course, if the account is satisfactory, which we shall assume to be the case). If the credit analyst is busy upstairs when a call is made, the salesman is kept waiting in line. With such a large store, there are sometimes many salesmen (and their customers) waiting for the credit analyst while he is busy answering requests. The management considers that the waiting time costs the Company $11 per hour for the salesman and $25 per hour in good will for the customer.

Credit requests are initiated by the salesmen at the rate of 12 per hour (Poisson), and the credit analyst can handle requests at the rate of 18 per hour (exponential).

a) The Company has been visited by the salesman for the Keen Komputer Kompany, which offers its new Keen Klever Koder Komputer to the Company for a rental price of $35 per hour. With this machine, the credit analyst can handle requests at an absolutely constant service time of 24 per hour. Should the computer be rented?

b) The credit analyst, who is unaccountably squeamish about computers, suggests that, if he had another credit analyst to work with him, they could work without getting in one another's way (i.e. maintaining the rate of 18 per hour exponential), and, at $8 per hour for the additional analyst, they could avoid the necessity for renting the computer. Your careful analysis of the job indicates that, if two men try to do the job at the same time, they will interfere with one another to a moderate extent. Actually, you feel that the capacity for each man would be 12 per hour instead of the 18, which one man can do alone. Analyze the credit analyst's suggestion both under his assumption (18 per hour) and your assumption (12 per hour). What do you recommend for the Company?

14–7. The Dazen Valley Electric Company finds that its customer's telephone requests for emergency service are randomly distributed throughout the day and occur at the average rate of 2 per hour.

The service department is considering *three* alternative vehicular systems for servicing these calls. There are two types of control systems available for the trucks. The *standard* trucks must return to the garage after each call to obtain information about the next call. *Radio* trucks are kept informed by radio and do not have to return to the garage between calls. Standard trucks cost the company $10.00 per hour each, and they can service *three* calls per hour each. Radio trucks cost the company $14.00 per hour each, and they can service *four* calls per hour each.

The company estimates that its customer relations cost for customers waiting for service in $10.00 per customer per hour. Which if the following three systems is most profitable for the company? What is the profitability of each?

System A, one standard truck
System B, one radio truck
System C, two standard trucks

14–8. The Shalad Laundry and Dry Cleaning Shoppe has two clerks. Both of them handle both dry cleaning and laundry at the rate of 10 customers per hour. The arrival rate is 15 customers per hour.

The manager seeks to decrease the waiting cost of customer time by making the clerks specialists; i.e., one for laundry and one for dry cleaning.

If $\frac{2}{3}$ of the customers come for dry cleaning and $\frac{1}{3}$ for laundry, and if clerk specialization increases productivity for either function to a capacity of 12 per hour, should such specialization be instituted? Assume that the customer waiting cost is five dollars per hour and that every customer is either a dry cleaning customer or a laundry customer, but not both. Assume that the system is Poisson-exponential.

14–9. Kew City has two airports. Westwood Airport services jet aircraft only and Eastwood Airport services propeller aircraft only. Airplanes arrive randomly into the area at the rate of 6 jets and 10 propeller aircraft per hour. The waiting cost in the system (the time between arrival into the Kew City metropolitan traffic control area and touchdown) is $1,000 per hour for jets and $600 per hour for the others.

a) What is the total waiting cost in the present system, whereby either airport can land 15 aircraft (exponential) per hour? The two airports do not interfere with one another.

b) How much will waiting cost be if the two airports are both modified to receive both types of aircraft and if they act as two channels serving a single queue? Arrival rates and service rates are unchanged.

14–10. Keenan Scalpo's barber shop had two chairs; but only one chair was operated, since Scalpo worked alone. He never had anyone waiting for a haircut, but he managed to keep satisfactorily and profitably busy, because he found that the next customer tended to enter the shop reasonably soon after he finished with the previous one. Actually, he was idle exactly 50 per cent of the time.

When his nephew, J. Brainwash Klipp, was graduated with the degree A.B. (awful barber) from the tonsorial curriculum at Science Tech., young Brainy asked if he could join his uncle and make it a two-barber shop. Uncle Scalpo thought that this was ridiculous since there couldn't possibly be any heads for Brainy to beautify since there never was more than one customer in the shop.

Brainy, who had studied queueing theory, argued the cause of voluntary truncation and asked for a two-week trial period. Uncle consented and he installed young Brainwash in the other chair. Lo and behold, they were *both* kept reasonably busy, but, still, the seats for waiting customers were *never* used.

a) If either barber can service 4 customers per hour, and if they are *both* idle now 40 per cent of the time, what percentage of their potential business do they lose as a consequence of voluntary truncation? (No one enters unless at least one barber is free.) Assume that the system is Poisson-exponential.

b) What per cent of his business did Uncle Keenan lose when he worked alone?

c) If Uncle Scalpo pays Brainy $2.50 per hour and if customers yield, on the average $3.00 each, does it pay for Scalpo to keep Brainy in his permanent employ?

d) Old Scalpo, impressed with the concept of voluntary truncation, decides to put heavy drapes on his windows, so that his potential customers are deprived of the information which they have used as the basis for their truncation. Now he can capture all his potential customers, and his profitability is increased; but he often has customers waiting. He decides that the waiting costs him in good will $6 per customer-hour *in the shop*. For $1 per hour per chair, he can mechanize his operation and be able to serve 5 customers per hour per chair instead of the present 4. Should be mechanize? Should he keep Brainy if he mechanizes?

14–11. The Haul-i-day Truck Renting Company has three trucks. These trucks rent for $30.00 per day, and their full cost to the Haul-i-day company is $20.00 per day, rented or not. The average customer uses a truck for two days and then returns it to Haul-i-day. Potential customers arrive at the Haul-i-day renting office at the rate of two per day, looking for trucks to rent, and, of course if trucks are available, they take them immediately; if any customers arrive when no trucks are available, the customers go across the street to the number-one company which always has trucks available.

If the system at the Haul-i-day company is Poisson-exponential,

a) What is the Haul-i-day's daily profit?

b) Of the 14 customers who arrive in a 7-day week (on the average), how many actually get a truck, on the average?

c) Should Haul-i-day buy another truck?

15

Markov Chains

15–1. Independent Trials. In most of the probability theory which we have considered thus far, we dealt with *independent trials.* That is, the outcome of any trial was independent of the results of any and all previous trials. The only exception which we have seen to this independency condition is sampling from a finite population without replacement. If a finite population of persons is half urban residents and half rural residents, and if a person is selected at random, the probability of selecting an urban resident is 0.5 on the first trial. If a second trial is made without replacement (that is, without replacing the person selected on the first trial), the probability of selecting a city-dweller on this second trial is not 0.5. It is less than 0.5 if a city dweller was selected on the first trial, and it is greater than 0.5 if a rural resident was selected on the first trial. Similarly, after many selections without replacement, the probability of any specified outcome on the next trial depends upon the outcomes of *all preceding trials.*

With the sole exception of this last kind of process involving sampling without replacement, we have thus far dealt exclusively with independent trials. Now we shall consider *Markov processes,* in which successive trials are not independent. Indeed, the essence of Markov processes is the unique relationship which exists between successive trials.

15–2. Markov Processes. In a Markov process, the probability of a particular outcome on any trial depends upon the outcome of the *single immediately preceding trial.* If the population of Ruritania is half urban and half rural, and if we select Ruritanian individuals at random *with replacement,* the probability of selecting a city-dweller is always 0.5. Suppose now that there is another population, Urbania, which is 80 per cent urban and only 20 per cent rural, and that we will select individuals from both populations according to the following rule. If an urban resident is selected on any drawing, the next drawing must be made from the population of Urbania, and if a rural resident is chosen, the next drawing must be made from the population of Ruritania. Thus, the conditional probabilities for the nth trial are, where U_n means an urban resident on the nth trial, and R_n means a rural resident on the nth trial:

$$P(U_n|U_{n-1}) = 0.8 \qquad P(R_n|U_{n-1}) = 0.2$$

$$P(U_n|R_{n-1}) = 0.5 \qquad P(R_n|R_{n-1}) = 0.5$$

That is, if an urban resident is selected on the $(n-1)^{th}$ trial, the next selection is made from Urbania, and the probabilities are 0.8 and 0.2 for urban and rural, respectively. However, if the $(n-1)^{th}$ trial yields a rural resident, the next trial is taken from the population of Ruritania, where the probabilities are 0.5 and 0.5. This is a Markov process. We can assume that all drawings are with replacement, so that the conditional probabilities given above do not change.

We shall find later that, in the long run, it does not matter which population we start with, but for the present let us specify arbitrarily that the initial drawing, the start, is made from Ruritania. Then, on each subsequent drawing, the probability of selecting an urban resident is 0.8 times the probability of selecting an urban resident on the previous trial *plus* 0.5 times the probability of selecting a rural resident on the previous trial:

$$P(U_n) = P(U_n \cap U_{n-1}) + P(U_n \cap R_{n-1}) \tag{15–2.1}$$

$$P(U_n) = P(U_n|U_{n-1})\,P(U_{n-1}) + P(U_n|R_{n-1})\,P(R_{n-1}) \tag{15–2.2}$$

$$P(U_n) = 0.8P(U_{n-1}) + 0.5P(R_{n-1}) \tag{15–2.3}$$

also

$$P(R_n) = 0.2P(U_{n-1}) + 0.5P(R_{n-1}) \tag{15–2.4}$$

Using the rule of Equation (15–2.3) we can compute $P(U)$, the probability of selecting an urban resident on each of a series of trials, beginning with an arbitrary decision to start with Ruritania. The computations are shown in Table 15–2.1. Notice that, as seen in the last column of the table,

TABLE 15–2.1

Successive Probabilities in a Markov Process

Trial					$P(U_n)$	Δ_1
(Start)					0.5	
1	(0.8)(0.5)	+ (0.5)(0.5)	= 0.40	+ 0.25	= 0.65	0.15
2	(0.8)(0.65)	+ (0.5)(0.35)	= 0.520	+ 0.175	= 0.695	0.045
3	(0.8)(0.695)	+ (0.5)(0.305)	= 0.5560	+ 0.1525	= 0.7085	0.0135
4	(0.8)(0.7085)	+ (0.5)(0.2915)	= 0.56680	+ 0.14575	= 0.71255	0.00405
5	(0.8)(0.71255)	+ (0.5)(0.28745)	= 0.570040	+ 0.143725	= 0.713765	0.001215

the difference between successive probabilities of $P(U_n)$ decreases as n increases. As a matter of fact, the differences would continue to shrink as $P(U_n)$ approaches a fixed value as its limit. This limit would seem to be somewhere in the vicinity of 0.714. However, before deriving the exact value of this limit let us look at an alternative representation of this process.

15–3. The Probability Tree. Figure 15–3.1 represents this Markov process as a probability tree. The U and R designations represent the

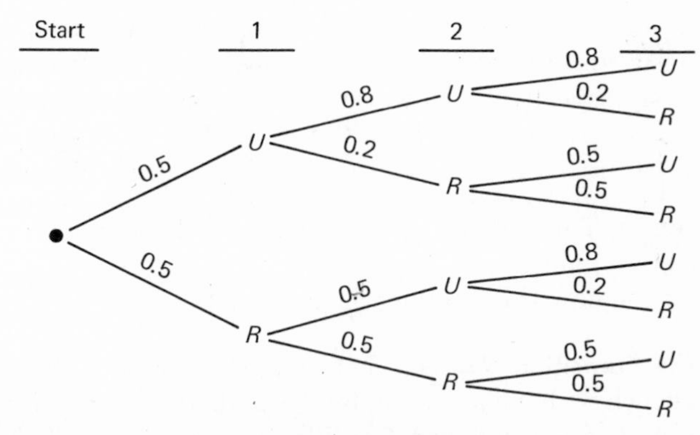

Fig. 15–3.1. A probablity tree representing the Markov process for the system described in Equations (15–2.3) and (15–2.4) and Table 15–2.1.

"states," urban and rural, and the numbers associated with each line represent the probability of that particular path from any state to the next state. Note that the probabilities for all of the paths leaving any state must sum to 1.0. The values of $P(U_n)$ as given in Table 15–2.1 may be computed from this tree diagram by multiplying the successive probabilities along any particular path and then summing the probabilities for the various alternative paths which lead to the same state. However, this computation method is long and burdensome. There are easier ways to arrive at the desired numerical results.

15–4. The Steady State. We noted in Table 15–2.1 that $P(U_n)$ seemed to approach some value as its limit. Indeed it does, and we shall call that limiting state, in which $P(U_n) = P(U_{n-1})$, the *steady state.* Of course, it may take a long time to *arrive* at the steady state. Theoretically, it takes an infinite number of trials. However, as Table 15–2.1 clearly shows, the approach may be so rapid that, after a relatively few trials, $P(U_n)$ becomes *quite close* to its steady state value.

The exact value of the steady state $P(U_n)$ is extremely easy to compute. From Equation (15–2.3),

$$P(U_n) = 0.8P(U_{n-1}) + 0.5P(R_{n-1}) \qquad (15\text{–}2.3)$$

Similarly

$$P(U_{n+1}) = 0.8P(U_n) + 0.5P(R_n) \tag{15–4.1}$$

But, by definition, at the steady state, $P(U_{n+1}) = P(U_n)$. Therefore, at the steady state,

$$P(U_n) = 0.8P(U_n) + 0.5P(R_n) \tag{15–4.2}$$

$$0.2P(U_n) = 0.5P(R_n)$$

$$P(U_n) = \frac{5}{2}P(R_n)$$

Then, since $P(U_n) + P(R_n) = 1$,

$$P(U_n) = \frac{5}{7} = 0.714286 \tag{15–4.3}$$

Thus, at the steady state, $P(U_n) = 0.714286$. Clearly, after only five trials, as seen on Table 15–2.1, $P(U_n)$ approached relatively close to its final steady state value.

Now let us see how this Markov model may be used.

15–5. The Transition Matrix. Let us modify slightly the numerical illustration which we have just used, but let us do it in such a way that the numerical aspects are unchanged. Consider the situation in which, in some country, Rurbania, the population consists of both rural and urban dwellers, but each year each person decides whether he will be an urban or rural resident for the following year. If one is an urban resident in any given year, the probability that he will remain in the city for the next year is 0.8; and if he is a rural dweller, the probability that he will remain on the farm is 0.5. Thus, again, the following equations from Section 15–2 are applicable:

$$P(U_n|U_{n-1}) = 0.8 \qquad P(R_n|U_{n-1}) = 0.2 \tag{15–5.1}$$

$$P(U_n|R_{n-1}) = 0.5 \qquad P(R_n|R_{n-1}) = 0.5 \tag{15–5.2}$$

The system may be portrayed simply by a matrix containing just these four numbers. These numbers are the *transition probabilities*, and the matrix is called a *transition matrix*. Figure 15–5.1 is the transition matrix

		Following State S_1 Urban	Following State S_2 Rural
Preceding State	S_1 Urban	0.8	0.2
	S_2 Rural	0.5	0.5

Fig. 15–5.1. Transition matrix for population shifts in Rurbania.

which describes this system. The two *states*, urban resident and rural resident, are entered on both axes of the matrix. At the left they represent the preceding state, or more specifically, the condition in which that person spent the year before the shift; and at the top the *same* two states represent the condition under which that person spent the year after the shift. The numbers in the matrix, the *transition probabilities*, are exactly the same conditional probabilities as in Equations (15–5.1) and (15–5.2) above. They may be designated p_{ij}, meaning the probability that an element in state i in the preceding period will be in state j in the following period. If we represent the states by the symbols S_1, S_2, S_3, etc., then

$$p_{ij} = P(S_j \text{ in the following period} \mid S_i \text{ in the preceding period}) \quad (15\text{–}5.3)$$

Note that, in this as in any transition matrix, the sum of the entries in any row must be 1.0. This is because the entries in any row must represent the probabilities for switching to all of the possible following states. Such a row, all of whose elements are nonnegative and whose sum is 1.0, is called a *probability vector*.

The general form of a transition matrix is shown in Figure 15–5.2. Also,

		Following State S_j				
		S_1	S_2	S_3	S_4	...
	S_1	p_{11}	p_{12}	p_{13}	p_{14}	...
	S_2	p_{21}	p_{22}	p_{23}	.	...
Preceding State S_i	S_3	p_{31}	.	.	.	
	S_4	.	.	.	.	
	.	.	.	.		
	.	.	.			

Fig. 15–5.2. General form for transition matrix.

it is often convenient to represent a transition matrix in the conventional mathematical matrix representation shown in Figure 15–5.3, which shows in mathematical notation the same data as the matrix of Figure 15–5.1.

In some situations, elements may enter or leave the population, such as, in this case, by births and deaths. In marketing applications, where the

$$\begin{bmatrix} 0.8 & 0.2 \\ 0.5 & 0.5 \end{bmatrix}$$

Fig. 15–5.3. Matrix notation for same data as in Figure 15–5.1.

various "states" are the brands of a product purchased, and the matrix is called a *brand-switching* matrix, persons may enter or leave the market as they begin to use a particular type of product or stop using it. When this happens, a new state or brand (i.e., "Brand X") is entered as a new column or row or both as needed. Then the probabilities assigned to this new state characterize those elements which enter or leave the market.

For a transition matrix to yield a true Markov chain, the rows cannot all be the same. For example, the transition matrix of Figure 15–5.4 does

$$\begin{bmatrix} 0.8 & 0.2 \\ 0.8 & 0.2 \end{bmatrix}$$

Fig. 15–5.4. A transition matrix in which $P(S_j)$ does not depend upon S_i.

not yield a *Markov chain*, because $P(S_j)$ does not depend upon S_i. Rather, each trial is an independent trial, since $P(S_j)$ is constant for each S_j, regardless of S_i.

A *Markov chain*, to which we have just referred, is defined as *an ordered series of states connected by a transition matrix*. Visually, such a chain may be seen in any path through the transition probability tree of Figure 15–3.1.

If, in a transition matrix, any $p_{ij} = 0$, that means that that transition does not occur. Conversely, if any $p_{ij} = 1$, every element in state S_i moves to state S_j in the next period. Also, if any $p_{ii} = 1$, i.e., if any transition probability on the main diagonal (from northwest to southeast) of the matrix is equal to 1, that state S_i is an *absorbing state;* i.e., it is not possible to leave this state. Finally, if a transition matrix, such as Figure 15–5.5, has at least one absorbing state, as in that case $p_{33} = 1$, and if it is possible to reach an absorbing state from every nonabsorbing state, then the Markov chain is an *absorbing Markov chain*. For example, in the Markov process depicted in Figure 15–5.5, eventually all elements will be in state S_3.

$$\begin{bmatrix} 0 & 0.8 & 0.2 & 0 \\ 0.2 & 0.3 & 0.1 & 0.4 \\ 0 & 0 & 1.0 & 0 \\ 0.1 & 0.1 & 0.6 & 0.2 \end{bmatrix}$$

Fig. 15–5.5. A transition matrix for an absorbing Markov chain.

Some processes which are cyclic in nature may be described by a transition matrix as, for example, the matrices of Figure 15–5.6. There

$$\begin{bmatrix} 0 & 1 & 0 & 0 \\ 0 & 0 & 1 & 0 \\ 0 & 0 & 0 & 1 \\ 1 & 0 & 0 & 0 \end{bmatrix} \qquad \begin{bmatrix} 0 & 0 & 0 & 1 \\ 0 & 0 & 1 & 0 \\ 1 & 0 & 0 & 0 \\ 0 & 1 & 0 & 0 \end{bmatrix}$$

Fig. 15–5.6. Cyclic transition matrices. Left: 1–2–3–4–1. Right: 1–4–2–3–1.

the left matrix is a cycle in which elements proceed 1–2–3–4–1, etc., and the right matrix represents the cycle 1–4–2–3–1, etc.

15–6. Brand Switching. As has been noted above, the transition matrix has been applied in marketing to describe brand-switching behavior in the market place. In that application, the states are the competing brands or products. We can illustrate why this application has been so attractive to marketing research analysts by continuing with the illustration of the population of Rurbania, as described in the familiar transition matrix of Figure 15–6.1, for the states S_1 = urban resident, S_2 = rural resident.

$$\begin{bmatrix} 0.8 & 0.2 \\ 0.5 & 0.5 \end{bmatrix}$$

Fig. 15–6.1. Transition matrix for urban–rural population shifting in Rurbania.

Using the data of Table 15–2.1, or Equation 15–2.3, we can construct Table 15–6.1, which shows the urban–rural division of the population at any time. Again, we shall start with the arbitrary starting point, 50 per cent urban and 50 per cent rural. The difference between Table 15–2.1 and Table 15–6.1 is that in Table 15–6.1, the data are presented, not as probabilities, but rather as percentages of the population in the various

TABLE 15–6.1

Urban-Rural Distribution of Rurbania Population Over Time
(distribution at year-end, after shift)

Year	Percentage Urban	Percentage Rural
0	50	50
1	65	35
2	69.5	30.5
3	70.85	29.15
4	71.255	28.745

states. Again we note that the percentages seem to be changing by ever smaller amounts as time goes on, and that consequently the population seems to be approaching some steady state urban–rural distribution. With the concept of population distribution which we are now using, there is a very easy way to solve for the numerical values of the steady state distribution.

Clearly, at the steady state, the number of persons leaving the cities must equal the number of persons going to the cities. The number leaving the cities is $0.2U^*$ where U^* is the steady-state percentage of urban dwellers, and the number entering the cities is $0.5R^*$, where R^* is the steady state percentage of rural residents. Then

$$0.2U^* = 0.5R^*$$

$$U^* = \frac{5}{2}R^*$$

Then, since $U^* + R^* = 100$ per cent,

$$U^* = \frac{5}{7} \cdot 100 = 71.4286\%$$

$$R^* = \frac{2}{7} \cdot 100 = 29.5714\%$$

This means that, in the long run, if the pattern of residence shifting described by the transition matrix of Figure 15–6.1 persists, the final population distribution of Rurbania will be 71.4 per cent urban and 29.6 per cent rural.

It should be noted that the steady state values which were derived above were derived with no reference at all to the current or starting population distribution. *All that was needed was the matrix of transition probabilities.* Therefore, it is clear that *the steady state distribution is uniquely determined by the transition matrix and is therefore independent of the starting state.*

This kind of model has been widely applied in marketing research to study consumer behavior with respect to brand loyalty and brand switching. In marketing applications, the results, of course, will be the steady-state *market shares* of the various brands. Otherwise the analysis is identical. The probabilities on the major diagonal represent "brand loyalty," while the probabilities off the diagonal refer to "brand switching."

Suppose there are three competing brands of tires: Achilles, Blubber, and Carshoo. Further, panel data studies yield the brand-switching pattern given in Figure 15–6.2, obtained from interviewing *the same people* twice, the second wave of interviews following the first by one purchase cycle.

This matrix tells us that the brand loyalty pattern is such that, in the period studied, 60 per cent of the buyers of Achilles tires were brand loyal, and that 90 per cent of the Blubber customers, but only 20 per cent of Carshoo customers, were brand loyal. In the case of Carshoo, the customers fled from the brand but did not differentially prefer Achilles or Blubber. Blubber suffered only a 10-per cent attrition of customers, and those leaving that brand were undifferentiated with respect to their choice of Achilles or Carshoo. However, the 40 per cent who left Achilles clearly preferred Blubber over Carshoo: 30 per cent compared to 10 per cent. It would seem, then, that sooner or later, if this brand switching pattern persists, Blubber will corner the market. Indeed, *if we can assume persistence of the transition matrix*, we can compute the steady-state market shares of these three brands. The arithmetic is, as we shall see, very easy. However, the assumption of persistence of the transition matrix is a massive assumption, one which is, in most marketing situations, totally unwarranted! This does not mean that the analysis is pointless. We shall see that the transition matrix is often a very useful tool, but first let us complete the arithmetic of the solution for the steady-state market shares in the tire market.

For each brand, the number of persons switching to the brand must, at the steady state, equal the number switching from the brand. Again representing the steady-state market shares by the symbols A^*, B^*, and C^*, we have, at the steady state,

$$\text{Switching out} = \text{Switching in}$$

$$0.4A^* = 0.05B^* + 0.4C^* \tag{15–6.1}$$

$$0.1B^* = 0.3A^* + 0.4C^* \tag{15–6.2}$$

$$0.8C^* = 0.1A^* + 0.05B^* \tag{15–6.3}$$

It might seem that this system of three equations is three independent equations with three unknowns and that therefore they can be solved simultaneously for the three unknowns. This is not the case. Because of the nature of the transition matrix, where the sum of the terms in every row is 1.0, these three equations are not independent. Actually, any two are independent, but the last is merely the sum of the other two, and it therefore does not provide new information not contained in the other two. The reader may verify this by adding Equations (15–6.1) and (15–6.2). First, Equation (15–6.2) is rearranged to read

$$-0.3A^* = -0.1B^* + 0.4C^* \tag{15–6.4}$$

Then this equation is added to Equation (15–6.1) to yield

$$0.1A^* = -0.05B^* + 0.8C^* \tag{15–6.5}$$

which is identical with equation (15–6.3).

Thus there are only two independent equations. However, there is a third equation. The brand shares must add to 1:

$$A^* + B^* + C^* = 1 \qquad (15\text{–}6.6)$$

Simultaneous solution of Equations (15–6.1), (15–6.2), and (15–6.6) yields the steady-state market shares, which are

$$A^* = \tfrac{12}{73} = 16.4\%$$

$$B^* = \tfrac{56}{73} = 76.7\%$$

$$C^* = \tfrac{5}{73} = 6.9\%$$

This result is to be interpreted to mean that, if the transition matrix of Figure 15–6.2 were to persist in the market place, the market shares of

		Present Purchase		
		Achilles	Blubber	Carshoo
Previous Purchase	Achilles	0.60	0.30	0.10
	Blubber	0.05	0.90	0.05
	Carshoo	0.40	0.40	0.20

Fig. 15–6.2. Transition matrix for the tire market.

the three competitors would approach the steady-state values given above. (See Exercise 15–4.)

We shall, in the next section, discuss the appropriateness of this persistence assumption in the real world of marketing, and we shall see that transition matrices *do* change over time, and that one of the functions of marketing and advertising executives is to try to change these transition matrices to increase their own brand loyalty and to stimulate brand shifting from their competitors' products to their own.

15–7. Usefulness of Stationary Markov Analysis. In the illustrations which we have considered thus far, we have found that it is quite simple to compute the steady-state market shares, given the transition matrix and the assumption that the transition probabilities will persist. Such a system, where the transition probabilities are constant over time, is known as a *stationary Markov process*. This simple model has been applied in marketing, and it had a spectacular but short-lived popularity.

It was not able to fulfill the promise which it seemed to hold for the analysts who at first embraced it. Perhaps the reason for the general disillusionment which followed is that too much was expected of it.

It was too unrealistic to assume that transition matrices would persist. Indeed, marketing and advertising efforts are usually directed toward changing transition probabilities. The real usefulness of simple Markov analysis in marketing is not to predict the actual long-term future market shares, but rather to show the current transition matrix which is itself a fruitful document for study, and also to point out the *direction* in which market shares are moving *under the present transition pattern* and perhaps also to provide forecasts of short term effects for periods during which the transition matrix may be relatively unchanged, i.e., for some products, for three, six, or even twelve months.

These studies can show marketing executives how loyal their and their competitors' customers are, to whom they are losing customers, from whom they are gaining customers, and where this will lead if no changes occur in the transition matrix. Of course *changes will occur*, and it is the enlightened and well-informed executive who will lead the way to his own firm's advantage. The kind of information which we have discussed above, while of very limited usefulness as a predictive tool, can be extremely helpful in making the kinds of *current* market analyses which he needs.

While stationary Markov analysis is of little or no usefulness *as a long-term predictive tool* in situations where transition matrices do not persist, it can be very useful in various nonmarketing applications where they do persist. In the following section we shall investigate an engineering situation in which the transition probabilities do persist, creating a true stationary Markov process.

15–8. A Replacement Application. The Embe Chemical Company has a large number of identical small heating coils installed at hundreds of points throughout the plant. These coils are used for ignition purposes and are very delicate. They all fail within 150 ignitions. There is an excess of coils in the plant in redundant positions, so that failure of any coil does not halt the operation of the plant. The actual failure pattern is given in Table 15–8.1. If we let the "periods" represent the number of ignitions, then the state S_i represents "surviving at beginning of ith fifty ignitions."

TABLE 15–8.1

Embe Chemical Company
Failure Pattern for Ignition Coils

Period i	Ignitions	P(survival at end of ith period)	P(failure during i^{th} period)	$P\left(\text{failure in } i^{\text{th}} \text{ period} \mid \text{survival into } i^{\text{th}} \text{ period}\right)$
1	1–50	0.60	0.40	0.40
2	51–100	0.15	0.45	0.75
3	101–150	0.00	0.15	1.00

No coils ever reach S_4. Rather, those which reach S_3 go next to S_1, meaning that they expire and are replaced by new ones.

Thus, from Table 15–8.1, it is clear that *if they are inspected and the faulty coils replaced at 50-ignition intervals*, of those in S_1, i.e., just starting, 40 per cent will fail and be replaced at fifty ignitions, and 60 per cent will enter S_2. Of those which are in S_2, 75 per cent will fail in the next period and 25 per cent will reach S_3, and all of those reaching S_3 will be replaced in the next period. These data are summarized in the transition probability matrix of Figure 15–8.1, which shows the probabilities of progressing

	S_1	S_2	S_3
S_1	0.40	0.60	0
S_2	0.75	0	0.25
S_3	1.00	0	0

Fig. 15–8.1. Transition matrix for coil replacement for Embe Chemical Company.

from state S_i to state S_{i+1} in one 50-ignition interval. Of course, from each state S_i, a coil can move only to S_{i+1} (if it survives) or to S_1 (if it is replaced). The state S_1 means "brand new." From this matrix, by the usual methods, the steady-state age distribution can be computed. The reader may easily verify that the steady-state percentage age distribution is $\frac{20}{35}$, $\frac{12}{35}$, and $\frac{3}{35}$, respectively, indicating that, if replacement is made after failure at 50-ignition intervals, $\frac{20}{35}$ or 57 per cent of the coils will be replaced at each inspection and replacement operation. This problem is also solved below in Section 15–10, Equations (15–10.3) to (15–10.9), to illustrate another method of solution.

The management of Embe Chemical Company may use this analysis to evaluate this particular inspection and replacement policy and, by similar analyses involving all of the relevant costs, evaluate other possible replacement policies to seek the optimal policy.

In this case, clearly, if the unit cost per coil of group replacement is less than 57 per cent of the unit cost of replacement after failure and inspection, then a policy of group replacement of *all* coils every 50 hours is preferable, and most likely, some alternative group replacement plan, possibly using different time intervals, about which we have no knowledge at present, would be even more economic.

15–9. Modifications and Variations. We have seen that stationary Markov analysis can and does give useful results about *transient* effects in the market place, but that it fails to provide the intensely desired prediction tool which it seemed to promise. This has led to attempts to modify the analysis to make it more useful, particularly in marketing ("brand-switching") applications.

One attempt has been to make the assumption that, although the transition matrix may not be constant, it may be able to be characterized by some consistent pattern of change. For example, if one takes three waves of interviews of a consumer panel, and creates the transition matrix between the first and second waves and also the transition matrix between the second and third waves, one can compare these two matrices and try to understand and describe the change from one transition matrix to the next. If this change is described mathematically, and *if one assumes that this change will persist,* then it is possible to derive the future transition matrices for any desired future number of periods and to apply these successively to the present market-share pattern to predict future market shares. This, of course, corresponds to observing a phenomenon at two points in time, noting the difference between the two observations, and forecasting on the basis of the assumption that that observed difference will persist into the future.

Other marketing applications have attempted to take into consideration not only the single previous purchase, but some small finite number of previous purchases and to predict future behavior on the basis of the observed patterns of successive purchases.

Other approaches have examined consumers' purchases over two *periods of time* (rather than *at two points in time*) and have measured the *amounts* purchased of each of the several competing brands or products. That is, the data for each period are in terms of amounts purchased and market shares, and the transitions are from one level of purchase or market share to another for each and all of the competing brands or products. Clearly, this analysis involves a huge number of individual pieces of numerical information. However, the transition patterns may be described mathematically and, if assumptions of persistence are made, forecasts can be produced. This approach leads to extremely complex results, but this is not necessarily the fault of the analysis. The market place and the behavior of consumers therein are immensely complex phenomena, and perhaps operations researchers and market analysts are overly optimistic when they hope to describe them by simple mathematical structures such as stationary Markov chains.

15–10. Introduction to Vector and Matrix Multiplication. In performing the arithmetic operations involved in Markov analysis, it is often helpful and efficient to use the notation and operations of vectors and matrices. Therefore, in this section, we shall present a brief survey of these mathematical materials.

1. *Vectors and Matrices.* A vector may be a *row vector* (n elements) or a *column vector* (m elements). If X is a row vector and Y is a column vector, each having the same number of components, i.e., in this case $m = n$,

$$X = [x_1 \quad x_2 \quad x_3 \quad \ldots \quad x_n]$$

$$Y = \begin{bmatrix} y_1 \\ y_2 \\ y_3 \\ \cdot \\ \cdot \\ \cdot \\ y_n \end{bmatrix}$$

then the product XY is defined as

$$XY = x_1y_1 + x_2y_2 + x_3y_3 + \cdots + x_ny_n = \sum_{i=1}^{n} x_iy_i$$

and it is a *scalar,* or simple, number. Note that *the row vector is always written first.*

Example: The cost of a market basket of three commodities with individual prices \$2, \$5, and \$3, respectively, for which quantities 7, 2, 4, respectively, are to be purchased, is the vector product of the price vector

$$P = [2 \quad 5 \quad 3]$$

and the quantity vector

$$Q = \begin{bmatrix} 7 \\ 2 \\ 4 \end{bmatrix}$$

$$PQ = [2 \quad 5 \quad 3] \begin{bmatrix} 7 \\ 2 \\ 4 \end{bmatrix} = 14 + 10 + 12 = \$36$$

A *matrix* is a rectangular array of elements with m rows and n columns, i.e., an $m \times n$ matrix. Note that the number of *rows* is always given first:

$$\begin{bmatrix} a_{11} & a_{12} & a_{13} & \cdots & a_{1n} \\ a_{21} & & & & \\ a_{31} & & & & \\ \cdot & & & & \\ \cdot & & & & \\ \cdot & & & & \\ a_{m1} & \cdots & & & a_{mn} \end{bmatrix}$$

Clearly, a vector is a special case of a matrix: a row vector is a $1 \times n$ matrix, and a column vector is a $m \times 1$ matrix.

2. *Vectors Multiplied with Matrices.* If X is an m-element row vector, its product with A, and $m \times n$ matrix, is defined as

$$XA = [x_1 \quad x_2 \quad x_3 \quad \cdots \quad x_m] \begin{bmatrix} a_{11} & a_{12} & \cdots & a_{1n} \\ a_{21} & a_{22} & & \\ \cdot & & & \\ \cdot & & & \\ \cdot & & & \\ a_{m1} & a_{m2} & \cdots & a_{mn} \end{bmatrix}$$

$$= [x_1a_{11} + x_2a_{21} + \cdots + x_ma_{m1}, x_1a_{12} + x_2a_{22} + \cdots + x_ma_{m2}, \ldots, x_1a_{1n} + x_2a_{2n} + \cdots + x_ma_{mn}]$$

The product is an n-element row vector, (note that commas are used here to separate the elements of the vector) the jth term of which is the *sum* of the respective products of the m elements of the vector X and the m elements of the jth *column* of the matrix A.

If Y is an n-element column vector, its produce with A, an $m \times n$ matrix, is defined as

$$AY = \begin{bmatrix} a_{11} & a_{12} & \cdots & a_{1n} \\ a_{21} & & & \\ \cdot & & & \\ \cdot & & & \\ \cdot & & & \\ a_{m1} & \cdots & & a_{mn} \end{bmatrix} \begin{bmatrix} y_1 \\ y_2 \\ \cdot \\ \cdot \\ \cdot \\ y_n \end{bmatrix} = \begin{bmatrix} a_{11}y_1 + a_{12}y_2 + \cdots + a_{1n}y_n \\ a_{21}y_2 + a_{22}y_2 + \cdots + a_{2n}y_n \\ \cdot \\ \cdot \\ \cdot \\ a_{m1}y_1 + a_{m2}y_2 + \cdots + a_{mn}y_n \end{bmatrix}$$

The product is an m-element column vector, the ith element of which is the sum of the respective products of the n elements of the ith row of the matrix A multiplied by the n elements of the vector Y.

3. *Matrices Multiplied by Matrices.* Two matrices, A and B, may be multiplied together to yield the product AB, (note carefully that this is usually *not* the same as BA; i.e., $AB \neq BA$), if the number of *columns* of A is the same as the number of *rows* of B.

If A is an $m \times k$ matrix

$$\begin{bmatrix} a_{11} & a_{12} & \cdots & a_{1k} \\ a_{21} & & & \\ \cdot & & & \\ \cdot & & & \\ \cdot & & & \\ a_{m1} & \cdots & & a_{mk} \end{bmatrix}$$

and B is a $k \times n$ matrix

$$\begin{bmatrix} b_{11} & b_{12} & \cdots & b_{1n} \\ b_{21} & & & \\ \cdot & & & \\ \cdot & & & \\ \cdot & & & \\ b_{k1} & \cdots & & b_{kn} \end{bmatrix}$$

the product AB is a $m \times n$ matrix

$$\begin{bmatrix} c_{11} & c_{12} & \cdots & c_{1n} \\ c_{21} & & & \\ \cdot & & & \\ \cdot & & & \\ \cdot & & & \\ c_{m1} & \cdots & & c_{mn} \end{bmatrix}$$

in which the ij^{th} term is the vector product of the ith *row* of A and the jth *column* of B.

$$c_{ij} = a_{i1}b_{1j} + a_{i2}b_{2j} + \cdots + a_{ik}b_{kj}$$

In matrix multiplication the associative law holds:

$$ABC = (AB)C = A(BC)$$

4. *The Powers of a Vector.* AA may be written A^2 and computed as indicated above for normal matrix multiplication, but A *must be a square matrix;* i.e., $m = n$.

5. *The Use of Vector Multiplication in Markov Chains.* We shall now put to use the techniques of matrix and vector multiplication that we have reviewed above. Let us therefore turn back to the first problem in this chapter. Here the transition matrix was

$$P = \begin{bmatrix} 0.8 & 0.2 \\ 0.5 & 0.5 \end{bmatrix}$$

and the initial step was given by the vector

$$p^{(0)} = [0.5 \quad 0.5]$$

Here we are defining the initial state as that which resulted from the *preliminary drawing*, since that was given in the statement of the problem. The next drawing shall be referred to as the *first drawing*.

The vector $p^{(1)}$, giving the probability of the states S_1 and S_2 after one drawing, is given by the *vector product:*

$$p^{(1)} = p^{(0)}P = [0.5 \quad 0.5]\begin{bmatrix} 0.8 & 0.2 \\ 0.5 & 0.5 \end{bmatrix} = [0.4 + 0.25 \quad 0.10 + 0.25]$$

$$= [0.65 \quad 0.35]$$

Similarly,

$$p^{(2)} = p^{(1)}P = [0.65 \quad 0.35]\begin{bmatrix} 0.8 & 0.2 \\ 0.5 & 0.5 \end{bmatrix} = [0.52 + 0.175 \quad 0.13 + 0.175]$$

$$= [0.695 \quad 0.305]$$

Clearly, then, since the associative law holds,

$$p^{(2)} = p^{(1)}P = (p^{(0)}P)P = p^{(0)}P^2$$

This process may be carried on for any number (r) of trials, and it may readily be seen that, where $p^{(r)}$ is the probability vector over the states S_1 and S_2 after r drawings,

$$p^{(r)} = p^{(0)}P^r$$

This has an important logical consequence, namely, that P^r is the matrix for the transition from S_i to S_j in r steps. That is, the ij^{th} entry is the probability of moving from S_i to S_j in r steps:

$$P^2 = \begin{bmatrix} 0.8 & 0.2 \\ 0.5 & 0.5 \end{bmatrix}\begin{bmatrix} 0.8 & 0.2 \\ 0.5 & 0.5 \end{bmatrix}$$

$$= \begin{bmatrix} (0.8)(0.8) + (0.2)(0.5) & (0.2)(0.8) + (0.2)(0.5) \\ (0.5)(0.8) + (0.5)(0.5) & (0.5)(0.2) + (0.5)(0.5) \end{bmatrix}$$

$$= \begin{bmatrix} 0.74 & 0.26 \\ 0.65 & 0.35 \end{bmatrix}$$

$$p^{(2)} = p^{(0)}P^2 = [0.5 \quad 0.5]\begin{bmatrix} 0.74 & 0.26 \\ 0.65 & 0.35 \end{bmatrix}$$

$$= [0.37 + 0.325 \quad 0.13 + 0.175] = [0.695 \quad 0.305]$$

which is the same result as was obtained above in two steps.

Now, it will be recalled that the *steady state probability vector* $p^{(n)}$ has the property that

$$p^{(n)} = p^{(n-1)}P \qquad \text{or} \qquad p^{(n)} = p^{(n)}P = t$$

The probability vector $p^{(n)}$, or t, is called the *fixed point* of the transformation P. The fixed point of the given transformation is

$$t = [0.7143 \quad 0.2857]$$

Now, let us see how this is derived by taking successive powers of P:

$$P = \begin{bmatrix} 0.8 & 0.2 \\ 0.5 & 0.5 \end{bmatrix} \qquad P^2 = \begin{bmatrix} 0.74 & 0.26 \\ 0.65 & 0.35 \end{bmatrix}$$

$$P^3 = \begin{bmatrix} 0.722 & 0.278 \\ 0.695 & 0.305 \end{bmatrix} \qquad P^4 = \begin{bmatrix} 0.7166 & 0.2834 \\ 0.7085 & 0.2915 \end{bmatrix}$$

$$P^5 = \begin{bmatrix} 0.71498 & 0.28502 \\ 0.71255 & 0.28745 \end{bmatrix} \qquad P^6 = \begin{bmatrix} 0.7145 & 0.2855 \\ 0.7138 & 0.2862 \end{bmatrix}$$

$$\lim_{n \to \infty} P^n = \begin{bmatrix} 0.7143 & 0.2857 \\ 0.7143 & 0.2857 \end{bmatrix} = T$$

The matrix T which is approached has, as its two rows, the probability vector which is the fixed point for that transformation. Clearly, any initial probability vector $p^{(0)}$ will yield

$$p^{(0)}T = t \tag{15–10.1}$$

since we have the form

$$[x \quad 1 - x]\begin{bmatrix} A^* & B^* \\ A^* & B^* \end{bmatrix} = [A^*x + A^*(1 - x) \quad B^*x + B^*(1 - x)]$$
$$= [A^* \quad B^*]$$

for any x. Thus, as we have noted above, the steady state probabilities in a Markov chain are independent of the starting configuration and depend *solely* on the transformation matrix.

The fixed point, t, is the row vector $[A^* \quad B^*]$ such that

$$tP = t \tag{15–10.2}$$

We can apply this formula to the Embe Chemical Company problem of Section 15–8 to derive the fixed point $[S_1^* \quad S_2^* \quad S_3^*]$, which we shall here designate $[A^* \quad B^* \quad C^*]$ for simplification:

$$[A^* \quad B^* \quad C^*]\begin{bmatrix} 0.4 & 0.6 & 0 \\ 0.75 & 0 & 0.25 \\ 1.00 & 0 & 0 \end{bmatrix} = [A^* \quad B^* \quad C^*]$$

$$0.4A^* + 0.75B^* + 1.00C^* = A^* \tag{15–10.3}$$

$$0.6A^* + 0 + 0 = B^* \tag{15–10.4}$$

$$0 + 0.25B^* + 0 = C^* \tag{15–10.5}$$

We know from Section 15–6, especially Equations (15–6.3), (15–6.4), and (15–6.5), that we may take any two of these equations and the equation

$$A^* + B^* + C^* = 1 \tag{15–10.6}$$

and solve the three equations simultaneously for A^*, B^*, and C^*. From Equation (15–10.4),

$$B^* = 0.6A^*$$

From Equations (15–10.5) and (15–10.6),

$$C^* = 0.25B^* = 0.15A^*$$

Then

$$A^* + 0.6A^* + 0.15A^* = 1$$

$$A^* = \frac{1}{1.75} = \frac{20}{35} \tag{15–10.7}$$

$$B^* = \frac{0.6}{1.75} = \frac{12}{35} \tag{15–10.8}$$

$$C^* = \frac{0.15}{1.75} = \frac{3}{35} \tag{15–10.9}$$

SUGGESTIONS FOR FURTHER READING

BHARUCHA-REID, A. T. *Elements of the Theory of Markov Processes and Their Applications.* New York: McGraw-Hill Book Co., Inc., 1960.

FELLER, W. *An Introduction to Probability Theory and Its Applications.* New York: John Wiley & Sons, Inc., Vol. 1 1957; Vol. 2, (2d ed.) 1966.

HOWARD R. A. *Dynamic Programming and Markov Processes.* New York: John Wiley & Sons, Inc., 1960.

KEMENY, J. G., and J. L. SNELL. *Finite Markov Chains.* Princeton, N.J.: D. Van Nostrand Company, Inc., 1960.

MAFFEI, R. B. "Brand Preferences and Simple Markov Processes," *Operations Research,* Vol. 8, No. 2 (March-April, 1960).

EXERCISES

15–1. The demand for cameras at the Jaz Camera shop is as given in Table 7–5.1. Ordering can be done only at the end of each week, and delivery is immediate. The inventory policy is to replenish the inventory level to 3 at the end of each week when the level on hand has fallen to 1 or 0, but to refrain from ordering if the level is 2 or 3. What are the probabilities of the various possible inventory levels *after* replenishment, if any?

15–2. Using the results of the analysis in Tables 7–6.1 through 7–6.4, compute the expected value of the net profit under the optimal inventory policy, which is specified in Table 7–6.4. (Be sure to note the lag of one week as described in the text in Section 7–6.)

15–3. The brand switching matrix for the two brands of cottage cheese sold in our town is given below. Compute the fixed point. Interpret your result.

	A	B
A	.6	.4
B	.1	.9

15–4. Show that the steady state market shares of Achilles, Blubber, and Carshoo are as given at the end of Section 15–6.

Part V
SCHEDULING MODELS

16

Sequencing and Scheduling Problems

16–1. The Traveling-Salesman Problem. There is a class of problem which involves consideration of the *order* in which tasks are performed. Perhaps the most widely known of these problems is the "traveling-salesman" problem. In its typical form, the traveling-salesman problem is the determination of the shortest route for a trip, starting in one city, visiting some number of other cities, and returning to the starting city, where the intercity distance for all city pairs is known. A familiar statement of this kind of problem is the determination of the shortest route starting from, say, Boston and back to Boston, touching each state capital of the 48 contiguous continental United States. There is no general analytic method for solving large problems of this type involving, say, 50 or more cities. However, there are computer-based methods for finding the optimal solution in relatively small problems, and there are other computer-based simulation procedures for finding good, if not optimal, solutions to even large problems.

The general form of the traveling-salesman problem occurs in various situations other than that described above. For example, the same problem is involved in deciding the order in which various tasks should be done, when the various task-to-task changeover times differ. In Figure 16–1.1 the matrix shows the job-to-job changeover times or the point-to-point travel times (or distances or costs).

At first glance, it might seem that this problem can be solved by the assignment method of Chapter 8, but on reflection it becomes evident that, if the best assignment from Boston to the next state capital is

	L_1	L_2	L_3	...	L_n
L_1	0	C_{12}	C_{13}	...	C_{1n}
L_2	C_{21}	0	C_{23}	...	C_{2n}
L_3	C_{31}	C_{32}	0	...	C_{3n}
.	.	.	.	...	.
.	.	.	.	...	.
L_n	C_{n1}	C_{n2}	C_{n3}	...	0

Fig. 16–1.1. Matrix for traveling-salesman problem. The tasks or locations are designated L, and the changeover times or costs are the C_{ij}.

selected, the traveler will go from Boston to Providence, and the best assignment from Providence brings him back to Boston. This completes his trip, and he has not visited all of the cities. Rather he has cycled through only two.

One might try to avoid this dilemma by specifying that he goes to the closest *unvisited* city. This would cycle him through all of the required cities, but it would not *necessarily* produce the optimal path. Indeed, it has been shown that, for this city-to-city version of the problem, the optimal path cannot have any intersections. A great deal is known about this problem, because many mathematicians have worked on it, but a general *analytical* method for the determination of the optimal sequence has not yet been developed.

There are, however, many approximate solutions; and with the advent of the electronic computer, excellent, though not necessarily optimal, sequences can be found for almost any specific problem of this type. The computer cannot solve by enumeration by evaluating *all* of the possible sequences in a large problem, because the number of them is astronomical, and even operating at electronic speeds, the computer could not evaluate all of the possible sequences for the problem involving the 48 state capitals. For example, with only 20 cities, the number of possible sequences is 20!, or 2.4×10^{18}, which as suggested in Section 8–3 would take millions of years to evaluate at even a thousand sequences per second.

A traveling salesman problem involving a small number of cities (or jobs) may be solved manually by first solving the assignment problem and then modifying the result, if necessary. Figure 16–1.2 shows the matrix for the highway distances between five United States cities. The desired solution is the shortest routing which visits all five cities. The application of the standard assignment method yields the first matrix in Figure 16–1.3. This was obtained by, first, replacing the zeros in Figure 16–1.2 with infinity signs to assure that these routes (from one city to itself) would not be chosen; and second, the application of the four steps

	Boston	Cleveland	Detroit	New York	Philadelphia
Boston	0	629	699	216	304
Cleveland	629	0	167	482	415
Detroit	699	167	0	647	570
New York	216	482	647	0	101
Philadelphia	304	415	570	101	0

Fig. 16–1.2. A small traveling-salesman problem.

described in Chapter 8; i.e., the smallest constant is subtracted from each column and each row and then "step 4" is applied.

This first matrix in Figure 16–1.3 does not constitute a solution to the traveling-salesman problem, although it is a solution to the assignment problem. The checkmarks identifying the selected zeros are not shown, but the reader can easily verify that this solution represents two cycles. One cycle is CLE–DET–CLE, and the other is BOS–PHL–NY–BOS. Therefore, this does not constitute a solution to the traveling-salesman problem. However, it is possible to work from this result (the first matrix of Figure 16–1.3) to a satisfactory solution to the traveling-salesman problem.

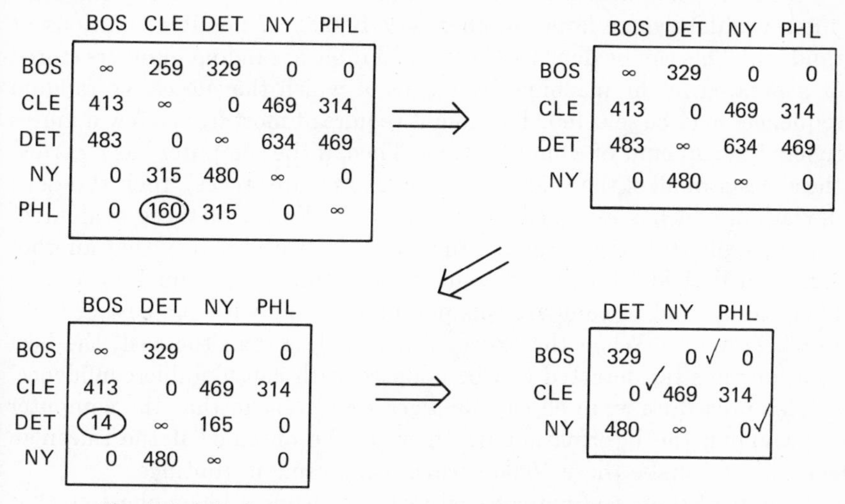

	BOS	CLE	DET	NY	PHL
BOS	∞	259	329	0	0
CLE	413	∞	0	469	314
DET	483	0	∞	634	469
NY	0	315	480	∞	0
PHL	0	(160)	315	0	∞

⟹

	BOS	DET	NY	PHL
BOS	∞	329	0	0
CLE	413	0	469	314
DET	483	∞	634	469
NY	0	480	∞	0

⟸

	BOS	DET	NY	PHL
BOS	∞	329	0	0
CLE	413	0	469	314
DET	(14)	∞	165	0
NY	0	480	∞	0

⟹

	DET	NY	PHL
BOS	329	0 ✓	0
CLE	0 ✓	469	314
NY	480	∞	0 ✓

Fig. 16–1.3. Solution to a small traveling-salesman problem.

The next step is the elimination of the smallest nonzero element in the matrix, thereby *agreeing to use that cell*, and seeking a solution to the rest of the matrix by applying the assignment technique to the reduced matrix. The smallest nonzero entry was 160 for PHL–CLE. Removing that entry and the entire column and row for that entry, yields the second matrix of

Figure 16–1.3, which is a 4 × 4 matrix. This may be solved by the usual assignment method to yield the third matrix shown in the figure. Again, the indicated solution yields cycles: PHL–CLE–DET–PHL, and BOS–NY–BOS.

The process is repeated. The smallest nonzero entry is 14 for DET–BOS. This entry and its column and row may be removed, indicating that we agree to use that cell, and then the reduced matrix shown as the last matrix constitutes a satisfactory solution. The optimal sequence then is, using the two eliminated cells PHL–CLE and DET–BOS: Boston, New York, Philadelphia, Cleveland, Detroit, Boston. Its total distance is 1,598 miles, and a glance at a map will indicate the obvious correctness of this solution. This method may, of course, be used only with small problems, and even then it is not sure to lead to the optimal solution since it may be that elimination of the smallest nonzero entry at some stage leads to a less desirable complete sequence than elimination (acceptance) of a more costly cell which, though more costly, could possibly lead to a better overall solution.

16–2. Computer Sampling. One ingenious method for solving large traveling-salesman problems and many similar kinds of problem involving the search for the best of a large number of possible solutions, is to sample from the astronomical number of possible solutions by having the computer evaluate some large number, say 10,000, of possible solutions at random.[1] This can be done by the use of a table of random numbers stored or generated in the machine, by means of which the successive random sequences may be selected. This might require at most from a few minutes to less than an hour of computer time. Then, if the computer has recorded the average of all of the 10,000 costs (or times or distances), their standard deviation, and has recorded the detail of the lowest of those evaluated, it is a simple statistical problem to estimate the probability that another sample will yield a lower cost solution, to estimate how much lower it is likely to be, and to compare this potential saving with the cost of additional sampling. When the expected gain is less than the cost, the best solution thus far detected can be adopted with considerable confidence.

This procedure is, in effect, *computer simulation* in that the computer is providing the information which would be obtained if the salesman actually did make these 10,000 trips, using random routings.

In spite of these computer-based methods, it must be emphasized that the human eye is so adept at pattern recognition that, in cases like the traveling-salesman problem, an intelligent person can quickly scan a geometrical representation, such as a map of the cities to be visited, and produce an excellent, if not optimal, solution. Indeed, experience has shown that often this simple free-hand geometrical solution is better than

[1] Heller (1960).

the best that the computer can generate after several hundred random trials.

It is evident that this sampling procedure can be made more efficient by restricting the computer's possible sequences in various ways to avoid the selection of sequences which are obviously not efficient. However, to do this may require more programming time than the savings may merit.

Also there are many computational algorithms which are far more sophisticated than the simple or restricted sampling suggested above. These techniques can lead to optimal solutions for even relatively large problems. Little[2] in 1963 solved a traveling salesman problem for 34 cities in less than 20 minutes of computer time. Others have applied dynamic programming approaches to the computer with promising results. The traveling-salesman problem, which has vexed the mathematician, has thus yielded to the electronic computer.

The computer sampling approach is completely general, and may be used with a wide variety of kinds of problem. It yields results which, although not optimal, are likely to be quite satisfactory.

16–3. Sequencing Through Stations. The term *job-shop* may be applied to any production system which is organized *functionally;* i.e., the system has two or more operations or specialized types of equipment, and various tasks or jobs are performed by these stations. This type of organization is generally quite different from the product-oriented production system which is characterized by an assembly line. An assembly line is usually set up to deal with a single product class, while the job-shop may produce diverse products which need have in common only the requirement for the application of similar operations or the use of certain specialized equipment. In the ideal assembly line, each job progresses successively through the stations in the same sequence, taking the same amount of time. The essence of job-shop problems is that they involve jobs which take different amounts of time at each station and which may require visiting the various stations in different sequence.

The technique which we are about to examine applies to jobs which consist of *single units* moving from station to station or, if jobs consist of many units, they occur in *batches* such that the units of any batch move together, and the next station cannot start on any units in the batch until all units in the batch have finished at the previous station.

Let us examine the relatively simple problem of sequencing a small number of jobs through a small number of stations, where each job has a different time requirement for each station, but where they all require the same sequence of stations.

The Reel Manufacturing Company has four jobs which may be scheduled in any order through two stations, but which must all go to

[2] Little, *et al.* (1963).

the grinding station first and the polishing station second. The times required at each station are given in Table 16–3.1. Each station requires 23 hours to work on the four jobs, but the entire processing operation can not be done in a 23-hour period, since the polishing station cannot begin to operate until the first job has emerged from grinding, and polishing must continue working after grinding has finished in order to process the last job through the system.

TABLE 16–3.1

Reel Manufacturing Company
Times Required for Four Jobs at Two Stations

Job i	First Station Grinding G_i	Second Station Polishing P_i
1	10	5
2	5	10
3	7	3
4	1	5
	23	23

The procedure for minimizing the length of the time interval required[3] for processing these four jobs through the two stations is to select the smallest of the G_i or P_i. If it is a G_i, schedule that job first. If it is a P_i, schedule that job last. If there are two tied for lowest, select either. Repeat this process with the remaining jobs, and the resulting schedule will be optimal in that the elapsed time between the start of grinding and the finish of polishing will be minimized. This minimizes waiting time for polishing, since grinding, the first station, will of course finish in 23 hours.

Applying this procedure to the data of Table 16–3.1, we find that job 4 should be scheduled first, job 3 should be last, and job 2 should be second. (Since Jobs 1 and 2 are tied, they could go in either order, with the same result as will be seen in the chart which follows.) Thus, the order is 4, 2, 1, 3. Figure 16–3.1 shows a Gantt chart for this problem. The elapsed time is 26 hours, since the polishing station must wait one hour at the start and two hours between jobs 1 and 3.

If there are *three* stations, the problem can be solved for minimum waiting by this method only if certain conditions are met. Table 16–3.2 shows the same data as given above, but now there are three operations to be performed, *all in the same order*. The method given above for scheduling

[3] Johnson (1954).

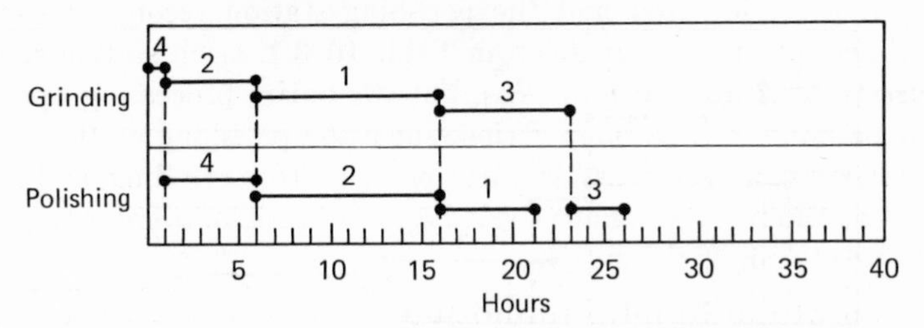

Fig. 16–3.1. Gantt chart for Reel Manufacturing Company optimal schedule.

these jobs through *two* stations can be used with *three* stations if the following condition is met.

$$\max P_i \leq \min G_i$$

or

$$\max P_i \leq \min S_i$$

That is, the largest of the times required at the *middle* station must be less than or equal to the smallest time required at one (or both) of the other two stations. That condition is met in Table 16–3.2, and the method may be used. First, add the $G_i + P_i$ and the $P_i + S_i$ to reduce the data to two columns as shown in the last two columns of Table 16–3.2.

TABLE 16–3.2

Reel Manufacturing Company
Times Required for Four Jobs at Three Stations
(hours)

Job i	Grinding G_i	Polishing P_i	Shipping S_i	$G_i + P_i$	$P_i + S_i$
1	10	5	12	15	17
2	5	10	18	15	28
3	7	3	15	10	18
4	1	5	20	6	25

Then using the same method as was used above for two stations, the optimal sequence of jobs is: 4, 3, 2, 1. The sequence: 4, 3, 1, 2 would be equally optimal. The Gantt chart for this is shown in Figure 16–3.2. The time for the entire operation is 71 hours. That is the optimal as is seen from the fact that shipping, once started, will never have to wait, and therefore the sooner it starts, the sooner it finishes. The technique of combining the times of the first two operations and choosing the job with the lowest sum to go first assured that the third operation would start as soon as possible. If the required condition had been met in the other direction, i.e., if $\max P_i \leq \min G_i$ instead of $\min S_i$, then there would be

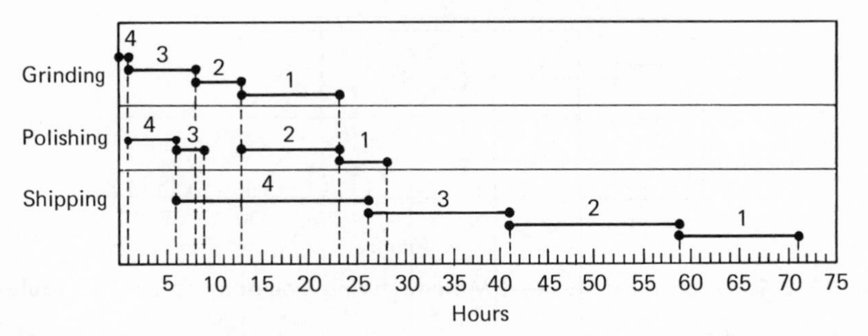

Fig. 16–3.2. Gantt chart for Reel Manufacturing Company with three stations.

waiting at the last station, but waiting would be scheduled so that shipping could finish up as soon after the others as possible. If the condition is not met, we cannot be sure that this method will yield the optimal schedule.

In some situations, some of the jobs do not go through the various stations in the same order, and the machines or stations also have requirements or preferences for the order in which they process the jobs. When this is the case, it is important to be sure that the required schedule is technically feasible. For example, if job 1 required the order G, P, and job 2 required the order P, G; but Grinding preferred to do job 2 before job 1, while Polishing preferred to do job 1 before job 2, this would be impossible. There is no way to start. In this simple situation, the inconsistency of the requirements is quite obvious, but in larger systems this may not be so obvious. The feasibility or lack of feasibility of a production program may be determined easily in a matrix worksheet. For a particular production program involving four jobs and four stations, the requirements are given in Table 16–3.3 for the Resac Machine Shop.

The feasibility of the requirements for this program can be evaluated

TABLE 16–3.3

Resac Machine Shop
Production Program Requirements for Four Jobs and Four Stations

Station Requirements		Job Requirements	
Station	Job Order	Job	Station Order
Cutting	1, 2, 4, 3	1	C, M, G, P
Grinding	3, 1, 2, 4	2	G, C, M, P
Machining	1, 2, 3, 4	3	C, M, G, P
Polishing	4, 2, 1, 3	4	C, G, M, P

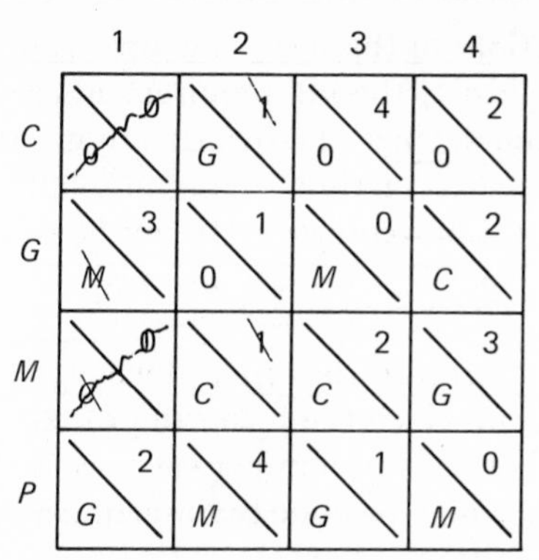

Fig. 16–3.3. Worksheet for determination of feasibility of program requirements of Resac Machine Shop.

in the matrix worksheet of Figure 16–3.3. The numbers in the worksheet are entered in the following way. The numbers in the upper right part of each cell are the station requirements for the *preceding* job. Thus the numbers in the top row are the job numbers for the preceding job at the cutting station. Since that station requires the order 1, 2, 4, 3, job 1 has no precedence requirement, job 2 must be preceded by job 1, job 4 by job 2, and job 3 by job 4. Similarly, for grinding, job 3 has no precedence requirement, job 1 must be preceded by job 3, and in this way, this and the other rows may be filled.

Similarly the *columns* may be filled with the letters in the lower left part of each cell. These represent the station precedence requirements of the jobs.

To satisfy the requirements of this program, specific *jobs* can be performed at specific *stations* only when *both* of the precedence requirements have been satisfied. Production can start with *job* 1 at cutting, since that combination has no precedence requirement. The completion of any job through a station satisfies *two* precedence requirements, one in the row and one in the column. Therefore, when the production operation represented by any cell is completed, the *letter* of that cell should be crossed out where it appears elsewhere in the *column*, and the *number* of that cell should be crossed out where it appears elsewhere in that *row*. Thus, when cell $(C, 1)$ is satisfied, the C in the column and the 1 in the row should be crossed out by hand, and that *cell* should be crossed out, preferably with a different color pencil.

Now, the precedence requirements for cell $(M, 1)$ are satisfied, so job 1 can go to machining. Then the M in the column and the 1 in that row should be crossed out as well as the cell $(M, 1)$ itself.

Now there is no cell which has all of its precedence requirements satisfied, and therefore the specified program is not feasible.

In real-world situations of this sort, of course, some of the requirements must be relaxed. Typically, the job requirements are far more rigid than the station requirements, since the former are usually technical requirements, and the latter cost- or time-saving injunctions. Thus, usually, at additional cost, the station requirements can be relaxed enough to make the program feasible, and the work can proceed. (See Exercise 16–1 at the end of this chapter.)

It is also necessary to record the order in which the cells are eliminated, since that is the order in which the jobs will proceed through the stations. The easiest way to do this is to number each crossed-out cell in sequence as it is eliminated. This may be done by inserting a number in the cell in a distinctive color or position.

16–4. Dynamic Programming. Dynamic programming is a decision-making technique for dealing with a *sequence of decisions*, each of which produces an outcome that influences the next. Thus each decision must take into account its effect on the next decision and, indeed, its effect on the succeeding chain of decisions. For example, we can not produce and deliver inferior merchandise in order to save inspection costs for this period without producing returned merchandise and lost customers in the next. We have seen something of this need for looking toward future decisions in Chapter 7, especially in Section 7–6. Here, we shall briefly introduce a new technique specifically relevant for successive decisions.

The basic technique of dynamic programming is to define the successive stages, optimize the effectiveness of the *last* stage for each of the possible inputs to that last stage, and then, since these are the outputs of the previous stage, that previous stage may now be solved in the same way. Thus, by successively working backwards by stages, the entire problem may be solved. This principle was developed by R. Bellman.

Let us illustrate this process by reference to a job-shop problem. The Gob Auto Body Shop has three departments: metal work; painting; touchup and polishing. All work must progress through these three departments in this same order. Each of the three departments has three parallel alternative channels. That is, there are three metal-working stations, three painting stations and three touchup stations, each with its own techniques, equipment, costs, and slightly different output characteristics affecting the costs in the next department.

A large job has just been towed in, and it must now be scheduled through *one* station in *each* department. The metal-working cost for this job is estimated to be \$400, \$420, or \$395, respectively, for metal-working stations 1, 2, and 3, and the costs for the other departments are given in Figure 16–4.1. Clearly, in this simple problem, the best route through the shop may be found by relatively easy enumeration. However, we shall use this simple problem to illustrate the concept of dynamic programming.

From Metal Working Station	Painting Station 1	2	3
1	40	50	45
2	50	35	40
3	45	60	70

From Painting Station	Touchup Station 1	2	3
1	18	24	15
2	21	18	20
3	12	15	5

Fig. 16–4.1. Gob Auto Body Shop. Cost estimates for each station. These costs are different for each station performing work in preceding department.

We start at the final stage, find the optimal, and work backward. Let us define $f(d, s)$ as the *optimum (in this case, minimum) value of the objective function (cost) attainable from a starting point*, (d,s), where d represents the department; i.e., $d = 0, m, p,$ or t, for, respectively: start, metal working, painting, and touchup departments; and $s = 1, 2, 3$, representing the three stations in each department. Thus $(p, 2)$ represents *2nd painting station.* Then, from the right-hand table of Figure 16–4.1,

$$f(p, 1) = 15 \quad \text{at } (t, 3)$$

$$f(p, 2) = 18 \quad \text{at } (t, 2)$$

$$f(p, 3) = 5 \quad \text{at } (t, 3)$$

These three statements give the *optimum cost* at the remaining department, touchup, for the job if it is in each of the three possible painting stations. This is the final stage problem, and, from the diagram, the optimal course of action at this stage is obviously $(t, 3)$ if at $(p, 1)$, $(t, 2)$ if at $(p, 2)$, and $(t, 3)$ if at $(p, 3)$. Clearly, under no condition should this particular job go to $(t, 1)$.

Let us now look at the two-stage problem.

$$\begin{aligned} f(m, 1) &= \min[40 + f(p, 1) \text{ or } 50 + f(p, 2) \text{ or } 45 + f(p, 3)] \\ &= \min[55 \text{ or } 68 \text{ or } 50] = 50 \end{aligned}$$

$$\begin{aligned} f(m, 2) &= \min[50 + f(p, 1) \text{ or } 35 + f(p, 2) \text{ or } 40 + f(p, 3)] \\ &= \min[65 \text{ or } 53 \text{ or } 45] = 45 \end{aligned}$$

$$\begin{aligned} f(m, 3) &= \min[45 + f(p, 1) \text{ or } 60 + f(p, 2) \text{ or } 70 + f(p, 3)] \\ &= \min[60 \text{ or } 78 \text{ or } 75] = 60 \end{aligned}$$

The three-stage problem is now:

$$\begin{aligned} f(0) &= \min[400 + f(m, 1) \text{ or } 420 + f(m, 2) \text{ or } 395 + f(m, 3)] \\ &= \min[450 \text{ or } 465 \text{ or } 455] = 450 \end{aligned}$$

The optimal routing is $(m, 1)$, $(p, 3)$, $(t, 3)$. Note that this result cannot be obtained by working forward and choosing the best decision at each stage. Even if one started with $(m, 1)$, if he selected the optimal station at each stage, he would select $(p, 1)$ and $(t, 3)$ for a total cost of $400 + 40 + 15 = \$455$. Note also that there are 27 possible routes through the system. If there had been another department with three stations, there would be 81 possible routes; however, there would be only one more stage analysis required, again comparing only three courses of action.

The general rule is that, at every stage, the relevant subsequent sequence of decisions is that which is the optimal policy for following each of the possible outputs of the decision at that stage. Then the optimal course of action at any stage is that whose effectiveness, when combined with the effectiveness of the optimal subsequent sequence, is optimum. Thus, an optimal policy is a policy such that, *at every stage, the remaining decisions constitute an optimal policy, given the conditions resulting from the preceding stage.*

Dynamic programming may be applied to many different kinds of problems, including some kinds of inventory and production scheduling problems. Clearly, in an ongoing manufacturing or merchandising system, one consequence of the current period's production or inventory decision is the inventory at the start of the next period. Thus, many inventory and production-scheduling problems may be regarded as sequences of decisions and thus amenable to dynamic programming analysis.

We shall now illustrate the application of dynamic programming to a simple production-scheduling and inventory problem in which the cost function is continuous, thereby requiring the use of differential calculus to arrive at optimality.

The Charbas Computer Company has contracted to manufacture and deliver a unique order of 18 units over the next 90 days. The contract calls for delivery of five units at the end of 30 days, five units at the end of 60 days, and eight units at the end of 90 days. Because of limited production facilities and the company's decision to work overtime rather than expand its facilities over this 90-day period, these units will be produced at increasing costs according to the following relationship, where m_i is the cost in dollars of manufacturing x_i units in the ith 30-day period:

$$m_i = 5{,}000 + 1{,}000x_i(x_i - 1) \qquad (16\text{–}4.1)$$

If any excess units or parts of units are manufactured and on hand at the end of any 30-day period, these may be carried over to the next period at a holding cost (interest, storage, security protection, special care, and testing, etc.) of \$1,000 for each unit carried over from one 30-day period to the next. Holding costs are proportional for partial units carried over. Thus, letting v_i be the number of units carried over *into* the ith period (i.e., it is the *starting* inventory for the ith period), the holding cost, h_i, is, in dollars,

$$h_i = 1{,}000v_i \tag{16–4.2}$$

In the following development, we shall simplify the arithmetic by expressing all costs in thousands of dollars. Thus, Equations (16–4.1) and (16–4.2) become

$$m_i = 5 + x_i(x_i - 1) \tag{16–4.3}$$

$$h_i = v_i \tag{16–4.4}$$

The company seeks to determine the optimal scheduling sequence to minimize the sum of the manufacturing and holding costs. There is no starting inventory. Carried-over inventories need not be integral numbers of units.

This problem is essentially a problem in *nonlinear programming* in which the objective function is to minimize:

$$\text{Total Cost (TC)} = h_1 + h_2 + h_3 + m_1 + m_2 + m_3 \tag{16–4.5}$$

subject to:

$$x_i \geq 0 \text{ for all } i \tag{16–4.6}$$

$$x_1 \geq 5 \tag{16–4.7}$$

$$x_1 + x_2 \geq 10 \tag{16–4.8}$$

$$x_1 + x_2 + x_3 = 18 \tag{16–4.9}$$

This is nonlinear, because although the restrictions, Equations (16–4.6) through (16–4.9), are linear, the objective function, Equation (16–4.5), is nonlinear. It is, with substitutions from Equations (16–4.3) and (16–4.4),

$$TC = v_1 + v_2 + v_3 + 15 + x_1(x_1 - 1) + x_2(x_2 - 1) + x_3(x_3 - 1) \tag{16–4.10}$$

but

$$v_1 = 0$$

$$v_2 = x_1 - 5$$

$$v_3 = x_1 + x_2 - 10$$

$$TC = x_1 - 5 + x_1 + x_2 - 10 + 15 + x_1^2 - x_1 + x_2^2 - x_2 + x_3^2 - x_3$$

$$TC = x_1 - x_3 + x_1^2 + x_2^2 + x_3^2 \tag{16–4.11}$$

The solution of this problem by nonlinear programming techniques is beyond the scope of this book. However, this problem is easily solved by the step-by-step procedure of dynamic programming. Indeed the simplicity of the following solution demonstrates the great power of this technique.

Let

$f(v_i,x_i^*)$ = the optimum total cost for the *remaining* production schedule starting at the start of the ith period, and

$c(v_i,x_i)$ = the total cost for the ith period *plus* the optimum total cost thereafter.

Thus, the fundamental dynamic programming expression which we shall use in this problem is

$$c(v_i,x_i) = h_i + m_i + f(v_{i+1},x_{i+1}^*) \qquad (16\text{–}4.12)$$

Following the usual dynamic programming procedure, we start at the last period, the 3rd 30-day period. The total cost in that 3rd period is

$$c(v_3,x_3) = h_3 + m_3 = v_3 + 5 + x_3(x_3 - 1)$$

Since the company is manufacturing only these 18 units, the optimal number to manufacture in the last period is the requirement, 8 units, less the initial inventory for that period.

$$x_3^* = 8 - v_3 \qquad (16\text{–}4.13)$$

Then

$$f(v_3,x_3^*) = v_3 + 5 + (8 - v_3)(7 - v_3)$$

$$= v_3 + 5 + 56 - 15v_3 + v_3^2$$

$$f(v_3,x_3^*) = 61 - 14v_3 + v_3^2 \qquad (16\text{–}4.14)$$

Since v_3 results from decisions made at earlier stages, we can not work further at this stage but must now work backward to the second period.

For the second period, the cost is

$$c(v_2,x_2) = h_2 + m_2 + f(v_3,x_3^*)$$

which is the relevant expression of the *fundamental dynamic programming idea;* i.e., it expresses the cost as the sum of the cost for the current period *plus* the *optimum* cost for *all* of the remaining periods.

Then,

$$c(v_2,x_2) = v_2 + 5 + x_2(x_2 - 1) + [61 - 14v_3 + v_3^2]$$

But the starting inventory in the 3rd period is the sum of the starting inventory of the previous period *plus* the production in that period, *less* the deliveries made in that period:

$$v_3 = v_2 + x_2 - 5$$

$$c(v_2,x_2) = 66 + v_2 + x_2^2 - x_2 - 14(v_2 + x_2 - 5) + (v_2 + x_2 - 5)^2 \qquad (16\text{–}4.15)$$

We differentiate Equation (16–4.15) with respect to x_2 and set the derivative equal to zero to obtain x_2^*:

$$\frac{d}{dx_2}[c(v_2,x_2)] = 2x_2 - 1 - 14 + 2(v_2 + x_2 - 5)$$

$$0 = -25 + 2v_2 + 4x_2^*$$

$$x_2^* = \frac{25 - 2v_2}{4} \tag{16–4.16}$$

It should be noted that we had no guarantee, at this point, that x_2^* would turn out to be large enough to meet the contract requirements. That is, in order to make the contracted deliveries on time, it is necessary that there be at least 5 units on hand at the end of the second 30-day period:

$$v_2 + x_2 \geq 5$$

Actually, in this case, it will turn out that x_2^* as computed from Equation (16–4.16) will be *feasible* by this criterion, but we cannot be sure of this until we have worked backward further and derived the value of v_2. If it should turn out that x_2^* is then too small to meet the delivery requirement, we would merely arbitrarily increase the production in that period to the minimum amount which meets that feasibility requirement.

Now that we have a value for x_2^*, we shall substitute it into Equation (16–4.15). We shall do this in two steps. First, substituting the value of x_2^* into the parenthetical expressions in Equation (16–4.15) yields

$$v_2 + x_2^* - 5 = v_2 + \frac{25 - 2v_2}{4} - 5 = \frac{5 + 2v_2}{4} \tag{16–4.17}$$

Then Equation (16–4.15) becomes

$$f(v_2,x_2^*) = 66 + v_2 + \left(\frac{25 - 2v_2}{4}\right)^2 - \left(\frac{25 - 2v_2}{4}\right) - 14\left(\frac{5 + 2v_2}{4}\right) + \left(\frac{5 + 2v_2}{4}\right)^2 \tag{16–4.18}$$

$$= \frac{169}{4} - \frac{11}{2}v_2 + \left(\frac{25 - 2v_2}{4}\right)^2 + \left(\frac{5 + 2v_2}{4}\right)^2 \tag{16–4.19}$$

There is no need to simplify Equation (16–4.19) further at this time. Finally, proceeding backwards to the first period, the dynamic programming expression for that period is

$$c(v_1,x_1) = h_1 + m_1 + f(v_2,x_2^*) \tag{16–14.20}$$

$$= v_1 + [5 + x_1(x_1 - 1)] + \left[\frac{169}{4} - \frac{11}{2}v_2 + \left(\frac{25 - 2v_2}{4}\right)^2 + \left(\frac{5 + 2v_2}{4}\right)^2\right]$$

but $v_1 = 0$, since there was no starting inventory, and $v_2 = x_1 - 5$; therefore,

$$\frac{25 - 2v_2}{4} = \frac{25 - 2x_1 + 10}{4} = \frac{35 - 2x_1}{4}$$

and

$$5 + 2v_2 = 5 + 2x_1 - 10 = 2x_1 - 5$$

therefore,

$$c(v_1,x_1) = c(0,x_1) = 0 + [5 + x_1^2 - x_1] + \left[\frac{169}{4} - \frac{11}{2}(x_1 - 5) + \left(\frac{35 - 2x_1}{4}\right)^2 + \left(\frac{2x_1 - 5}{4}\right)^2\right]$$

We could, at this point, combine terms and simplify this last equation, but it is simpler to differentiate it in this form, since many terms will drop out:

$$\frac{d}{dx_1}[c(v_1,x_1)] = 2x_1 - 1 - \frac{11}{2} + 2\left(\frac{35 - 2x_1}{4}\right)\left(-\frac{1}{2}\right) + 2\left(\frac{2x_1 - 5}{4}\right)\left(\frac{1}{2}\right)$$

Now, setting the derivative equal to zero,

$$0 = 2x_1^* - \frac{13}{2} - \frac{35}{4} + \frac{x_1^*}{2} + \frac{x_1^*}{2} - \frac{5}{4}$$

$$3x_1^* = \frac{66}{4}$$

$$x_1^* = \frac{66}{12} = 5\frac{1}{2} \text{ units}$$

Then

$$v_2 = \frac{1}{2}$$

and, from Equation (16–4.16),

$$x_2^* = \frac{25 - 2v_2}{4} = 6$$

$$v_3 = v_2 + x_2 - 5 = \frac{1}{2} + 6 - 5 = 1\frac{1}{2}$$

$$x_3^* = 8 - v_3 = 6\frac{1}{2}$$

Thus the optimal schedule, the minimum cost schedule which satisfies the delivery requirements, is to manufacture, in the three 30-day periods, respectively, $5\frac{1}{2}$ units, 6 units, and $6\frac{1}{2}$ units.

It may be interesting to compare the cost of this schedule with some of the many other possible schedules. We shall select for comparison, first, manufacturing for the delivery deadlines, and, second, manufacturing a uniform amount each period. The total cost of these production schedules or of any others may be computed easily from Equation (16–4.11).

$$TC = x_1 - x_3 + x_1^2 + x_2^2 + x_3^2 \qquad (16\text{–}4.11)$$

Looking first at the policy of manufacturing for the *delivery deadlines*, i.e., producing, respectively, 5, 5, 8, the "deadline" cost, TC_d, is

$$TC_d = 5 - 8 + 25 + 25 + 64 = \$111 \text{ (thousands)}$$

Next, the policy of manufacturing a *uniform* amount, namely 6 units, each period yields a "uniform" cost, TC_u, of

$$TC_u = 6 - 6 + 36 + 36 + 36 = \$108 \text{ (thousands)}$$

The *optimal* production schedule, $5\frac{1}{2}$, 6, and $6\frac{1}{2}$ units, yields a cost, TC^*, of

$$TC^* = 5\tfrac{1}{2} - 6\tfrac{1}{2} + 30.25 + 36 + 42.25 = \$107.5 \text{ (thousands)}$$

There are, of course, many other feasible schedules, but this is the least costly. This cost saving may not seem impressive in this simple illustration, but it should be quite clear that, in larger and more complex problems, the savings achievable by careful analysis of this sort may be large indeed.

16–5. Simulation. We have seen in earlier chapters many kinds of problems which could be solved analytically. In this chapter, however, we have encountered problems which could not be solved *analytically*, but which could be solved or somehow handled *numerically*. When a model is used to describe a system for the purpose of determining the value of the output for many alternative possible configurations of the input variables in order to be able to identify that course of action which leads to the optimum output, that model is a *simulation model*, and this process is called *simulation*.

Many simulation models in business are characterized by the linking of a chain of two or more systems such that the output of one system is the input of the next. It is this interdependency of several subsystems which makes analytic solution very difficult or impossible and which made such systems intractable until the advent of the electronic computer, which made simulation, really a brute-force repetitive computational process, a feasible and often surprisingly efficient method of solution.

Some managements have tried to construct simulations of large segments of or even all of their company operations so that they can, in effect, deal with a model of their real-world operations much as players do with the now familiar *business games*. Business games are simulations of all or part of some contrived business environment in which "players," as firms, make decisions about products, prices, promotion, financial operations, production, construction, research, etc., and the computer, using hypothetical demand functions, production functions, advertising-return functions, contrived business-cycle meanderings, research-effectiveness functions, etc., computes market shares, financial performance, inventories, and all relevant profit-and-loss and balance-sheet items for the period past so that the players may make a new set of decisions for the future.

These games have been found to be interesting and exciting and useful for certain pedogogical purposes, especially in helping students learn about the interrelations of the various functions of a business. For example, if a team consisting of three last-term students majoring in marketing, finance, and production, respectively, plays a business game as a firm, the individuals are sure to learn something new about each other's fields, build a new respect for the functions and responsibilities of those other fields, and learn something about decision delegation and responsibility in business. All this happens even though the actual mathematical functions in the computer model may be, by most standards, poor approximations to reality.

Most simulations have the characteristic that, among other things, they make it possible to simulate reality with a compressed time scale. That is, the activities of a month or a quarter or a year may be simulated in a few seconds. Thus, it is possible to examine a long history of simulated experience under varying conditions in a very short time.

Managements' efforts at building simulation models of their firms have sought to construct adequate models of the real-world business environment, so that they could experiment with various configurations of their controllable variables, observe the output, and hopefully learn something about probable real-world responses to their future managerial decisions. Some companies have met with some degree of success in this attempt, but the process is still new, and we can anticipate very extensive developments in this area as computers become easier to communicate with, less expensive, and more capacious, and as both managers and computers become more sophisticated.

Many inputs to real-world systems are probabilistic in nature. This is true of demand, arrival patterns, servicing patterns, replacement and maintenance requirements, absenteeism, employee resignations and recruitment, and many other phenomena. These phenomena may be simulated in a simulation model by the *Monte Carlo* method, which is the name given to the technique of *simulation by sampling*, whereby the desired probability distribution is either stored or generated in the computer, and a table of random numbers, also either stored or generated in the computer, is used to make random selections from the population of the appropriate random variable. These selected values of the random variable are then entered into the simulation model, and the logical consequences of those particular random events are computed. This technique has been extremely useful in designing traffic-control patterns, maintenance facilities, and warehouse locations, and in many other areas characterized by complex but observable stochastic input variables. (See Section 14–15 above.)

SUGGESTIONS FOR FURTHER READING

BELLMAN, R. *Dynamic Programming*, Princeton, N.J.: Princeton University Press, 1957.

GARETT, J. W. "Three Heuristic Rules for Sequencing Jobs to a Single Production Facility," *Management Science*, 11:166–76 (June, 1965).

GERE, W. S., JR. "Heuristics in Job Shop Scheduling," *Management Science*, 13:167–90 (November, 1966).

HELLER, J. "Some Numerical Experiments for an M × J Flow Shop and Its Decision Theoretic Aspects," *Operations Research*, Vol. 8, No. 2 (March-April, 1960).

HOWARD R. A. "Dynamic Programming," *Management Science*, Vol. 12, No. 5 (January, 1966).

JOHNSON, S. M., "Optimal Two- and Three-Stage Production Schedules with Setup Times Included," *Naval Research Logistics Quarterly*, Vol. 1, No. 1 (March, 1954).

LITTLE, J. D. C., K. G. MURTY, D. W. SWEENEY, and C. KAREL. "An Algorithm for the Traveling Salesman Problem," *Operations Research*, (November-December, 1963).

McMILLIN, C., and R. F. GONZALEZ. *Systems Analysis: A Computer Approach to Decision Models*, Homewood, Ill.: Richard D. Irwin, Inc., 1965.

SASIENI, M., A. YASPAN, and L. FRIEDMAN. *Operations Research: Methods and Problems*. New York: John Wiley & Sons, Inc., 1959.

SISSON, R. L. "Sequencing Theory," Chapter 7 in *Progress in Operations Research*, Vol. 1 (R. L. Ackoff, ed.). John Wiley & Sons, Inc., 1961.

EXERCISES

16–1. If the station requirements given in Table 16–3.3 were relaxed only to the extent that the grinding station can take the jobs in the order: 1–2–3–4, is the program feasible? If so, specify a feasible program and construct a Gantt chart. How long should the entire production program take if each job stays exactly one hour in each station?

16–2. The machine shop of Jarn Electric Corporation has three machines, and there are three jobs to be scheduled today. The jobs must progress through the machines in the job requirements order indicated below, and the machine change-over effort is minimized if the jobs progress through the machines in the machine preference order shown.

a) Can this schedule be observed? Explain (very briefly).

b) How long should it take (optimally) to service the three jobs through the shop, if the machine preferences are ignored. Each job takes one hour on each machine. Ignore change-over times.

Job requirements		Machine preferences	
Job	Machine Order	Machine	Job Order
Arc	Grind, Polish, Spray	Grinder	Arc, Cam, Bar
Bar	Grind, Spray, Polish	Polisher	Bar, Arc, Cam
Cam	Grind, Polish, Spray	Sprayer	Cam, Arc, Bar

16–3. In the Charbas Computer Company problem in Section 16–4, what would be the optimal production schedule if the holding costs were half as great (only $500 per unit carried over)?

17

PERT

17–1. Introduction. PERT (Project Evaluation and Review Technique) is a technique for analysis, coordination and control of progress on a project. The method was developed in 1958 in connection with the United States Navy's *Polaris* project. It has been estimated that the use of PERT saved up to two years in the completion of that project. Since that time, PERT has been extensively used in military and civilian activities, and though still relatively new, it has become a managerial tool of major importance.

It is most useful in application to projects or activities which are not recurrent in a routine sense, but which are, at least in some degree, unique. However, to the extent that certain recurrent or continuing activities can be converted into or viewed as projects, PERT can be successfully applied.

17–2. The PERT Network. Basic to the PERT system is the PERT network. This network is essentially a flow chart which diagrammatically depicts the flow of the work. The project is first analyzed into tasks (there may be relatively few or many hundreds) and the network presents the entire project as a series of *events* connected by *activities.* This is illustrated in Figure 17–2.1. Each node of the network (represented in the diagram by a rectangular box) is a milestone or *event.* It represents an *instant of time* and it is generally described as the *start* or *completion* of some activity. The arrows or lines between events are *activities,* i.e., the tasks which must be performed in order that the *successor events* may occur. Thus, an activity is the work which must take place between events, and in the network, an activity is a *period of time.* It is the period necessary to move from the *predecessor event* (at the tail of the arrow) to the *successor event*

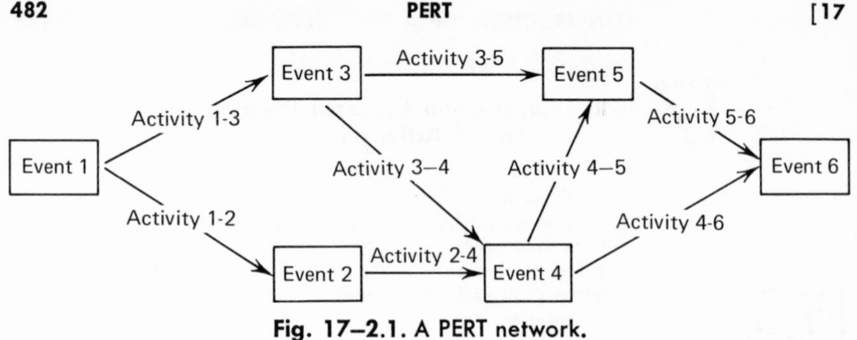

Fig. 17–2.1. A PERT network.

(at the head of the arrow). Clearly, implicit in this time definition of each activity is some decision about resource allocation to that activity.

In Figure 17–2.1, each event is so numbered that the arrows always proceed from a lower number to a higher number. The lengths of the arrows bear no necessary relationship to the lengths of the time spans which they represent.

The PERT network is so designed that, in the network, the precedence relationship between events and activities is inviolate. All preceding input activities common to an event must be completed before the event can take place, and no activity can start until its predecessor event or events, have occurred.

In the network, each event is represented by some geometrical shape. Some analysts like to use several different shapes in the same network, with each shape representing some particular class of events, i.e., departmental responsibility, reporting level, etc. We shall use simple rectangles throughout. Also, many analysts like to have the word *start* or *complete* appear in the description of every event. We shall here follow that procedure. The use of the word *complete* insures that each node (event) so designated does indeed represent a completed task.

17–3. Construction of a PERT Network. Let us illustrate the PERT technique by applying it to a research project of the BORIY Corporation (Basic Operations Research in Industrial Yields). The first step is to analyze the project into separate tasks. In any real situation, the analyst must decide how far to carry the subdivision of tasks. This is not always an easy decision; but once this is accomplished, the project may be defined in terms of a list of tasks, such as is shown in Table 17–3.1. The order in this list is not important. The list of activities in Table 17–3.1 was produced by the project director, thinking in terms of groups of activities and the person or persons responsible for their execution.

The list is then revised into task-sequence order as is shown in Table 17–3.2. There are many possible correct ways in which these might be listed. The major requirement is that any task which must precede

TABLE 17–3.1

BORIY Corporation Research Project
List of Activities

Prepare outline
Construct and debug computer program
Design field work
Conduct field work
Analyze data and write report
Read proofs
Prepare index
Distribute books to client offices
Negotiate for printing and binding
Printer sets type
Design book
Printer corrects errors, prints, and binds

another task in the project must be listed above it in the table. From the list in Table 17–3.2, the PERT network is constructed.

Beginning at the end, i.e., with the "Complete project" box, and working backwards, the analyst constructs the network as shown in Figure 17–3.1.

TABLE 17–3.2

BORIY Corporation Research Project
List of Activities in Task Sequence

1. Prepare outline
2. Design field work
3. Negotiate for printing and binding
4. Design book
5. Construct and debug computer program
6. Conduct field work
7. Analyze data and write report
8. Printer sets type
9. Read proofs
10. Prepare index
11. Printer corrects errors, prints, and binds
12. Distribute books to client offices

The network in Figure 17–3.1 shows both the events and the activity titles. In actual practice, these are not usually both shown. Often only one set of titles is shown, and the other is implied.

In Figure 17–3.1, one of the boxes embedded in the network is labeled "Start typesetting and cover manufacture." This is the only box besides the first with the word "start" in the title. This box is added for convenience only. It is not essential, but this way of handling a process with three activity inputs seems to make a neat presentation. Two points are

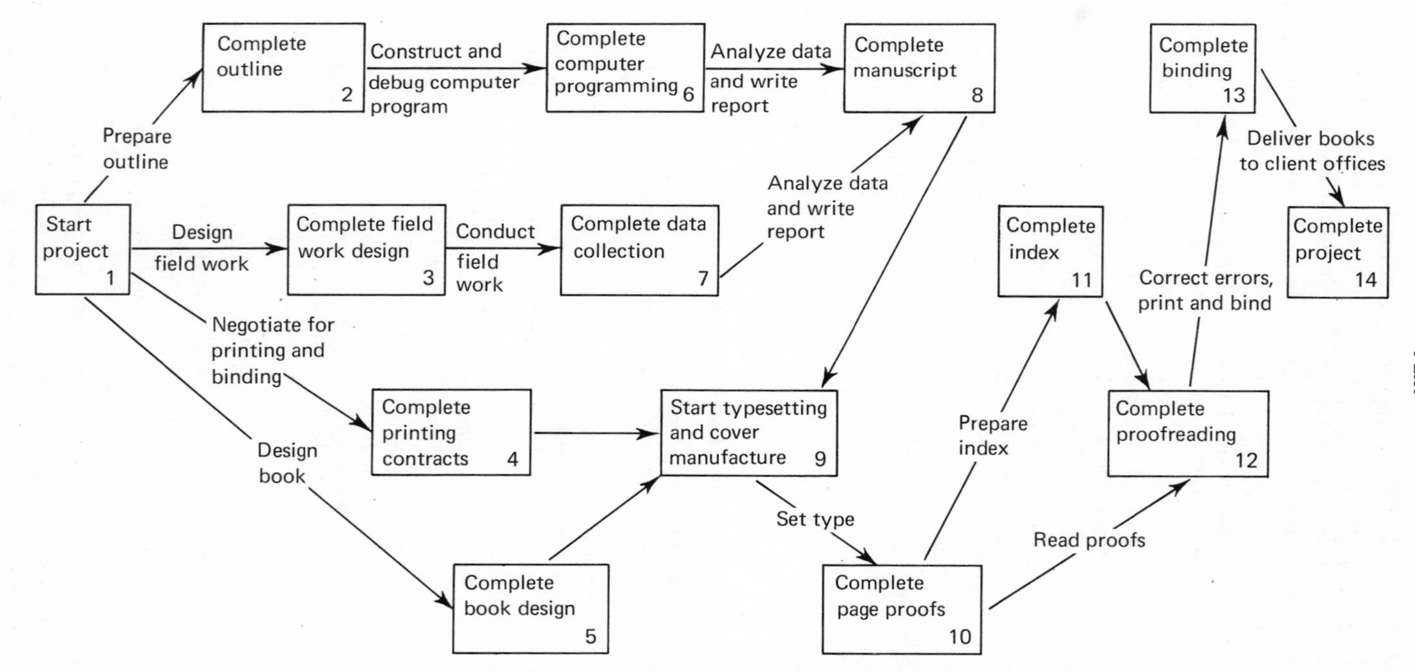

Fig. 17–3.1. PERT network for BORIY Corporation research project.

to be noted. First, all of the activities preceding it are *dummy activities;* i.e., they do not represent any real activities, and, as we shall see, they take zero time. That is, typesetting can begin as soon as the three predecessor *events* have occurred, and arrows could have been drawn from these three events directly to the event "Complete page proofs," with all three labeled "Set type." This method was used for event 8. Alternatively, for event 8, we could have inserted dummy activities from events 6 and 7 to an event labeled "Start manuscript." This last method of presentation, which is that used for event 9, is generally preferred, since it seems a bit clearer and easier to understand. Thus, in Figure 17–3.1, we find both ways of handling an activity with two or more predecessor events. Preference between these is a matter of individual taste, and dummy activities of this sort may be inserted as deemed desirable.

Second, the BORIY analyst has limited his subdivision of the tasks to those of his own company. The printing company might well perform its own PERT analysis for the tasks it must perform in setting type, making cuts, proofing operations, cover manufacture, printing, and binding. However, in this project, the BORIY Corporation has contracted with the printer and its needs are satisfied by the network subdivisions as shown.

17–4. Critical Path with Time Certainty. There is a variation of the method called the CPM (*Critical Path Method*) which emphasizes the *activities*, and whose network usually shows the nodes as numbered shapes only. CPM was originally developed in nonmilitary applications, and the system has had somewhat different methods of time analysis. Also, some authors distinguish between PERT and CPM by noting that PERT emphasizes the events, and CPM emphasizes the activities. We shall, in this volume, not try to distinguish between these two methods. The distinction in practice has all but disappeared. We shall here refer to the entire analysis as PERT, and we shall indicate the extreme importance of the *critical path* in the PERT network.

Each PERT activity is associated with a measure of duration and a description of resource allocation. If, for example, the times for the various activities are known with certainty and are those numbers, in days, shown in Figure 17–4.1, then the project duration may be computed by the use of the form shown in Table 17–4.1. In that table, the several activities are identified by the numbers of their predecessor and successor events.

In this time computation, normally, actual calendar dates are used for the last two columns in the table. Here, however, for simplicity, we shall assume that the project begins on day 1; and the third and fourth columns in Table 17–4.1 represent the number of days which have passed when the activity starts and finishes, respectively. When two or more activities

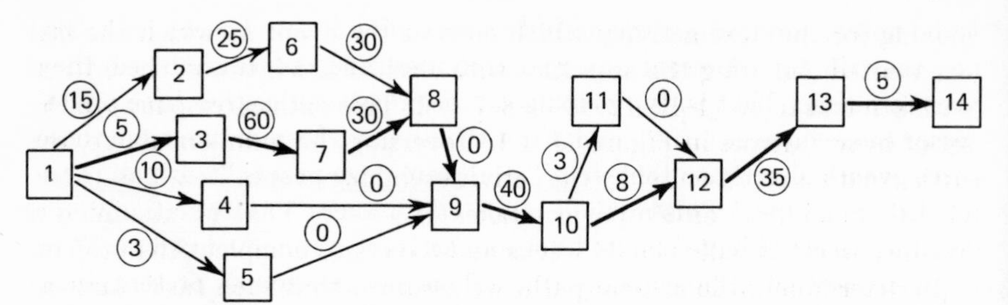

Fig. 17–4.1. PERT network for BORIY research project with exact activity durations entered for all activities. Critical path shown in heavy arrows.

TABLE 17–4.1

Computation of Project Duration via Critical Path

Activity (1)	Duration (2)		Days Passed when Activity Starts (3)		Days Passed when Activity Finishes (4)
1–2	15	+	0	=	15
1–3	5	+	0	=	5
1–4	10	+	0	=	10
1–5	3	+	0	=	3
2–6	25	+	15	=	40
3–7	60	+	5	=	65
4–9	0	+	10	=	~~10~~
5–9	0	+	3	=	~~3~~
6–8	30	+	40	=	~~70~~
7–8	30	+	65	=	95
8–9	0	+	95	=	95
9–10	40	+	95	=	135
10–11	3	+	135	=	138
10–12	8	+	135	=	143
11–12	0	+	138	=	~~138~~
12–13	35	+	143	=	178
13–14	5	+	178	=	183

terminate in the same event, we draw a line through the completion times of all but the last one to terminate, and these slashed earlier times are *ignored* in timing the succeeding activities. In this way, the time of the *longest* path through the network is represented by the last number in the last column. This is, of course, the *earliest* time by which the project can be completed.

Of course, the time units used for this analysis may be hours, days, weeks, months, or whatever units are most convenient. *Weeks* are probably the most common. Here, where the project is relatively small, we shall use *days* throughout.

The *critical path*, i.e., the route through the network which takes the most time, may be determined by working backward through Table 17–4.1, starting with activity 13–14, and working upward in column (1), looking for the next activity which ends at the event at which the last one started. Ignoring the activities with slashed finish times, the critical path is found to be 14–13–12–10–9–8–7–3–1. This path corresponds to the set of heavy arrows in Figure 17–4.1. Reversing the numbers above, the critical path is represented by the activities linking events: 1–3–7–8–9–10–12–13–14, and the entire project takes 183 days. That is, assuming a five-day week, it will take 36 weeks and 3 days to complete the project.

In determining the critical path, we assumed that each task starts as soon as possible, i.e., as soon as its predecessor event (or events) has occurred. Clearly, this is not necessary for any activity not on the critical path. For example, activity 10–12 takes eight days, while activities 10–11 and 11–12 take three days. Therefore, there is slack time of five days in the path 10–11–12, indicating that activity 10–11 may be delayed up to five days without causing slippage in the entire project.

However, on the critical path, any delay in any of the tasks causes a delay in the completion of the entire project.

The controllable variables in this system, with *certainty* in the time estimates, are the resource allocations to the various subtasks. Clearly, if management seeks to shorten the time for the entire project without adding to the cost, efforts could be made to shift resources from noncritical activities to critical activities, and if additional resources are available, they should be allocated to critical activities.

Optimal balance for earliest completion at a fixed cost would theoretically occur when resources are so shifted that all paths have the same duration. This is, of course, seldom possible in the real world because of indivisibilities in inputs and outputs, but it indicates the direction in which resource shifts should be made to advance the completion date.

17–5. Uncertain Time Estimates. In the last section, we assumed that the durations for all activities were known with certainty. This is seldom the case. The PERT method has become identified with an ingenious procedure for dealing with probabilistic estimates of activity durations. This procedure, which is based on psychological studies, assumes that the distribution of certain kinds of estimates of durations resembles the beta distribution. These estimates are obtained from the technical staff.

The person responsible for each activity is asked to provide three estimates of the time required for that activity. These estimates are: the *most likely time* (m), the *optimistic time* (a), and the *pessimistic time* (b). The latter two, the optimistic time and the pessimistic time, are usually associated with a subjective probability less than 0.01. That is, as described to the technical man who must make the estimate, the optimistic time is that time which, under normal circumstances, with no changes or breakthroughs, but with good luck at every point, could be attained or bettered less than once in 100 similar runs. The pessimistic time estimate is sought by a similar statement; i.e., that time which, without catastrophe, would be exceeded less than once in 100 runs. Actually, the mathematical methodology of PERT, using beta distributions, assumes that the optimistic time will not be bettered and the pessimistic time will not be exceeded.

These time estimates are entered on the PERT network diagram as a–m–b, where a is the *optimistic* time, m is the *most likely* time, and b is the *pessimistic* time. This is shown in Figure 17–5.1.

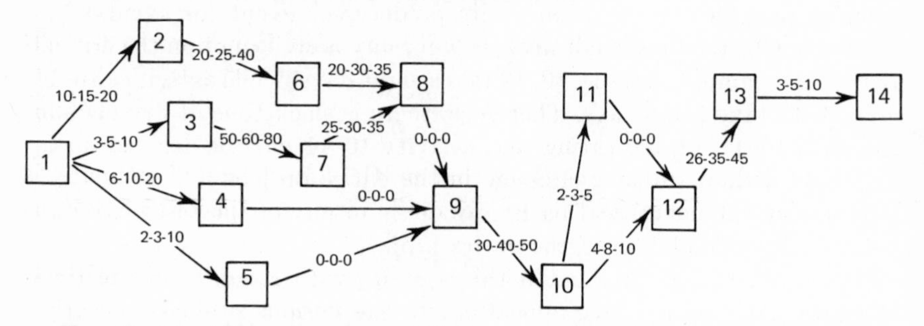

Fig. 17–5.1. PERT network for BORIY research project with three time estimates shown for each activity.

From the three time estimates, the mean time, t_e, is computed. As we have noted above, this computation is based on the assumption that a set of three time estimates, such as these, tend to resemble certain beta distributions, as shown in Figure 17–5.2. In other words, PERT assumes

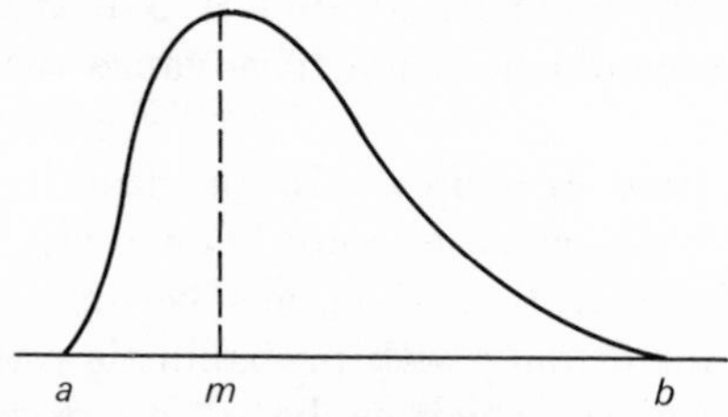

Fig. 17–5.2. Beta distribution with optimistic, most likely, and pessimistic time estimates.

that the duration of an activity is *a chance variable with beta distribution.* From Equation (6–10.1), the *pdf* for the beta distribution is

$$f(x) = \frac{(\alpha + \beta + 1)!}{\alpha!\,\beta!}\,x^{\alpha}(1 - x)^{\beta} \qquad \text{for } 0 < x < 1$$

Here α and β are used for the parameters of the beta distribution to distinguish them from a and b, the optimistic and pessimistic time estimates. (We here reserve the symbols a and b for the PERT time estimates, since they are almost universally used in that application.)

The theoretical formulas for the mean and standard deviation of a beta distribution are, from Equation (6–10.6),

$$E(x) = \mu = \frac{\alpha + 1}{\alpha + \beta + 2} \tag{17–5.1}$$

and, from Equation (6–10.11),

$$\sigma^2 = \frac{(\alpha + 1)(\beta + 1)}{(\alpha + \beta + 2)^2(\alpha + \beta + 3)} \tag{17–5.2}$$

The mode of a beta distribution, it will be recalled from Exercise 6–10, is

$$m = \frac{\alpha}{\alpha + \beta} \tag{17–5.3}$$

PERT makes the assumptions that m, the "most likely" estimate, is the mode of the beta distribution, that the mean or expected value, t_e, is

$$t_e = \frac{a + 4m + b}{6} \tag{17–5.4}$$

and that the expected standard deviation is $\frac{1}{6}$ the range from a to b:

$$\sigma_{t_e} = \frac{b - a}{6} \tag{17–5.5}$$

These assumptions are an integral part of the PERT method for dealing with uncertainty in the time durations of activities.

Let us examine these assumptions in the light of our knowledge about beta distributions. For simplicity, we shall let $a = 0$ and $b = 1$. This is a simple linear transformation for any values of a and b which might be estimated. Then, $0 \leq m \leq 1$, and the PERT assumptions are

$$t_e = \frac{4m + 1}{6} \tag{17–5.6}$$

and

$$\sigma_{t_e} = \frac{1}{6} \tag{17–5.7}$$

The assumption about the mean, i.e., that $t_e = \mu$, is, from Equations (17–5.6), (17–5.3), and (17–5.1), that

$$\frac{4\left(\dfrac{\alpha}{\alpha + \beta}\right) + 1}{6} = \frac{\alpha + 1}{\alpha + \beta + 2}$$

$$\frac{4\alpha + \alpha + \beta}{6(\alpha + \beta)} = \frac{\alpha + 1}{\alpha + \beta + 2}$$

$$\frac{5\alpha + \beta}{6(\alpha + \beta)} = \frac{\alpha + 1}{\alpha + \beta + 2} \tag{17–5.8}$$

For a beta distribution with $\alpha = 1$, $\beta = 3$, such as is shown in Figure 17–5.3, this assumption is met perfectly. For other beta distributions,

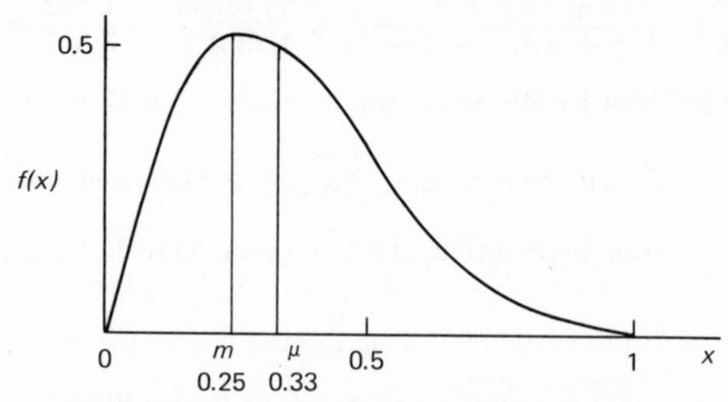

Fig. 17–5.3. Beta distribution with $\alpha = 1$, $\beta = 3$.

this assumption is not likely to introduce serious error. For example, in the negatively skewed beta distribution of Figure 6–10.1, where $\alpha = 6$, $\beta = 2$, the condition of Equation (17–5.8) yields for the PERT estimate

$$t_e = \frac{5\alpha + \beta}{6(\alpha + \beta)} = \frac{32}{48} = 0.67$$

for the exact beta distribution mean

$$\mu = \frac{\alpha + 1}{\alpha + \beta + 2} = \frac{7}{10} = 0.70$$

and the difference is small.

Finally, let us look at the beta distributions of Figure 6–10.1, where $\alpha = \beta$. There, of course,

$$\mu = \frac{\alpha + 1}{\alpha + \beta + 2} = \frac{\alpha + 1}{2\alpha + 2} = \frac{1}{2}$$

and similarly,

$$m = \frac{\alpha}{\alpha + \beta} = \frac{1}{2}$$

showing that a beta distribution in which $\alpha = \beta$ is symmetrical, since then $\mu = m$; i.e., the arithmetic mean equals the median.

For a symmetrical beta distribution, the PERT estimate of the mean is

$$t_e = \frac{5\alpha + \beta}{6(\alpha + \beta)} = \frac{6\alpha}{6(2\alpha)} = \frac{1}{2}$$

and the PERT assumption is exactly met for symmetrical distributions.

Similarly, for the standard deviation, for $\alpha = 1$, $\beta = 3$, the true standard deviation is, from Equation (17–5.2),

$$\sigma = \sqrt{\frac{(\alpha + 1)(\beta + 1)}{(\alpha + \beta + 2)^2(\alpha + \beta + 3)}} = \sqrt{\frac{(2)(4)}{(36)(7)}} = \frac{1}{3}\sqrt{\frac{2}{7}} = 0.18$$

as compared to the PERT assumption of 1/6, or 0.17 (to two decimal places).

For the beta distribution with $\alpha = 6$, $\beta = 2$, the exact formula yields

$$\sigma = \sqrt{\frac{(\alpha + 1)(\beta + 1)}{(\alpha + \beta + 2)^2(\alpha + \beta + 3)}} = \sqrt{\frac{(7)(3)}{(100)(11)}} = 0.14$$

as compared to 0.17 for the PERT assumption, and, for the symmetrical distributions of Figure 6–10.1:

for $\alpha = \beta = 1$

$$\sigma = \sqrt{\frac{4}{(16)(5)}} = \sqrt{0.05} = 0.22$$

and for $\alpha = \beta = 2$

$$\sigma = \sqrt{\frac{9}{(36)(7)}} = \frac{1}{2}\sqrt{\frac{1}{7}} = 0.19$$

as compared to the PERT assumption of 0.17.

In general, we can conclude that the assumptions made by the PERT technique seem to be reasonably well justified.

In summary, then, PERT makes three seemingly quite reasonable assumptions in the treatment of uncertainty in the time estimates. First, it assumes that the duration of an activity is a random variable with beta distribution, with mode m the *most likely time estimate.* Second, it assumes that the mean time is t_e, as given by Equation (17–5.4) for the *expected time:*

$$t_e = \frac{a + 4m + b}{6} \tag{17–5.4}$$

where: a is the optimistic estimate
m is the most likely estimate
b is the pessimistic estimate

Third, it assumes that the standard deviation is given by Equation (17–5.5);

$$\sigma_{t_e} = \frac{b - a}{6} \tag{17–5.5}$$

In Table 17–5.1, the mean duration, t_e, and the variance, $\sigma_{t_e}^2$, for each activity are computed from Equations (17–5.4) and (17–5.5) for later use. The computations are carried to one decimal place only. Greater precision would be both unwarranted and useless.

TABLE 17–5.1

BORIY Corporation Research Project
Computation of Expected Durations and Variances

Activity	a	m	b	$t_e = \frac{a + 4m + b}{6}$	$\sigma_{t_e} = \frac{b - a}{6}$	$\sigma_{t_e}^2$
1–2	10	15	20	15.0	1.7	2.9
1–3	3	5	10	5.5	1.2	1.4
1–4	6	10	20	11.0	2.3	5.3
1–5	2	3	10	4.0	1.3	1.7
2–6	20	25	40	26.7	3.3	10.9
3–7	50	60	80	61.7	5.0	25.0
4–9	0	0	0	0	0	0
5–9	0	0	0	0	0	0
6–8	20	30	35	29.2	2.5	6.3
7–8	25	30	35	30.0	1.7	2.9
8–9	0	0	0	0	0	0
9–10	30	40	50	40.0	3.3	10.9
10–11	2	3	5	3.2	0.5	0.3
10–12	4	8	10	7.7	1.0	1.0
11–12	0	0	0	0	0	0
12–13	26	35	45	35.2	3.2	10.2
13–14	3	5	10	5.5	1.2	1.4

17–6. Time Calculations. In order to illustrate the PERT procedures, we shall continue to analyze the BORIY research problem introduced in Section 17–3 and portrayed in Figures 17–3.1 and 17–5.1. The three time estimates of Figure 17–5.1 will be used, and a table similar to Table 17–4.1 is computed using the t_e values. This is shown in Table 17–6.1, which, in any sizeable project, would be prepared by an electronic computer, as would Table 17–5.1, on which it is based. Computer programs to perform the required PERT analyses and computations are readily available.

The entries in the column headed T_E are the day (or date) on which the successor event is expected to be achieved, i.e., the day on which the activity is expected to be completed. The value of T_E for each activity's successor event is computed by adding to the T_E for the predecessor event the t_e for the activity. When two or more activities have the same successor event, different values of T_E will usually result. We mark all but the largest with a slash as before and ignore these slashed values of T_E when calculating T_E for succeeding events.

The subscript in the symbol T_E may be understood to represent "earliest," and T_E is the *earliest expected time* for the event to be achieved. True, it represents the longest, in time, of all paths leading to that event, but the event cannot be achieved until all preceding activities have been completed, and therefore the end of the longest path represents the earliest time in which the event can be achieved.

TABLE 17–6.1

BORIY Corporation Research Project
PERT Computations

Event: Predecessor	Event: Successor	Activity Description	Expected Duration t_e	Expected Variance $\sigma_{t_e}^2$	Day (Successor Event) Expected T_E	Latest Day Allowed T_L	Slack $T_L - T_E$
1	2	Prepare outline	15.0	2.9	15.0	41.3	26.3
1	3	Design field work	5.5	1.4	5.5	5.5	0
1	4	Negotiate for printing	11.0	5.3	11.0	97.2	86.2
1	5	Design book	4.0	1.7	4.0	97.2	93.2
2	6	Prepare computer program	26.7	10.9	41.7	68.0	26.3
3	7	Conduct field work	61.7	25.0	67.2	67.2	0
4	9	———	0.0	0	~~11.0~~	97.2	86.2
5	9	———	0.0	0	~~4.0~~	97.2	93.2
6	8	Analysis and writing	29.2	6.3	~~70.9~~	97.2	26.3
7	8	Analysis and writing	30.0	2.9	97.2	97.2	0
8	9	———	0.0	0	97.2	97.2	0
9	10	Printer set type	40.0	10.9	137.2	137.2	0
10	11	Prepare index	3.2	0.3	140.4	144.9	4.5
10	12	Read proofs	7.7	1.0	144.9	144.9	0
11	12	———	0.0	0	~~140.4~~	144.9	4.5
12	13	Print and bind	35.2	10.2	180.1	180.1	0
13	14	Distribute books	5.5	1.4	185.6	185.6	0

T_E figures with line drawn through them are not true T_E for their respective events since, for each, there is another, more time-consuming path with a later T_E.

In Table 17–6.1, as in Table 17–4.1, the critical path is seen to be 1–3–7–8–9–10–12–13–14, and the expected time of finishing, T_E, is 185.6 days. We could, as many might wish to do, round all t_e on the table upward to the next complete day, thereby assuming that, if a task is finished sometime during a day, the rest of the day is not usable for starting the next task. However, we shall not do this. These t_e are *expected* durations, and the consistent bias which such a rounding procedure would introduce is unwarranted. Figure 17–6.1 shows the network with the expected durations on the activity arrows and the T_E circled in the event boxes.

Slack is the difference between the expected time (T_E) and the *latest allowable completion time* (T_L). Let us see how T_L is computed, and then we shall be in a position to see the implications of the slack. Note that T_E and T_L, which we are about to consider, refer to *events*, i.e., the successor events for the appropriate activity.

To compute T_L for each event, start at the scheduled completion date,

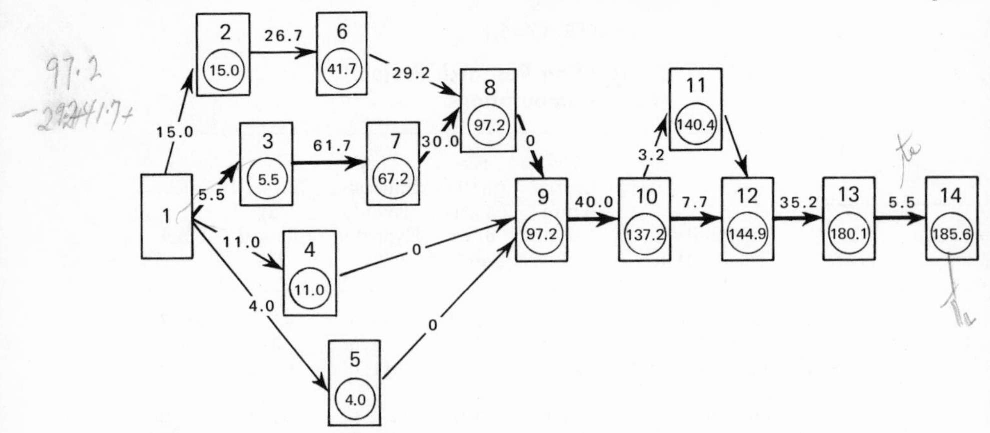

Fig. 17–6.1. PERT network for BORIY research project with t_e shown on arrows and T_E circled in boxes.

or if as in this case there is none given, start at the T_E for the final event. Subtract from it the t_e for the preceding activity to arrive at the latest allowable completion time (T_L) for the predecessor event. Enter the resulting T_L value on the line for the activity for which that event is successor. Continue working backward through the network (upward on the table), subtracting from the T_L of each successor event the t_e of the preceding activity, to arrive at the T_L for the predecessor event, and enter the T_L on the line for the activity for which that event is successor. T_L is the latest allowable time for that successor event because it is *the latest allowable time for starting the succeeding activity.* When an event has two or more successor events, the T_L which is used is the *lowest.* For example, event 10 in the table on the line for activity 9–10, shows $T_L = 137.2$. This is the lower of the 137.2 generated on the path 10–12 and the (discarded) value 141.7 generated on the path 10–11–12.

Each entry in the *slack* column in Table 17–6.1 is the number of days which the *successor* event may be delayed beyond its T_E without causing the final project completion date to slip. Note that the slack refers to the complete path. That is, the slack value of 26.3 days refers to the *path* 1–2–6–8, and the slack value of 86.2 days refers to the *path* 1–4–9. Similarly, the slack value of 93.2 days refers to the path 1–5–9, and the slack value of 4.5 days refers to the path 10–11–12. The delay represented by the slack may be applied at management's discretion at any point along the slack path. On the critical path, there is no slack, and conversely, all events with zero slack, i.e., all events on zero-slack paths, may be called *critical events.*

Wherever there is a great deal of slack, management may wish to consider shifting resources from that path to expedite activities on the critical path. Conversely, low slack values indicate that that path, while not critical, could become critical if relatively small changes occur in time durations.

17–7. Statistical Inference in Time Estimates. Thus far we have used the t_e values, the *expected values,* and the results which we have obtained are the *average* or *expected* completion times, slack times, etc. Now, since we have estimates of the standard deviations of all the t_e, we can make inferential statements about these results.

Even without the standard deviation, we could say that, since t_e and T_E are *expected values,*

$$P(t < t_e) = 0.5 \qquad \text{and} \qquad P(T < T_E) = 0.5$$

where t and T are *actual* durations and completion times, respectively

However, since we do have the standard deviations, we can make more useful statements.

The variance of the T_E for the entire project may be found by summing the variances of all the activities along the critical path. That is

$$\sigma_{T_E}{}^2 = \Sigma\sigma^2 \tag{17–7.1}$$

where: $\Sigma\sigma^2$ is the sum of the activity variances along the path
$\sigma_{T_E}{}^2$ is the variance for that path

Many analysts prefer to use $\Sigma\sigma^2$ in order to emphasize that it is a *sum* of individual activity variances.

It has been found empirically that, for a path consisting of several activities, the distribution of time to complete the path is well approximated by the normal distribution with mean T_E and variance $\sigma_{T_E}{}^2 = \Sigma\sigma^2$.

In Table 17–6.1 the column headed $\sigma_{t_e}{}^2$ has been taken from Table 17–5.1. The sum of the eight variances along the critical path, i.e., those on the same line with zero slack values, is $\Sigma\sigma^2 = 52.8$. Therefore,

$$\sigma_{T_E} = \sqrt{\Sigma\sigma^2} = \sqrt{52.8} = 7.27 \text{ days}$$

This may be interpreted to mean that the time to complete the project is a random variable, normally distributed, with mean 185.6 days and standard deviation 7.27 days. This distribution is shown in Figure 17–7.1.

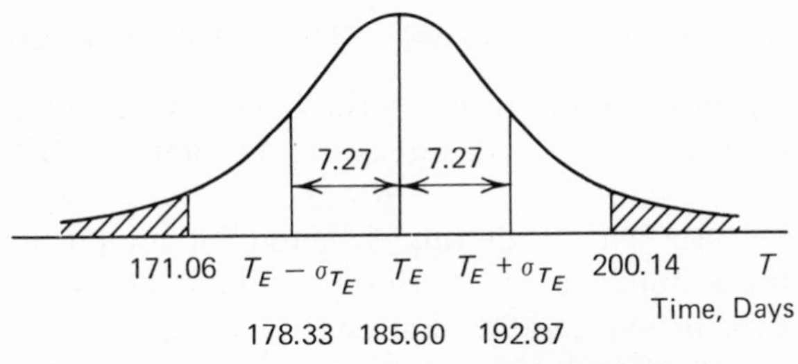

Fig. 17–7.1. Distribution of T_E on critical path for the BORIY research project.

From the diagram, we can see that the probability is 95.5 that the task will be completed in the period roughly between 171 days and 200 days. If our scheduled deadline (T_S) is 198 days, the probability that we will meet the deadline is computed in the usual way. Let T be the time in which the project is completed; then,

$$z = \frac{T_S - T_E}{\sigma_{T_E}} = \frac{198.0 - 185.6}{7.27} = \frac{12.4}{7.27} = 1.71$$

$$P(T \leq T_S) = F(1.71) = 0.95637$$

The probability that the deadline will be met is 0.96. Also, if there is a bonus for completion in 180 days (T_B),

$$z = \frac{T_B - T_E}{\sigma_{T_E}} = \frac{180.0 - 185.6}{7.27} = -\frac{5.6}{7.27} = -0.77$$

$$P(T \leq T_B) = F(-0.77) = 0.22065$$

The probability that the bonus will be earned is 0.22.

Actually, the probabilities are slightly less than those computed here, since it is possible, though very unlikely here, that the project will miss the bonus or miss the deadline because of time loss *along some other path, which then turns out to be in fact the critical path.* In practice, where the critical path does not differ so markedly, the computation should be performed over every possible path.

We shall illustrate this by considering the probability of making the bonus.

The probability of *failing* to make the bonus on the critical path, 1–3–7–8–9–10–11–12–13–14, is 0.78.

Along the noncritical path, 1–2–6–8–9–10–11–12–13–14, the slack is $26.3 + 4.5 = 30.8$ days, indicating that T_E along that path is 154.8 days. Also, $\Sigma\sigma^2 = 42.9$ along that path, and $\sqrt{42.9} = 6.55$. The probability of failing to make the bonus along that path is $P(T > 180)$ in a normal distribution, with mean 154.8 and standard deviation 6.55.

$$z = \frac{180.0 - 154.8}{6.55} = \frac{25.2}{6.55} = 3.85$$

$$P(T > 180) = 1 - F(3.85) = 1 - 0.99994 = 0.00006$$

The probability of failing to make the bonus along any of the other paths in this illustration is even smaller and is not worth bothering to compute.

It should be clear that, while this technique for computing the probability of failure is applicable to a relatively simple network in which all noncritical paths have a great deal of slack and therefore the probability of failure along those paths is close to zero, it cannot be applied to networks which have noncritical paths with *small* amounts of slack. The computation of the probability of failure in large networks with many low-slack noncritical paths can become extremely complex. This is because the probability of failure along some one of the other paths becomes large and, indeed, the probability of their union may easily exceed the probability of failure on the critical path.

Then, we might say that the path which we have referred to as the critical path is in actuality the *most likely critical path*, and when a complex project is actually conducted, the probability that this most likely critical path will turn out to be the actual critical path may be very small. That is, this *first* critical path is the *most likely* of all paths, but its likelihood may nevertheless be very small.

In very complex networks, the probability that this first critical path will turn out to be the actual critical path may be so small that management can be quite confident that some other path will turn out to be critical. For this reason, it is common to evaluate and observe the second, third, fourth, etc., critical paths as well as the first, and to observe continuously the actual progress of the project with the additional purpose of ascertaining and anticipating changes in the critical path. Clearly, this is an extremely important and valuable use of the PERT technique.

17–8. The Value and Extensions of PERT. Today PERT is widely used in nonmilitary as well as military projects. Its benefits go beyond the obvious control capability which it imparts to management. That is, not only can management detect when a project schedule is in danger and identify the location of the difficulty, but it enables management to look ahead in time and anticipate and correct possible difficulties before they actually arise.

Also, the precise, disciplined requirements for the construction of a PERT network force management to analyze the project with more care and detail than might otherwise be the case. In some cases, the introduction of PERT has changed not only the scheduling and planning functions, but the entire structure and management of organizations.

Recently, intensive efforts have been directed toward enlarging the scope of PERT by adding cost and, sometimes, profit calculations.

The methodology which we have studied in this chapter is often called PERT/TIME to distinguish it from PERT/COST and PERT/PROFIT, techniques being developed to enable control of the cost and, ultimately, the profit of a project as well as the time. It is in the combinations of PERT with cost and profit considerations that one seeks to analyze the costs involved in the addition of new resources to the project, the shifting of resources from slack paths to the critical path, and the balance of cost objectives against time objectives for the purpose of optimal allocation of resources over the life of the project. The basic requirement for these analyses is a set of estimates of the costs as well as the time for each activity. That is, the cost of the minimum time operation may be quite different from the cost for some longer time. Also, the time required for the minimum cost completion of an activity can be expected to be quite different from the time for a more costly procedure.

Armed with estimates of these times and costs and with estimates of the relationship between cost changes and time changes for all, or at least the decisive, activities, the manager can proceed to balance the time and cost objectives and plan for the minimum-cost procedure that will meet some time schedule, or, conversely, he may seek the minimum-time procedure subject to specified cost constraints. Ultimately, he should try to measure both time and costs on some single objective-function scale and seek to schedule the project to optimize this objective function over the whole project or even over a set of projects.

SUGGESTIONS FOR FURTHER READING

Evarts, H. F. *Introduction to PERT*. Boston: Allyn & Bacon, Inc., 1964.

Hansen, B. J. *Practical PERT*, Washington, D.C.: American Aviation Publications, 1964.

MacCrimmon, K. R., and C. A. Ryavec. "An Analytic Study of the PERT Assumptions," *Operations Research*, Vol. 12, No. 1 (January-February, 1964).

Malcolm, D. G., J. H. Roseboom, C. E. Clark, and W. Fazar. "Application of a Technique for Research and Development Program Evaluation," *Operations Research*, Vol. 7, No. 5, (September-October, 1959).

PERT, Program Evaluation Research Task, Phase I Summary Report, Special Projects Office, Bureau of Ordnance, Department of the Navy, Washington, D.C., July, 1958.

Starr, M. K. *Production Management: Systems and Synthesis*. Englewood Cliffs, N.J.: Prentice-Hall, Inc., 1964.

Part VI

DECISION THEORY

18

Game Theory

18–1. Decision Making Under Conflict. Decision making *under conflict* was one of the four categories of decisions which were evolved in the discussion of the decision model in Section 1-11. It will be recalled that this decision situation is that in which there are two or more possible states of nature, and the decision maker knows that these states of nature are controlled by an adverse intellect, i.e., an opponent whose interests are contrary to his own. The states of nature for the first decision maker, whom we shall call A, are actually the courses of action of his opponent, B, and B's states of nature are A's courses of action. The analysis of this kind of situation is the subject matter of *game theory.*

At the outset we must emphasize that game theory has had only very limited success in application to business situations. The kinds of situations with which game theory deals most successfully simply do not occur frequently or widely in business, if at all. We shall examine the reasons for this presently. Clearly, the reason is not that business situations lack the interplay of opposing interests. Indeed marketing competition and labor-management negotiations are two areas of business which are characterized by direct conflict of interests. Nevertheless, for even these situations, the requirements for the application of game theory are seldom met. It is probably safe to say that the most successful applications of game theory to actual situations have been in the military. Certainly that is where it has been most extensively applied.

However, it does not follow from this that those of us who are interested primarily in business applications should ignore game theory. Far from it. Game theory offers a well-conceived and well-thought-out discipline for analyzing the consequences of certain clear and well-defined assumptions about a system, and as such it can provide us with a sharpened understanding of many types of real-world situations, even though these real situations do not conform to the carefully specified assumptions of some areas of game theory.

18–2. Two-Person Zero-Sum Games. We shall look first at two-person zero-sum games. This is the class of games for which the theory has been most satisfactorily developed and for which solutions are always available.

A two-person zero-sum game is one in which, first, there are two opposing players or interests. These may be individuals, firms, or groups. Second, when one player gains, the other loses, and the more one gains, the more the other loses. That is, the two interests are *strictly competitive.* It is not possible for the two interests to agree to conspire together to their mutual interest. Clearly, if they could both gain by cooperating with one another, such gain must be at the expense of yet another party, such as when two selling competitors agree to raise prices to the disadvantage of their customers. Then, of course, it is not a two-person game, there being more than two opposing interests.

In a two-person zero-sum game, there are only two opposing interests, and the qualification *zero-sum* derives from the fact that, since one's gain is the other's loss, the *sum* of payoffs to the two players is zero; i.e., they are equal and opposite.

18–3. Courses of Action. A course of action in game theory is a *complete* plan of action. It may be a single- or a multiple-step plan such as, for example, in a labor contract negotiation, a single-step management course of action might be simply "Refuse any increase," or "Accept any union demand below $.25 per hour and thus keep production rolling," or "Offer half of the union's first demand." A multiple-step course of action might be, for example, "Offer half of the union's first demand, and if that is not accepted, continue to increase the offer at the rate of 2¢ to 5¢ per day of hard bargaining until agreement is reached."

18–4. The Game Matrix. We shall deal with *finite* games. That is, there is, for each player, a finite number of courses of action. The first player, A, has m courses of action available, and the second player, B, has n courses of action available. For each combination of courses of action, A_i and B_j, there is a known outcome E_{ij}, and the whole game may be represented by an $m \times n$ matrix such as is shown in Figure 18–4.1. The entries in the body of the matrix may be interpreted as payoffs from player B to player A, so that A wishes a large (algebraically) value of E_{ij} and B seeks a small value.

Each player is assumed to know all of the information contained in the matrix. That is, each knows (1) all of the courses of action available to

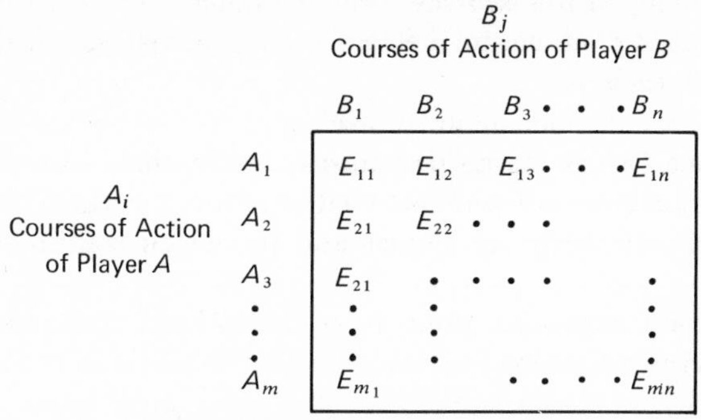

B_j
Courses of Action of Player B

A_i
Courses of Action of Player A

	B_1	B_2	$B_3 \cdots$	$\cdot B_n$
A_1	E_{11}	E_{12}	$E_{13} \cdots$	$\cdot E_{1n}$
A_2	E_{21}	$E_{22} \cdots$		
A_3	E_{21}	$\cdots$	$\cdots$	$\cdot$
$\vdots$	$\vdots$	$\vdots$		$\vdots$
A_m	E_{m_1}		$\cdots$	$\cdot E_{mn}$

Fig. 18–4.1. Matrix representation of a two-person finite zero-sum game. The entries E_{ij} are the payoffs from player B to player A.

both himself and his opponent, (2) the entire pattern of outcomes, and (3) the preference pattern of each. When the outcomes are expressed in numerical terms in payoff units, such as for example money or A's market-share points, such that A prefers high values and B prefers low values, then the preference patterns are clear. We shall assume that we can describe the payoffs in such numerical terms and that these numbers do indeed represent utility values to A and disutility values to B.

Clearly, as we have noted, situations such as this do not arise often except in athletics or in competitive games of skill. They may sometimes arise, however, in labor–management bargaining, competitive bidding, or bilateral trade, and of course, in war. Although such two-person zero-sum games are not common, they are important because the framework of these relatively simple games is essential for understanding the more complex n-person, non–zero-sum games, which probably approach reality more closely but for which solutions are not so readily available.

18–5. A Game with a Saddle Point. Let us consider the *two-person finite zero-sum game* represented in Figure 18–5.1. The situation

	B_1	B_2	B_3	B_4
A_1	40†	34	30*	33
A_2	38	35*†	36	37
A_3	28*	33	37†	38†

Fig. 18–5.1. A 3 × 4 two-person finite zero-sum game with a saddle point.

may be taken to represent negotiation between a buyer B and a seller A for a fixed amount of goods or services, where the courses of action for each are bargaining courses of action involving bids, offers, timing, bluffing, etc. The entries are the prices in dollars which will result from each combination of an A_i and a B_j. Since these are payments from B to A, this is a zero-sum game.

The basic assumption made by each player in selecting his course of action in game theory is the pessimistic assumption that the opponent will select his best counter course of action. Since each player must select his course of action *without* knowledge of his opponent's selection, he selects his *safest* course of action.

As player A surveys his possible courses of action, he sees that (as indicated by the asterisks)

If he selects A_1, the minimum he can get is \$30
If he selects A_2, the minimum he can get is \$35
If he selects A_3, the minimum he can get is \$28.

Therefore, by selecting A_2, he can assure himself *at least* \$35. That is the maximum of the minima. It is the most revenue he can assure for himself, and A_2 is A's *maximin course of action.*

Similarly, player B surveys his possible courses of action and notes that (as indicated by the daggers)

If he selects B_1, the maximum which he must pay is \$40
If he selects B_2, the maximum which he must pay is \$35
If he selects B_3, the maximum which he must pay is \$37
If he selects B_4, the maximum which he must pay is \$38.

Therefore, by selecting B_2, he can assure that he will pay *at most* \$35. That is the minimum of the maxima. It is the least cost he can assure for himself, and B_2 is B's *minimax course of action.*

In the matrix of Figure 18–5.1, the maximin (the maximum of the row minima) has the same value as the minimax (the minimum of the column maxima). This occurs at the point A_2,B_2. This point is called a *saddle point* or an *equilibrium point,* and the courses of action A_2 and B_2 are called an *equilibrium pair of courses of action.* These two courses of action are said to be *in equilibrium.*

In such an equilibrium situation, each player, by choosing the best outcome of which he can be sure, is said to optimize his *security level,* and if either player were to learn in advance the course of action of the other, he could not improve himself by changing his own course of action.

An equilibrium point such as A_2,B_2 in this illustration is called a *saddle point,* because it is at the same time the row minimum and the column maximum. This corresponds to the concept of the saddle point in meteorological maps or geographical contours, as shown in Figure 18–5.2. In the figure, imagine that the two points marked H are the peaks of two hills, and the lines are lines of constant elevation. Then the saddle point is the

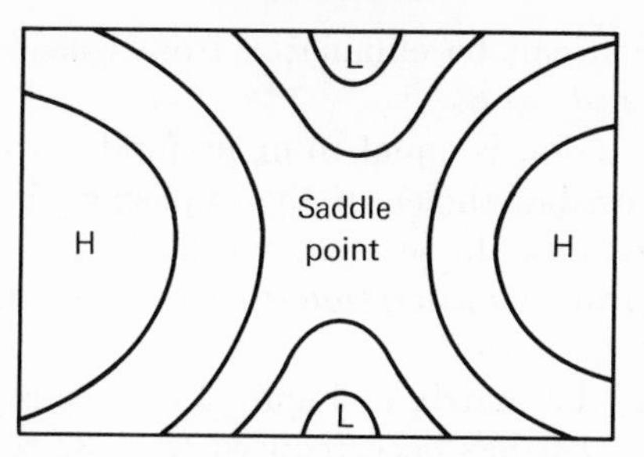

Fig. 18–5.2. A saddle point as seen on a weather map or a contour plan.

highest point on a north–south pass between these hills. Its similarity to a saddle shape should be evident.

Thus, at the saddle point, no other outcome in the column is preferable to A and no other outcome in the row is preferable to B. Neither player can improve the outcome by changing his course of action if the other player does not. Each has made the best possible counter choice against the other.

Not all games have saddle points. When there is no saddle point, the solution is different, and we shall examine this kind of situation below in Section 18–9. To ascertain whether there is a saddle point, identify all of the row minima, as we have done with asterisks in Figure 18–5.1, and identify all of the column maxima, as we have done with daggers in Figure 18–5.1. If any point has both identifying marks, that is the saddle point. In working with pencil and paper, it is usually more convenient to identify these row maxima by a more distinct mark, such as encircling the appropriate numbers. Then the column minima may be identified by enclosing them in squares or by encircling them in a different color pencil. If there is more than one saddle point, all should be marked. They must, of course, all have the same value.

18–6. The Value of the Game. In the game represented by the matrix of Figure 18–5.1, the *value of the game* is $35. That is the payoff entry at the saddle point. It is the largest amount which A can be sure of getting, and it is the minimum amount which B can be required to pay, if both players select their optimal courses of action. If A were to be required to pay to play this game (and if his other costs were all zero), then he should be willing to pay up to $35 to play the game. It is not worth more, and it should not be made available for less.

18–7. Dominance. In Figure 18–5.1, course of action B_4 would never be selected by player B, because for any and every A_i, B_3 is preferable to B_4. That is, every entry in the B_4 column is higher than the respective row entry in column B_3. Clearly then, B_4 will never be selected, and that course of action can be eliminated from consideration. Course of action B_4 is *dominated* by B_3.

If one course of action is equal to or preferable to another course of action for every possible choice of the opposing player, then the first course of action *dominates* the second, and the dominated course of action may be eliminated from consideration since the *dominant* course of action will always be preferable to it.

In Figure 18–7.1, the matrix of Figure 18–5.1 is reproduced with but one change, namely, E_{33} has been reduced from 37 to 35. However, this

	B_1	B_2	B_3	B_4
A_1	40	34	30	33
A_2	38	35	36	37
A_3	28	33	35	38

Fig. 18–7.1. Game matrix with dominance.

change makes for successive dominance. That is, column B_4 may be eliminated since it is dominated by B_3. Then, with that column missing, the bottom row may be eliminated, since A_3 is then dominated by A_2. Then, B_1 is dominated by either of the remaining two B_j. Finally, A_1 is now dominated by A_2, and then B_3 is dominated by B_2, leaving only the saddle point at A_2,B_2. The solution and the value of the game are therefore unchanged. However, in the solution of games by algebraic methods, as we shall see below, it is extremely helpful to simplify the matrix by the elimination of dominated courses of action. Thus, in any attempted solution of a game matrix, the first step should always be examination for dominance and elimination of dominated courses of action, taking advantage of such successive dominance as may occur.

18–8. A Military Illustration. Probably the most widely known real-world illustration of game theory is that reported by and analyzed by O. G. Haywood[1] dealing with the Rabaul–Lae convoy situation in the struggle for New Guinea in February 1943 in World War II. Haywood points out that the doctrine of decision of the armed forces of the United States is based on enemy *capabilities* rather than enemy *intentions*. That is, a commander should choose his course of action on the basis of his estimate of what the enemy *is able to do* in response, rather than on the basis of his estimate of what the enemy *is going to do*. (If General Washington had been so indoctrinated, would he have crossed the Delaware River on that fateful night?)

[1] Haywood, O. G., Jr., "Military Decision and Game Theory," *Journal of the Operations Research Society of America*, 2:365–85, 1954.

In any event, this doctrine of being guided by enemy capabilities is consistent with the conservative game-theoretic solution of seeking out the optimum security level.

In the Pacific naval situation described by Haywood, the Allied Air Forces in the Southwest Pacific Area received intelligence reports indicating that a Japanese convoy was assembling at Rabaul (New Britain) for movement to Lae (New Guinea).

General Kenney, the American commander, recognized that the Japanese commander had two routes from which to select. He could proceed north of New Britain or south of it. Either route would require three days for the trip.

General Kenney's problem was the deployment of his reconnaissance aircraft, with a view to discovering the convoy as soon as possible, to maximize the length of time in which the convoy would be subject to bombing from the air. He could concentrate his search effort on the northerly route or on the southerly route. Visibility was expected to be poor on the northerly route but good on the southerly route.

Measuring the outcome in terms of days of bombing, General Kenney reasoned that, if he selected the northerly route for concentration of his search effort, and the convoy sailed on the northerly route, the search effort would be hampered by poor visibility, and the convoy would not be discovered until the second day, with the result that there would be two days of attack; and if the convoy went south, a small reconnaissance force there also would, in the clear weather, discover the convoy on the second day, giving two days of bombing.

If, however, the reconnaissance effort were concentrated in the south, the convoy would be discovered on the first day if it went south, resulting in three days of bombing; and if the convoy went north, the limited search force there, in the poor visibility, would not discover the convoy until the third day, with the result of only one day of bombing. This situation is represented in game-theoretic matrix formulation in Figure 18–8.1. A rough map of the area is shown in Figure 18–8.2.

			Convoy Route	
			B_1 North	B_2 South
Allied Air Search	A_1	North	2 days* †	2 days*
	A_2	South	1 day*	3 days†

Fig. 18–8.1. Matrix representation of Rabaul-Lae convoy situation.

The courses of action A_1, B_1 clearly constitute a saddle point. Both General Kenney and the Japanese commander selected the northerly

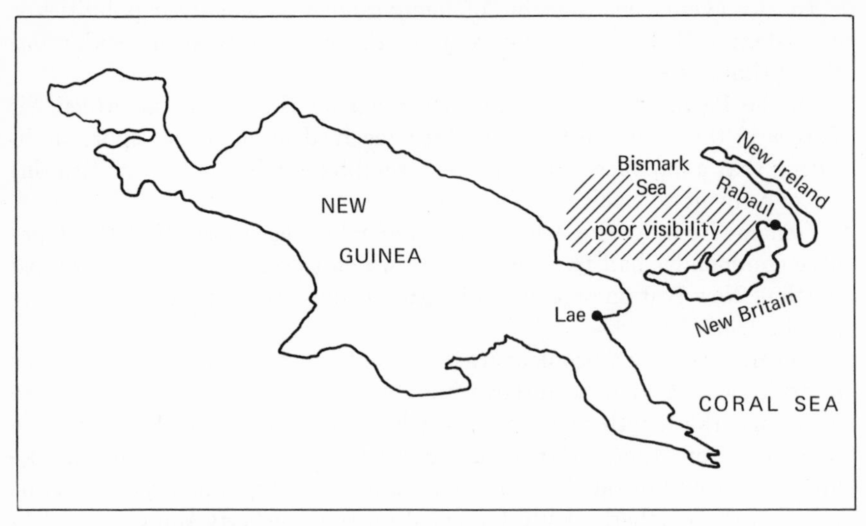

Fig. 18–8.2. Map of the New Guinea–New Britain area.

route. The result was, as predicted, two days of bombing and the disastrous defeat for the Japanese in what has become known as the Battle of the Bismarck Sea.

The Japanese disaster did not result from an error of decision on the part of the Japanese commander. His decision was the correct one under the circumstances that the trip had to be attempted. Indeed, examination of the matrix of Figure 18–8.1 indicates that B_1 is a dominant course of action. Under no circumstances should the convoy have sailed on the southerly route.

18–9. A Game Without a Saddle Point. The simplest case of a two-person zero-sum game without a saddle point is any 2×2 game in which the two lowest values are on one diagonal and the two highest are on the other diagonal, as shown in Figure 18–9.1. In the situation repre-

	B_1	B_2
A_1	5*	35†
A_2	20†	10*

Fig. 18–9.1. Two-person zero-sum game without a saddle point.

sented by that figure, there is no saddle point. A's maximin course of action is A_2, yielding a security level of 10, while B's minimax course of action is B_1, with its security level of 20. Thus, as A sees it, his optimal course of action yields him a "revenue" of 10 from B, while B finds that his optimal course of action involves a "payment" of 20 to A. Clearly, there is a difference in the amount which A expects to receive and that which B expects to pay, and, of course, each player would like to appropriate as much of this difference as possible.

It will be recalled that, in the previous illustrations with saddle points, if each player knew the other's course of action, there was still no benefit to be derived by changing courses of action. It is not so here. If B reasons that A will select his maximin course of action, A_2, costing B 20 if B, at the same time, selects his minimax course of action, B_1; then B might decide to be wily and select B_2, thereby reducing his cost to 10. However, then A might reason that B will do exactly that, expecting A to adhere to his maximin, and being shrewd A might surprise B by selecting A_1, which increases B's cost and A's revenue to 35. However, B might be sufficiently wily to anticipate A's devious reasoning and select B_1, reducing his cost to 5. But A, who has been a skillful gamesman all his life may be able to reconstruct this entire planning process of B, and to frustrate it by selecting A_2. Now they have made a full circuit of the matrix, and still nothing is solved. This "He knows that I know that he knows that . . . , etc." type of reasoning has no necessary stopping point. Is there a way to solve the problem? Yes there is, and this is one of the major contributions of Von Neumann and Morganstern in their classic *Theory of Games and Economic Behavior.*

18–10. Mixed Strategies. Any single course of action, A_i or B_j, which a player may select, is referred to as a *pure strategy*, and in the illustrations prior to that of the last section, the equilibrium pairs were pure strategies. Let us now enlarge the set of available strategies to include not only the listed set of courses of action, but also now the set of *mixed strategies*, where a mixed strategy is a probabilistic combination of courses of action. For example, if the player's available courses of action are the set $\{A_1, A_2, \ldots, A_m\}$, and if $(x_1, x_2, \ldots, x_m)$ is a probability vector, where $\sum_{i=1}^{m} x_i = 1$, then a mixed strategy is a decision to perform some chance process (select from a table of random numbers, cast dice, spin a rotating pointer, etc.) with m exhaustive and mutually exclusive outcomes with probabilities $x_1, x_2, \ldots, x_m$, respectively, and to adopt A_i if the ith outcome occurs. Thus, in effect, a *strategy* consists of a set of probabilities $(x_1, x_2, \ldots, x_m)$ such that each course of action A_i will be selected with probability x_i; i.e., $x_i = P(A_i)$. In a *mixed strategy*, at least two of the probabilities are greater than zero. In a *pure strategy*, one of the probabilities is equal to 1, and all the others are equal to zero.

The famous minimax theorem first proved by Von Neumann states that, for *every* two-person zero-sum game, there is a set of equilibrium strategies. We have seen that, when there is a saddle point, these equilibrium strategies are pure strategies. Now we shall find that, when there is no saddle point, the equilibrium strategies are mixed strategies but the characteristics of the solution are the same. That is, neither player has any incentive to change his strategy even if he discovers his opponent's strategy. A's selected mixed strategy is his *maximin mixed strategy,* and B's is his *minimax mixed strategy.* Also, the *value of the game* is uniquely determined by the mixed strategies, just as it was by the pure strategies in the case of the games with saddle points.

The maximin mixed strategy for player A is such that his *expected* payoff, v, is the highest of all possible minimum values, and B's minimax mixed strategy will keep A's expected payoff from exceeding v. Thus, v is the value of the game, and all of the characteristics of the pure strategy solutions to the saddle point games are met by the mixed strategy solutions to the general case.

We can now solve the 2×2 two-person zero-sum game of Figure 18–9.1. In the simple 2×2 case, we find the optimal mixed strategy by asserting that the expected payoff for each player must be independent of the strategy selected by the other player. Thus, for A, if $x_i = P(A_i)$, then,

If B selects B_1, A's expected payoff is $5x_1 + 20x_2$
If B selects B_2, A's expected payoff is $35x_1 + 10x_2$

Setting these expected payoffs equal,

$$5x_1 + 20x_2 = 35x_1 + 10x_2$$
$$10x_2 = 30x_1$$
$$x_2 = 3x_1$$

Then, since $x_1 + x_2 = 1$,

$$x_1 = 0.25$$
$$x_2 = 0.75$$

$$v = (5)(0.25) + (20)(0.75) = 1.25 + 15.00 = 16.25$$

or

$$v = (35)(0.25) + (10)(0.75) = 8.75 + 7.50 = 16.25$$

Thus, by adopting the mixed strategy (0.25, 0.75), A can assure himself an expected payoff of 16.25, regardless of B's strategy, be it pure or mixed. Since it is 16.25 for either of B's pure strategies, it must also be 16.25 for *any mixture* of those strategies.

Player B can compute his optimal mixed strategy in the same way. Let $y_j = P(B_j)$; then

$$5y_1 + 35y_2 = 20y_1 + 10y_2$$

$$25y_2 = 15y_1$$

$$y_2 = \frac{3}{5}y_1$$

$$y_2 = \frac{3}{8} = 0.375$$

$$y_1 = \frac{5}{8} = 0.625$$

and again,

$$v = (5)(0.625) + (35)(0.375) = 3.125 + 13.125 = 16.25$$

or

$$v = (20)(0.625) + (10)(0.375) = 12.50 + 3.75 = 16.25$$

The solution then is that A's maximin mixed strategy is (0.25, 0.75), and B's minimax mixed strategy is (0.625, 0.375); and the value of the game, the expected payoff to A, is 16.25.

The use of *expected values* again raises questions related to individuals' views of probability and utility. We shall defer discussion of these matters to the next chapter. For the present we shall, as we have done before, assume that people seek to maximize their expected values and that the relevant utility functions are linear.

18–11. Graphical Solution to a Game. A two-person zero-sum 2×2 game may be solved by graphical methods to determine the mixed strategy of either player and the value of the game. In the trivial case where there is a saddle point, the mixed strategy which emerges is a pure strategy, giving one course of action a probability value of 1, and the other, zero. The graphical solution for player A in the game of Figure 18–9.1 is shown in Figure 18–11.1, where the vertical axis represents the payoff to A. The horizontal axis is $P(A_2)$. Thus, the right end of the scale, where $P(A_2) = 1.0$, represents the pure strategy A_2. Similarly, the left end of the scale represents the pure strategy A_1. From the matrix, it is noted that, if B selects B_1, then A_1 yields 5 and A_2 yields 20. These points are plotted as (0, 5) and (1.0, 20), and the line labeled B_1 is drawn between them. Similarly, the line B_2 is drawn between the two points (0, 35) and (1.0, 10). These lines indicate the payoff which A can obtain for various values of $P(A_2)$. Since B's interests are opposed to A's, B will select that line which is the lower for any value of $P(A_2)$ which A selects. That is, A can obtain the payoff along the broken line which is the lower

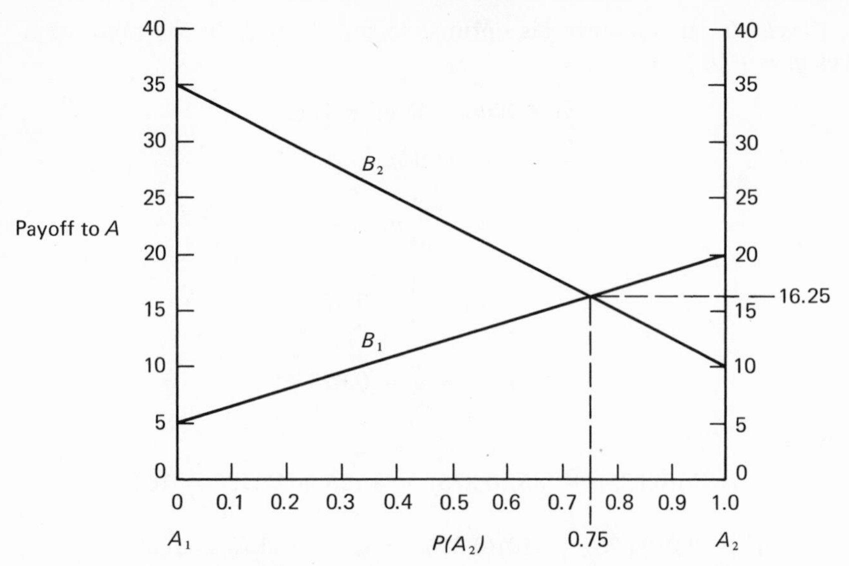

Fig. 18–11.1. Graphical solution for player A to the game of Figure 18–9.1. $P(A_2) = 0.75, v = 16.25$.

of B's two strategy lines. This corresponds to the feasible region in the graphical solution to linear programming problems. Since A wishes his payoff to be as high as possible, he picks that value of $P(A_2)$ for which the lower of B's strategy lines is highest. Clearly, in the figure, this is at the intersection, where $P(A_2) = 0.75$.

The solution for player B may be found in much the same way. See Exercise 18–1 at the end of this chapter. The graphical solution is possible for any player with only two courses of action, regardless of the number available to the other player. We shall examine such a problem in the next section.

18–12. General Algebraic Solution to $m \times n$ Games. The simple algebraic solution which we used in Section 18–10 is applicable only for 2×2 games. When there are more than two courses of action available, that method cannot be used. Consider graphically the game given in Figure 18–12.1. Since A has only two courses of action, a graphical solution to A's problem is possible. Note that the first two columns are

	B_1	B_2	B_3	B_4
A_1	5	35	10	25
A_2	20	10	15	5

Fig. 18–12.1. Game matrix for a 2×4 game.

exactly the same as those in the game of Figures 18–9.1 and 18–11.1. Therefore the entire graph of Figure 18–11.1 is *part* of the graph for A's solution to this game, as is shown in Figure 18–12.2. Clearly, A's optimal strategy is indicated at the intersection of lines B_3 and B_4. Since these two lines determine x_1 and x_2, and v, we can solve as before:

$$10x_1 + 15x_2 = 25x_1 + 5x_2$$

$$10x_2 = 15x_1$$

$$x_2 = \frac{3}{2}x_1$$

$$x_2 = 0.6$$

$$x_1 = 0.4$$

$$\text{from } B_3 \qquad v = (10)(0.4) + (15)(0.6) = 4 + 9 = 13$$

$$\text{from } B_4 \qquad v = (25)(0.4) + (5)(0.6) = 10 + 3 = 13$$

It is important to note that, using this mixed strategy (0.4, 0.6), A's expected payoff is greater than v if B selects either of his two other courses of action:

If B_1, $E(A\text{'s payoff}) = (5)(0.4) + (20)(0.6) = 14$
If B_2, $E(A\text{'s payoff}) = (35)(0.4) + (10)(0.6) = 20$

These results may be seen also on the graph in Figure 18–12.2.

That graph also indicates the relationship between a dominant and a dominated course of action. That is, for player B, course of action B_4 dominates B_2. Since B's objective is to minimize A's payoff, B_2 would never be selected since it lies above B_4 at all points. Clearly, if two lines do not cross, one dominates the other.

Let us now proceed to solve this problem without recourse to a graph. The algebraic solution to A's problem is to select (x_1, x_2) so that A's expected payoff is *greater than or equal to v for all of B's* courses of action. This is of course exactly what A accomplished via the graphical solution. To solve the problem algebraically, first eliminate the dominated course of action B_2; then x_1 and x_2 must be such that, for each of the remaining three B_j in turn,

$$\text{from } B_1 \qquad 5x_1 + 20x_2 \geq v \qquad (18\text{–}12.1)$$

$$\text{from } B_3 \qquad 10x_1 + 15x_2 \geq v \qquad (18\text{–}12.2)$$

$$\text{from } B_4 \qquad 25x_1 + 5x_2 \geq v \qquad (18\text{–}12.3)$$

also

$$x_1 \geq 0 \qquad (18\text{–}12.4)$$

$$x_2 \geq 0 \qquad (18\text{–}12.5)$$

$$x_1 + x_2 = 1 \qquad (18\text{–}12.6)$$

This system has six expressions but only three unknowns. Therefore, any solution involves at least three equations and at most three inequations. The problem is to find which, in addition to Equation (18–12.6), are equations and which are inequations. We may proceed by trial and error, assuming that we do not have the graph available.

Let the first two expressions as well as the last be equations. Then $x_1 > 0$, and $x_2 > 0$. Trying this as a possible solution:

$$\text{from } B_1 \qquad 5x_1 + 20x_2 = v \tag{18–12.7}$$

$$\text{from } B_3 \qquad 10x_1 + 15x_2 = v \tag{18–12.8}$$

Solving simultaneously,

$$25x_2 = v$$

$$x_2 = \frac{v}{25}$$

and from Equation (18–12.6),

$$x_1 = 1 - \frac{v}{25}$$

Substituting these results back into Equation (18–12.7) yields

$$5\left(1 - \frac{v}{25}\right) + 20\left(\frac{v}{25}\right) = v$$

$$5 - \frac{v}{5} + \frac{4}{5}v = v$$

$$\frac{2}{5}v = 5$$

$$v = 12.5$$

Then,

$$x_1 = 0.5 \qquad \text{and} \qquad x_2 = 0.5$$

Now we have a trial set of values for x_1, x_2 and v. We must now try them to see whether this mixed strategy will yield this value of v (or more) against the other of B's courses of action. Thus, we substitute these values of x_1 and x_2 into Equation (18–12.3), which has not yet been brought into the analysis. From Equation (18–12.3),

$$(25)(0.5) + (5)(0.5) = 15 > v = 12.5$$

Therefore, this system of equations is consistent. If B selects B_4, A will gain even more. It is a feasible solution. But is it optimal for A? To find out, let us repeat the process, this time trying Equations (18–12.1) and (18–12.3) as equalities:

$$\text{from } B_1 \qquad 5x_1 + 20x_2 = v \tag{18–12.9}$$

$$\text{from } B_4 \qquad 25x_1 + 5x_2 = v \tag{18–12.10}$$

$$25x_1 + 100x_2 = 5v$$

$$25x_1 + 5x_2 = v$$

$$95x_2 = 4v$$

$$x_2 = \frac{4}{95}v$$

$$x_1 = 1 - \frac{4}{95}v$$

Substituting in Equation (18–12.9),

$$5\left(1 - \frac{4}{95}v\right) + 20\left(\frac{4}{95}v\right) = v$$

$$5 - \frac{4}{19}v + \frac{16}{19} = v$$

$$\frac{7}{19}v = 5$$

$$v = \frac{95}{7} = 13\frac{4}{7}$$

Then,

$$x_1 = \frac{3}{7} \qquad \text{and} \qquad x_2 = \frac{4}{7}$$

This value of v is higher than the previous value (12.5), but can it be achieved by this mixed strategy against B's other course of action, B_3? Let us substitute these values of x_1 and x_2 into inequation (18–2.2). It yields

$$(10)\left(\frac{3}{7}\right) + (15)\left(\frac{4}{7}\right) = \frac{90}{7} < v = \frac{95}{7}$$

Thus, this solution is *not* consistent. This is not a feasible solution. The value of $v = \dfrac{95}{7} = 13\dfrac{4}{7}$ is not a maximin payoff.

Finally, we must try the last two inequations, (18–12.2) and (18–12.3), as equations:

$$\text{from } B_3 \qquad 10x_1 + 15x_2 = v \tag{18–12.11}$$

$$\text{from } B_4 \qquad 25x_1 + 5x_2 = v \tag{18–12.12}$$

$$10x_1 + 15x_2 = v$$

$$75x_1 + 15x_2 = 3v$$

$$65x_1 = 2v$$

$$x_1 = \frac{2}{65}v$$

$$x_2 = 1 - \frac{2}{65}v$$

Substituting in Equation (18–12.11),

$$(10)\left(\frac{2}{65}v\right) + (15)\left(1 - \frac{2}{65}v\right) = v$$

$$\frac{20}{65}v + 15 - \frac{30}{65}v = v$$

$$\frac{75}{65}v = 15$$

$$v = 13$$

Then,

$$x_1 = 0.4 \qquad \text{and} \qquad x_2 = 0.6$$

This value of v is higher than that of the other feasible solution (12.5), but can it be achieved by this mixed strategy against B's other course of action, B_1? Let us substitute these values of x_1 and x_2 into inequation (18–2.1). It yields

$$(5)(0.4) + (20)(0.6) = 2 + 12 = 14 > v = 13$$

Thus, this system of equations is consistent. The mixed strategy (0.4, 0.6) will yield $v = 13$ against B_3 or B_4. If B selects B_1, A will gain even more. Since this value of $v = 13$ is higher than the other achievable value (12.5), *this solution (0.4, 0.6) is the optimal solution.*

The reader should follow this reasoning on the graph of Figure 18–12.2, where it can be seen that the intersection of B_1 and B_3 and the intersection of B_3 and B_4 are both feasible but the latter is optimal. Also, the intersection of B_1 and B_4 is not feasible.

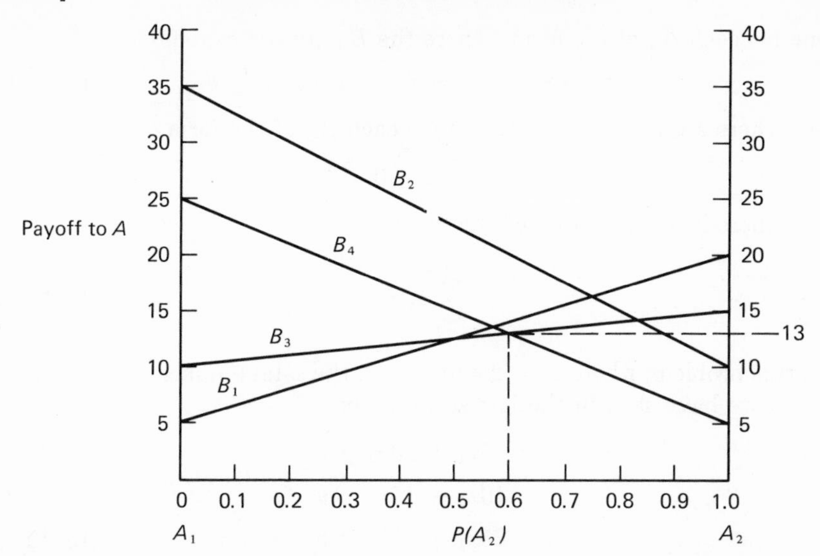

Fig. 18–12.2. Graphical solution for player A to the game of Figure 18–12.1. $P(A_2) = 0.6$, $v = 13$.

This problem may also be solved for B's mixed strategy. See Exercise 18–2 at the end of this chapter.

This rather tedious procedure may, in the mind of the reader, suggest similarities to linear programming. Actually, such problems as this are indeed most easily solved by the methods of linear programming as we shall see in the next section.

18–13. Solution to Games by Linear Programming. A two-person zero-sum $m \times n$ game may be converted into a linear programming problem and solved by the usual linear programming methods. We shall illustrate this procedure by solving the same problem which was solved in the last section. This problem, which was originally stated in the matrix of Figure 18–12.1, is, after reduction by removal of dominated course of action B_2, shown in Figure 18–13.1.

	B_1	B_3	B_4
A_1	5	10	25
A_2	20	15	5

Fig. 18–13.1. The game matrix of Figure 18–12.1 reduced by the removal of dominated course of action B_2.

From the pattern of Equations (18–12.1) to (18–12.6), we can conclude that, in an $m \times n$ game, solving for player A, there are n inequations, one for each B_j, of the form (where the E_{ij} are the payoffs)

$$E_{1j}x_1 + E_{2j}x_2 + \cdots + E_{mj}x_m \geq v \tag{18–13.1}$$

also there are m inequations, one for each A_i, of the form

$$x_i \geq 0 \tag{18–13.2}$$

and there is one equation of the form

$$\sum_{i=1}^{m} x_i = 1 \tag{18–13.3}$$

In this problem, where $m = 2$ and $n = 3$, the total number of expressions is, as we have seen in the last section, six:

$$5x_1 + 20x_2 \geq v \tag{18–12.1}$$

$$10x_1 + 15x_2 \geq v \tag{18–12.2}$$

$$25x_1 + 5x_2 \geq v \tag{18–12.3}$$

$$x_1 \geq 0 \tag{18–12.4}$$

$$x_2 \geq 0 \tag{18–12.5}$$

$$x_1 + x_2 = 1 \tag{18–12.6}$$

To convert this statement of the game problem into a linear programming problem, let us first consider the objective function. That is, of course, v, the value of the game. A wishes to maximize v, subject to the restrictions imposed by his opponent, B. It is essential to the procedure that v be positive. If there is any doubt about this, i.e., if there are several negative payoff values in the matrix, then a constant may be added to every term in the payoff matrix. This will not change the final x_i which will emerge, but it will increase v by that constant amount, and therefore if this procedure is followed, the constant must be subtracted from the derived v to get the true value of the game. In this illustration, all of the payoff values are positive, and therefore v is sure to be positive.

Second, we divide all of the $m + n + 1$ expressions by v, yielding n inequations of the form

$$E_{1j}\frac{x_1}{v} + E_{2j}\frac{x_2}{v} + \cdots + E_{mj}\frac{x_m}{v} \geq 1 \tag{18–13.4}$$

m inequations of the form

$$\frac{x_i}{v} \geq 0 \tag{18–13.5}$$

and one equation of the form

$$\sum_{i=1}^{m} \frac{x_i}{v} = \frac{1}{v} \tag{18–13.6}$$

Finally, we substitute for the fractions $\frac{x_i}{v}$ by introducing the symbol

$$X_i = \frac{x_i}{v} \tag{18–13.7}$$

and the final set of expressions is:

n inequations of the form

$$E_{1j}X_1 + E_{2j}X_2 + \cdots + E_{mj}X_m \geq 1 \tag{18–13.8}$$

m inequations of the form

$$X_i \geq 0 \tag{18–13.9}$$

and one equation of the form

$$\sum_{i=1}^{m} X_i = \frac{1}{v} \tag{18–13.10}$$

From Equation (18–13.10), it can be seen that the objective function is

$$v = \frac{1}{\sum_{i=1}^{m} X_i} \quad \text{to be maximized} \tag{18–13.11}$$

or

$$\frac{1}{v} = \sum_{i=1}^{m} X_i \quad \text{to be minimized} \tag{18–13.12}$$

The final statement of the linear programming problem, then is:

Minimize:

$$\frac{1}{v} = \sum_{i=1}^{m} X_i \tag{18–13.12}$$

Subject to n inequations of the form

$$E_{1j}X_1 + E_{2j}X_2 + \cdots + E_{mj}X_m \geq 1 \tag{18–13.8}$$

Applying this format to the game problem of Equations (18–12.1) to (18–12.6), we obtain:

Minimize:

$$\frac{1}{v} = X_1 + X_2 \tag{18–13.13}$$

Subject to:

$$5X_1 + 20X_2 \geq 1 \tag{18–13.14}$$

$$10X_1 + 15X_2 \geq 1 \tag{18–13.15}$$

$$25X_1 + \ 5X_2 \geq 1 \tag{18–13.16}$$

This problem may be solved by the simplex algorithm in the usual way, and since it is a two dimensional problem, it may also be solved graphically. The graphic solution is shown in Figure 18–13.2. The optimal solu-

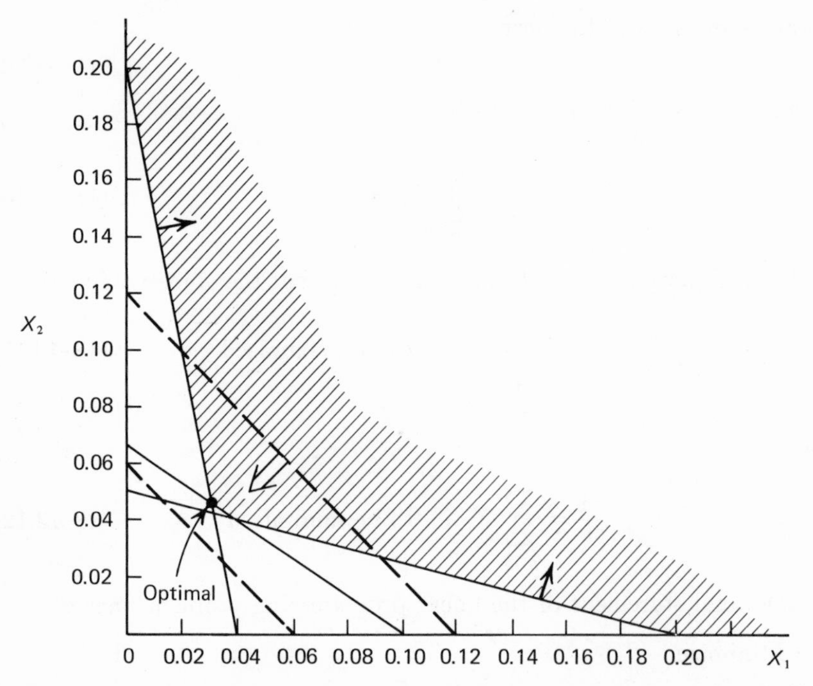

Fig. 18–13.2. Graphical solution to linear programming statement of Figure 18–13.1.

tion is at the corner defined by the lines

$$10X_1 + 15X_2 = 1 \tag{18–13.17}$$

$$25X_1 + 5X_2 = 1 \tag{18–13.18}$$

Solve simultaneously,

$$65X_1 = 2$$

$$X_1 = \frac{2}{65}$$

Then, from Equation (18–13.17),

$$(10)\left(\frac{2}{65}\right) + 15X_2 = 1$$

$$X_2 = \frac{3}{65}$$

and from Equation (18–13.13),

$$\frac{1}{v} = \frac{2}{65} + \frac{3}{65} = \frac{5}{65} = \frac{1}{13}$$

$$v = 13$$

$$x_1 = X_1 v = \left(\frac{2}{65}\right)(13) = \frac{2}{5} = 0.4$$

$$x_2 = X_2 v = \left(\frac{3}{65}\right)(13) = \frac{3}{5} = 0.6$$

This is the same result which was obtained above by direct game-theoretic methods.

The linear program as stated may be solved by the simplex method, or if preferred, its dual may be solved. In this case, obviously the dual may be solved more easily, since the primal will require three artificial variables. An important aspect of the linear programming solution to games is that *the solution to the primal yields A's solution, i.e., A's maximin strategy, and the solution to the dual yields B's minimax solution to the game.* We shall now state and solve the dual:

Maximize:

$$\frac{1}{v} = Y_1 + Y_3 + Y_4 \tag{18–13.19}$$

Subject to:

$$5Y_1 + 10Y_3 + 25Y_4 \leq 1 \tag{18–13.20}$$

$$20Y_1 + 15Y_3 + \ 5Y_4 \leq 1 \tag{18–13.21}$$

Note that we have not followed the practice of numbering the dual variables starting with $m + 1$, as is common in standard linear programming dual problems. The reason for this is that here the dual problem is just as real as the primal; i.e., it is B's solution. The procedure we have followed, i.e., designating the real variables Y_1, Y_3, and Y_4, maintains the relationship

$$y_j = Y_j v = P(B_j)$$

without confusion of subscripts. The slack variables in this dual problem will be designated Y_5 and Y_6, respectively. In the matrix transposition

		Y_1	Y_3	Y_4
$\frac{1}{v}$	0	1	1	1
Y_5	1	−5	−10	(−25)
Y_6	1	−20	−15	−5

⟹

		Y_1	Y_3	Y_5
$\frac{1}{v}$	$\frac{1}{25}$	$\frac{4}{5}$	$\frac{3}{5}$	$-\frac{1}{25}$
Y_4	$\frac{1}{25}$	$-\frac{1}{5}$	$-\frac{2}{5}$	$-\frac{1}{25}$
Y_6	$\frac{4}{5}$	(−19)	−13	$\frac{1}{5}$

⇙

		Y_6	Y_3	Y_5
$\frac{1}{v}$	$\frac{7}{95}$	$-\frac{4}{95}$	$\frac{1}{19}$	$-\frac{3}{95}$
Y_4	$\frac{3}{95}$	$\frac{1}{95}$	$-\frac{5}{19}$	$-\frac{4}{95}$
Y_1	$\frac{4}{95}$	$-\frac{1}{19}$	($-\frac{13}{19}$)	$\frac{1}{95}$

⟹

		Y_6	Y_1	Y_5
$\frac{1}{v}$	$\frac{1}{13}$	$-\frac{3}{65}$	$-\frac{1}{13}$	$-\frac{2}{65}$
Y_4	$\frac{1}{65}$	$\frac{2}{65}$	$\frac{5}{13}$	$-\frac{3}{65}$
Y_3	$\frac{4}{65}$	$-\frac{1}{13}$	$-\frac{19}{13}$	$\frac{1}{65}$

Fig. 18–13.3. Simplex solution of dual, yielding B's minimax solution to the game of Figure 18–13.1.

to produce the primal solution from the dual, these will represent the probabilities for A, of selection of A_1 and A_2 in that order.

The simplex tableaux for the solution of the dual problem are given in Figure 18–13.3. The result of that analysis is

$$v = 13$$

$$P(B_1) = y_1 = Y_1 v = 0$$

$$P(B_3) = y_3 = Y_3 v = \left(\frac{4}{65}\right)(13) = \frac{4}{5} = 0.8$$

$$P(B_4) = y_4 = Y_4 v = \left(\frac{1}{65}\right)(13) = \frac{1}{5} = 0.2$$

Therefore, the minimax solution for B is to use the mixed strategy (0, 0.8, 0.2) over the three courses of action B_1, B_3, and B_4, respectively.

A's solution may be obtained by transposing the final matrix, i.e., interchanging the rows and columns and changing the signs. This is shown in Figure 18–13.4, where the row and column designations have been changed to X_i's, with the numbering system such that X_1 and X_2 (which correspond respectively to Y_5 and Y_6 of the dual) are the real variables $\frac{P(A_1)}{v}$ and $\frac{P(A_2)}{v}$, respectively, and X_3, X_4, and X_5 (which correspond, respectively, to Y_1, Y_3, and Y_4 of the dual) are slack variables. The result shown in the right side of Figure 18–13.4 may alternatively

		Y_1	Y_5	Y_6
$\frac{1}{V}$	$\frac{1}{13}$	$-\frac{1}{13}$	$-\frac{2}{65}$	$-\frac{3}{65}$
Y_3	$\frac{4}{65}$	$-\frac{19}{13}$	$\frac{1}{65}$	$-\frac{1}{13}$
Y_4	$\frac{1}{65}$	$\frac{5}{13}$	$-\frac{3}{65}$	$\frac{2}{65}$

Dual — *B's* Solution

		X_4	X_5
$-\frac{1}{V}$	$-\frac{1}{13}$	$-\frac{4}{65}$	$\frac{1}{65}$
X_3	$\frac{1}{13}$	$\frac{19}{13}$	$-\frac{5}{13}$
X_1	$\frac{2}{65}$	$-\frac{1}{65}$	$\frac{3}{65}$
X_2	$\frac{3}{65}$	$\frac{1}{13}$	$-\frac{2}{65}$

Primal — *A's* Solution

Fig. 18–13.4. Maximin solution for player A to the game of Figure 18–13.1, obtained from solution to dual.

be obtained directly by simplex solution of the primal. This is left as an exercise for the student (see Exercise 18–4 at the end of this chapter).

The solution to A's decision problem, as given in Figure 18–13.4 is

$$v = 13$$

$$P(A_1) = x_1 = X_1 v = \left(\frac{2}{65}\right)(13) = \frac{2}{5} = 0.4$$

$$P(A_2) = x_2 = X_2 v = \left(\frac{3}{65}\right)(13) = \frac{3}{5} = 0.6$$

This result is clearly the same as that obtained both graphically and algebraically in Section 18–12 and graphically by linear programming earlier in this section.

18–14. Comments on Mixed Strategies. The concept of the mixed strategy raises serious and disturbing questions. In order to pursue a mixed strategy, the decision maker must flip a coin, consult a table of random numbers, or otherwise utilize some stochastic process with probabilities corresponding to those of the desired mixed strategy. He must follow the dictates of the outcome of the stochastic process, and then his expected value is as determined in the solution. The problem is whether a real decision maker can agree to be bound by a coin flip. Can we imagine a business executive allowing a coin flip to make a real decision about, say, whether to market a new product or to change his price? Probably not!

If the making of decisions by the use of stochastic processes seems untenable in this kind of nonrecurring situation, let us be reminded that there are other situations in which coin flips, random numbers, and pointer spinning are not unthinkable as decision making devices. In search problems, both the searching element and the evading element can and do rely on such procedures. Consider the wartime problem of a ship traveling through waters infested with enemy submarines. One evasive policy which the surface vessel may follow is zigzag by a stochastic process which determines the exact new heading for the ship and the length of time to hold that heading until the chance process selects a new heading and a new time period until the next change, etc. The great strength of this procedure is that the future exact position of the evading ship cannot be predicted by an attacker. Indeed its own captain does not know exactly where it will be after some relatively short period into the future. This procedure of evasion is probably superior to any fixed pattern of zigzagging, since if a fixed pattern is used, a potential attacker could conceivably lurk at some distance and observe the evasive pattern long enough to be able to predict future movements. This is a decision process in which we can probably all accept the notion of stochastic control.

The acceptance of stochastic control in many single-event situations is questionable not only for mixed strategies in game theory, but even in simple situations involving expected values of payoffs. We can define rational decision making as involving *desire to maximize expected values* and, indeed, we do so in most of our treatment of decision problems. However, as we shall see, serious questions can be raised about the willingness of real decision makers to do this in real-world problems. Let us defer this matter for the next chapter.

18–15. *n*-Person Non-Zero-Sum Games. In our treatment of game theory, we have confined our interest to two-person zero-sum games. There is good reason for this. The solution to such games is well defined and relatively simple, but this is not true for more complex games.

When the number of players exceeds two, the possibility of coalitions arises, and game theorists must speculate about how much player A might be willing to offer player B to form a coalition against player C, who might also be offering either of the other two players a side payment to combine with him against the third. With more players, the process becomes very complex as the number of possibilities is multiplied.

Non-zero-sum games, even two-person games, offer the possibility for the two players to combine against some third interest which may not be an active player at all. For example, a management–labor bargaining situation is not a zero-sum game, because those two interests might agree to a wage boost, both knowing that a price boost will follow from which they both might conceivably gain. Similarly, the typical competitive marketing situation, even with two-seller oligopoly, is not a zero-sum game, because both competitors can gain by increasing the size of the market, by raising prices, or by some other device which renders their opposition to one another something less than strictly competitive as we have stipulated it; i.e., whatever one gains, the other loses.

The well-known *prisoners' dilemma* is often cited as an example of a two-person non-zero-sum game. Two prisoners, suspected of committing a crime together have been apprehended and questioned separately. Each is offered a very light penalty as an incentive to confess and a heavy punishment if he is convicted by his accomplice's confession, with some middle penalty if they both confess. This is shown in Figure 18–15.1,

		B: Confess	*B*: Not Confess
A	Confess	Both: 3 years	A: 30 days B: 10 years
A	Not confess	A: 10 years B: 30 days	Both: 1 year for carrying a gun

Fig. 18–15.1. The prisoners' dilemma. Entries are prison terms.

where the additional condition of a significant penalty if both do not confess makes confession a dominant strategy for both. Nevertheless, if both could agree not to confess, neither of them would do worse than one year. It can be expected that, in this situation, both will confess. However, it may also be that confession does not occur, but the reason might well be additional non-zero-sum aspects of the situation not shown in the matrix, such as the knowledge that if one confessed and the other did not, the family and friends of a languishing 10-year prisoner might have something to say to the 30-day loquacious chap when he emerged from prison.

The prisoners' dilemma is the same kind of situation as faced by farmers, diamond merchants, or others, who may have agreed to restrict production to keep prices elevated. If they adhere to the agreement, it is highly advantageous for any one of them to defect and increase his production and sales at the high price. However, if they all defect, prices fall, and all of them lose. In this situation, as in the prisoners' dilemma, defection is probably generally to be expected in the absence of external enforcement.

These are only a few illustrations of the possible kinds of situations which may be described when the games become more complex than the two-person zero-sum games which have been the main subject of this chapter. We shall not here pursue the subject further.

SUGGESTIONS FOR FURTHER READING

Luce, R. D. and H. Raiffa. *Games and Decisions.* New York: John Wiley & Sons, Inc., 1957.

Rapoport, A. *Fights, Games and Debates.* Ann Arbor: University of Michigan Press, 1960.

SHUBIK, M. "The Uses of Game Theory in Management Science," *Management Science*, Vol. 2, No. 1 (October, 1955).
———. *Strategy and Market Structure.* New York: John Wiley & Sons, Inc., 1959.
VON NEUMANN, J., and O. MORGENSTERN. *Theory of Games and Economic Behavior.* Princeton: Princeton University Press, 1944.
WAGNER, H. "Advances in Game Theory: A Review Article," *American Economic Review*, 48:368–87 (1958).
WILLIAMS, J. D. *The Compleat Strategyst*, New York: McGraw-Hill Book Co., Inc., 1954.

EXERCISES

18–1. Solve the game of Figure 18–8.1 for player B graphically.

18–2. Solve the matrix of Figure 18–12.1 for player B algebraically.

18–3. Show that, for a two-by-two zero-sum two-person game, the maximin strategy for A is:

$$x_1 = \frac{E_{22} - E_{21}}{(E_{11} - E_{12}) + (E_{22} - E_{21})}$$

$$x_2 = \frac{E_{11} - E_{12}}{(E_{11} - E_{12}) + (E_{22} - E_{21})}$$

18–4. Solve by simplex the primal for the problem stated in Equations (18–13.13) through (18–13.16), whose dual is solved in the text in Figure 18–13.3.

18–5. The management of the Darad Radio Corporation is in the process of deciding whether to agree to negotiate with the striking union (Amalgamated Monkeywrench Throwers) now, or to delay. The decision is difficult because the management does not know what the union leadership position is. The union leaders may be adamant and insist on their original demands, they can be ready to compromise, or they can be ready to yield and accept the original management offer. The matrix of payoffs to management, as management sees it, in millions of dollars, is:

Union Position

	B_1 Adamant	B_2 Compromise	B_3 Yield
A_1 Negotiate	−2	1	2
A_2 Delay	5	−2	−3

a) Solve management's problem graphically.
b) Solve management's problem algebraically.
c) Solve management's problem by linear programming.
d) What should be the union's strategy?
e) Discuss the implications of a conclusion to adopt a mixed strategy.

Is this a valid policy for a real-life situation? Would your conclusions be different if this were a situation which tended to recur frequently?

19

Applications of Decision Theory

19–1. Usefulness of Decision Theory. The subject of decision theory has already been introduced (in Chapters 1, 4, 7, and 18) and the reader is, at this point, encouraged to reread Sections 1–5 through 1–11 as an introduction to the material of this chapter. In addition, we shall find ourselves using various topics in probability theory, and the reader is encouraged to reread, by way of review, Sections 4–1 through 4–11, with special emphasis on Section 4–11, *Bayes' Theorem.* He may also wish to review the material in Section 7–12.

At the outset it must be emphasized that the study and application of decision theory *does not add* to the amount of information available to the decision maker. To the extent that decision theory is useful in practice, it is so as a consequence of its having helped the decision maker to organize his available input information into a system which, under the assumption of *rationality*, as we shall define that word, leads to the selection of a particular course of action. If the decision maker himself is instinctively rational in this sense, and in his own way naturally uses all the information this system does, then decision theory will be of little practical use to him in making decisions, since his decisions will be the same without the theory.

However, decision theory can help by improving the decisions of all but those few favored with such magnificent natural talents. Also, for all decision making—even by those favored few—decision theory, by organizing the input elements, makes it possible for others who come later to understand and to analyze how a decision was made and to identify those aspects or inputs with which they may find agreement or disagreement. For example, the reduction of a large set of instincts, intuitions, and lessons of experience into a single identified number, a subjective probability, and the use of it in the decision-theoretic framework, make it possible for observers to analyze the decision maker's system of reasoning, to agree with the framework and accept all of the observational data which were used, but disagree with the final decision as to course of action because of disagreement about the subjective factors which are the basis for the subjective probability values used.

19–2. Expected Values and Utilities. We have, many times in this volume, especially in Chapters 7 and 18, made the assumption that people act in the way to maximize their expected values. For example, in the Marchand problem in Section 7–3, we specifically noted that our solution was based on the assumption that *expected profit* (in dollars) was to be maximized.

The assumption that the expected value of some money function is to be maximized is, in fact, two assumptions. One is that *the utility of money is linear*, and the other is that *the expected value is what we do, or should, seek to maximize.* Both assumptions are open to question, and, indeed volumes have been written about both. We shall discuss them briefly in the sections which follow, and the interested reader may consult any of the many available references, some of which are cited at the end of this chapter. However, in solving problems, what we have done and shall continue to do in this volume is to assume linearity of the utility of the objective functions and to define *rational behavior* as that which seeks to maximize (or minimize, as the case may be) the *expected value* of the objective function. Now, before we leave the subject let us examine certain aspects of these assumptions.

19–3. Rationality and Ethics. In this volume we assume that the decision maker knows what his objective function is, and that he wishes to optimize its expected value. From this, it follows that, in order to achieve this objective, he *should* select the course of action which leads to that optimum expected value, and throughout this volume we identify that course of action as the "right" solution to the decision problem. This, however, in no way suggests that this is the best answer according to some other criteria, and particularly does not assure that the selected course of action is a "good" one for him, for his organization, or for society.

That is, there is no attempt here to equate the word "rational" with the words "good" or "ethical." We define rational decision making as the optimization of the expected value of some previously defined measure of effectiveness. The methodology used in this volume does not take into account the ethical aspects of the objective function. This is the province of the decision maker whose value system has led to the choice of the objective function, and of course we hope that that value system is wise and thoughtful and ethical in the broadest sense. But the methodology of decision theory is as indifferent to ethical values as is the arithmetic operation which determines that one peacemaker plus one peacemaker equals two peacemakers and equally efficiently determines that one murderer plus one murderer equals two murderers.

On the other hand, as Boulding (1966) pointed out, by increasing the efficiency and reducing the burdensomeness of information processing, these techniques may make it even easier for decision makers to broaden the kinds of problems and considerations to which they can address themselves and easier therefore to include ethical considerations in their planning. Conceivably this may, in some part, help to lead to a generally heightened appreciation of, and service to, ethical values.

19–4. Linearity of the Utility Function. In directing our decision apparatus toward the selection of that course of action which maximizes the expected value of, say, monetary income, we have assumed that, within the range of monetary payoffs being considered, a payoff of twice as much money is twice as desirable. That is, only if \$2.00 is twice as desirable as \$1.00 can we expect a decision maker to be indifferent between a certain payoff of \$1.00 and a lottery with payoff of \$2.00 with probability $p_1 = 0.5$ and payoff of zero with probability $p_2 = 0.5$. This situation is pictured in the familiar matrix form in Figure 19–4.1 where the payoffs

	(0.50) B_1	(0.50) B_2	
A_1	2	0	$E(A_1) = (2)(0.5)+(0)(0.5) = 1.00$
A_2	1	1	$E(A_2) = \qquad = 1.00$

Fig. 19–4.1. Two courses of action with equal expected values. The numbers in cells represent sums of money.

are in dollars and the numbers in parentheses are the $P(B_j)$. The expected values are the same for both courses of action, and the decision maker should be indifferent between them. On the other hand, in Figure 19–4.2,

	(0.55) B_1	(0.45) B_2	
A_1	2	0	$E(A_1) = (2)(0.55) = 1.10$
A_2	1	1	$E(A_2) = \qquad = 1.00$

Fig. 19–4.2. Two courses of action with slightly different expected values. The numbers in the cells represent sums of money.

the same matrix is presented with a slight change in probabilities. Clearly, A_1 has the higher expected value, and it is to be preferred, *if the utility of money is linear* in the range of payoffs under consideration. Let the reader think about this for a moment. If he were faced with the decision situation depicted in Figure 19–4.2, and if the payoffs were 0, 1, and 2 *cents*, would he select A_1? If they were *dollars*, would he select A_1? If they were *hundreds of dollars* would he select A_1? If they were *thousands of dollars* would he select A_1? For most people, there is some point in the preceding sequence of questions at which they would answer negatively. *A bird in the hand is worth two in the bush,* and a bird in the hand may be preferable to several in the bush if one is hungry and one bird constitutes a meal.

The reason for this is the familiar decrease in marginal utility. The marginal utility of money, or almost any other desirable goods or services, is generally conceived of as tapering off as the amount available increases, as is shown in Figure 19–4.3.

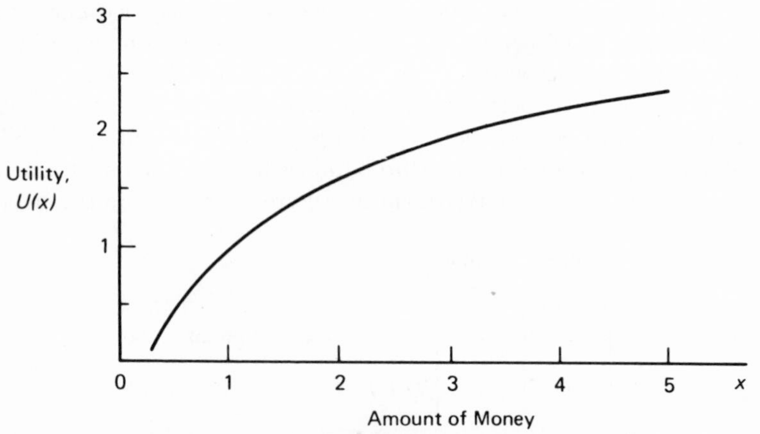

Fig. 19–4.3. Graph of diminishing marginal utility of money. $U(x) = 1 + 2 \log x$.

The actual function used in constructing that graph is

$$U(x) = 1 + 2 \log x \qquad \text{for } x \geq 0.35 \tag{19–4.1}$$

There is no particular reason for using this specific function except that it yields a curve of the desired configuration. Its use here does not imply that a logarithmic function of this sort does actually reflect the utility function of any real person, although it may be quite close for many persons in various ranges of monetary payoff.

However, let us assume for the purpose of illustration that it does accurately reflect the utility function of this decision maker at this time. The numbers plotted in Figure 19–4.3 are derived in Table 19–4.1. From

TABLE 19–4.1

Computations for Figure 19–4.3

Dollars x	$\log x$	Utility $U(x) = 1 + 2 \log x$
0.35	−0.46	0.08
0.5	−0.30	0.40
1	0.00	1.00
2	0.30	1.60
3	0.48	1.96
4	0.60	2.20
5	0.70	2.40
6	0.78	2.56

Table 19–4.1, we note that the utility of one dollar is one *utile*, the name commonly given to a measure of utility, and the utility of $2 is 1.6 utiles. Then the decision matrix of Figure 19–4.2 may be rewritten in utility terms as shown in Figure 19–4.4. Then A_2 is preferable to A_1, because,

	(0.55) B_1	(0.45) B_2	
A_1	1.6	0	$E(A_1) = (1.6)(0.55) = 0.88$
A_2	1	1	$E(A_2) = \quad = 1.00$

Fig. 19–4.4. The payoff matrix of Figure 19–4.2 rewritten so that the numbers in the cells represent utility values.

after all, it is the expected value of utility that, by definition, we always seek to maximize. That is, we might define utility as that function which we seek to maximize.

The reader is correct if he has observed a circularity in the definition of the preceding sentence. That is, we can define utility as that function, the expected value of which we always seek to maximize when we make decisions; and we can define our rational decision-making criterion as the maximization of the expected value of utility. While these definitions are indeed circular, the reader may find it helpful to think about the definitions of these terms in this way. The circularity does not impair their usefulness. The real problem is in finding the operational measures (sales, profits, assets, costs, time, etc.) of utility.

This simple example illustrates the danger of reliance on the assumption of linearity of the utility of money. The optimal course of action changes from A_1 to A_2 when account is taken of the nonlinearity of the utility function.

Of course, in any decision situation in which we select among courses of action on the basis of expected values, we make the assumption that the utility of the objective function is linear. This is tantamount to saying that the expected value of our utility will be maximized *only when the entries in the payoff matrix are valid measures of utility.* Normally, in practical problems we do make the assumption that the level of sales, profits, costs, time, etc., or whatever measure of effectiveness is used, does indeed reflect utility; i.e., that its utility is linear. However, a truly sophisticated decision maker should ideally take into account non-linearities in the utility function and perform the analysis in terms of utility values as was done above in Table 19–4.1 and Figure 19–4.4.

19–5. Maximization of Expected Values. In the previous section we considered the possible shortcomings involved in the assumption that we seek to maximize the expected value of the objective function by raising the question whether the utility of the objective function (measure of effectiveness) is linear. In this section we shall ask whether, *even if the utility of the measure of effectiveness is linear,* we do indeed seek to maximize its expected value.

Consider the payoff matrix of Figure 19–4.2, which is reproduced in Figure 19–5.1, and assume that although the entries are dollars, they do

	(0.55) B_1	(0.45) B_2
A_1	2	0
A_2	1	1

Fig. 19–5.1

in fact represent utilities; i.e., for this sum of money, the utility of money is linear for this decision maker at this time.

Clearly, if the decision were to be made again and again for a long series of trials, the decision maker could expect that in the long run the average payoff to A_1 would be the expected value at \$1.10. Presumably the decision maker would then select A_1 for each and every trial and enjoy the average income of \$1.10 and *never* select A_2. If we agree with this conclusion, does that help us decide what the decision maker would or should do *if this is a once-in-a-lifetime decision?* To be consistent with our assumptions we must agree that he should (and would) select A_1. If a real decision maker in such a situation did select A_2, we would have to conclude that the payoff values in the matrix did not represent utilities, and we would have to increase the payoff in cell 11 before A_1 would be preferred.

Actually, we could use an experiment of this sort to measure utility. We could change the stochastic process to one in which $P(B_1) = P(B_2) = 0.5$ and then increase the payoff in cell 11 until the decision maker was indifferent between A_1 and A_2, and then assign to that amount of money the utility value of 2. Then, with that payoff in cell 11, if the stochastic process were changed back to that pictured above with $P(B_1) = 0.55$, he would now prefer A_1. If the decision maker's utility function happened to be that shown in Table 19–4.1 and Figure 19–4.3, the required monetary payoff would be about $3.16, as can be determined from Table 19–4.1 and Appendix G.

This method of measuring the utility of a sum of money may again seem to be circular reasoning, but it is a consequence of our basic concept of utility as *that function whose expected value we seek to maximize.*

We cannot leave this subject without indicating that there is further cause for reservation and that, even in the case of the repetitive experiment, people may not naturally seek to maximize their expected values—or what seem to be their expected values. Consider the payoff matrix of Figure 19–5.2. If, in this matrix, the payoffs are relatively small amounts

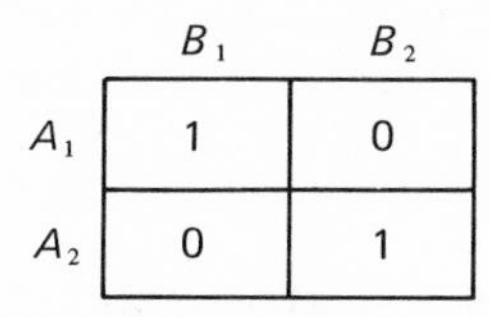

Fig. 19–5.2

of money, say, dollars or quarters or dimes, then we should expect that a decision maker would pick A_1 if $P(B_1) > P(B_2)$ and A_2 if the reverse were true, and that he would be indifferent between A_1 and A_2 if the probabilities of B_1 and B_2 were equal.

If, for example, $P(B_1) = 0.7$, his best course of action is to select A_1 with expected value 0.7, and if the experiment were to be repeated many times, he should select A_1 every time and expect to win the payoff 70 per cent of the time in the long run.

Unfortunately, it does not seem that people always behave in this way. Certain experiments have been performed which suggest that at least some people tend to prefer to try to *event-match;* that is, they would, in this case, try to pick A_1 70 per cent of the time and A_2 30 per cent of the time, thereby seeking to win always, but actually winning only 58 per cent of the time. That is, if they randomly select A_1 and A_2 with probabilities of 0.7 and 0.3, respectively, and if "nature" independently selects B_1 and B_2 with probabilities of 0.7 and 0.3, respectively, the probability that they will win is, from Equations (4–8.5) and (4–9.1),

$$\begin{aligned} P(\text{Win}) &= P[(A_1 \cap B_1) \cup (A_2 \cap B_2)] \\ &= P(A_1 \cap B_1) + P(A_2 \cap B_2) \\ &= P(A_1)P(B_1) + P(A_2)P(B_2) \\ &= (0.7)(0.7) + (0.3)(0.3) = 0.49 + 0.09 = 0.58 \end{aligned}$$

Let us take a moment to describe an experiment in which people seem to tend to seek to event-match and actually receive a payoff that is less than that which they could and would get if they were consistently to select that A_i with the higher expected value.

The person is seated at a console, depicted schematically in Fig. 19–5.3, with four lights, two red and two yellow, and two buttons, one red and

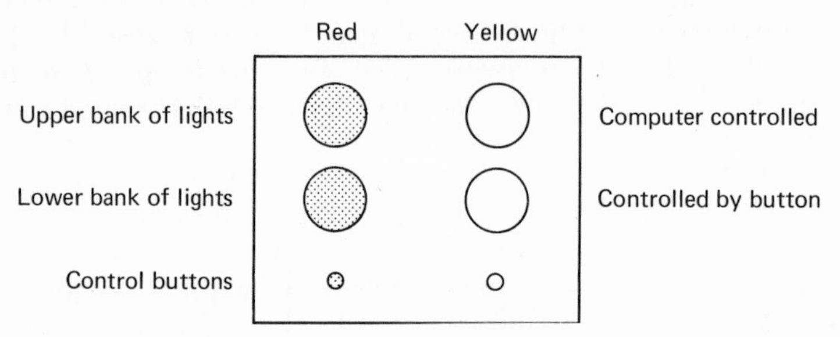

Fig. 19–5.3. Schematic representation of event-matching experiment.

one yellow. The upper bank of lights is controlled by a computer, and the lower bank of lights is controlled by the decision maker's control buttons. If the decision maker presses the yellow button the lower yellow light will light, and if he presses the red button the lower red light will light. However, when he presses a button, he also lights one of the two upper lights, but he does not know which one. The computer selects either the red or yellow of the upper bank, but does not light it. Instead it signals the decision maker that it has made its decision and that he may now make his selection and press the button implementing both decisions. That is, the light in the lower bank corresponding to the selected button color will light, and the computer's selection in the upper bank will light, but this is independent of the color of the button selected. It has been preselected by the computer. If the two lights which light are of the same color, the decision maker receives his payoff, and if they are of different colors, he receives nothing. This decision situation is exactly that portrayed in the decision matrix of Figure 19–5.2.

Now, if the decision maker has an opportunity to try this experiment many times, and if he concludes that, although he cannot predict the outcome of any particular trial, the computer seems to select red 70 per cent of the time. Then, as we noted above, he should select red *all* of the time and win 70 per cent of the time. However this is not always the case. People seem to tend to try to event-match, i.e., use a mixed strategy, as described above, and win less often than 70 per cent of the time.

The tendency toward event-matching vs. maximization of expected dollar payoff seems to depend upon a complex of personal and cultural characteristics of the decision maker, and, indeed, one can not be sure that the decision maker is not maximizing the expected value of his utility if he finds a utility-yielding payoff in personal satisfaction in trying to "beat" the machine.

It must not be concluded that event-matching is necessarily irrational as we have defined that word. That is, the decision maker might indulge in event-matching and still be maximizing the expected value of some objective function. He might understand thoroughly the entire process and seek to maximize his expected value by event-matching if his objective function is not just the monetary payoff. He may enjoy playing the game and trying to beat the system, which he may very well be able to do in the short run just by luck. In the illustration given above, the expected value of the optimal course of action was 0.70, and the expected value of event matching was 0.58. Yet in the short run a player could by event-matching obtain a return in excess of 0.58, and even in excess of 0.70. He could also, of course, do much worse. Indeed, since this is a probabilistic system, any result can occur in the short run. That is, he could go through n trials, winning all or losing all, regardless of the expected values. Under event-matching there is the hope that one may win more than 70 per cent of the time, even in a large number of trials, by actually matching the outcomes of the probabilistic process. The emotional—or even financial, if his utility function is extremely nonlinear—payoff for doing this may be so high that the player, by following this *mixed strategy*, does indeed maximize the expected value of his payoff *as he sees it*.

With these reservations in mind, we shall, in the succeeding sections of this volume, continue to assume that our objective functions are linear with utility, and we shall continue to observe our definition of rational behavior as being that which maximizes the expected value of those objective functions.

19–6. Decision Making Under Complete Ignorance. We shall now introduce an illustrative problem which originally appeared in the Second Edition of the author's *Statistical Analysis*. We shall analyze that problem much as it is analyzed there, and then we shall proceed to develop the technique further. We shall refer to this problem as "Alox at the Falls."

Alox is an enterprising young businessman. Each morning during the tourist season, Alox drives his vending truck to the Falls and sells refreshments to the tourists. The weather at the Falls is characterized by extremes; and, in fact, there are only two kinds of weather situations at the Falls during the tourist season. Either it is sunny and warm (B_1), or it is cloudy and cold (B_2). In the latter case, it may even rain; but, for our purposes, this is no different from cloudiness without rain, and it is included in the classification, B_2, "cloudy."

His decision problem stems from the fact that he must decide each day's course of action on the previous day, and he has two courses of action available. He may take the insulated ice cream truck (A_1), or he may take the awning truck with its urns of hot coffee (A_2).

On a sunny day, he can sell 1,250 bars of ice cream, which cost him 8¢ each, at 20¢; and on a cloudy day, he can sell 2,500 cups of hot coffee at 15¢. The coffee costs him only 4¢ per cup, but it must all be brewed in advance. Thus, each day, he invests exactly $100; and, if he makes the right decision, on sunny days, his gross sales income is $250, yielding a net profit of $150; while, on cloudy days, his gross income is $375, yielding a profit of $275. Clearly, he prefers bad weather!

If he misjudges the weather and brings the wrong truck, he sells nothing; and, in fact, he loses his entire investment for the day, since the ice cream will melt, or the coffee will deteriorate, whichever the case may be. His profit matrix is shown in Figure 19–6.1.

Courses of Action A_i	States of Nature B_j: B_1 Sunny	B_2 Cloudy
A_1 Ice Cream	150	−100
A_2 Coffee	−100	275

Fig. 19–6.1. Decision matrix. Alox at the Falls.

Clearly, he would like always to bring the ice cream truck when the weather is sunny and the coffee truck when the weather is cloudy. If he could do this, he would always earn either $150 or $275 per day. However, he always runs the risk of losing $100. Since he knows *absolutely nothing* about the weather, what is he to do? He knows nothing more than is shown in the matrix; i.e., each day may be sunny or cloudy. How can he decide which course of action to follow?

Clearly this is an unrealistic situation. It is probably impossible for us to imagine a real situation in which this entrepreneur could be so completely ignorant about the likelihood of the states of nature. For the sake of the illustration, however, we shall assume for the moment that Alox has *no weather information at all.* That is, it may be sunny every day, it may never be sunny, or cloudy and sunny days may occur in any proportion or sequence. And furthermore we shall, for the moment, not permit Alox to accumulate weather data as the season progresses. That is, his decision problem and his complete lack of weather information are unchanged throughout the season. In this event, Alox finds himself in the situation which, in Chapter 1, we have described as *decision making under complete ignorance*, and he may then wish to apply any of the alternative techniques which were described in Section 1–11. However, each of these is open to question and each may select a course of action which can turn out to be disastrous for Alox if his luck is bad. Given the payoff matrix and no additional information, Alox can, as we shall see, achieve a positive and satisfactory expected value by using a mixed strategy. True, his luck can go against him, even with this strategy; but he wishes to maximize his expected value, and the mixed strategy technique gives him a sound basis for operating with a definite computable expected value.

When Alox decides to use the mixed strategy of game theory, then he is in effect regarding his problem as a *game against nature*, and he is treating nature as if it were a rational opponent whose purpose is to minimize Alox's gain. It will be recalled from Chapter 18 that, in a game-theoretic situation, with no saddle point, the maximin strategy is a *mixed strategy*.

Using a mixed strategy involves making his selection each day by tossing a coin, selecting a number from a table of random numbers, or by using some other probabilistic process. The probabilities which must be assigned to A_1 and A_2 may be found easily from the fact that the essence of the solution is that the expected value of his profit under the mixed strategy must be the same, regardless of the state of nature.

Let x_1 be the probability of A_1, and x_2 be the probability of B_2. Then,

$$\text{Expected profit, if } B_1 \text{ occurs,} = (150)(x_1) + (-100)(x_2)$$

and

$$\text{Expected profit, if } B_2 \text{ occurs,} = (-100)(x_1) + (275)(x_2)$$

But these two expected values must be equal; therefore,

$$150x_1 - 100x_2 = -100x_1 + 275x_2$$

$$250x_1 = 375x_2$$

$$x_1 = 1.5x_2$$

but, since there are only two courses of action,

$$x_1 + x_2 = 1$$

$$1.5x_2 + x_2 = 1$$

$$x_2 = 0.4;\ x_1 = 0.6$$

Therefore, the required probabilities for his chance process must be 0.6 and 0.4, respectively, or, in other words, 3:2 in favor of A_1, the ice cream.

If he uses a chance process which will direct him to select A_1 with a probability of 0.6 and A_2 with a probability of 0.4, his expected profit will be the same, *regardless of the weather!* It will be \$50. This is the *value of the game.*

$$\text{If } B_1\text{: Expected profit} = (150)(0.6) + (-100)(0.4) = 90 - 40 = \$50$$

$$\text{If } B_2\text{: Expected profit} = (-100)(0.6) + (275)(0.4) = -60 + 110 = \$50$$

Therefore, if every night Alox consults his table of random numbers, tosses his die, or otherwise satisfies the probability requirements of this mixed strategy, and if he then chooses and acts upon the course of action indicated by the chance result, he can *expect* to earn \$50 per day in the long run, regardless of whether it is sunny every day or it is cloudy every day, or nature intersperses these two types of weather in any diabolical, heavenly, or other kind of order.

This result may be obtained graphically, using the technique introduced in Chapter 18. Figure 19–6.2 shows that the maximin mixed strategy for Alox is $P(A_1) = 0.6$, and the expected profit is \$50.

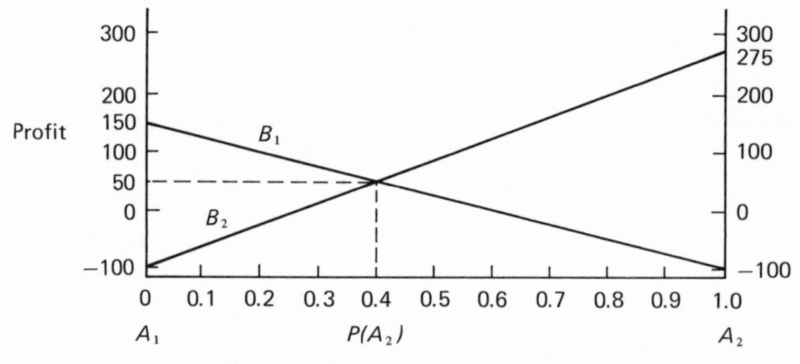

Fig. 19–6.2. Graphical determination of optimal mixed strategy. Alox at the Falls.

19–7. Decision Making Under Risk. Clearly, if Alox had some information about the weather, even if it were only historical climatological data, he could do better than his pitiful game-theoretic solution with its expected value of \$50.

Presumably, what he would do is use his weather information to characterize the likelihood of the states of nature. That is, if he had perfect information about the next day's weather, his decision problem would be that which we have characterized as *decision making under certainty.* Then, his decision matrix each day would consist only of a single column, i.e., that for the correct B_j. He would then always bring the correct truck, and his yield over the season would depend upon the frequencies with which the two kinds of weather situations actually occur.

If his information is not perfect, then he will not be certain about the next day's weather, but he will have an estimate of the probabilities associated with the various states of nature. Then, he will be in the decision situation which we have characterized as *decision making under risk*, and then, under the behavioral assumptions discussed in the earlier sections in this chapter, his optimal strategy is to adopt the course of action with the higher expected value.

Now we shall permit Alox to have some additional information. For the present, we shall let him have only climatological information; i.e., he knows the weather history for previous years, but he knows nothing about each individual day this year except that it is a day which may be characterized as one of a set of days similar to those whose history he has studied. The historical facts are that, for many years now, the weather has been sunny during the tourist season on 70 per cent of the days, and it has been cloudy on 30 per cent of the days. He therefore concludes, quite reasonably, that, in the absence of additional information for specific days, he will treat each day as a random selection from a set of days, 70 per cent of which are sunny, and he then assigns a probability of 0.7 to the event B_1. That is, he concludes that the probability of sunny weather on any day is 0.7.

With this information, he now can treat his problem as a standard problem in decision making under risk. His decision matrix, with the probabilities of the states of nature entered, is as given in Figure 19–7.1.

	(0.7) B_1	(0.3) B_2
A_1	150	−100
A_2	−100	275

Fig. 19–7.1. Decision matrix. Alox at the Falls. Climatological probabilities shown.

Now, he can compute the expected values of the two courses of action, and he finds them to be:

$$E(A_1) = (150)(0.7) + (-100)(0.3) = 105 - 30 = \$75$$

$$E(A_2) = (-100)(0.7) + (275)(0.3) = -70 + 82.5 = \$12.50$$

On the basis of this analysis, Alox decides to select A_1 every day. His expected profit is \$75 per day. This is a considerable improvement over his expected profit (\$50) under the mixed strategy when he had no weather information, and it leads to a very interesting and helpful concept, *the value of information.*

19–8. The Value of Information. Since without the climatological information Alox's best strategy seemed to be the mixed strategy with its expected value of $50, and with the climatological information his best strategy is to adopt the course of action A_1 every day with its expected value of $75, it is correct to say that the value of the additional information, the climatological probabilistic information about the frequency of sunny days, is $25 per day. We shall have many occasions to use this concept of value of information. Simply stated, the value of information is *the increase in the expected value of the objective function which is brought about by the availability and optimal use of that information,* as compared with the expected value without that information.

For example, we can digress for a moment and ask how much perfect information would be worth. That is, how much additional profit could Alox earn if he had perfect information about the weather? Since he already knows that the weather is sunny 70 per cent of the time, the additional information which he would need to have perfect information is the precise advance identification of which days are to be the sunny days and which are to be the cloudy days. We can agree in advance that this degree of perfection in weather information is, at least in the area of the Falls, impossible of attainment within the present state of the art and science of meteorology. However, we can ask what his profit would be *if he did have such ideal information.* He would choose A_1 on the sunny days, 70 per cent of the days, and he would choose A_2 on the cloudy days, 30 per cent of the days, and his profit would be:

$$\begin{aligned}\text{Expected profit under perfect information} &= (150)(0.7) + (275)(0.3)\\ &= 105 + 82.5 = \$187.50\end{aligned}$$

His expected average profit would be $187.50 per day, which is the average of 70 per cent of the days at $150 and 30 per cent of the days at $275. This expected average daily profit is $112.50 more than he could earn with the climatological information alone; and it indicates that the precise forecast, if it were available, would be worth $112.50 per day.

We have agreed that such omniscience is impossible, but we well know that the present state of weather science can usually be expected to provide information which is incremental to and which has value over and above that of simple weather history. In order to examine the value of a less-than-perfect weather forecast, we shall find it desirable to look first at Bayes' theorem, which it will be recalled has been previously mentioned as an important aid in using observational information to modify probabilities of states of nature and applying such observations in decision making.

19–9. Bayes' Theorem and Bayesians. Bayes' theorem has been introduced and discussed in its general form in Section 4–11. There it was seen to be a mathematical procedure for manipulating probabilities. Now, it will be used in a very special way. It enables us to start with the *prior probability,* i.e., the probability of a state of nature as we viewed it prior to our acquiring additional observational information, to take into account the additional information, and to emerge with the *posterior probability,* i.e., the revised probability as modified by that additional information. This seems simple enough, and the formula for Bayes' theorem is also quite simple; yet there is not complete agreement among statisticians with respect to the *use* of Bayes' theorem. The basis for the disagreement has not been Bayes' theorem itself, but rather the interpretation of the inputs and the outputs.

Bayes' theorem, as we have seen in Section 4–11 and shall see again here, is the result of simple algebraic manipulations of certain basic probability rules. No one can argue with the derivation of the theorem; but what distinguishes the so-called *Bayesians* from non-Bayesians is their willingness, first, to use subjective probabilities as the prior probabilities to be applied to what we have called *states of nature,* and second, to modify these prior probabilities on the basis of experimental or observational evidence. We have already, especially in Chapter 4 and earlier in this chapter, said a great deal about the first, subjective probabilities. Now let us devote a few paragraphs to the second.

A statistical hypothesis generally characterizes some population or sample space, and from the hypothesis we can usually, by simple deductive reasoning, assign probabilities under the hypothesis to the various events (subsets of the sample space) which may occur when we draw random samples from that population. For example, if the hypothesis (B) is that the daily demand is normally distributed with mean \$200 and variance \$10, the probability of the observation (X) that a random day's demand will be under \$180 can be easily computed. That is, $P(X|B) = 0.023$. This is a direct logical consequence of the definitions, and there can be no disagreement. It represents *objective* probability in that we have used the word "random" to avoid messy real-world problems such as how the day is actually to be selected.

On the other hand, suppose that, on some real day, we observed X, that the demand was less than \$180. What can we then say about the hypothesis? That is, can we evaluate $P(B|X)$? More correctly, *are we willing* to use probabilities in this way? Bayesians are. Non-Bayesians are not. The rest of this chapter may be characterized as "Bayesian."

In the "classical" view of statistical inference, one could, upon observing X, decide to "accept" or "reject" the hypothesis B. However, the concept of *the probability that the hypothesis B is true* does not exist in the classical interpretation. Similarly therefore, in the classical interpretation, the concept of *the probability of a state of nature* does not exist. States of nature are there taken to be descriptions of reality which may be true or false, but to which probabilities may not properly be applied. Bayesians are willing to apply probabilities to states of nature and to modify those probabilities in the light of additional evidence. This last step is precisely what Bayes' theorem does by providing the mechanism for computing $P(B|X)$, the probability of the state of nature (hypothesis), given the observed evidence.

19–10. The Prior Probabilities. In the Alox problem, the prior probabilities are the 0.7 and 0.3 which refer to the historical distribution of sunny and cloudy days, and in a sense these probabilities are not without some objective basis which may make them palatable to some non-Bayesians who might object to other, more clearly subjective, probability situations. (One such purely subjective situation might be the probability of innocence or guilt of an accused at trial and the modification of the judge's subjective probability as new items of evidence are introduced.) For this reason, we shall introduce this technique using the Alox problem with its historical "relative frequency" basis for the prior probabilities. However, the technique is the same regardless of the source of the prior probabilities.

In any event, the general procedure is to start with the *prior* probabilities $P(B_j)$, perform some experiment or consult some data, and having observed the data, X, compute the *posterior* probability of the states of nature $P(B_j|X)$.

It should be clear to the reader that, in order to use the techniques described here, it is essential that prior probabilities be available. The key to these prior probabilities is that they represent the best knowledge of the decision maker—the distillate of all that he has learned that in any way bears on the phenomenon—and that these subjective prior probabilities are to be estimated by the method prescribed in Section 4–2.

19–11. Using Bayes' Theorem. The first input to the use of Bayes' theorem is the set of prior probabilities over the states of nature. The second input is the probability of the observation, given the state of nature (hypothesis). The output is the posterior probability of the states of nature—*posterior to, and revised by, the observational data.*

In the Alox problem, let us designate the observational possibilities (sample space) as:

X_1: a forecast of sunny weather for tomorrow
X_2: a forecast of cloudy weather for tomorrow

These two possible forecasts are determined by the configuration of weather phenomena recorded by the weather bureau, and the probabilities of various observational or experimental results, given the hypothesis or state of nature are assumed to be known to be:

$$P(X_1|B_1) = 0.9 \quad \text{and} \quad P(X_1|B_2) = 0.2$$

From these, it follows that

$$P(X_2|B_1) = 0.1 \quad \text{and} \quad P(X_2|B_2) = 0.8$$

We can take this to mean that, in the past, when the weather has been sunny, those sunny days had been correctly forecast 90 per cent of the time. Similarly, on the occasions when it has been cloudy, the forecast had incorrectly predicted sunny weather 20 per cent of the time.

Forecasts such as these are clearly quite different from the perfect knowledge which we would like to have; but we shall find, nevertheless, that they do provide very valuable information. Let us now see how to use this information.

First, we shall compute the probability of a forecast of sunny weather, X_1. Since there are only two states of nature, sunny, B_1, with $P(B_1) = 0.7$, and cloudy, B_2, with $P(B_2) = 0.3$, the forecast of sunshine may occur in only two ways. Either there is a forecast of sunshine, and there is sunshine; or there is a forecast of sunshine, and there is cloudiness. Therefore,

$$P(X_1) = P(X_1 \cap B_1) + P(X_1 \cap B_2) \qquad (19\text{–}11.1)$$

From Equation (4-10.7),

$$P(X_1 \cap B_1) = P(B_1)P(X_1|B_1) \qquad (19\text{–}11.2)$$

and

$$P(X_1 \cap B_2) = P(B_2)P(X_1|B_2) \qquad (19\text{–}11.3)$$

Therefore,

$$P(X_1) = P(B_1)P(X_1|B_1) + P(B_2)P(X_1|B_2) \qquad (19\text{–}11.4)$$

and, since we know the values of all the terms on the right side of Equation (19–11.4), we can compute the probability of X_1.

Also, from Equation (4–10.6) the formula for compound probabilities may be expressed as

$$P(X_1 \cap B_1) = P(X_1)P(B_1|X_1) \qquad (19\text{–}11.5)$$

The last factor on the right side of this equation is the desired posterior probability. It is *the probability of sunshine, given that there is a forecast of sunshine.* Since we know the values of all the other terms in the equation, we can solve for this posterior probability. The rearrangement of this equation to solve it for $P(B_j|X_i)$ is

$$P(B_1|X_1) = \frac{P(X_1 \cap B_1)}{P(X_1)} \qquad (19\text{–}11.6)$$

Now, utilizing the relationships of Equations (19–11.2) and (19–11.4), we derive *Bayes' theorem:*

$$P(B_1|X_1) = \frac{P(B_1)P(X_1|B_1)}{P(B_1)P(X_1|B_1) + P(B_2)P(X_1|B_2)} \qquad (19\text{–}11.7)$$

The general statement of Bayes' theorem is

$$P(B_j|X_i) = \frac{P(B_j)P(X_i|B_j)}{\sum_j P(B_j)P(X_i|B_j)} \qquad (19\text{–}11.8)$$

where the symbol $\sum_j$ is to be read "the sum over all j"

We are now in a position to solve Equation (19–11.7) for Alox and his decision problem. If there is a forecast of sunny weather, the posterior probability of sunny weather, i.e., the probability of sunny weather, given that sunny weather has been predicted, is

$$P(B_1|X_1) = \frac{(0.7)(0.9)}{(0.7)(0.9) + (0.3)(0.2)} = \frac{0.63}{0.69}$$

$$P(B_1|X_1) = 0.91$$

Therefore, if there is a forecast of sunny weather, the posterior probability of sunny weather is 0.91, and Alox's matrix, with the probabilities entered,

	(0.91) B_1	(0.09) B_2
A_1	150	−100
A_2	−100	275

Fig. 19–11.1

is as given in Figure 19–11.1. His evaluation of the expected values of his two courses of action becomes

$$E(A_1) = (150)(0.91) + (-100)(0.09) = 136.5 - 9.0 = \$127.50$$

$$E(A_2) = (-100)(0.91) + (275)(0.09) = -91.00 + 24.75 = -\$66.25$$

Clearly, if there is a forecast of sunny weather, Alox is well advised to bring the ice cream truck. However, what should be his course of action if there is a forecast of cloudy weather? From Equation (19–11.8), we can compute the posterior probabilities of the B_j, given X_2:

$$P(B_1|X_2) = \frac{P(B_1)P(X_2|B_1)}{P(B_1)P(X_2|B_1) + P(B_2)P(X_2|B_2)} \tag{19–11.9}$$

$$P(B_1|X_2) = \frac{(0.7)(0.1)}{(0.7)(0.1) + (0.3)(0.8)} = \frac{0.07}{0.31}$$

$$P(B_1|X_2) = 0.23 \quad \text{and} \quad P(B_2|X_2) = 0.77$$

Therefore, if there is a forecast of cloudy weather, the posterior probability of cloudy weather is 0.77, and Alox's matrix is as given in Figure

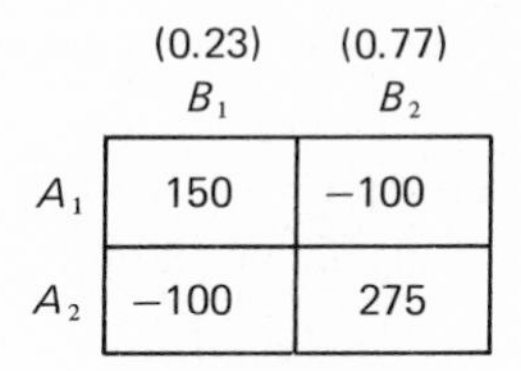

	(0.23) B_1	(0.77) B_2
A_1	150	−100
A_2	−100	275

Fig. 19–11.2

19–11.2. His evaluation of the expected values of his two courses of action now is

$$E(A_1) = (150)(0.23) + (-100)(0.77) = 34.5 - 77.0 = -\$42.50$$

$$E(A_2) = (-100)(0.23) + (275)(0.77) = -23.00 + 211.75 = \$188.75$$

Clearly, if there is a forecast of cloudy weather, Alox is well advised to bring the coffee truck.

The optimal over-all policy for Alox to follow is obviously to hear the forecast and to choose the course of action which is consistent with the forecast. When there is a forecast of sunny weather, he will take the ice cream truck, and his expected daily profit will be \$127.50; and, when there is a forecast of cloudy weather, he will take the coffee truck, and his expected daily profit will then be \$188.75. His expected average daily profit throughout the season will be a weighted average of these, with the $P(X_i)$ as the weights. These $P(X_i)$ are the denominators of Equations (19–11.7) and (19–11.9), respectively; and the values are seen to be $P(X_1) = 0.69$, and $P(X_2) = 0.31$. Since, when X_1 occurs, he chooses A_1, and, when X_2 occurs, he chooses A_2, his expected average daily profit for the season is

$$\begin{aligned} \text{Expected daily profit} &= E(A_1|X_1)P(X_1) + E(A_2|X_2)P(X_2) \qquad (19\text{–}11.10) \\ &= (127.50)(0.69) + (188.75)(0.31) \\ &= 87.98 + 58.51 = \$146.49 \end{aligned}$$

Summarizing Alox's use of incremental information and the value of that information to him: (1) with no information, his expected daily profit was \$50; (2) with climatological historical information, his expected daily profit was \$75, and the climatological information was worth \$25 per day; (3) with the meteorological forecast, his expected daily profit was \$146.49, indicating that the forecast was worth an additional \$71.49 per day. It was also noted that the *absolute optimum* expected average daily profit, if he had perfect weather information, was \$187.50, indicating that Alox's residual ignorance of the weather, even after the forecast, was costing him \$41.01 per day, the difference between his expected profit with the forecast (\$146.49) and the optimum possible value.

Since the local meteorologist had the climatological information available to him, he could have saved Alox the trouble of making all these computations by simply announcing, when he forecasted sunny weather, that his probability estimate for the forecast was 0.91, and, when he forecasted cloudy weather, that his probability estimate that the forecast was correct was 0.77. Alox could then follow the indication of the forecast, and he would realize the average daily profit of \$146.49.

These measures which we have computed of the value of the information at each stage suggest that, when a decision maker is faced with a decision as to whether to purchase information or to try to get along without it, he can calculate how much he should be willing to pay for the information. We know exactly what Alox should be willing to pay for the weather forecast or for the climatological information, if he were faced with the decision of buying the information or doing without it.

This has general implications in that the same kinds of techniques can be applied to other testing and research problems in which there is a decision to be made as to whether additional information should be secured. If the cost of a proposed study is known, one can calculate whether the anticipated study information will be worth the cost. We shall develop the methodology for this procedure in Section 19–14.

Alternatively, if there is a decision to be made about the elaborateness of the test, such as a decision as to the optimal sample size, it may be possible to treat the design of the test as part of the total decision problem, and to calculate the optimal sample size by balancing the cost of the additional observations against the value of the additional information to be gained. Attempts to include all these considerations within a single decision problem can make the analysis extremely complex.

Finally, a last note about the prior probabilities. Clearly, the entire apparatus of Bayes' theorem, including what is yet to be covered in this chapter, cannot be used if the prior probabilities are not available. Also, the greater the amount of information that is added subsequently, the less is the importance of the prior probabilities in determining the eventual values of the posterior probabilities. Therefore, no matter how difficult it may seem to assign values to the prior probabilities, this must be done; and as consolation and comfort, it may be borne in mind that these values will not be damaging to the final results if a large amount of observational information is subsequently added via Bayes' theorem, possibly even by successive applications of the procedure as more and more observational information is added. When there is no prior knowledge at all, some investigators suggest that it may be feasible to start with the assignment of equal probabilities to the various states of nature, even though this may surely not be the case. However, it is difficult to imagine a real situation in which there is absolutely no information to permit the assignment of tentative values to the subjective probabilities essential to the utilization of Bayes' theorem.

19–12. Bounding the Probabilities. In the previous section we noted that, if the weather forecaster had said that his probability estimate associated with his forecast of sunny weather was 0.91, Alox would proceed to bring his ice cream truck whenever there was a forecast of sunny weather. This is obviously correct, but does the probability have to be quite that high in order for Alox correctly to choose A_1? Clearly, no! How high must the probability be in order to lead to a decision for A_1? We can answer this question by asking what the probability must be in order for the two courses of action to be of equal value. Let this critical value of $P(B_1)$ be designated p. Then,

$$E(A_1) = 150p + (-100)(1 - p)$$

and

$$E(A_2) = -100p + (275)(1 - p)$$

Set these equal in order to find the value of p for $E(A_1) = E(A_2)$:

$$150p - 100 + 100p = -100p + 275 - 275p$$

$$625p = 375$$

$$p = 0.60$$

If $P(B_1) = 0.60$, then

$$E(A_1) = (150)(0.60) + (-100)(0.40) = \$50$$

$$E(A_2) = (-100)(0.60) + (275)(0.40) = \$50$$

Thus, if the probability of sunny weather is 0.60 or greater, Alox should choose A_1. If the weather forecaster forecasts sunny weather, and his probability estimate associated with the forecast is 0.60 or greater, he should cause our hero to bring his ice cream truck to the Falls. Of course, we have already seen that, by just picking a random day during the season, the probability of sunny weather is 0.7; and, of course, with that knowledge, Alox did decide to merchandise the ice cream.

The fact that the weatherman could give him a forecast with assigned probability of 0.91 and thereby cause him to select a particular course of action, whereas he would have selected that same course of action if the probability had been 0.6 or higher, leads to a very useful conclusion. Often, when it is very difficult to assign a particular number to the probability of a particular event, it is helpful to compute the *bounding value* of the probability, where the bounding value is defined as the value such that, if the probability is higher than that, one of the A_i will be selected, and, if it is lower, another one of the A_i will be selected. Often, when this is done, it is easy to select the appropriate A_i, because, although the decision maker cannot assign a precise value to the probability, he may be perfectly able and willing to agree that it lies above (or below) the bounding value. In the case of Alox at the Falls, Alox need only agree that the probability of sunny weather was 0.6 or higher in order to decide to bring his ice cream truck.

The value of the bounding probability may be found graphically. The result is the same as above, but the graph provides a new and somewhat different way of viewing the problem. In Figure 19–12.1, the horizontal

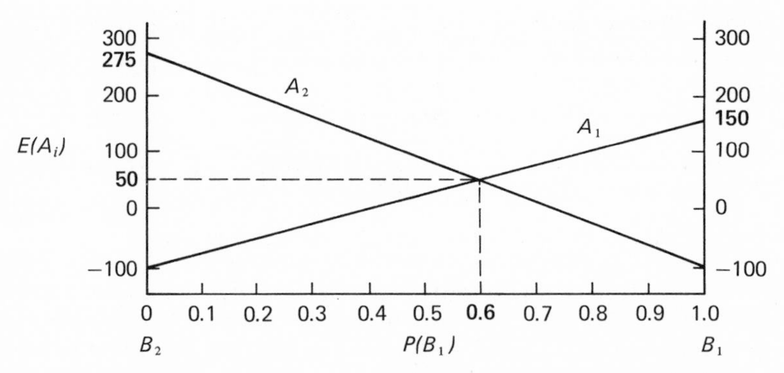

Fig. 19–12.1. Graphic solution for bounding value of $P(B_1)$.

axis is $P(B_1)$, and the left end of that scale, $P(B_1) = 0$, represents the state of nature B_2. Conversely, the right end of the scale $P(B_1) = 1$ represents the state of nature B_1. The two straight lines, labeled A_1 and A_2, represent the expected profit for Alox under each of these respective courses of action for all possible probability distributions over the states of nature. The graph indicates which course of action is optimal for Alox for all $P(B_1)$. That is, he should select the A_i whose line is the higher for any specific $P(B_1)$.

As we have already discovered, for $P(B_1) = 0.7$, the optimal course of action is A_1, with its expected value of \$75. The "break-even" point is at $P(B_1) = 0.6$, where the payoff is \$50 for either course of action. For higher $P(B_1)$, A_1 is preferred, and for lower $P(B_1)$, A_2 is preferred. This graph is similar to that which "nature" might construct to select its optimal mixed strategy, if nature were indeed a rational opponent.

The reader may wish to compare this graph with that of Fig. 19–6.2. In either or both of these graphs, the direction of the horizontal axis could be reversed with no effect on the result. If the horizontal axis of either *one* of these two graphs were to be reversed, it would then look exactly like the other.

19–13. Marginal, Conditional, and Joint Probabilities. The arithmetic involved in computing the posterior probabilities may seem complex as worked out in Section 19–11. However, the procedure used there was selected to illustrate the theoretical basis rather than to demonstrate the simplicity of the computations. The matrices of probability values shown in Figure 19–13.1 have all of the necessary computations for working out the Alox problem. Matrix I in Figure 19–13.1 has the conditional

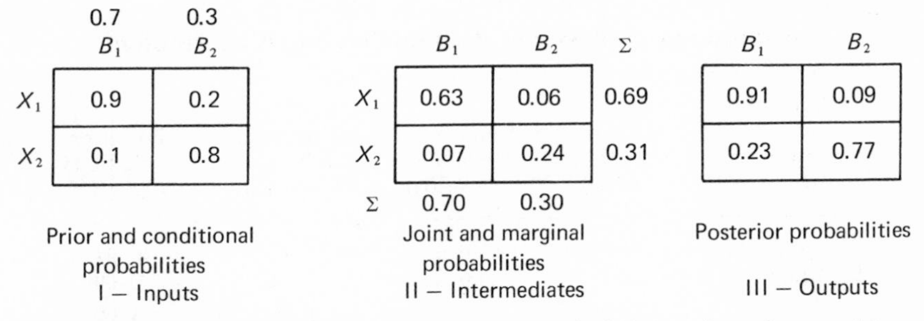

	0.7 B_1	0.3 B_2
X_1	0.9	0.2
X_2	0.1	0.8

Prior and conditional probabilities
I — Inputs

	B_1	B_2	Σ
X_1	0.63	0.06	0.69
X_2	0.07	0.24	0.31
Σ	0.70	0.30	

Joint and marginal probabilities
II — Intermediates

B_1	B_2
0.91	0.09
0.23	0.77

Posterior probabilities
III — Outputs

Fig. 19–13.1. Computation of posterior probabilities for Alox problem. Matrix I has inputs—prior probabilities $P(B_j)$ across the top, and conditional probabilities $P(X_i|B_j)$ in the body. Matrix II computed from Matrix I—each entry in body is $P(B_j)P(X_i|B_j) = P(B_j \cap X_i)$; marginal probabilities by addition. Matrix III computed from Matrix II—each entry is $P(B_j \cap X_i)/P(X_i) = P(B_j|X_i)$.

probabilities $P(X_i|B_j)$ as the cell entries in the body of the matrix and the prior probabilities across the top. These are the *inputs.*

The cell entries in Matrix II in Figure 19–13.1 are computed by multiplying the corresponding cell entries in Matrix I by the appropriate $P(B_j)$ given at the top of the column. These *joint* probabilities are, of course, $P(B_j \cap X_i)$:

$$P(B_j)P(X_i|B_j) = P(B_j \cap X_i) \qquad (19\text{–}13.1)$$

Then, the marginal probabilities shown in the right and bottom margins of Matrix II are obtained by adding across and down, respectively.

$$\sum_j P(B_j \cap X_i) = P(B_j) \tag{19–13.2}$$

$$\sum_i P(B_j \cap X_i) = P(X_i) \tag{19–13.3}$$

Of course the marginal probabilities at the bottom of Matrix II are the original prior probabilities.

Finally, the cell entries in Matrix III are the desired posterior probabilities obtained from Matrix II by dividing the corresponding cell entries by the marginal probability $P(X_i)$:

$$\frac{P(X_i \cap B_i)}{P(X_i)} = P(B_j|X_i) \tag{19–13.4}$$

Alternatively, this whole procedure can very conveniently be performed in a tabular format as is shown in Table 19–13.1. There the analysis is

TABLE 19–13.1

Computation of Posterior Probabilities for Alox Problem

State of Nature B_j	Prior Probability $P(B_j)$	Conditional Probability $P(X_1\|B_j)$	Joint Probability $P(X_1 \cap B_j)$	Posterior Probability $P(B_j\|X_1)$
B_1: Sunny	0.7	0.9	0.63	0.91
B_2: Cloudy	0.3	0.2	0.06	0.09
			0.69	1.00

done only for X_1. Three additional columns would be required to obtain corresponding results for X_2. However, in real problems the evidence consists of *some* X_i, and then the computation need be done only for the X_i which actually did occur. Thus, the simple five-column format of Table 19–13.1 is all that is normally required.

This technique can, of course, be applied to decision problems involving any number of A_i and B_j. All that is required is a set of prior probabilities, $P(B_j)$ for all j, and a set of conditional probabilities giving the probability of the observed experimental result, X, under each of the possible states of nature, i.e., $P(X|B_j)$ for all j.

19–14. Predicting the Value of Information. The foregoing analysis of the value of information has been, in a sense, "after the fact." That is, we obtained each successive increment of information, evaluated it, and then determined how much it was worth. Often, a situation arises in which the decision alternatives are either to undertake or not to undertake a study whose purpose is to acquire information bearing on a decision to be made. In such a situation, one might wish to try to evaluate in advance the worth of the information to be provided by the study and thereby decide whether to undertake the study. Clearly, we would not want to spend $50,000 for a study whose worth, in terms of the value of the information provided, is only, say, $10,000.

This advance prediction or evaluation of the worth of information is usually quite difficult but nevertheless often an exercise well worth trying. The general approach is quite simple. The difficulty is in estimating the possible payoffs and the probabilities associated with each. We can illustrate this kind of situation by again referring to the Alox problem.

First, let us agree that *information has no value unless it causes us to change our course of action.* For example, suppose that we have decided to adopt course of action A_1; if we then do a study which shows that the expected profit is different from our expectation, but that A_1 is still the optimal course of action, *that information is worth nothing.* For example, if, before Alox obtained the meteorological forecast, when he was content with A_1 and its expected value of $75, a study were to show that the expected value of A_1 was actually $100 instead of $75 and that the expected value of A_2 was still below that of A_1, then the information provided by that study would have no value to him because it would not change his course of action. True, it might make him feel better, but the information has no operational impact in that it does not affect his actions; and therefore it has no value, as we define that term here.

It should be noted that, in the foregoing analysis of successive information stages in the Alox problem, the information added at each stage always had a positive value because it always led to a change in his course of action.

Let us return to the Alox problem and consider that stage at which only historical climatological information is available, and at which A_1, with its expected value of $75 per day, is preferable to A_2, with its expected value of $12.50 per day. Now, let us suppose that no regular meteorological forecast is available, but that suddenly there appears on the scene a supermeteorologist who can predict the weather with complete (100 per cent) accuracy. This perfect forecaster offers to forecast the weather for Alox and give him an absolutely correct forecast every day. What should this forecast be worth to Alox?

From the analysis of Section 19–8, wherein we saw that perfect information led to an expected value of $187.50 per day, we can easily reason that such perfect information should be worth the difference between the $187.50 per day and the then optimum expected value of $75 per day.

That difference is \$112.50 per day, and that is indeed the expected value of the perfect forecast, if his policy without the forecast is to select A_1 every day.

Now we shall show that we can arrive at the same measure of the expected value of the information by using an alternative method, and we shall, in the process, develop a powerful new tool. At that stage in the analysis at which only historical climatological information is available, Alox selects A_1, the ice cream truck, and therefore, at that stage, a perfect forecast of sunny weather, B_1, would not change his course of action. Thus, at that stage, a perfectly dependable, 100-per cent certain forecast of B_1 for the next day (or any specific day) would have a value of zero to him. Conversely, a perfect forecast of cloudy weather, B_2, for a specific day would change his course of action from A_1 to A_2, the coffee truck, and he would then earn \$275 on that day. Without that forecast, he would have continued to select A_1, and he would have lost \$100. Therefore, a perfect forecast of B_2 for any specific day would have a value of \$375 for that day.

Since the weather is actually sunny 70 per cent of the days and cloudy 30 per cent of the days, the perfect forecaster will correctly forecast B_1 with probability 0.7 and B_2 with probability 0.3. Therefore, the expected value of the perfect forecast is

$$E \text{ (perfect forecast)} = (0)(0.7) + (375)(0.3) = \$112.50 \text{ per day}$$

which is the same result as was obtained above.

Now we can proceed to use this technique to solve for the value of information in more complex problems. The important idea to be noted in the preceding analysis is this: If one can, in advance, describe all of the possible states of nature in a decision problem, and if he can assign probabilities to each, he can, *with that very information*, predict the value of the information which might be provided by a study which would identify precisely which of the states of nature is the true one. This last sentence is rather complex, but it is a complete summary statement. In different words, it says that, *if a decision problem can be stated as a problem in decision making under risk*—that is, if all of the A_i, B_j, E_{ij}, and $P(B_j)$ are known—*then it is possible to predict the expected value of such information as would convert the problem into a problem in decision making under certainty*. The procedure is:

(1) Compute the $E(A_i)$ for all i and select the optimal A_i in the usual way for a problem in decision making under risk.
(2) Define the value of the information that each B_j is the true state of nature as the difference between E_{ij} and E_{kj}, where E_{ij} is the payoff under the optimal A_i selected in step (1) above, and E_{kj} is the payoff under the *best* course of action for each respective

j^{th} state of nature. Clearly this difference $E_{kj} - E_{ij}$ (of course, the reverse of this would be used when E is measured in, say, costs, and therefore low values are sought) can be only positive or zero. It is zero in those cases where $k = i$; that is, where the specific information does not change the optimal course of action. Thus, the additional information can have only positive or zero value. Its value can never be negative; i.e., additional (correct) information can never hurt.

(3) Compute the predicted expected value of the information as

$$E \text{ (perfect information)} = \sum_j (E_{kj} - E_{ij})P(B_j) \qquad (19\text{–}14.1)$$

where $E_{kj} - E_{ij}$ is either positive or zero

We shall now apply this same reasoning to a more complex problem in which we shall deal with the expected values of expected values and predict the value of the information which a more elaborate kind of study might generate for Alox.

Let us again return to the stage at which Alox has no meteorological forecast of any kind. That is, he is at the stage wherein his decision problem is a problem in decision making under risk, using the historical climatological information which has already been described. Now, let us suppose that some question has arisen about the accuracy of the information given in Figure 19–7.1. It now seems that the payoffs and the probabilities may not be correct or complete as shown there. Possibly a climatologist tells Alox that the weather data may be wrong and that he would like to conduct a new historical study to determine the correct probabilities of the B_j. Or perhaps a marketing man wants to conduct a study to determine more accurately just how much ice cream and coffee can be sold under the two weather conditions. Or perhaps a combined study is proposed. If there is no possibility that the outcome of the study will change the optimal course of action from A_1 to A_2, then the value of the information which that study might provide is zero, and the study should not be undertaken. This is true even if the study were to indicate that the expected values are different from those which have led Alox to his preference for A_1. If, however, the study information might divert him from A_1 to A_2, then that information does have value, and whether it should be performed or not depends upon the relationship between the expected cost of the study and the expected value of the information which it will generate.

We can compute in advance the expected value of this information *only if we can identify the possible outcome or outcomes of the study and determine the probability of each.* Let us assume that, in Alox's case, he could identify four possible study outcomes, each of which leads to an expected value for each A_i, if that A_i is selected every day as a consistent policy. This entire pre-study analysis is pictured in Figure 19–14.1. The numbers in the body of the matrix are to be understood to be the expected values

	Study Outcome			
	I	II	III	IV
A_1	75	100	60	100
A_2	12.50	60	70	150

Fig. 19–14.1. Four possible results of a contemplated study expressed as expected values of Alox's courses of action under each possible study outcome.

of the A_i under each of the four possible information outputs of the study. The reader will recognize that these four possible study results are actually the four possible *states of nature.* (We assume that the study or studies will be properly conducted and their results accurate.)

Let us designate these states of nature B_{I}, B_{II}, B_{III}, and B_{IV}, respectively, and look at them more closely. In Figure 19–14.1 we see that possible study outcome I indicates that Alox's current estimates of the expected values are correct. Clearly, if the study shows that B_{I} is indeed the case, his optimal course of action (A_1) is unchanged, as is its expected value ($75). In that case, the study does not lead to a change of course of action and therefore it has no value. He would have had the same course of action and expected value without the study.

If, on the other hand, the study yields outcome II, which indicates that B_{II} is the true state of nature, that would change Alox's view of the world and tell him that the expected values for A_1 and A_2 are, respectively, $100 per day and $60 per day. If this is the case, his reward will be quite different from his previous estimates. However, he still will select A_1, and therefore the information is of no value to him. True, this information tells him that the expected value of A_1 is $100 rather than $75 as he had previously thought, but if he did not have the information he would still have selected A_1. True, he now will be pleasantly surprised to find his earnings higher than he had estimated, but *this is not a consequence of the study, rather it is a consequence of the true state of nature, and this was the case even without the study. The study information has no value because his course of action and its attendant expected value are the same both with and without the study.*

However, if the study should indicate that the true state of nature is B_{III} or B_{IV}, then the study information does have value to Alox. Either of those two study results would change his optimal course of action from A_1 to A_2, and the value of the information in each case is the difference between the expected value of A_2 and the expected value of A_1, *given that state of nature.* That is, study result III is worth \$10 per day, and study result IV is worth \$50 per day. These are, in each case, the difference between the expected value of the course of action which he would select with the study (he would select A_2) and the expected value of the course of action which he would select without the study (he would select A_1).

Assuming that the study will be correct, these four possible study outcomes are the four possible *true* states of nature in a decision problem. Furthermore, if Alox can assign probabilities to these four possible study ourcomes, or states of nature, then he has converted his problem (before the study) to a problem in *decision making under risk.* This he has done, and his subjective probabilities are shown in Figure 19–14.2, which also

	State of Nature			
	B_{I}	B_{II}	B_{III}	B_{IV}
Value of Information	0	0	10	50
Probability	0.4	0.3	0.2	0.1

Fig. 19–14.2. Expected value of information. The states of nature are the study outcomes of Figure 19–14.1. The probabilities are Alox's subjective estimates.

shows the value of the study information for each of these four possible study outcomes.

Alox may now use the familiar technique for solving problems in decision making under risk. The expected values of the two courses of action A *without the study information* are:

$$E(A_1) = (75)(0.4) + (100)(0.3) + (60)(0.2) + (100)(0.1) = \$82 \text{ per day}$$

$$E(A_2) = (12.5)(0.4) + (60)(0.3) + (70)(0.2) + (150)(0.1) = \$52 \text{ per day}$$

And the expected value of the *best* course of action *with the study information,* where A_k is the best course of action for each respective state of nature, is:

$$E(A_k) = (75)(0.4) + (100)(0.3) + (70)(0.2) + (150)(0.1) = \$89 \text{ per day}$$

Clearly, then, without the study information, but with this new information about the possible states of nature, Alox's best course of action is still A_1, and its expected value is now \$82 per day. However, with the study information, the expected value of his optimal policy is \$89 per day, indicating that the expected value of the study information is \$7 per day.

This measure of the expected value of the information may alternatively be computed directly from the data given in Figure 19–14.2, using Equation (19–14.1).

$$\text{Expected value of information} = (0)(0.4) + (0)(0.3) + (10)(0.2) + (50)(0.1)$$
$$= \$7 \text{ per day}$$

Therefore, if the study can be performed for less than \$7 per day, it should be undertaken. That is, if Alox will use the results of the study over a period of, say, 120 days, then he should be willing to pay up to \$840 for the study. If the study costs more than this figure of \$7 per day, it should not be performed, even though it can, and presumably would, change the decision problem from one of decision making under risk to one of decision making under certainty. It simply would not be worth the price!

19–15. The Contribution of Decision Theory to Management. The contribution to management of decision theory is the prescription that decisions can and should be so structured and analyzed that the course of action which maximizes the expected value of the objective function can be selected. This recommendation is not, as some may hastily surmise, an instruction to ignore "judgement" in making decisions. On the contrary, this concept of decision making helps one to call upon and use his experience and judgement in an orderly and understandable way, namely by: (1) selecting and defining the appropriate objective function; (2) identifying the permissible courses of action; and (3) assigning subjective probabilities to states of nature, especially *future* states of nature, about which available information is incomplete.

19–16. Operations Research and Management Information. The reader who has now completed his tour through this introduction to operations research and management decision making has been exposed to many ideas and has seen and worked his way through a multitude of techniques which he has been told are useful in management decision making. Hopefully, he has enjoyed this broad sampling of ideas and techniques and has encountered at least some that he found to be exciting and that appealed to his individual needs or tastes and that he will wish to pursue beyond the level treated in this book.

However, the reader may, at this point, wish to ask broad questions about the real relevance of operations research and about the place and function of operations research in the organization. Is it a concept which can be characterized as merely leading to interesting and useful tasks for a group of specialists who constitute an "operations research group" within the organization and who do occasional special project work for operating departments when, as, and if requested? Or does operations research have some higher, more central place in the management of business, governmental, educational, eleemosynary, and other organizations? I submit that the concept or approach which has been dubbed "operations research" and which has been defined and described in Chapter 1 above, and aspects of which constitute the subject of this entire volume, is of central, crucial, and, indeed, *dominant* importance in almost any purposeful organization. Now that the reader has completed his tour of the substantive material of this volume and has become familiar with what we understand operations research to mean, we can proceed to demonstrate why *this must be so.*

Implicit in our discussion and description of operations research is a concept and view of the organizations in which decision making takes place: Organizations are information-processing entities. They may be viewed as networks of information flows converging or intersecting at points which may be called *decision-making nodes.* At these nodes, information inputs from various sources in the information system are assembled and processed. From these nodes output information streams—some carrying the results of newly made decisions—flow on to other decision-making nodes for action and for additional processing.

This assemblage of information and the flow pattern of the information movements, from the original data gathering to the inputs and outputs at the topmost managerial level, may be called the *management information system,* and the theory and design of management information systems has become an important area of interest for management scientists.

When we examine—as we shall now do—the concept and requirements of an ideal management information system, we shall see that the three concepts: management information systems, decision making, and operations research, are so closely interrelated that it is impossible to think of one without the other two. The decision function is the *raison d'être* of the organization, the information system makes that function possible, and operations research tells what the information system must do in order to accomplish that purpose.

A management information system *must supply to each decision-making node the information which is used and useful in making the decisions for which that organizational point is responsible.* This definition of purpose is very brief, and management information theorists have much more to say as, for example, about the currency and the sparseness of these information inputs and about many other aspects, but, for our purposes, the above statement is adequate. If, now, with this definition in mind, one were to seek to design a management information system for some organization, he would inevitably have to proceed through the following four steps.

1. Identify and describe each and every kind of decision that must be made in the organization, according to some concept of optimality for the organization and its objectives.

2. Construct a model for each kind of decision, identifying, for each, the objective function, the controllable and uncontrollable input variables and, to the extent feasible, the functional relationships among these quantities.
3. Design the necessary data definitions and the appropriate data-collection methods and information-flow patterns according to some concept of optimality for the organization and its objectives.
4. Build in a system of information feedback for control and improvement of the decision models and the information system as a whole.

Clearly, the second step (with its implications for the fourth step also) above is precisely the task which we have described as the function of operations research. Equally clearly from the above sequence, it is not possible to construct a rational management information system unless these decision models exist. Thus, *without this step, it is not possible to proceed*. The inevitable and inescapable conclusion, then, is that the operations research function is central and critical in the organization.

Every organization in existence—yesterday, today, and tomorrow—necessarily has its inherent management information system, for better or for worse, and that management information system presupposes and is based upon some model, implicit or explicit, of each of the kinds of decisions that must be made within the organization, as indicated in step 2 above. This is essential, whether the management consciously planned it or is even unaware of it. Operations researchers seek to make more and more of these models explicit, rational, and effective.

SUGGESTIONS FOR FURTHER READING

Anderson, N. H., and D. A. Grant. "A Test of a Statistical Learning Theory Model for Two-Choice Behavior with Double Stimulus Events," *Journal of Experimental Psychology*, 54:305–17 (1957).

Boulding, K. E. "The Ethics of Rational Decision," *Management Science*, Vol. 12, No. 6 (February, 1966).

Chernoff, H., and L. E. Moses. *Elementary Decision Theory*. New York: John Wiley & Sons, Inc., 1957.

Churchman, C. W. "Decision and Value Theory," in *Progress in Operations Research*, Vol. 1 (R. L. Ackoff, ed.). New York: John Wiley & Sons, Inc., 1961.

Davidson, D., P. Suppes, and S. Siegel. *Decision Making, An Experimental Approach*. Stanford, Calif.: Stanford University Press, 1957.

Good, I. J. *The Estimation of Probabilities*, Cambridge, Mass.: M.I.T. Press, 1965.

Luce, R. D., and H. Raiffa. *Games and Decisions*. New York: John Wiley & Sons, Inc., 1957.

Pratt, J. W., H. Raiffa, and R. Schlaifer. "The Foundations of Decision Under Uncertainty: An Elementary Exposition," *Journal of the American Statistical Association*, Vol. 59, No. 306 (June, 1964).

Raiffa, H., and R. Schlaifer. *Applied Statistical Decision Theory*. Boston:

Harvard University Division of Research, Graduate School of Business Administration, 1961.
SAVAGE, L. J. *The Foundations of Statistics.* New York: John Wiley & Sons, Inc., 1954.
SCHLAIFER, R. *Probability and Statistics for Business Decisions.* New York: McGraw-Hill Book Co., Inc., 1959.
SIMON, H. A. *Models of Man.* New York: John Wiley & Sons, Inc., 1957.
SIMON, H. A. "Theories of Decision-Making in Economics," *American Economic Review,* Vol. 49, No. 3 (June, 1959).
WEISS, L. *Statistical Decision Theory.* New York: McGraw-Hill Book Co., Inc., 1961.

EXERCISES

19–1. The Hawoff Company inspection department has just received a large lot of electronic components for inspection. Experience indicates that there are only two possible compositions of the lot; B_1, 5% defective or B_2, 10% defective. Empirical evidence also tells that $P(B_1) = 0.7$ and $P(B_2) = 0.3$. The payoff matrix for the decision problem is given below, in thousands of dollars of cost of error. These are the only relevant costs.

	B_1	B_2
A_1 Accept	0	5
A_2 Accept	3	0

a) Should the lot be accepted if there is no additional evidence?
b) Should the lot be accepted if a sample of two units is drawn and both are defective?
c) What is the value of the information which that specific sample provided in that specific case?
d) What is the *expected value* of the information provided by a sample of two units?
(Hint: To compute the *expected value of sample information,* examine each of the possible sample outcomes and compute the expected value of the course of action selected after each outcome. Then compute the expected value of these expected values, using the probabilities of each of the possible sample outcomes. Compare this result with the expected value of the course of action which would have been adopted without the sample information. This yields the expected value of the sample information.)
e) If testing costs $37 per unit tested, should there be any testing, or should lots just be accepted?
(Hint: Compute the expected value of the information provided by a sample of *one* unit.)

19–2. The Sparkle Corporation is about to introduce a new detergent, but the company management is undecided as to whether to bring out the new product now or next spring. The chief competitor of the Sparkle Corporation is Radiance, Inc., which, as is widely known, also has a new product to introduce. Since Sparkle's present product is superior to Radiance's present product, if they both wait, Sparkle will gain. If they both introduce their products now, Radiance will gain, since Sparkle cannot match Radiance's current marketing capability. However, if Radiance alone introduces now, Sparkle will be able to keep afloat this year because of its superior product and will clobber Radiance next spring. If Radiance happens to have two products and introduces one now and one next spring, Sparkle had best hold its new product for the fierce competition next spring.

The entire picture, as seen by Sparkle in terms of profits for Sparkle in millions of dollars, is summarized in the following matrix.

		Radiance		
		B_1 Now	B_2 Next Spring	B_3 Both
Sparkle	A_1 Now	−4	8	−6
	A_2 Next Spring	10	5	6

a) If Sparkle management has no additional information, what are the company's possible strategies? What are their expected values?

b) If the president of Sparkle has information which gives him subjective probabilities of: 0.2, 0.6, 0.2 for the respective B_j, what should be his course of action? What is its expected value?

c) What would be the expected value to Sparkle of the information provided by a study which could tell *exactly* which course of action Radiance will adopt?

d) The president decides not to conduct that study (in part *c* above) and, instead, conducts his own experiment to test Radiance's intentions and obtains a response, R, such that, in his opinion:

$$P(R|B_1) = 0.1$$

$$P(R|B_2) = 0.7$$

$$P(R|B_3) = 0.3$$

What should now be his course of action, and what is its expected value?

APPENDIX

A

Areas and Ordinates of the Normal Curve

Table of Areas
Column (2) Shows

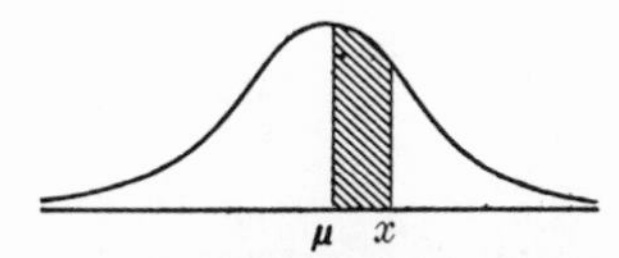

Table of Ordinates
Column (3) Shows

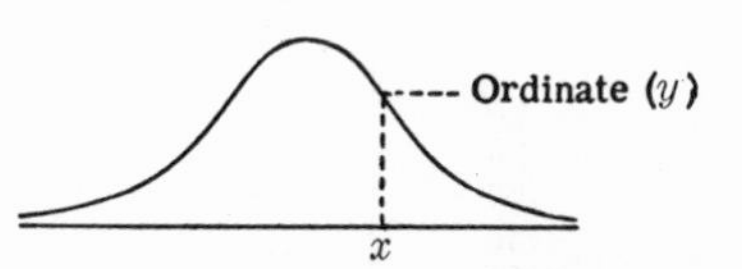

$\frac{x-\mu}{\sigma}$ (1)	Area Under the Curve between μ and x (2)	Ordinate (y) of the curve at x (3)	$\frac{x-\mu}{\sigma}$ (1)	Area Under the Curve between μ and x (2)	Ordinate (y) of the curve at x (3)
.00	.00000	.39894	.20	.07926	.39104
.01	.00399	.39892	.21	.08317	.39024
.02	.00798	.39886	.22	.08706	.38940
.03	.01197	.39876	.23	.09095	.38853
.04	.01595	.39862	.24	.09483	.38762
.05	.01994	.39844	.25	.09871	.38667
.06	.02392	.39822	.26	.10257	.38568
.07	.02790	.39797	.27	.10642	.38466
.08	.03188	.39767	.28	.11026	.38361
.09	.03586	.39733	.29	.11409	.38251
.10	.03983	.39695	.30	.11791	.38139
.11	.04380	.39654	.31	.12172	.38023
.12	.04776	.39608	.32	.12552	.37903
.13	.05172	.39559	.33	.12930	.37780
.14	.05567	.39505	.34	.13307	.37654
.15	.05962	.39448	.35	.13683	.37524
.16	.06356	.39387	.36	.14058	.37391
.17	.06749	.39322	.37	.14431	.37255
.18	.07142	.39253	.38	.14803	.37115
.19	.07535	.39181	.39	.15173	.36973

$\frac{x-\mu}{\sigma}$ (1)	Area Under the Curve between μ and x (2)	Ordinate (y) of the curve at x (3)	$\frac{x-\mu}{\sigma}$ (1)	Area Under the Curve between μ and x (2)	Ordinate (y) of the curve at x (3)
.40	.15542	.36827	.85	.30234	.27798
.41	.15910	.36678	.86	.30511	.27562
.42	.16276	.36526	.87	.30785	.27324
.43	.16640	.36371	.88	.31057	.27086
.44	.17003	.36213	.89	.31327	.26848
.45	.17364	.36053	.90	.31594	.26609
.46	.17724	.35889	.91	.31859	.26369
.47	.18082	.35723	.92	.32121	.26129
.48	.18439	.35553	.93	.32381	.25888
.49	.18793	.35381	.94	.32639	.25647
.50	.19146	.35207	.95	.32894	.25406
.51	.19497	.35029	.96	.33147	.25164
.52	.19847	.34849	.97	.33398	.24923
.53	.20194	.34667	.98	.33646	.24681
.54	.20540	.34482	.99	.33891	.24439
.55	.20884	.34294	1.00	.34134	.24197
.56	.21226	.34105	1.01	.34375	.23955
.57	.21566	.33912	1.02	.34614	.23713
.58	.21904	.33718	1.03	.34850	.23471
.59	.22240	.33521	1.04	.35083	.23230
.60	.22575	.33322	1.05	.35314	.22988
.61	.22907	.33121	1.06	.35543	.22747
.62	.23237	.32918	1.07	.35769	.22506
.63	.23565	.32713	1.08	.35993	.22265
.64	.23891	.32506	1.09	.36214	.22025
.65	.24215	.32297	1.10	.36433	.21785
.66	.24537	.32086	1.11	.36650	.21546
.67	.24857	.31874	1.12	.36864	.21307
.68	.25175	.31659	1.13	.37076	.21069
.69	.25490	.31443	1.14	.37286	.20831
.70	.25804	.31225	1.15	.37493	.20594
.71	.26115	.31006	1.16	.37698	.20357
.72	.26424	.30785	1.17	.37900	.20121
.73	.26730	.30563	1.18	.38100	.19886
.74	.27035	.30339	1.19	.38298	.19652
.75	.27337	.30114	1.20	.38493	.19419
.76	.27637	.29887	1.21	.38686	.19186
.77	.27935	.29659	1.22	.38877	.18954
.78	.28230	.29431	1.23	.39065	.18724
.79	.28524	.29200	1.24	.39251	.18494
.80	.28814	.28969	1.25	.39435	.18265
.81	.29103	.28737	1.26	.39617	.18037
.82	.29389	.28504	1.27	.39796	.17810
.83	.29673	.28269	1.28	.39973	.17585
.84	.29955	.28034	1.29	.40147	.17360

$\frac{x-\mu}{\sigma}$ (1)	Area Under the Curve between μ and x (2)	Ordinate (y) of the curve at x (3)	$\frac{x-\mu}{\sigma}$ (1)	Area Under the Curve between μ and x (2)	Ordinate (y) of the curve at x (3)
1.30	.40320	.17137	1.75	.45994	.08628
1.31	.40490	.16915	1.76	.46080	.08478
1.32	.40658	.16694	1.77	.46164	.08329
1.33	.40824	.16474	1.78	.46246	.08183
1.34	.40988	.16256	1.79	.46327	.08038
1.35	.41149	.16038	1.80	.46407	.07895
1.36	.41309	.15822	1.81	.46485	.07754
1.37	.41466	.15608	1.82	.46562	.07614
1.38	.41621	.15395	1.83	.46638	.07477
1.39	.41774	.15183	1.84	.46712	.07341
1.40	.41924	.14973	1.85	.46784	.07206
1.41	.42073	.14764	1.86	.46856	.07074
1.42	.42220	.14556	1.87	.46926	.06943
1.43	.42364	.14350	1.88	.46995	.06814
1.44	.42507	.14146	1.89	.47062	.06687
1.45	.42647	.13943	1.90	.47128	.06562
1.46	.42786	.13742	1.91	.47193	.06438
1.47	.42922	.13542	1.92	.47257	.06316
1.48	.43056	.13344	1.93	.47320	.06195
1.49	.43189	.13147	1.94	.47381	.06077
1.50	.43319	.12952	1.95	.47441	.05959
1.51	.43448	.12758	1.96	.47500	.05844
1.52	.43574	.12566	1.97	.47558	.05730
1.53	.43699	.12376	1.98	.47615	.05618
1.54	.43822	.12188	1.99	.47670	.05508
1.55	.43943	.12001	2.00	.47725	.05399
1.56	.44062	.11816	2.01	.47778	.05292
1.57	.44179	.11632	2.02	.47831	.05186
1.58	.44295	.11450	2.03	.47882	.05082
1.59	.44408	.11270	2.04	.47932	.04980
1.60	.44520	.11092	2.05	.47982	.04879
1.61	.44630	.10915	2.06	.48030	.04780
1.62	.44738	.10741	2.07	.48077	.04682
1.63	.44845	.10567	2.08	.48124	.04586
1.64	.44950	.10396	2.09	.48169	.04491
1.65	.45053	.10226	2.10	.48214	.04398
1.66	.45154	.10059	2.11	.48257	.04307
1.67	.45254	.09893	2.12	.48300	.04217
1.68	.45352	.09728	2.13	.48341	.04128
1.69	.45449	.09566	2.14	.48382	.04041
1.70	.45543	.09405	2.15	.48422	.03955
1.71	.45637	.09246	2.16	.48461	.03871
1.72	.45728	.09089	2.17	.48500	.03788
1.73	.45818	.08933	2.18	.48537	.03706
1.74	.45907	.08780	2.19	.48574	.03626

$\frac{x-\mu}{\sigma}$ (1)	Area Under the Curve between μ and x (2)	Ordinate (y) of the curve at x (3)	$\frac{x-\mu}{\sigma}$ (1)	Area Under the Curve between μ and x (2)	Ordinate (y) of the curve at x (3)
2.20	.48610	.03547	2.65	.49598	.01191
2.21	.48645	.03470	2.66	.49609	.01160
2.22	.48679	.03394	2.67	.49621	.01130
2.23	.48713	.03319	2.68	.49632	.01100
2.24	.48745	.03246	2.69	.49643	.01071
2.25	.48778	.03174	2.70	.49653	.01042
2.26	.48809	.03103	2.71	.49664	.01014
2.27	.48840	.03034	2.72	.49674	.00987
2.28	.48870	.02965	2.73	.49683	.00961
2.29	.48899	.02898	2.74	.49693	.00935
2.30	.48928	.02833	2.75	.49702	.00909
2.31	.48956	.02768	2.76	.49711	.00885
2.32	.48983	.02705	2.77	.49720	.00861
2.33	.49010	.02643	2.78	.49728	.00837
2.34	.49036	.02582	2.79	.49736	.00814
2.35	.49064	.02522	2.80	.49744	.00792
2.36	.49086	.02463	2.81	.49752	.00770
2.37	.49111	.02406	2.82	.49760	.00748
2.38	.49134	.02349	2.83	.49767	.00727
2.39	.49158	.02294	2.84	.49774	.00707
2.40	.49180	.02239	2.85	.49781	.00687
2.41	.49202	.02186	2.86	.49788	.00668
2.42	.49224	.02134	2.87	.49795	.00649
2.43	.49245	.02083	2.88	.49801	.00631
2.44	.49266	.02033	2.89	.49807	.00613
2.45	.49286	.01984	2.90	.49813	.00595
2.46	.49305	.01936	2.91	.49819	.00578
2.47	.49324	.01889	2.92	.49825	.00562
2.48	.49343	.01842	2.93	.49831	.00545
2.49	.49361	.01797	2.94	.49836	.00530
2.50	.49379	.01753	2.95	.49841	.00514
2.51	.49396	.01709	2.96	.49846	.00499
2.52	.49413	.01667	2.97	.49851	.00485
2.53	.49430	.01625	2.98	.49856	.00471
2.54	.49446	.01585	2.99	.49861	.00457
2.55	.49461	.01545	3.00	.49865	.00443
2.56	.49477	.01506	3.01	.49869	.00430
2.57	.49492	.01468	3.02	.49874	.00417
2.58	.49506	.01431	3.03	.49878	.00405
2.59	.49520	.01394	3.04	.49882	.00393
2.60	.49534	.01358	3.05	.49886	.00381
2.61	.49547	.01323	3.06	.49889	.00370
2.62	.49560	.01289	3.07	.49893	.00358
2.63	.49573	.01256	3.08	.49897	.00348
2.64	.49585	.01223	3.09	.49900	.00337

$\frac{x-\mu}{\sigma}$ (1)	Area Under the Curve between μ and x (2)	Ordinate (y) of the curve at x (3)	$\frac{x-\mu}{\sigma}$ (1)	Area Under the Curve between μ and x (2)	Ordinate (y) of the curve at x (3)
3.10	.49903	.00327	3.55	.49981	.00073
3.11	.49906	.00317	3.56	.49981	.00071
3.12	.49910	.00307	3.57	.49982	.00068
3.13	.49913	.00298	3.58	.49983	.00066
3.14	.49916	.00288	3.59	.49983	.00063
3.15	.49918	.00279	3.60	.49984	.00061
3.16	.49921	.00271	3.61	.49985	.00059
3.17	.49924	.00262	3.62	.49985	.00057
3.18	.49926	.00254	3.63	.49986	.00055
3.19	.49929	.00246	3.64	.49986	.00053
3.20	.49931	.00238	3.65	.49987	.00051
3.21	.49934	.00231	3.66	.49987	.00049
3.22	.49936	.00224	3.67	.49988	.00047
3.23	.49938	.00216	3.68	.49988	.00046
3.24	.49940	.00210	3.69	.49989	.00044
3.25	.49942	.00203	3.70	.49989	.00042
3.26	.49944	.00196	3.71	.49990	.00041
3.27	.49946	.00190	3.72	.49990	.00039
3.28	.49948	.00184	3.73	.49990	.00038
3.29	.49950	.00178	3.74	.49991	.00037
3.30	.49952	.00172	3.75	.49991	.00035
3.31	.49953	.00167	3.76	.49992	.00034
3.32	.49955	.00161	3.77	.49992	.00033
3.33	.49957	.00156	3.78	.49992	.00031
3.34	.49958	.00151	3.79	.49992	.00030
3.35	.49960	.00146	3.80	.49993	.00029
3.36	.49961	.00141	3.81	.49993	.00028
3.37	.49962	.00136	3.82	.49993	.00027
3.38	.49964	.00132	3.83	.49994	.00026
3.39	.49965	.00127	3.84	.49994	.00025
3.40	.49966	.00123	3.85	.49994	.00024
3.41	.49968	.00119	3.86	.49994	.00023
3.42	.49969	.00115	3.87	.49995	.00022
3.43	.49970	.00111	3.88	.49995	.00021
3.44	.49971	.00107	3.89	.49995	.00021
3.45	.49972	.00104	3.90	.49995	.00020
3.46	.49973	.00100	3.91	.49995	.00019
3.47	.49974	.00097	3.92	.49996	.00018
3.48	.49975	.00094	3.93	.49996	.00018
3.49	.49976	.00090	3.94	.49996	.00017
3.50	.49977	.00087	3.95	.49996	.00016
3.51	.49978	.00084	3.96	.49996	.00016
3.52	.49978	.00081	3.97	.49996	.00015
3.53	.49979	.00079	3.98	.49997	.00014
3.54	.49980	.00076	3.99	.49997	.00014

B

Binomial Distribution Function

$$P\{x\} = \frac{n!}{x!(n-x)!} p^x q^{n-x}$$

n	x	.05	.10	.15	.20	.25	.30	.35	.40	.45	.50
						p					
1	0	.9500	.9000	.8500	.8000	.7500	.7000	.6500	.6000	.5500	.5000
	1	.0500	.1000	.1500	.2000	.2500	.3000	.3500	.4000	.4500	.5000
2	0	.9025	.8100	.7225	.6400	.5625	.4900	.4225	.3600	.3025	.2500
	1	.0950	.1800	.2550	.3200	.3750	.4200	.4550	.4800	.4950	.5000
	2	.0025	.0100	.0225	.0400	.0625	.0900	.1225	.1600	.2025	.2500
3	0	.8574	.7290	.6141	.5120	.4219	.3430	.2746	.2160	.1664	.1250
	1	.1354	.2430	.3251	.3840	.4219	.4410	.4436	.4320	.4084	.3750
	2	.0071	.0270	.0574	.0960	.1406	.1890	.2389	.2880	.3341	.3750
	3	.0001	.0010	.0034	.0080	.0156	.0270	.0429	.0640	.0911	.1250
4	0	.8145	.6561	.5220	.4096	.3164	.2401	.1785	.1296	.0915	.0625
	1	.1715	.2916	.3685	.4096	.4219	.4116	.3845	.3456	.2995	.2500
	2	.0135	.0486	.0975	.1536	.2109	.2646	.3105	.3456	.3675	.3750
	3	.0005	.0036	.0115	.0256	.0469	.0756	.1115	.1536	.2005	.2500
	4	.0000	.0001	.0005	.0016	.0039	.0081	.0150	.0256	.0410	.0625
5	0	.7738	.5905	.4437	.3277	.2373	.1681	.1160	.0778	.0503	.0312
	1	.2036	.3280	.3915	.4096	.3955	.3602	.3124	.2592	.2059	.1562
	2	.0214	.0729	.1382	.2048	.2637	.3087	.3364	.3456	.3369	.3125
	3	.0011	.0081	.0244	.0512	.0879	.1323	.1811	.2304	.2757	.3125
	4	.0000	.0004	.0022	.0064	.0146	.0284	.0488	.0768	.1128	.1562
	5	.0000	.0000	.0001	.0003	.0010	.0024	.0053	.0102	.0185	.0312
6	0	.7351	.5314	.3771	.2621	.1780	.1176	.0754	.0467	.0277	.0156
	1	.2321	.3543	.3993	.3932	.3560	.3025	.2437	.1866	.1359	.0938
	2	.0305	.0984	.1762	.2458	.2966	.3241	.3280	.3110	.2780	.2344
	3	.0021	.0146	.0415	.0819	.1318	.1852	.2355	.2765	.3032	.3125
	4	.0001	.0012	.0055	.0154	.0330	.0595	.0951	.1382	.1861	.2344
	5	.0000	.0001	.0004	.0015	.0044	.0102	.0205	.0369	.0609	.0938
	6	.0000	.0000	.0000	.0001	.0002	.0007	.0018	.0041	.0083	.0156

n	x	.05	.10	.15	.20	.25	.30	.35	.40	.45	.50
7	0	.6983	.4783	.3206	.2097	.1335	.0824	.0490	.0280	.0152	.0078
	1	.2573	.3720	.3960	.3670	.3115	.2471	.1848	.1306	.0872	.0547
	2	.0406	.1240	.2097	.2753	.3115	.3177	.2985	.2613	.2140	.1641
	3	.0036	.0230	.0617	.1147	.1730	.2269	.2679	.2903	.2918	.2734
	4	.0002	.0026	.0109	.0287	.0577	.0972	.1442	.1935	.2388	.2734
	5	.0000	.0002	.0012	.0043	.0115	.0250	.0466	.0774	.1172	.1641
	6	.0000	.0000	.0001	.0004	.0013	.0036	.0084	.0172	.0320	.0547
	7	.0000	.0000	.0000	.0000	.0001	.0002	.0006	.0016	.0037	.0078
8	0	.6634	.4305	.2725	.1678	.1002	.0576	.0319	.0168	.0084	.0039
	1	.2793	.3826	.3847	.3355	.2670	.1977	.1373	.0896	.0548	.0312
	2	.0515	.1488	.2376	.2936	.3115	.2065	.2587	.2090	.1569	.1094
	3	.0054	.0331	.0839	.1468	.2076	.2541	.2786	.2787	.2568	.2188
	4	.0004	.0046	.0185	.0459	.0865	.1361	.1875	.2322	.2627	.2734
	5	.0000	.0004	.0026	.0092	.0231	.0467	.0808	.1239	.1719	.2188
	6	.0000	.0000	.0002	.0011	.0038	.0100	.0217	.0413	.0403	.1094
	7	.0000	.0000	.0000	.0001	.0004	.0012	.0033	.0079	.0164	.0312
	8	.0000	.0000	.0000	.0000	.0000	.0001	.0002	.0007	.0017	.0039
9	0	.6302	.3874	.2316	.1342	.0751	.0404	.0207	.0101	.0046	.0020
	1	.2985	.3874	.3679	.3020	.2253	.1556	.1004	.0605	.0339	.0176
	2	.0629	.1722	.2597	.3020	.3003	.2668	.2162	.1612	.1110	.0703
	3	.0077	.0446	.1069	.1762	.2336	.2668	.2716	.2508	.2119	.1641
	4	.0006	.0074	.0283	.0661	.1168	.1715	.2194	.2508	.2600	.2461
	5	.0000	.0008	.0050	.0165	.0389	.0735	.1181	.1672	.2128	.2461
	6	.0000	.0001	.0006	.0028	.0087	.0210	.0424	.0743	.1160	.1641
	7	.0000	.0000	.0000	.0003	.0012	.0039	.0098	.0212	.0407	.0703
	8	.0000	.0000	.0000	.0000	.0001	.0004	.0013	.0035	.0083	.0176
	9	.0000	.0000	.0000	.0000	.0000	.0000	.0001	.0003	.0008	.0020
10	0	.5987	.3487	.1969	.1074	.0563	.0282	.0135	.0060	.0025	.0010
	1	.3151	.3874	.3474	.2684	.1877	.1211	.0725	.0403	.0207	.0098
	2	.0746	.1937	.2759	.3020	.2816	.2335	.1757	.1209	.0763	.0439
	3	.0105	.0574	.1298	.2013	.2503	.2668	.2522	.2150	.1665	.1172
	4	.0010	.0112	.0401	.0881	.1460	.2001	.2377	.2508	.2384	.2051
	5	.0001	.0015	.0085	.0264	.0584	.1029	.1536	.2007	.2340	.2461
	6	.0000	.0001	.0012	.0055	.0162	.0368	.0689	.1115	.1596	.2051
	7	.0000	.0000	.0001	.0008	.0031	.0090	.0212	.0425	.0746	.1172
	8	.0000	.0000	.0000	.0001	.0004	.0014	.0043	.0106	.0229	.0439
	9	.0000	.0000	.0000	.0000	.0000	.0001	.0005	.0016	.0042	.0098
	10	.0000	.0000	.0000	.0000	.0000	.0000	.0000	.0001	.0003	.0010
11	0	.5688	.3138	.1673	.0859	.0422	.0198	.0088	.0036	.0014	.0005
	1	.3293	.3835	.3248	.2362	.1549	.0932	.0518	.0266	.0125	.0054
	2	.0867	.2131	.2866	.2953	.2581	.1998	.1395	.0887	.0513	.0269
	3	.0137	.0710	.1517	.2215	.2581	.2568	.2254	.1774	.1259	.0806
	4	.0014	.0158	.0536	.1107	.1721	.2201	.2428	.2365	.2060	.1611
	5	.0001	.0025	.0132	.0388	.0803	.1321	.1830	.2207	.2360	.2256
	6	.0000	.0003	.0023	.0097	.0268	.0566	.0985	.1471	.1931	.2256
	7	.0000	.0000	.0003	.0017	.0064	.0173	.0379	.0701	.1128	.1611
	8	.0000	.0000	.0000	.0002	.0011	.0037	.0102	.0234	.0462	.0806
	9	.0000	.0000	.0000	.0000	.0001	.0005	.0018	.0052	.0126	.0269
	10	.0000	.0000	.0000	.0000	.0000	.0000	.0002	.0007	.0021	.0054
	11	.0000	.0000	.0000	.0000	.0000	.0000	.0000	.0000	.0002	.0005
12	0	.5404	.2824	.1422	.0687	.0317	.0138	.0057	.0022	.0008	.0002
	1	.3413	.3766	.3012	.2062	.1267	.0712	.0368	.0174	.0075	.0029
	2	.0988	.2301	.2924	.2835	.2323	.1678	.1088	.0639	.0339	.0161
	3	.0173	.0852	.1720	.2362	.2581	.2397	.1954	.1419	.0923	.0537
	4	.0021	.0213	.0683	.1329	.1936	.2311	.2367	.2128	.1700	.1208
	5	.0002	.0038	.0193	.0532	.1032	.1585	.2039	.2270	.2225	.1934
	6	.0000	.0005	.0040	.0155	.0401	.0792	.1281	.1766	.2124	.2256
	7	.0000	.0000	.0006	.0033	.0115	.0291	.0591	.1009	.1489	.1934
	8	.0000	.0000	.0001	.0005	.0024	.0078	.0199	.0420	.0762	.1208
	9	.0000	.0000	.0000	.0001	.0004	.0015	.0048	.0125	.0277	.0537

n	x	.05	.10	.15	.20	.25	.30	.35	.40	.45	.50
						p					
12	10	.0000	.0000	.0000	.0000	.0000	.0002	.0008	.0025	.0068	.0161
	11	.0000	.0000	.0000	.0000	.0000	.0000	.0001	.0003	.0010	.0029
	12	.0000	.0000	.0000	.0000	.0000	.0000	.0000	.0000	.0001	.0002
13	0	.5133	.2542	.1209	.0550	.0238	.0097	.0037	.0013	.0004	.0001
	1	.3512	.3672	.2774	.1787	.1029	.0540	.0259	.0113	.0045	.0016
	2	.1109	.2448	.2937	.2680	.2059	.1388	.0836	.0453	.0220	.0095
	3	.0214	.0997	.1900	.2457	.2517	.2181	.1651	.1107	.0660	.0349
	4	.0028	.0277	.0838	.1535	.2097	.2337	.2222	.1845	.1350	.0873
	5	.0003	.0055	.0266	.0691	.1258	.1803	.2154	.2214	.1989	.1571
	6	.0000	.0008	.0063	.0230	.0559	.1030	.1546	.1968	.2169	.2095
	7	.0000	.0001	.0011	.0058	.0186	.0442	.0833	.1312	.1775	.2095
	8	.0000	.0001	.0001	.0011	.0047	.0142	.0336	.0656	.1089	.1571
	9	.0000	.0000	.0000	.0001	.0009	.0034	.0101	.0243	.0495	.0873
	10	.0000	.0000	.0000	.0000	.0001	.0006	.0022	.0065	.0162	.0349
	11	.0000	.0000	.0000	.0000	.0000	.0001	.0003	.0012	.0036	.0095
	12	.0000	.0000	.0000	.0000	.0000	.0000	.0000	.0001	.0005	.0016
	13	.0000	.0000	.0000	.0000	.0000	.0000	.0000	.0000	.0000	.0001
14	0	.4877	.2288	.1028	.0440	.0178	.0068	.0024	.0008	.0002	.0001
	1	.3593	.3559	.2539	.1539	.0832	.0407	.0181	.0073	.0027	.0009
	2	.1229	.2570	.2912	.2501	.1802	.1134	.0634	.0317	.0141	.0056
	3	.0259	.1142	.2056	.2501	.2402	.1943	.1366	.0845	.0462	.0222
	4	.0037	.0349	.0998	.1720	.2202	.2290	.2022	.1549	.1040	.0611
	5	.0004	.0078	.0352	.0860	.1468	.1963	.2178	.2066	.1701	.1222
	6	.0000	.0013	.0093	.0322	.0734	.1262	.1759	.2066	.2088	.1833
	7	.0000	.0002	.0019	.0092	.0280	.0618	.1082	.1574	.1952	.2095
	8	.0000	.0000	.0003	.0020	.0082	.0232	.0510	.0918	.1398	.1833
	9	.0000	.0000	.0000	.0003	.0018	.0066	.0183	.0408	.0762	.1222
	10	.0000	.0000	.0000	.0000	.0003	.0014	.0049	.0136	.0312	.0611
	11	.0000	.0000	.0000	.0000	.0000	.0002	.0010	.0033	.0093	.0222
	12	.0000	.0000	.0000	.0000	.0000	.0000	.0001	.0005	.0019	.0056
	13	.0000	.0000	.0000	.0000	.0000	.0000	.0000	.0001	.0002	.0009
	14	.0000	.0000	.0000	.0000	.0000	.0000	.0000	.0000	.0000	.0001
15	0	.4633	.2059	.0874	.0352	.0134	.0047	.0016	.0005	.0001	.0000
	1	.3658	.3432	.2312	.1319	.0668	.0305	.0126	.0047	.0016	.0005
	2	.1348	.2669	.2856	.2309	.1559	.0916	.0476	.0219	.0090	.0032
	3	.0307	.1285	.2184	.2501	.2252	.1700	.1110	.0634	.0318	.0139
	4	.0049	.0428	.1156	.1876	.2252	.2186	.1792	.1268	.0780	.0417
	5	.0006	.0105	.0449	.1032	.1651	.2061	.2123	.1859	.1404	.0916
	6	.0000	.0019	.0132	.0430	.0917	.1472	.1906	.2066	.1914	.1527
	7	.0000	.0003	.0030	.0138	.0393	.0811	.1319	.1771	.2013	.1964
	8	.0000	.0000	.0005	.0035	.0131	.0348	.0710	.1181	.1647	.1964
	9	.0000	.0000	.0001	.0007	.0034	.0116	.0298	.0612	.1048	.1527
	10	.0000	.0000	.0000	.0001	.0007	.0030	.0096	.0245	.0515	.0916
	11	.0000	.0000	.0000	.0000	.0001	.0006	.0024	.0074	.0191	.0417
	12	.0000	.0000	.0000	.0000	.0000	.0001	.0004	.0016	.0052	.0139
	13	.0000	.0000	.0000	.0000	.0000	.0000	.0001	.0003	.0010	.0032
	14	.0000	.0000	.0000	.0000	.0000	.0000	.0000	.0000	.0001	.0005
	15	.0000	.0000	.0000	.0000	.0000	.0000	0000	.0000	.0000	.0000
16	0	.4401	.1853	.0743	.0281	.0100	.0033	.0010	.0003	.0001	.0000
	1	.3706	.3294	.2097	.1126	.0535	.0228	.0087	.0030	.0009	.0002
	2	.1463	.2745	.2775	.2111	.1336	.0732	.0353	.0150	.0056	.0018
	3	.0359	.1423	.2285	.2463	.2079	.1465	.0888	.0468	.0215	.0085
	4	.0061	.0514	.1311	.2001	.2252	.2040	.1553	.1014	.0572	.0278
	5	.0008	.0137	.0555	.1201	.1802	.2099	.2008	.1623	.1123	.0667
	6	.0001	.0028	.0180	.0550	.1101	.1649	.1982	.1983	.1684	.1222
	7	.0000	.0004	.0045	.0197	.0524	.1010	.1524	.1889	.1969	.1746
	8	.0000	.0001	.0009	.0055	.0197	.0487	.0923	.1417	.1812	.1964
	9	.0000	.0000	.0001	.0012	.0058	.0185	.0442	.0840	.1318	.1746

n	x	.05	.10	.15	.20	.25	.30	.35	.40	.45	.50
						p					
16	10	.0000	.0000	.0000	.0002	.0014	.0056	.0167	.0392	.0755	.1222
	11	.0000	.0000	.0000	.0000	.0002	.0013	.0049	.0142	.0337	.0667
	12	.0000	.0000	.0000	.0000	.0000	.0002	.0011	.0040	.0115	.0278
	13	.0000	.0000	.0000	.0000	.0000	.0000	.0002	.0008	.0029	.0085
	14	.0000	.0000	.0000	.0000	.0000	.0000	.0000	.0001	.0005	.0018
	15	.0000	.0000	.0000	.0000	.0000	.0000	.0000	.0000	.0001	.0002
	16	.0000	.0000	.0000	.0000	.0000	.0000	.0000	.0000	.0000	.0000
17	0	.4181	.1668	.0631	.0225	.0075	.0023	.0007	.0002	.0000	.0000
	1	.3741	.3150	.1893	.0957	.0426	.0169	.0060	.0019	.0005	.0001
	2	.1575	.2800	.2673	.1914	.1136	.0581	.0260	.0102	.0035	.0010
	3	.0415	.1556	.2359	.2393	.1893	.1245	.0701	.0341	.0144	.0052
	4	.0076	.0605	.1457	.2093	.2209	.1868	.1320	.0796	.0411	.0182
	5	.0010	.0175	.0668	.1361	.1914	.2081	.1849	.1379	.0875	.0472
	6	.0001	.0039	.0236	.0680	.1276	.1784	.1991	.1839	.1432	.0944
	7	.0000	.0007	.0065	.0267	.0668	.1201	.1685	.1927	.1841	.1484
	8	.0000	.0001	.0014	.0084	.0279	.0644	.1134	.1606	.1883	.1855
	9	.0000	.0000	.0003	.0021	.0093	.0276	.0611	.1070	.1540	.1855
	10	.0000	.0000	.0000	.0004	.0025	.0095	.0263	.0571	.1008	.1484
	11	.0000	.0000	.0000	.0001	.0005	.0026	.0090	.0242	.0525	.0944
	12	.0000	.0000	.0000	.0000	.0001	.0006	.0024	.0081	.0215	.0472
	13	.0000	.0000	.0000	.0000	.0000	.0001	.0005	.0021	.0068	.0182
	14	.0000	.0000	.0000	.0000	.0000	.0000	.0001	.0004	.0016	.0052
	15	.0000	.0000	.0000	.0000	.0000	.0000	.0000	.0001	.0003	.0010
	16	.0000	.0000	.0000	.0000	.0000	.0000	.0000	.0000	.0000	.0001
	17	.0000	.0000	.0000	.0000	.0000	.0000	.0000	.0000	.0000	.0000
18	0	.3972	.1501	.0536	.0180	.0056	.0016	.0004	.0001	.0000	.0000
	1	.3763	.3002	.1704	.0811	.0338	.0126	.0042	.0012	.0003	.0001
	2	.1683	.2835	.2556	.1723	.0958	.0458	.0190	.0069	.0022	.0006
	3	.0473	.1680	.2406	.2297	.1704	.1046	.0547	.0246	.0095	.0031
	4	.0093	.0700	.1592	.2153	.2130	.1681	.1104	.0614	.0291	.0117
	5	.0014	.0218	.0787	.1507	.1988	.2017	.1664	.1146	.0666	.0327
	6	.0002	.0052	.0301	.0816	.1436	.1873	.1941	.1655	.1181	.0708
	7	.0000	.0010	.0091	.0350	.0820	.1376	.1792	.1892	.1657	.1214
	8	.0000	.0002	.0022	.0120	.0376	.0811	.1327	.1734	.1864	.1669
	9	.0000	.0000	.0004	.0033	.0139	.0386	.0794	.1284	.1694	.1855
	10	.0000	.0000	.0001	.0008	.0042	.0149	.0385	.0771	.1248	.1669
	11	.0000	.0000	.0000	.0001	.0010	.0046	.0151	.0374	.0742	.1214
	12	.0000	.0000	.0000	.0000	.0002	.0012	.0047	.0145	.0354	.0708
	13	.0000	.0000	.0000	.0000	.0000	.0002	.0012	.0045	.0134	.0327
	14	.0000	.0000	.0000	.0000	.0000	.0000	.0002	.0011	.0039	.0117
	15	.0000	.0000	.0000	.0000	.0000	.0000	.0000	.0002	.0009	.0031
	16	.0000	.0000	.0000	.0000	.0000	.0000	.0000	.0000	.0001	.0006
	17	.0000	.0000	.0000	.0000	.0000	.0000	.0000	.0000	.0000	.0001
	18	.0000	.0000	.0000	.0000	.0000	.0000	.0000	.0000	.0000	.0000
19	0	.3774	.1351	.0456	.0144	.0042	.0011	.0003	.0001	.0000	.0000
	1	.3774	.2852	.1529	.0685	.0268	.0093	.0029	.0008	.0002	.0000
	2	.1787	.2852	.2428	.1540	.0803	.0358	.0138	.0046	.0013	.0003
	3	.0533	.1796	.2428	.2182	.1517	.0869	.0422	.0175	.0062	.0018
	4	.0112	.0798	.1714	.2182	.2023	.1491	.0909	.0467	.0203	.0074
	5	.0018	.0266	.0907	.1636	.2023	.1916	.1468	.0933	.0497	.0222
	6	.0002	.0069	.0374	.0955	.1574	.1916	.1844	.1451	.0949	.0518
	7	.0000	.0014	.0122	.0443	.0974	.1525	.1844	.1797	.1443	.0961
	8	.0000	.0002	.0032	.0166	.0487	.0981	.1489	.1797	.1771	.1442
	9	.0000	.0000	.0007	.0051	.0198	.0514	.0980	.1464	.1771	.1762
	10	.0000	.0000	.0001	.0013	.0066	.0220	.0528	.0976	.1449	.1762
	11	.0000	.0000	.0000	.0003	.0018	.0077	.0233	.0532	.0970	.1442
	12	.0000	.0000	.0000	.0000	.0004	.0022	.0083	.0237	.0529	.0961
	13	.0000	.0000	.0000	.0000	.0001	.0005	.0024	.0085	.0233	.0518
	14	.0000	.0000	.0000	.0000	.0000	.0001	.0006	.0024	.0082	.0222

n	x	p									
		.05	.10	.15	.20	.25	.30	.35	.40	.45	.50
19	15	.0000	.0000	.0000	.0000	.0000	.0000	.0001	.0005	.0022	.0074
	16	.0000	.0000	.0000	.0000	.0000	.0000	.0000	.0001	.0005	.0018
	17	.0000	.0000	.0000	.0000	.0000	.0000	.0000	.0000	.0001	.0003
	18	.0000	.0000	.0000	.0000	.0000	.0000	.0000	.0000	.0000	.0000
	19	.0000	.0000	.0000	.0000	.0000	.0000	.0000	.0000	.0000	.0000
20	0	.3585	.1216	.0388	.0115	.0032	.0008	.0002	.0000	.0000	.0000
	1	.3774	.2702	.1368	.0576	.0211	.0068	.0020	.0005	.0001	.0000
	2	.1887	.2852	.2293	.1369	.0669	.0278	.0100	.0031	.0008	.0002
	3	.0596	.1901	.2428	.2054	.1339	.0718	.0323	.0123	.0040	.0011
	4	.0133	.0898	.1821	.2182	.1897	.1304	.0738	.0350	.0139	.0046
	5	.0022	.0319	.1028	.1746	.2023	.1789	.1272	.0746	.0365	.0148
	6	.0003	.0089	.0454	.1091	.1686	.1916	.1712	.1244	.0746	.0370
	7	.0000	.0020	.0160	.0545	.1124	.1643	.1844	.1659	.1221	.0739
	8	.0000	.0004	.0046	.0222	.0609	.1144	.1614	.1797	.1623	.1201
	9	.0000	.0001	.0011	.0074	.0271	.0654	.1158	.1597	.1771	.1602
	10	.0000	.0000	.0002	.0020	.0099	.0308	.0686	.1171	.1593	.1762
	11	.0000	.0000	.0000	.0005	.0030	.0120	.0336	.0710	.1185	.1602
	12	.0000	.0000	.0000	.0001	.0008	.0039	.0136	.0355	.0727	.1201
	13	.0000	.0000	.0000	.0000	.0002	.0010	.0045	.0146	.0366	.0739
	14	.0000	.0000	.0000	.0000	.0000	.0002	.0012	.0049	.0150	.0370
	15	.0000	.0000	.0000	.0000	.0000	.0000	.0003	.0013	.0049	.0148
	16	.0000	.0000	.0000	.0000	.0000	.0000	.0000	.0003	.0013	.0046
	17	.0000	.0000	.0000	.0000	.0000	.0000	.0000	.0000	.0002	.0011
	18	.0000	.0000	.0000	.0000	.0000	.0000	.0000	.0000	.0000	.0002
	19	.0000	.0000	.0000	.0000	.0000	.0000	.0000	.0000	.0000	.0000
	20	.0000	.0000	.0000	.0000	.0000	.0000	.0000	.0000	.0000	.0000

C

Poisson Distribution

Values of $e^{-m}\frac{m^x}{x!}$

x	m = 0.1	0.2	0.3	0.4	0.5	0.6	0.7	0.8	0.9	1.0	x
0	.9048	.8187	.7408	.6703	.6065	.5488	.4966	.4493	.4066	.3679	0
1	.0905	.1637	.2222	.2681	.3033	.3293	.3476	.3595	.3659	.3679	1
2	.0045	.0164	.0333	.0536	.0758	.0988	.1217	.1438	.1647	.1839	2
3	.0002	.0011	.0033	.0072	.0126	.0198	.0284	.0383	.0494	.0613	3
4	.0000	.0001	.0002	.0007	.0016	.0030	.0050	.0077	.0111	.0153	4
5	.0000	.0000	.0000	.0001	.0002	.0004	.0007	.0012	.0020	.0031	5
6	.0000	.0000	.0000	.0000	.0000	.0000	.0001	.0002	.0003	.0005	6
7	.0000	.0000	.0000	.0000	.0000	.0000	.0000	.0000	.0000	.0001	7

x	m = 1.1	1.2	1.3	1.4	1.5	1.6	1.7	1.8	1.9	2.0	x
0	.3329	.3012	.2725	.2466	.2231	.2019	.1827	.1653	.1496	.1353	0
1	.3662	.3614	.3543	.3452	.3347	.3230	.3106	.2975	.2842	.2707	1
2	.2014	.2169	.2303	.2417	.2510	.2584	.2640	.2678	.2700	.2707	2
3	.0738	.0867	.0998	.1128	.1255	.1378	.1496	.1607	.1710	.1804	3
4	.0203	.0260	.0324	.0395	.0471	.0551	.0636	.0723	.0812	.0902	4
5	.0045	.0062	.0084	.0111	.0141	.0176	.0216	.0260	.0309	.0361	5
6	.0008	.0012	.0018	.0026	.0035	.0047	.0061	.0078	.0098	.0120	6
7	.0001	.0002	.0003	.0005	.0008	.0011	.0015	.0020	.0027	.0034	7
8	.0000	.0000	.0001	.0001	.0001	.0002	.0003	.0005	.0006	.0009	8
9	.0000	.0000	.0000	.0000	.0000	.0000	.0001	.0001	.0001	.0002	9

x	m = 2.1	2.2	2.3	2.4	2.5	2.6	2.7	2.8	2.9	3.0	x
0	.1225	.1108	.1003	.0907	.0821	.0743	.0672	.0608	.0550	.0498	0
1	.2572	.2438	.2306	.2177	.2052	.1931	.1815	.1703	.1596	.1494	1
2	.2700	.2681	.2652	.2613	.2565	.2510	.2450	.2384	.2314	.2240	2
3	.1890	.1966	.2033	.2090	.2138	.2176	.2205	.2225	.2237	.2240	3
4	.0992	.1082	.1169	.1254	.1336	.1414	.1488	.1557	.1622	.1680	4
5	.0417	.0476	.0538	.0602	.0668	.0735	.0804	.0872	.0940	.1008	5
6	.0146	.0174	.0206	.0241	.0278	.0319	.0362	.0407	.0455	.0504	6
7	.0044	.0055	.0068	.0083	.0099	.0118	.0139	.0163	.0188	.0216	7
8	.0011	.0015	.0019	.0025	.0031	.0038	.0047	.0057	.0068	.0081	8
9	.0003	.0004	.0005	.0007	.0009	.0011	.0014	.0018	.0022	.0027	9
10	.0001	.0001	.0001	.0002	.0002	.0003	.0004	.0005	.0006	.0008	10
11	.0000	.0000	.0000	.0000	.0000	.0001	.0001	.0001	.0002	.0002	11
12	.0000	.0000	.0000	.0000	.0000	.0000	.0000	.0000	.0000	.0001	12

x	m = 3.1	3.2	3.3	3.4	3.5	3.6	3.7	3.8	3.9	4.0	x
0	.0450	.0408	.0369	.0334	.0302	.0273	.0247	.0224	.0202	.0183	0
1	.1397	.1304	.1217	.1135	.1057	.0984	.0915	.0850	.0789	.0733	1
2	.2165	.2087	.2008	.1929	.1850	.1771	.1692	.1615	.1539	.1465	2
3	.2237	.2226	.2209	.2186	.2158	.2125	.2087	.2046	.2001	.1954	3
4	.1734	.1781	.1823	.1858	.1888	.1912	.1931	.1944	.1951	.1954	4
5	.1075	.1140	.1203	.1264	.1322	.1377	.1429	.1477	.1522	.1563	5
6	.0555	.0608	.0662	.0716	.0771	.0826	.0881	.0936	.0989	.1042	6
7	.0246	.0278	.0312	.0348	.0385	.0425	.0466	.0508	.0551	.0595	7
8	.0095	.0111	.0129	.0148	.0169	.0191	.0215	.0241	.0269	.0298	8
9	.0033	.0040	.0047	.0056	.0066	.0076	.0089	.0102	.0116	.0132	9
10	.0010	.0013	.0016	.0019	.0023	.0028	.0033	.0039	.0045	.0053	10
11	.0003	.0004	.0005	.0006	.0007	.0009	.0011	.0013	.0016	.0019	11
12	.0001	.0001	.0001	.0002	.0002	.0003	.0003	.0004	.0005	.0006	12
13	.0000	.0000	.0000	.0000	.0001	.0001	.0001	.0001	.0002	.0002	13
14	.0000	.0000	.0000	.0000	.0000	.0000	.0000	.0000	.0000	.0001	14

x	m = 4.1	4.2	4.3	4.4	4.5	4.6	4.7	4.8	4.9	5.0	x
0	.0166	.0150	.0136	.0123	.0111	.0101	.0091	.0082	.0074	.0067	0
1	.0679	.0630	.0583	.0540	.0500	.0462	.0427	.0395	.0365	.0337	1
2	.1393	.1323	.1254	.1188	.1125	.1063	.1005	.0948	.0894	.0842	2
3	.1904	.1852	.1798	.1743	.1687	.1631	.1574	.1517	.1460	.1404	3
4	.1951	.1944	.1933	.1917	.1898	.1875	.1849	.1820	.1789	.1755	4
5	.1600	.1633	.1662	.1687	.1708	.1725	.1738	.1747	.1753	.1755	5
6	.1093	.1143	.1191	.1237	.1281	.1323	.1362	.1398	.1432	.1462	6
7	.0640	.0686	.0732	.0778	.0824	.0869	.0914	.0959	.1002	.1044	7
8	.0328	.0360	.0393	.0428	.0463	.0500	.0537	.0575	.0614	.0653	8
9	.0150	.0168	.0188	.0209	.0232	.0255	.0280	.0307	.0334	.0363	9
10	.0061	.0071	.0081	.0092	.0104	.0118	.0132	.0147	.0164	.0181	10
11	.0023	.0027	.0032	.0037	.0043	.0049	.0056	.0064	.0073	.0082	11
12	.0008	.0009	.0011	.0014	.0016	.0019	.0022	.0026	.0030	.0034	12
13	.0002	.0003	.0004	.0005	.0006	.0007	.0008	.0009	.0011	.0013	13
14	.0001	.0001	.0001	.0001	.0002	.0002	.0003	.0003	.0004	.0005	14
15	.0000	.0000	.0000	.0000	.0001	.0001	.0001	.0001	.0001	.0002	15

x	m = 5.1	5.2	5.3	5.4	5.5	5.6	5.7	5.8	5.9	6.0	x
0	.0061	.0055	.0050	.0045	.0041	.0037	.0033	.0030	.0027	.0025	0
1	.0311	.0287	.0265	.0244	.0225	.0207	.0191	.0176	.0162	.0149	1
2	.0793	.0746	.0701	.0659	.0618	.0580	.0544	.0509	.0477	.0446	2
3	.1348	.1293	.1239	.1185	.1133	.1082	.1033	.0985	.0938	.0892	3
4	.1719	.1681	.1641	.1600	.1558	.1515	.1472	.1428	.1383	.1339	4
5	.1753	.1748	.1740	.1728	.1714	.1697	.1678	.1656	.1632	.1606	5
6	.1490	.1515	.1537	.1555	.1571	.1584	.1594	.1601	.1605	.1606	6
7	.1086	.1125	.1163	.1200	.1234	.1267	.1298	.1326	.1353	.1377	7
8	.0692	.0731	.0771	.0810	.0849	.0887	.0925	.0962	.0998	.1033	8
9	.0392	.0423	.0454	.0486	.0519	.0552	.0586	.0620	.0654	.0688	9
10	.0200	.0220	.0241	.0262	.0285	.0309	.0334	.0359	.0386	.0413	10
11	.0093	.0104	.0116	.0129	.0143	.0157	.0173	.0190	.0207	.0225	11
12	.0039	.0045	.0051	.0058	.0065	.0073	.0082	.0092	.0102	.0113	12
13	.0015	.0018	.0021	.0024	.0028	.0032	.0036	.0041	.0046	.0052	13
14	.0006	.0007	.0008	.0009	.0011	.0013	.0015	.0017	.0019	.0022	14
15	.0002	.0002	.0003	.0003	.0004	.0005	.0006	.0007	.0008	.0009	15
16	.0001	.0001	.0001	.0001	.0001	.0002	.0002	.0002	.0003	.0003	16
17	.0000	.0000	.0000	.0000	.0000	.0001	.0001	.0001	.0001	.0001	17

x	m = 6.1	6.2	6.3	6.4	6.5	6.6	6.7	6.8	6.9	7.0	x
0	.0022	.0020	.0018	.0017	.0015	.0014	.0012	.0011	.0010	.0009	0
1	.0137	.0126	.0116	.0106	.0098	.0090	.0082	.0076	.0070	.0064	1
2	.0417	.0390	.0364	.0340	.0318	.0296	.0276	.0258	.0240	.0223	2
3	.0848	.0806	.0765	.0726	.0688	.0652	.0617	.0584	.0552	.0521	3
4	.1294	.1249	.1205	.1162	.1118	.1076	.1034	.0992	.0952	.0912	4
5	.1579	.1549	.1519	.1487	.1454	.1420	.1385	.1349	.1314	.1277	5
6	.1605	.1601	.1595	.1586	.1575	.1562	.1546	.1529	.1511	.1490	6
7	.1399	.1418	.1435	.1450	.1462	.1472	.1480	.1486	.1489	.1490	7
8	.1066	.1099	.1130	.1160	.1188	.1215	.1240	.1263	.1284	.1304	8
9	.0723	.0757	.0791	.0825	.0858	.0891	.0923	.0954	.0985	.1014	9
10	.0441	.0469	.0498	.0528	.0558	.0588	.0618	.0649	.0679	.0710	10
11	.0245	.0265	.0285	.0307	.0330	.0353	.0377	.0401	.0426	.0452	11
12	.0124	.0137	.0150	.0164	.0179	.0194	.0210	.0227	.0245	.0264	12
13	.0058	.0065	.0073	.0081	.0089	.0098	.0108	.0119	.0130	.0142	13
14	.0025	.0029	.0033	.0037	.0041	.0046	.0052	.0058	.0064	.0071	14
15	.0010	.0012	.0014	.0016	.0018	.0020	.0023	.0026	.0029	.0033	15
16	.0004	.0005	.0005	.0006	.0007	.0008	.0010	.0011	.0013	.0014	16
17	.0001	.0002	.0002	.0002	.0003	.0003	.0004	.0004	.0005	.0006	17
18	.0000	.0001	.0001	.0001	.0001	.0001	.0001	.0002	.0002	.0002	18
19	.0000	.0000	.0000	.0000	.0000	.0000	.0000	.0001	.0001	.0001	19

x	7.1	7.2	7.3	7.4	7.5	7.6	7.7	7.8	7.9	8.0	x
					m						
0	.0008	.0007	.0007	.0006	.0006	.0005	.0005	.0004	.0004	.0003	0
1	.0059	.0054	.0049	.0045	.0041	.0038	.0035	.0032	.0029	.0027	1
2	.0208	.0194	.0180	.0167	.0156	.0145	.0134	.0125	.0116	.0107	2
3	.0492	.0464	.0438	.0413	.0389	.0366	.0345	.0324	.0305	.0286	3
4	.0874	.0836	.0799	.0764	.0729	.0696	.0663	.0632	.0602	.0573	4
5	.1241	.1204	.1167	.1130	.1094	.1057	.1021	.0986	.0951	.0916	5
6	.1468	.1445	.1420	.1394	.1367	.1339	.1311	.1282	.1252	.1221	6
7	.1489	.1486	.1481	.1474	.1465	.1454	.1442	.1428	.1413	.1396	7
8	.1321	.1337	.1351	.1363	.1373	.1382	.1388	.1392	.1395	.1396	8
9	.1042	.1070	.1096	.1121	.1144	.1167	.1187	.1207	.1224	.1241	9
10	.0740	.0770	.0800	.0829	.0858	.0887	.0914	.0941	.0967	.0993	10
11	.0478	.0504	.0531	.0558	.0585	.0613	.0640	.0667	.0695	.0722	11
12	.0283	.0303	.0323	.0344	.0366	.0388	.0411	.0434	.0457	.0481	12
13	.0154	.0168	.0181	.0196	.0211	.0227	.0243	.0260	.0278	.0296	13
14	.0078	.0086	.0095	.0104	.0113	.0123	.0134	.0145	.0157	.0169	14
15	.0037	.0041	.0046	.0051	.0057	.0062	.0069	.0075	.0083	.0090	15
16	.0016	.0019	.0021	.0024	.0026	.0030	.0033	.0037	.0041	.0045	16
17	.0007	.0008	.0009	.0010	.0012	.0013	.0015	.0017	.0019	.0021	17
18	.0003	.0003	.0004	.0004	.0005	.0006	.0006	.0007	.0008	.0009	18
19	.0001	.0001	.0001	.0002	.0002	.0002	.0003	.0003	.0003	.0004	19
20	.0000	.0000	.0001	.0001	.0001	.0001	.0001	.0001	.0001	.0002	20
21	.0000	.0000	.0000	.0000	.0000	.0000	.0000	.0000	.0001	.0001	21

x	8.1	8.2	8.3	8.4	8.5	8.6	8.7	8.8	8.9	9.0	x
					m						
0	.0003	.0003	.0002	.0002	.0002	.0002	.0002	.0002	.0001	.0001	0
1	.0025	.0023	.0021	.0019	.0017	.0016	.0014	.0013	.0012	.0011	1
2	.0100	.0092	.0086	.0079	.0074	.0068	.0063	.0058	.0054	.0050	2
3	.0269	.0252	.0237	.0222	.0208	.0195	.0183	.0171	.0160	.0150	3
4	.0544	.0517	.0491	.0466	.0443	.0420	.0398	.0377	.0357	.0337	4
5	.0882	.0849	.0816	.0784	.0752	.0722	.0692	.0663	.0635	.0607	5
6	.1191	.1160	.1128	.1097	.1066	.1034	.1003	.0972	.0941	.0911	6
7	.1378	.1358	.1338	.1317	.1294	.1271	.1247	.1222	.1197	.1171	7
8	.1395	.1392	.1388	.1382	.1375	.1366	.1356	.1344	.1332	.1318	8
9	.1256	.1269	.1280	.1290	.1299	.1306	.1311	.1315	.1317	.1318	9
10	.1017	.1040	.1063	.1084	.1104	.1123	.1140	.1157	.1172	.1186	10
11	.0749	.0776	.0802	.0828	.0853	.0878	.0902	.0925	.0948	.0970	11
12	.0505	.0530	.0555	.0579	.0604	.0629	.0654	.0679	.0703	.0728	12
13	.0315	.0334	.0354	.0374	.0395	.0416	.0438	.0459	.0481	.0504	13
14	.0182	.0196	.0210	.0225	.0240	.0256	.0272	.0289	.0306	.0324	14
15	.0098	.0107	.0116	.0126	.0136	.0147	.0158	.0169	.0182	.0194	15
16	.0050	.0055	.0060	.0066	.0072	.0079	.0086	.0093	.0101	.0109	16
17	.0024	.0026	.0029	.0033	.0036	.0040	.0044	.0048	.0053	.0058	17
18	.0011	.0012	.0014	.0015	.0017	.0019	.0021	.0024	.0026	.0029	18
19	.0005	.0005	.0006	.0007	.0008	.0009	.0010	.0011	.0012	.0014	19
20	.0002	.0002	.0002	.0003	.0003	.0004	.0004	.0005	.0005	.0006	20
21	.0001	.0001	.0001	.0001	.0001	.0002	.0002	.0002	.0002	.0003	21
22	.0000	.0000	.0000	.0000	.0001	.0001	.0001	.0001	.0001	.0001	22

x	m = 9.1	9.2	9.3	9.4	9.5	9.6	9.7	9.8	9.9	10	x
0	.0001	.0001	.0001	.0001	.0001	.0001	.0001	.0001	.0001	.0000	0
1	.0010	.0009	.0009	.0008	.0007	.0007	.0006	.0005	.0005	.0005	1
2	.0046	.0043	.0040	.0037	.0034	.0031	.0029	.0027	.0025	.0023	2
3	.0140	.0131	.0123	.0115	.0107	.0100	.0093	.0087	.0081	.0076	3
4	.0319	.0302	.0285	.0269	.0254	.0240	.0226	.0213	.0201	.0189	4
5	.0581	.0555	.0530	.0506	.0483	.0460	.0439	.0418	.0398	.0378	5
6	.0881	.0851	.0822	.0793	.0764	.0736	.0709	.0682	.0656	.0631	6
7	.1145	.1118	.1091	.1064	.1037	.1010	.0982	.0955	.0928	.0901	7
8	.1302	.1286	.1269	.1251	.1232	.1212	.1191	.1170	.1148	.1126	8
9	.1317	.1315	.1311	.1306	.1300	.1293	.1284	.1274	.1263	.1251	9
10	.1198	.1210	.1219	.1228	.1235	.1241	.1245	.1249	.1250	.1251	10
11	.0991	.1012	.1031	.1049	.1067	.1083	.1098	.1112	.1125	.1137	11
12	.0752	.0776	.0799	.0822	.0844	.0866	.0888	.0908	.0928	.0948	12
13	.0526	.0549	.0572	.0594	.0617	.0640	.0662	.0685	.0707	.0729	13
14	.0342	.0361	.0380	.0399	.0419	.0439	.0459	.0479	.0500	.0521	14
15	.0208	.0221	.0235	.0250	.0265	.0281	.0297	.0313	.0330	.0347	15
16	.0118	.0127	.0137	.0147	.0157	.0168	.0180	.0192	.0204	.0217	16
17	.0063	.0069	.0075	.0081	.0088	.0095	.0103	.0111	.0119	.0128	17
18	.0032	.0035	.0039	.0042	.0046	.0051	.0055	.0060	.0065	.0071	18
19	.0015	.0017	.0019	.0021	.0023	.0026	.0028	.0031	.0034	.0037	19
20	.0007	.0008	.0009	.0010	.0011	.0012	.0014	.0015	.0017	.0019	20
21	.0003	.0003	.0004	.0004	.0005	.0006	.0006	.0007	.0008	.0009	21
22	.0001	.0001	.0002	.0002	.0002	.0002	.0003	.0003	.0004	.0004	22
23	.0000	.0001	.0001	.0001	.0001	.0001	.0001	.0001	.0002	.0002	23
24	.0000	.0000	.0000	.0000	.0000	.0000	.0000	.0001	.0001	.0001	24

x	m = 11	12	13	14	15	16	17	18	19	20	x
0	.0000	.0000	.0000	.0000	.0000	.0000	.0000	.0000	.0000	.0000	0
1	.0002	.0001	.0000	.0000	.0000	.0000	.0000	.0000	.0000	.0000	1
2	.0010	.0004	.0002	.0001	.0000	.0000	.0000	.0000	.0000	.0000	2
3	.0037	.0018	.0008	.0004	.0002	.0001	.0000	.0000	.0000	.0000	3
4	.0102	.0053	.0027	.0013	.0006	.0003	.0001	.0001	.0000	.0000	4
5	.0224	.0127	.0070	.0037	.0019	.0010	.0005	.0002	.0001	.0001	5
6	.0411	.0255	.0152	.0087	.0048	.0026	.0014	.0007	.0004	.0002	6
7	.0646	.0437	.0281	.0174	.0104	.0060	.0034	.0018	.0010	.0005	7
8	.0888	.0655	.0457	.0304	.0194	.0120	.0072	.0042	.0024	.0013	8
9	.1085	.0874	.0661	.0473	.0324	.0213	.0135	.0083	.0050	.0029	9
10	.1194	.1048	.0859	.0663	.0486	.0341	.0230	.0150	.0095	.0058	10
11	.1194	.1144	.1015	.0844	.0663	.0496	.0355	.0245	.0164	.0106	11
12	.1094	.1144	.1099	.0984	.0829	.0661	.0504	.0368	.0259	.0176	12
13	.0926	.1056	.1099	.1060	.0956	.0814	.0658	.0509	.0378	.0271	13
14	.0728	.0905	.1021	.1060	.1024	.0930	.0800	.0655	.0514	.0387	14
15	.0534	.0724	.0885	.0989	.1024	.0992	.0906	.0786	.0650	.0516	15
16	.0367	.0543	.0719	.0866	.0960	.0992	.0963	.0884	.0772	.0646	16
17	.0237	.0383	.0550	.0713	.0847	.0934	.0963	.0936	.0863	.0760	17
18	.0145	.0256	.0397	.0554	.0706	.0830	.0909	.0936	.0911	.0844	18
19	.0084	.0161	.0272	.0409	.0557	.0699	.0814	.0887	.0911	.0888	19
20	.0046	.0097	.0177	.0286	.0418	.0559	.0692	.0798	.0866	.0888	20
21	.0024	.0055	.0109	.0191	.0299	.0426	.0560	.0684	.0783	.0846	21
22	.0012	.0030	.0065	.0121	.0204	.0310	.0433	.0560	.0676	.0769	22
23	.0006	.0016	.0037	.0074	.0133	.0216	.0320	.0438	.0559	.0669	23
24	.0003	.0008	.0020	.0043	.0083	.0144	.0226	.0328	.0442	.0557	24
25	.0001	.0004	.0010	.0024	.0050	.0092	.0154	.0237	.0336	.0446	25
26	.0000	.0002	.0005	.0013	.0029	.0057	.0101	.0164	.0246	.0343	26
27	.0000	.0001	.0002	.0007	.0016	.0034	.0063	.0109	.0173	.0254	27
28	.0000	.0000	.0001	.0003	.0009	.0019	.0038	.0070	.0117	.0181	28
29	.0000	.0000	.0001	.0002	.0004	.0011	.0023	.0044	.0077	.0125	29
30	.0000	.0000	.0000	.0001	.0002	.0006	.0013	.0026	.0049	.0083	30
31	.0000	.0000	.0000	.0000	.0001	.0003	.0007	.0015	.0030	.0054	31
32	.0000	.0000	.0000	.0000	.0001	.0001	.0004	.0009	.0018	.0034	32
33	.0000	.0000	.0000	.0000	.0000	.0001	.0002	.0005	.0010	.0020	33
34	.0000	.0000	.0000	.0000	.0000	.0000	.0001	.0002	.0006	.0012	34
35	.0000	.0000	.0000	.0000	.0000	.0000	.0000	.0001	.0003	.0007	35
36	.0000	.0000	.0000	.0000	.0000	.0000	.0000	.0001	.0002	.0004	36
37	.0000	.0000	.0000	.0000	.0000	.0000	.0000	.0000	.0001	.0002	37
38	.0000	.0000	.0000	.0000	.0000	.0000	.0000	.0000	.0000	.0001	38
39	.0000	.0000	.0000	.0000	.0000	.0000	.0000	.0000	.0000	.0001	39

D

A Short Table of Derivatives

In this table, those results which are derived or presented in the text are identified by the equation number which they are assigned in the text. The symbols u and v represent functions of x, and a and n are used to represent constants. The symbol e represents the irrational number $e = 2.71828\ldots$, the base of natural logarithms, and $\ln x = 2.303 \log_{10} x$.

1. $$\frac{d}{dx}(a) = 0$$

2. $$\frac{d}{dx}(x) = 1$$

3. $$\frac{d}{dx}(ax^n) = nax^{n-1} \qquad (2\text{–}5.4)$$

4. $$\frac{d}{dx}(au) = a\frac{du}{dx}$$

5. $$\frac{d}{dx}(u + v) = \frac{du}{dx} + \frac{dv}{dx}$$

6. $$\frac{d}{dx}(uv) = u\frac{dv}{dx} + v\frac{du}{dx} \qquad (2\text{–}7.3)$$

7. $$\frac{d}{dx}\left(\frac{u}{v}\right) = \frac{v\dfrac{du}{dx} - u\dfrac{dv}{dx}}{v^2} \qquad (2\text{–}7.4)$$

8. $$\frac{d}{dx}(\ln x) = \frac{1}{x} \qquad (2\text{–}9.5)$$

9. $$\frac{d}{dx}(e^x) = e^x \qquad (2\text{–}9.6)$$

10. $$\frac{d}{dx}(f(u)) = \frac{d}{du}(f(u))\frac{du}{dx} \qquad (2\text{–}7.1)$$

11. $$\frac{d}{dx}(\ln u) = \frac{1}{u}\frac{du}{dx}$$

12. $$\frac{d}{dx}(e^u) = e^u\frac{du}{dx}$$

13. $$\frac{d}{dx}(u^n) = nu^{n-1}\frac{du}{dx}$$

14. $$\frac{d}{dx}(a^u) = a^u \ln a\frac{du}{dx}$$

15. $$\frac{d}{dx}(u^v) = vu^{v-1}\frac{du}{dx} + u^v \ln u\frac{dv}{dx}$$

16. $$\frac{d}{dx}(\sin x) = \cos x \qquad (2\text{–}8.26)$$

17. $$\frac{d}{dx}(\cos x) = -\sin x \qquad (2\text{–}8.27)$$

18. $$\frac{d}{dx}(\tan x) = \sec^2 x \qquad (2\text{–}8.28)$$

19. $$\frac{d}{dx}(\sin u) = \cos u\frac{du}{dx} \qquad (2\text{–}8.29)$$

20. $$\frac{d}{dx}(\cos u) = -\sin u\frac{du}{dx} \qquad (2\text{–}8.30)$$

E

A Short Table of Integrals

In this table, those results which are derived or presented in the text are identified by the equation number which they are assigned in the text. The symbols u and v represent functions of x, and a, b, and n are used to represent constants.

1. $$\int 0 \, dx = C$$

2. $$\int dx = x + C$$

3. $$\int du = u + C$$

4. $$\int f'(x) \, dx = f(x) + C \qquad (5\text{–}1.10)$$

5. $$\int af(x) \, dx = a \int f(x) \, dx \qquad (5\text{–}5.2)$$

6. $$\int (u + v) \, dx = \int u \, dx + \int v \, dx \qquad (5\text{–}5.1)$$

7. $$\int ax^n \, dx = \frac{ax^{n+1}}{n+1} + C, \text{ for } n \neq -1 \qquad (5\text{–}2.7)$$

8. $$\int \frac{dx}{x} = \ln x + C \qquad (5\text{–}5.4)$$

9. $$\int \ln x \, dx = x \ln x - x + C \qquad (5\text{–}5.5)$$

10. $$\int u \, dv = uv - \int v \, du \qquad (5\text{–}5.6)$$

11. $$\int u^n \, du = \frac{u^{n+1}}{n+1} + C, \text{ for } n \neq -1 \qquad (5\text{–}5.7)$$

12. $$\int \frac{du}{u} = \ln u + C \qquad (5\text{–}5.8)$$

13. $$\int e^u \, du = e^u + C \qquad (5\text{–}5.9)$$

14. $$\int a^u \, du = \frac{a^u}{\ln a} + C \qquad (5\text{–}5.10)$$

15. $$\int \ln u \, du = u \ln u - u + C \qquad (5\text{–}5.11)$$

16. $$\int \sin u \, du = -\cos u + C \qquad (5\text{–}5.12)$$

17. $$\int \cos u \, du = \sin u + C \qquad (5\text{–}5.13)$$

Some useful definite integrals:

18. $$\int_A^B f(x) \, dx = F(B) - F(A) \qquad (5\text{–}4.7)$$

19. $$\int_{-\infty}^{\infty} e^{-z^2/2} \, dz = \sqrt{2\pi}$$

20. $$\int_0^{\infty} x^2 e^{-bx} \, dx = \frac{a!}{b^{a+1}}, \text{ if } a \text{ is a positive integer and } b > 0$$

21. $$\int_0^1 x^a (1-x)^b \, dx = \frac{a!b!}{(a+b+1)!}$$

F

Values of e^{-m}

m	e^{-m}	m	e^{-m}
0.0	1.00000	2.5	.08208
0.1	.90484	2.6	.07427
0.2	.81873	2.7	.06721
0.3	.74082	2.8	.06081
0.4	.67032	2.9	.05502
0.5	.60653	3.0	.04979
0.6	.54881	3.2	.04076
0.7	.49659	3.4	.03337
0.8	.44933	3.6	.02732
0.9	.40657	3.8	.02237
1.0	.36788	4.0	.01832
1.1	.33287	4.2	.01500
1.2	.30119	4.4	.01228
1.3	.27253	4.6	.01005
1.4	.24660	4.8	.00823
1.5	.22313	5.0	.00674
1.6	.20190	5.5	.00409
1.7	.18268	6.0	.00248
1.8	.16530	6.5	.00150
1.9	.14957	7.0	.00091
2.0	.13534	7.5	.00055
2.1	.12246	8.0	.00034
2.2	.11080	8.5	.00020
2.3	.10026	9.0	.00012
2.4	.09072	10.0	.00005

G

Five-Place Common Logarithms

100 - 130

N	Log 0	1	2	3	4	5	6	7	8	9
100	00 000	043	087	130	173	217	260	303	346	389
101	432	475	518	561	604	647	689	732	775	817
102	860	903	945	988	*030	*072	*115	*157	*199	*242
103	01 284	326	368	410	452	494	536	578	620	662
104	703	745	787	828	870	912	953	995	*036	*078
105	02 119	160	202	243	284	325	366	407	449	490
106	531	572	612	653	694	735	776	816	857	898
107	938	979	*019	*060	*100	*141	*181	*222	*262	*302
108	03 342	383	423	463	503	543	583	623	663	703
109	743	782	822	862	902	941	981	*021	*060	*100
110	04 139	179	218	258	297	336	376	415	454	493
111	532	571	610	650	689	727	766	805	844	883
112	922	961	999	*038	*077	*115	*154	*192	*231	*269
113	05 308	346	385	423	461	500	538	576	614	652
114	690	729	767	805	843	881	918	956	994	*032
115	06 070	108	145	183	221	258	296	333	371	408
116	446	483	521	558	595	633	670	707	744	781
117	819	856	893	930	967	*004	*041	*078	*115	*151
118	07 188	225	262	298	335	372	408	445	482	518
119	555	591	628	664	700	737	773	809	846	882
120	918	954	990	*027	*063	*099	*135	*171	*207	*243
121	08 279	314	350	386	422	458	493	529	565	600
122	636	672	707	743	778	814	849	884	920	955
123	991	*026	*061	*096	*132	*167	*202	*237	*272	*307
124	09 342	377	412	447	482	517	552	587	621	656
125	691	726	760	795	830	864	899	934	968	*003
126	10 037	072	106	140	175	209	243	278	312	346
127	380	415	449	483	517	551	585	619	653	687
128	721	755	789	823	857	890	924	958	992	*025
129	11 059	093	126	160	193	227	261	294	327	361
130	394	428	461	494	528	561	594	628	661	694
N	Log 0	1	2	3	4	5	6	7	8	9

Proportional parts

	44	43	42
1	4.4	4.3	4.2
2	8.8	8.6	8.4
3	13.2	12.9	12.6
4	17.6	17.2	16.8
5	22.0	21.5	21.0
6	26.4	25.8	25.2
7	30.8	30.1	29.4
8	35.2	34.4	33.6
9	39.6	38.7	37.8

	41	40	39
1	4.1	4.0	3.9
2	8.2	8.0	7.8
3	12.3	12.0	11.7
4	16.4	16.0	15.6
5	20.5	20.0	19.5
6	24.6	24.0	23.4
7	28.7	28.0	27.3
8	32.8	32.0	31.2
9	36.9	36.0	35.1

	38	37	36
1	3.8	3.7	3.6
2	7.6	7.4	7.2
3	11.4	11.1	10.8
4	15.2	14.8	14.4
5	19.0	18.5	18.0
6	22.8	22.2	21.6
7	26.6	25.9	25.2
8	30.4	29.6	28.8
9	34.2	33.3	32.4

.00000 — .11694

N	Log	0	1	2	3	4	5	6	7	8	9
130	11	394	428	461	494	528	561	594	628	661	694
131		727	760	793	826	860	893	926	959	992	*024
132	12	057	090	123	156	189	222	254	287	320	352
133		385	418	450	483	516	548	581	613	646	678
134		710	743	775	808	840	872	905	937	969	*001
135	13	033	066	098	130	162	194	226	258	290	322
136		354	386	418	450	481	513	545	577	609	640
137		672	704	735	767	799	830	862	893	925	956
138		988	*019	*051	*082	*114	*145	*176	*208	*239	*270
139	14	301	333	364	395	426	457	489	520	551	582
140		613	644	675	706	737	768	799	829	860	891
141		922	953	983	*014	*045	*076	*106	*137	*168	*198
142	15	229	259	290	320	351	381	412	442	473	503
143		534	564	594	625	655	685	715	746	776	806
144		836	866	897	927	957	987	*017	*047	*077	*107
145	16	137	167	197	227	256	286	316	346	376	406
146		435	465	495	524	554	584	613	643	673	702
147		732	761	791	820	850	879	909	938	967	997
148	17	026	056	085	114	143	173	202	231	260	289
149		319	348	377	406	435	464	493	522	551	580
150		609	638	667	696	725	754	782	811	840	869
151		898	926	955	984	*013	*041	*070	*099	*127	*156
152	18	184	213	241	270	298	327	355	384	412	441
153		469	498	526	554	583	611	639	667	696	724
154		752	780	808	837	865	893	921	949	977	*005
155	19	033	061	089	117	145	173	201	229	257	285
156		312	340	368	396	424	451	479	507	535	562
157		590	618	645	673	700	728	756	783	811	838
158		866	893	921	948	976	*003	*030	*058	*085	*112
159	20	140	167	194	222	249	276	303	330	358	385
160		412	439	466	493	520	548	575	602	629	656
161		683	710	737	763	790	817	844	871	898	925
162		952	978	*005	*032	*059	*085	*112	*139	*165	*192
163	21	219	245	272	299	325	352	378	405	431	458
164		484	511	537	564	590	617	643	669	696	722
165		748	775	801	827	854	880	906	932	958	985
166	22	011	037	063	089	115	141	167	194	220	246
167		272	298	324	350	376	401	427	453	479	505
168		531	557	583	608	634	660	686	712	737	763
169		789	814	840	866	891	917	943	968	994	*019
170	23	045	070	096	121	147	172	198	223	249	274
171		300	325	350	376	401	426	452	477	502	528
172		553	578	603	629	654	679	704	729	754	779
173		805	830	855	880	905	930	955	980	*005	*030
174	24	055	080	105	130	155	180	204	229	254	279
175		304	329	353	378	403	428	452	477	502	527
176		551	576	601	625	650	674	699	724	748	773
177		797	822	846	871	895	920	944	969	993	*018
178	25	042	066	091	115	139	164	188	212	237	261
179		285	310	334	358	382	406	431	455	479	503
180		527	551	575	600	624	648	672	696	720	744
181		768	792	816	840	864	888	912	935	959	983
182	26	007	031	055	079	102	126	150	174	198	221
183		245	269	293	316	340	364	387	411	435	458
184		482	505	529	553	576	600	623	647	670	694
185		717	741	764	788	811	834	858	881	905	928

Proportional parts

	35	34	33
1	3.5	3.4	3.3
2	7.0	6.8	6.6
3	10.5	10.2	9.9
4	14.0	13.6	13.2
5	17.5	17.0	16.5
6	21.0	20.4	19.8
7	24.5	23.8	23.1
8	28.0	27.2	26.4
9	31.5	30.6	29.7

	32	31	30
1	3.2	3.1	3.0
2	6.4	6.2	6.0
3	9.6	9.3	9.0
4	12.8	12.4	12.0
5	16.0	15.5	15.0
6	19.2	18.6	18.0
7	22.4	21.7	21.0
8	25.6	24.8	24.0
9	28.8	27.9	27.0

	29	28	27
1	2.9	2.8	2.7
2	5.8	5.6	5.4
3	8.7	8.4	8.1
4	11.6	11.2	10.8
5	14.5	14.0	13.5
6	17.4	16.8	16.2
7	20.3	19.6	18.9
8	23.1	22.4	21.6
9	26.1	25.2	24.3

	26	25
1	2.6	2.5
2	5.2	5.0
3	7.8	7.5
4	10.4	10.0
5	13.0	12.5
6	15.6	15.0
7	18.2	17.5
8	20.8	20.0
9	23.4	22.5

	24	23
1	2.4	2.3
2	4.8	4.6
3	7.2	6.9
4	9.6	9.2
5	12.0	11.5
6	14.4	13.8
7	16.8	16.1
8	19.2	18.4
9	21.6	20.7

N Log 0 1 2 3 4 5 6 7 8 9 Proportional parts

185 - 240

N	Log	0	1	2	3	4	5	6	7	8	9
185	26	717	741	764	788	811	834	858	881	905	928
186		951	975	998	*021	*045	*068	*091	*114	*138	*161
187	27	184	207	231	254	277	300	323	346	370	393
188		416	439	462	485	508	531	554	577	600	623
189		646	669	692	715	738	761	784	807	830	852
190		875	898	921	944	967	989	*012	*035	*058	*081
191	28	103	126	149	171	194	217	240	262	285	307
192		330	353	375	398	421	443	466	488	511	533
193		556	578	601	623	646	668	691	713	735	758
194		780	803	825	847	870	892	914	937	959	981
195	29	003	026	048	070	092	115	137	159	181	203
196		226	248	270	292	314	336	358	380	403	425
197		447	469	491	513	535	557	579	601	623	645
198		667	688	710	732	754	776	798	820	842	863
199		885	907	929	951	973	994	*016	*038	*060	*081
200	30	103	125	146	168	190	211	233	255	276	298
201		320	341	363	384	406	428	449	471	492	514
202		535	557	578	600	621	643	664	685	707	728
203		750	771	792	814	835	856	878	899	920	942
204		963	984	*006	*027	*048	*069	*091	*112	*133	*154
205	31	175	197	218	239	260	281	302	323	345	366
206		387	408	429	450	471	492	513	534	555	576
207		597	618	639	660	681	702	723	744	765	785
208		806	827	848	869	890	911	931	952	973	994
209	32	015	035	056	077	098	118	139	160	181	201
210		222	243	263	284	305	325	346	366	387	408
211		428	449	469	490	510	531	552	572	593	613
212		634	654	675	695	715	736	756	777	797	818
213		838	858	879	899	919	940	960	980	*001	*021
214	33	041	062	082	102	122	143	163	183	203	224
215		244	264	284	304	325	345	365	385	405	425
216		445	465	486	506	526	546	566	586	606	626
217		646	666	686	706	726	746	766	786	806	826
218		846	866	885	905	925	945	965	985	*005	*025
219	34	044	064	084	104	124	143	163	183	203	223
220		242	262	282	301	321	341	361	380	400	420
221		439	459	479	498	518	537	557	577	596	616
222		635	655	674	694	713	733	753	772	792	811
223		830	850	869	889	908	928	947	967	986	*005
224	35	025	044	064	083	102	122	141	160	180	199
225		218	238	257	276	295	315	334	353	372	392
226		411	430	449	468	488	507	526	545	564	583
227		603	622	641	660	679	698	717	736	755	774
228		793	813	832	851	870	889	908	927	946	965
229		984	*003	*021	*040	*059	*078	*097	*116	*135	*154
230	36	173	192	211	229	248	267	286	305	324	342
231		361	380	399	418	436	455	474	493	511	530
232		549	568	586	605	624	642	661	680	698	717
233		736	754	773	791	810	829	847	866	884	903
234		922	940	959	977	996	*014	*033	*051	*070	*088
235	37	107	125	144	162	181	199	218	236	254	273
236		291	310	328	346	365	383	401	420	438	457
237		475	493	511	530	548	566	585	603	621	639
238		658	676	694	712	731	749	767	785	803	822
239		840	858	876	894	912	931	949	967	985	*003
240	38	021	039	057	075	093	112	130	148	166	184
N	Log	0	1	2	3	4	5	6	7	8	9

Proportional parts

	24	23
1	2.4	2.3
2	4.8	4.6
3	7.2	6.9
4	9.6	9.2
5	12.0	11.5
6	14.4	13.8
7	16.8	16.1
8	19.2	18.4
9	21.6	20.7

	22	21
1	2.2	2.1
2	4.4	4.2
3	6.6	6.3
4	8.8	8.4
5	11.0	10.5
6	13.2	12.6
7	15.4	14.7
8	17.6	16.8
9	19.8	18.9

	20
1	2.0
2	4.0
3	6.0
4	8.0
5	10.0
6	12.0
7	14.0
8	16.0
9	18.0

	19
1	1.9
2	3.8
3	5.7
4	7.6
5	9.5
6	11.4
7	13.3
8	15.2
9	17.1

	18
1	1.8
2	3.6
3	5.4
4	7.2
5	9.0
6	10.8
7	12.6
8	14.4
9	16.2

Proportional parts

240 - 295

N	Log 0	1	2	3	4	5	6	7	8	9
240	38 021	039	057	075	093	112	130	148	166	184
241	202	220	238	256	274	292	310	328	346	364
242	382	399	417	435	453	471	489	507	525	543
243	561	578	596	614	632	650	668	686	703	721
244	739	757	775	792	810	828	846	863	881	899
245	917	934	952	970	987	*005	*023	*041	*058	*076
246	39 094	111	129	146	164	182	199	217	235	252
247	270	287	305	322	340	358	375	393	410	428
248	445	463	480	498	515	533	550	568	585	602
249	620	637	655	672	690	707	724	742	759	777
250	794	811	829	846	863	881	898	915	933	950
251	967	985	*002	*019	*037	*054	*071	*088	*106	*123
252	40 140	157	175	192	209	226	243	261	278	295
253	312	329	346	364	381	398	415	432	449	466
254	483	500	518	535	552	569	586	603	620	637
255	654	671	688	705	722	739	756	773	790	807
256	824	841	858	875	892	909	926	943	960	976
257	993	*010	*027	*044	*061	*078	*095	*111	*128	*145
258	41 162	179	196	212	229	246	263	280	296	313
259	330	347	363	380	397	414	430	447	464	481
260	497	514	531	547	564	581	597	614	631	647
261	664	681	697	714	731	747	764	780	797	814
262	830	847	863	880	896	913	929	946	963	979
263	996	*012	*029	*045	*062	*078	*095	*111	*127	*144
264	42 160	177	193	210	226	243	259	275	292	308
265	325	341	357	374	390	406	423	439	455	472
266	488	504	521	537	553	570	586	602	619	635
267	651	667	684	700	716	732	749	765	781	797
268	813	830	846	862	878	894	911	927	943	959
269	975	991	*008	*024	*040	*056	*072	*088	*104	*120
270	43 136	152	169	185	201	217	233	249	265	281
271	297	313	329	345	361	377	393	409	425	441
272	457	473	489	505	521	537	553	569	584	600
273	616	632	648	664	680	696	712	727	743	759
274	775	791	807	823	838	854	870	886	902	917
275	933	949	965	981	996	*012	*028	*044	*059	*075
276	44 091	107	122	138	154	170	185	201	217	232
277	248	264	279	295	311	326	342	358	373	389
278	404	420	436	451	467	483	498	514	529	545
279	560	576	592	607	623	638	654	669	685	700
280	716	731	747	762	778	793	809	824	840	855
281	871	886	902	917	932	948	963	979	994	*010
282	45 025	040	056	071	086	102	117	133	148	163
283	179	194	209	225	240	255	271	286	301	317
284	332	347	362	378	393	408	423	439	454	469
285	484	500	515	530	545	561	576	591	606	621
286	637	652	667	682	697	712	728	743	758	773
287	788	803	818	834	849	864	879	894	909	924
288	939	954	969	984	*000	*015	*030	*045	*060	*075
289	46 090	105	120	135	150	165	180	195	210	225
290	240	255	270	285	300	315	330	345	359	374
291	389	404	419	434	449	464	479	494	509	523
292	538	553	568	583	598	613	627	642	657	672
293	687	702	716	731	746	761	776	790	805	820
294	835	850	864	879	894	909	923	938	953	967
295	982	997	*012	*026	*041	*056	*070	*085	*100	*114
N	Log 0	1	2	3	4	5	6	7	8	9

Proportional parts

	18	17	16	15	14
1	1.8	1.7	1.6	1.5	1.4
2	3.6	3.4	3.2	3.0	2.8
3	5.4	5.1	4.8	4.5	4.2
4	7.2	6.8	6.4	6.0	5.6
5	9.0	8.5	8.0	7.5	7.0
6	10.8	10.2	9.6	9.0	8.4
7	12.6	11.9	11.2	10.5	9.8
8	14.4	13.6	12.8	12.0	11.2
9	16.2	15.3	14.4	13.5	12.6

log e = 0.43429

295 - 350

N	Log 0	1	2	3	4	5	6	7	8	9
295	46 982	997	*012	*026	*041	*056	*070	*085	*100	*114
296	47 129	144	159	173	188	202	217	232	246	261
297	276	290	305	319	334	349	363	378	392	407
298	422	436	451	465	480	494	509	524	538	553
299	567	582	596	611	625	640	654	669	683	698
300	712	727	741	756	770	784	799	813	828	842
301	857	871	885	900	914	929	943	958	972	986
302	48 001	015	029	044	058	073	087	101	116	130
303	144	159	173	187	202	216	230	244	259	273
304	287	302	316	330	344	359	373	387	401	416
305	430	444	458	473	487	501	515	530	544	558
306	572	586	601	615	629	643	657	671	686	700
307	714	728	742	756	770	785	799	813	827	841
308	855	869	883	897	911	926	940	954	968	982
309	996	*010	*024	*038	*052	*066	*080	*094	*108	*122
310	49 136	150	164	178	192	206	220	234	248	262
311	276	290	304	318	332	346	360	374	388	402
312	415	429	443	457	471	485	499	513	527	541
313	554	568	582	596	610	624	638	651	665	679
314	693	707	721	734	748	762	776	790	803	817
315	831	845	859	872	886	900	914	927	941	955
316	969	982	996	*010	*024	*037	*051	*065	*079	*092
317	50 106	120	133	147	161	174	188	202	215	229
318	243	256	270	284	297	311	325	338	352	365
319	379	393	406	420	433	447	461	474	488	501
320	515	529	542	556	569	583	596	610	623	637
321	651	664	678	691	705	718	732	745	759	772
322	786	799	813	826	840	853	866	880	893	907
323	920	934	947	961	974	987	*001	*014	*028	*041
324	51 055	068	081	095	108	121	135	148	162	175
325	188	202	215	228	242	255	268	282	295	308
326	322	335	348	362	375	388	402	415	428	441
327	455	468	481	495	508	521	534	548	561	574
328	587	601	614	627	640	654	667	680	693	706
329	720	733	746	759	772	786	799	812	825	838
330	851	865	878	891	904	917	930	943	957	970
331	983	996	*009	*022	*035	*048	*061	*075	*088	*101
332	52 114	127	140	153	166	179	192	205	218	231
333	244	257	270	284	297	310	323	336	349	362
334	375	388	401	414	427	440	453	466	479	492
335	504	517	530	543	556	569	582	595	608	621
336	634	647	660	673	686	699	711	724	737	750
337	763	776	789	802	815	827	840	853	866	879
338	892	905	917	930	943	956	969	982	994	*007
339	53 020	033	046	058	071	084	097	110	122	135
340	148	161	173	186	199	212	224	237	250	263
341	275	288	301	314	326	339	352	364	377	390
342	403	415	428	441	453	466	479	491	504	517
343	529	542	555	567	580	593	605	618	631	643
344	656	668	681	694	706	719	732	744	757	769
345	782	794	807	820	832	845	857	870	882	895
346	908	920	933	945	958	970	983	995	*008	*020
347	54 033	045	058	070	083	095	108	120	133	145
348	158	170	183	195	208	220	233	245	258	270
349	283	295	307	320	332	345	357	370	382	394
350	407	419	432	444	456	469	481	494	506	518
N	Log 0	1	2	3	4	5	6	7	8	9

Proportional parts

	15	14	13	12
1	1.5	1.4	1.3	1.2
2	3.0	2.8	2.6	2.4
3	4.5	4.2	3.9	3.6
4	6.0	5.6	5.2	4.8
5	7.5	7.0	6.5	6.0
6	9.0	8.4	7.8	7.2
7	10.5	9.8	9.1	8.4
8	12.0	11.2	10.4	9.6
9	13.5	12.6	11.7	10.8

$\log \pi = 0.49715$

350 - 405

N	Log	0	1	2	3	4	5	6	7	8	9
350	54	407	419	432	444	456	469	481	494	506	518
351		531	543	555	568	580	593	605	617	630	642
352		654	667	679	691	704	716	728	741	753	765
353		777	790	802	814	827	839	851	864	876	888
354		900	913	925	937	949	962	974	986	998	*011
355	55	023	035	047	060	072	084	096	108	121	133
356		145	157	169	182	194	206	218	230	242	255
357		267	279	219	303	315	328	340	352	364	376
358		388	400	413	425	437	449	461	473	485	497
359		509	522	534	546	558	570	582	594	606	618
360		630	642	654	666	678	691	703	715	727	739
361		751	763	775	787	799	811	823	835	847	859
362		871	883	895	907	919	931	943	955	967	979
363		991	*003	*015	*027	*038	*050	*062	*074	*086	*098
364	56	110	122	134	146	158	170	182	194	205	217
365		229	241	253	265	277	289	301	312	324	336
366		348	360	372	384	396	407	419	431	443	455
367		467	478	490	502	514	526	538	549	561	573
368		585	597	608	620	632	644	656	667	679	691
369		703	714	726	738	750	761	773	785	797	808
370		820	832	844	855	867	879	891	902	914	926
371		937	949	961	972	984	996	*008	*019	*031	*043
372	57	054	066	078	089	101	113	124	136	148	159
373		171	183	194	206	217	229	241	252	264	276
374		287	299	310	322	334	345	357	368	380	392
375		403	415	426	438	449	461	473	484	496	507
376		519	530	542	553	565	576	588	600	611	623
377		634	646	657	669	680	692	703	715	726	738
378		749	761	772	784	795	807	818	830	841	852
379		864	875	887	898	910	921	933	944	955	967
380		978	990	*001	*013	*024	*035	*047	*058	*070	*081
381	58	092	104	115	127	138	149	161	172	184	195
382		206	218	229	240	252	263	274	286	297	309
383		320	331	343	354	365	377	388	399	410	422
384		433	444	456	467	478	490	501	512	524	535
385		546	557	569	580	591	602	614	625	636	647
386		659	670	681	692	704	715	726	737	749	760
387		771	782	794	805	816	827	838	850	861	872
388		883	894	906	917	928	939	950	961	973	984
389		995	*006	*017	*028	*040	*051	*062	*073	*084	*095
390	59	106	118	129	140	151	162	173	184	195	207
391		218	229	240	251	262	273	284	295	306	318
392		329	340	351	362	373	384	395	406	417	428
393		439	450	461	472	483	494	506	517	528	539
394		550	561	572	583	594	605	616	627	638	649
395		660	671	682	693	704	715	726	737	748	759
396		770	780	791	802	813	824	835	846	857	868
397		879	890	901	912	923	934	945	956	966	977
398		988	999	*010	*021	*032	*043	*054	*065	*076	*086
399	60	097	108	119	130	141	152	163	173	184	195
400		206	217	228	239	249	260	271	282	293	304
401		314	325	336	347	358	369	379	390	401	412
402		423	433	444	455	466	477	487	498	509	520
403		531	541	552	563	574	584	595	606	617	627
404		638	649	660	670	681	692	703	713	724	735
405		746	756	767	778	788	799	810	821	831	842

Proportional parts

	13	12	11	10
1	1.3	1.2	1.1	1.0
2	2.6	2.4	2.2	2.0
3	3.9	3.6	3.3	3.0
4	5.2	4.8	4.4	4.0
5	6.5	6.0	5.5	5.0
6	7.8	7.2	6.6	6.0
7	9.1	8.4	7.7	7.0
8	10.4	9.6	8.8	8.0
9	11.7	10.8	9.9	9.0

N Log 0 1 2 3 4 5 6 7 8 9 Proportional parts

405 - 460

N	Log 0	1	2	3	4	5	6	7	8	9
405	60 746	756	767	778	788	799	810	821	831	842
406	853	863	874	885	895	906	917	927	938	949
407	959	970	981	991	*002	*013	*023	*034	*045	*055
408	61 066	077	087	098	109	119	130	140	151	162
409	172	183	194	204	215	225	236	247	257	268
410	278	289	300	310	321	331	342	352	363	374
411	384	395	405	416	426	437	448	458	469	479
412	490	500	511	521	532	542	553	563	574	584
413	595	606	616	627	637	648	658	669	679	690
414	700	711	721	731	742	752	763	773	784	794
415	805	815	826	836	847	857	868	878	888	899
416	909	920	930	941	951	962	972	982	993	*003
417	62 014	024	034	045	055	066	076	086	097	107
418	118	128	138	149	159	170	180	190	201	211
419	221	232	242	252	263	273	284	294	304	315
420	325	335	346	356	366	377	387	397	408	418
421	428	439	449	459	469	480	490	500	511	521
422	531	542	552	562	572	583	593	603	613	624
423	634	644	655	665	675	685	696	706	716	726
424	737	747	757	767	778	788	798	808	818	829
425	839	849	859	870	880	890	900	910	921	931
426	941	951	961	972	982	992	*002	*012	*022	*033
427	63 043	053	063	073	083	094	104	114	124	134
428	144	155	165	175	185	195	205	215	225	236
429	246	256	266	276	286	296	306	317	327	337
430	347	357	367	377	387	397	407	417	428	438
431	448	458	468	478	488	498	508	518	528	538
432	548	558	568	579	589	599	609	619	629	639
433	649	659	669	679	689	699	709	719	729	739
434	749	759	769	779	789	799	809	819	829	839
435	849	859	869	879	889	899	909	919	929	939
436	949	959	969	979	988	998	*008	*018	*028	*038
437	64 048	058	068	078	088	098	108	118	128	137
438	147	157	167	177	187	197	207	217	227	237
439	246	256	266	276	286	296	306	316	326	335
440	345	355	365	375	385	395	404	414	424	434
441	444	454	464	473	483	493	503	513	523	532
442	542	552	562	572	582	591	601	611	621	631
443	640	650	660	670	680	689	699	709	719	729
444	738	748	758	768	777	787	797	807	816	826
445	836	846	856	865	875	885	895	904	914	924
446	933	943	953	963	972	982	992	*002	*011	*021
447	65 031	040	050	060	070	079	089	099	108	118
448	128	137	147	157	167	176	186	196	205	215
449	225	234	244	254	263	273	283	292	302	312
450	321	331	341	350	360	369	379	389	398	408
451	418	427	437	447	456	466	475	485	495	504
452	514	523	533	543	552	562	571	581	591	600
453	601	619	629	639	648	658	667	677	686	696
454	706	715	725	734	744	753	763	772	782	792
455	801	811	820	830	839	849	858	868	877	887
456	896	906	916	925	935	944	954	963	973	982
457	992	*001	*011	*020	*030	*039	*049	*058	*068	*077
458	66 087	096	106	115	124	134	143	153	162	172
459	181	191	200	210	219	229	238	247	257	266
460	276	285	295	304	314	323	332	342	351	361
N	Log 0	1	2	3	4	5	6	7	8	9

Proportional parts

	11	10	9
1	1.1	1.0	0.9
2	2.2	2.0	1.8
3	3.3	3.0	2.7
4	4.4	4.0	3.6
5	5.5	5.0	4.5
6	6.6	6.0	5.4
7	7.7	7.0	6.3
8	8.8	8.0	7.2
9	9.9	9.0	8.1

460 - 515

N	Log	0	1	2	3	4	5	6	7	8	9
460	66	276	285	295	304	314	323	332	342	351	361
461		370	380	389	398	408	417	427	436	445	455
462		464	474	483	492	502	511	521	530	539	549
463		558	567	577	586	596	605	614	624	633	642
464		652	661	671	680	689	699	708	717	727	736
465		745	755	764	773	783	792	801	811	820	829
466		839	848	857	867	876	885	894	904	913	922
467		932	941	950	960	969	978	987	997	*006	*015
468	67	025	034	043	052	062	071	080	089	099	108
469		117	127	136	145	154	164	173	182	191	201
470		210	219	228	237	247	256	265	274	284	293
471		302	311	321	330	339	348	357	367	376	385
472		394	493	413	422	431	440	449	459	468	477
473		486	495	504	514	523	532	541	550	560	569
474		578	587	596	605	614	624	633	642	651	660
475		669	679	688	697	706	715	724	733	742	752
476		761	770	779	788	797	806	815	825	834	843
477		852	861	870	879	888	897	906	916	925	934
478		943	952	961	970	979	988	997	*006	*015	*024
479	68	034	043	052	061	070	079	088	097	106	115
480		124	133	142	151	160	169	178	187	196	205
481		215	224	233	242	251	260	269	278	287	296
482		305	314	323	332	341	350	359	368	377	386
483		395	404	413	422	431	440	449	458	467	476
484		485	494	502	511	520	529	538	547	556	565
485		574	538	592	601	610	619	628	637	646	655
486		664	673	681	690	699	708	717	726	735	744
487		753	762	771	780	789	797	806	815	824	833
488		842	851	860	869	878	886	895	904	913	922
489		931	940	949	958	966	975	984	993	*002	*011
490	69	020	028	037	046	055	064	073	082	090	099
491		108	117	126	135	144	152	161	170	179	188
492		197	205	214	223	232	241	249	258	267	276
493		285	294	302	311	320	329	338	346	355	364
494		373	381	390	399	408	417	425	434	443	452
495		461	469	478	487	496	504	513	522	531	539
496		548	557	566	574	583	592	601	609	618	627
497		636	644	653	662	671	679	688	697	705	714
498		723	732	740	749	758	767	775	784	793	801
499		810	819	827	836	845	854	862	871	880	888
500		897	906	914	923	932	940	949	958	966	975
501		984	992	*001	*010	*018	*027	*036	*044	*053	*062
502	70	070	079	088	096	105	114	122	131	140	148
503		157	165	174	183	191	200	209	217	226	234
504		243	252	260	269	278	286	295	303	312	321
505		329	338	346	355	364	372	381	389	398	406
506		415	424	432	441	449	458	467	475	484	492
507		501	509	518	526	535	544	552	561	569	578
508		586	595	603	612	621	629	638	646	655	663
509		672	680	689	697	706	714	723	731	740	749
510		757	766	774	783	791	800	808	817	825	834
511		842	851	859	868	876	885	893	902	910	919
512		927	935	944	952	961	969	978	986	995	*003
513	71	012	020	029	037	046	054	063	071	079	088
514		096	105	113	122	130	139	147	155	164	172
515		181	189	198	206	214	223	231	240	248	257
N	Log	0	1	2	3	4	5	6	7	8	9

Proportional parts

	10
1	1.0
2	2.0
3	3.0
4	4.0
5	5.0
6	6.0
7	7.0
8	8.0
9	9.0

	9
1	0.9
2	1.8
3	2.7
4	3.6
5	4.5
6	5.4
7	6.3
8	7.2
9	8.1

	8
1	0.8
2	1.6
3	2.4
4	3.2
5	4.0
6	4.8
7	5.6
8	6.4
9	7.2

Proportional parts

515 - 570

N	Log	0	1	2	3	4	5	6	7	8	9
515	71	181	189	198	206	214	223	231	240	248	257
516		265	273	282	290	299	307	315	324	332	341
517		349	357	366	374	383	391	399	408	416	425
518		433	441	450	458	466	475	483	492	500	508
519		517	525	533	542	550	559	567	575	584	592
520		600	609	617	625	634	642	650	659	667	675
521		684	692	700	709	717	725	734	742	750	759
522		767	775	784	792	800	809	817	825	834	842
523		850	858	867	875	883	892	900	908	917	925
524		933	941	950	958	966	975	983	991	999	*008
525	72	016	024	032	041	049	057	066	074	082	090
526		099	107	115	123	132	140	148	156	165	173
527		181	189	198	206	214	222	230	239	247	255
528		263	272	280	288	296	304	313	321	329	337
529		346	354	362	370	378	387	395	403	411	419
530		428	436	444	452	460	469	477	485	493	501
531		509	518	526	534	542	550	558	567	575	583
532		591	599	607	616	624	632	640	648	656	665
533		673	681	689	697	705	713	722	730	738	746
534		754	762	770	779	787	795	803	811	819	827
535		835	843	852	860	868	876	884	892	900	908
536		916	925	933	941	949	957	965	973	981	989
537		997	*006	*014	*022	*030	*038	*046	*054	*062	*070
538	73	078	086	094	102	111	119	127	135	143	151
539		159	167	175	183	191	199	207	215	223	231
540		239	247	255	263	272	280	288	296	304	312
541		320	328	336	344	352	360	368	376	384	392
542		400	408	416	424	432	440	448	456	464	472
543		480	488	496	504	512	520	528	536	544	552
544		560	568	576	584	592	600	608	616	624	632
545		640	648	656	664	672	679	687	695	703	711
546		719	727	735	743	751	759	767	775	783	791
547		799	807	815	823	830	838	846	854	862	870
548		878	886	894	902	910	918	926	933	941	949
549		957	965	973	981	989	997	*005	*013	*020	*028
550	74	036	044	052	060	068	076	084	092	099	107
551		115	123	131	139	147	155	162	170	178	186
552		194	202	210	218	225	233	241	249	257	265
553		273	280	288	296	304	312	320	327	335	343
554		351	359	367	374	382	390	398	406	414	421
555		429	437	445	453	461	468	476	484	492	500
556		507	515	523	531	539	547	554	562	570	578
557		586	593	601	609	617	624	632	640	648	656
558		663	671	679	687	695	702	710	718	726	733
559		741	749	757	764	772	780	788	796	803	811
560		819	827	834	842	850	858	865	873	881	889
561		896	904	912	920	927	935	943	950	958	966
562		974	981	989	997	*005	*012	*020	*028	*035	*043
563	75	051	059	066	074	082	089	097	105	113	120
564		128	136	143	151	159	166	174	182	189	197
565		205	213	220	228	236	243	251	259	266	274
566		282	289	297	305	312	320	328	335	343	351
567		358	366	374	381	389	397	404	412	420	427
568		435	442	450	458	465	473	481	488	496	504
569		511	519	526	534	542	549	557	565	572	580
570		587	595	603	610	618	626	633	641	648	656
N	Log	0	1	2	3	4	5	6	7	8	9

Proportional parts

	9
1	0.9
2	1.8
3	2.7
4	3.6
5	4.5
6	5.4
7	6.3
8	7.2
9	8.1

	8
1	0.8
2	1.6
3	2.4
4	3.2
5	4.0
6	4.8
7	5.6
8	6.4
9	7.2

570 - 625

N	Log 0	1	2	3	4	5	6	7	8	9
570	75 587	595	603	610	618	626	633	641	648	656
571	664	671	679	686	694	702	709	717	724	732
572	740	747	755	762	770	778	785	793	800	808
573	815	823	831	838	846	853	861	868	876	884
574	891	899	906	914	921	929	937	944	952	959
575	967	974	982	989	997	*005	*012	*020	*027	*035
576	76 042	050	057	065	072	080	087	095	103	110
577	118	125	133	140	148	155	163	170	178	185
578	193	200	208	215	223	230	238	245	253	260
579	268	275	283	290	298	305	313	320	328	335
580	343	350	358	365	373	380	388	395	403	410
581	418	425	433	440	448	455	462	470	477	485
582	492	500	507	515	522	530	537	545	552	559
583	567	547	582	589	597	604	612	619	626	634
584	641	649	656	664	671	678	686	693	701	708
585	716	723	730	738	745	753	760	768	775	782
586	790	797	805	812	819	827	834	842	849	856
587	864	871	879	886	893	901	908	916	923	930
588	938	945	953	960	967	975	982	989	997	*004
589	77 012	019	026	034	041	048	056	063	070	078
590	085	093	100	107	115	122	129	137	144	151
591	159	166	173	181	188	195	203	210	217	225
592	232	240	247	254	262	269	276	283	291	298
593	305	313	320	327	335	342	349	357	364	371
594	379	386	393	401	408	415	422	430	437	444
595	452	459	466	474	481	488	495	503	510	517
596	525	532	539	546	554	561	568	576	583	590
597	597	605	612	619	627	634	641	648	656	663
598	670	677	685	692	699	706	714	721	728	735
599	743	750	757	764	772	779	786	793	801	808
600	815	822	830	837	844	851	859	866	873	880
601	887	895	902	909	916	924	931	938	945	952
602	960	967	974	981	988	996	*003	*010	*017	*025
603	78 032	039	046	053	061	068	075	082	089	097
604	104	111	118	125	132	140	147	154	161	168
605	176	183	190	197	204	211	219	226	233	240
606	247	254	262	269	276	283	290	297	305	312
607	319	326	333	340	347	355	362	369	376	383
608	390	398	405	412	419	426	433	440	447	455
609	462	469	476	483	490	497	504	512	519	526
610	533	540	547	554	561	569	576	583	590	597
611	604	611	618	625	633	640	647	654	661	668
612	675	682	689	696	704	711	718	725	732	739
613	746	753	760	767	774	781	789	796	803	810
614	817	824	831	838	845	852	859	866	873	880
615	888	895	902	909	916	923	930	937	944	951
616	958	965	972	979	986	993	*000	*007	*014	*021
617	79 029	036	043	050	057	064	071	078	085	092
618	099	106	113	120	127	134	141	148	155	162
619	169	176	183	190	197	204	211	218	225	232
620	239	246	253	260	267	274	281	288	295	302
621	309	316	323	330	337	344	351	358	365	372
622	379	386	393	400	407	414	421	428	435	442
623	449	456	463	470	477	484	491	498	505	511
624	518	525	532	539	546	553	560	567	574	581
625	588	595	602	609	616	623	630	637	644	650
N	Log 0	1	2	3	4	5	6	7	8	9

Proportional parts

	8
1	0.8
2	1.6
3	2.4
4	3.2
5	4.0
6	4.8
7	5.6
8	6.4
9	7.2

	7
1	0.7
2	1.4
3	2.1
4	2.8
5	3.5
6	4.2
7	4.9
8	5.6
9	6.3

625 - 680

N	Log	0	1	2	3	4	5	6	7	8	9
625	79	588	595	602	609	616	623	630	637	644	650
626		657	664	671	678	685	692	699	706	713	720
627		727	734	741	748	754	761	768	775	782	789
628		796	803	810	817	824	831	837	844	851	858
629		865	872	879	886	893	900	906	913	920	927
630		934	941	948	955	962	969	975	982	989	996
631	80	003	010	017	024	030	037	044	051	058	065
632		072	079	085	092	099	106	113	120	127	134
633		140	147	154	161	168	175	182	188	195	202
634		209	216	223	229	236	243	250	257	264	271
635		277	284	291	298	305	312	318	325	332	339
636		346	353	359	366	373	380	387	393	400	407
637		414	421	428	434	441	448	455	462	468	475
638		482	489	496	502	509	516	523	530	536	543
639		550	557	564	570	577	584	591	598	604	611
640		618	625	632	638	645	652	659	665	672	679
641		686	693	699	706	713	720	726	733	740	747
642		754	760	767	774	781	787	794	801	808	814
643		821	828	835	841	848	855	862	868	875	882
644		889	895	902	909	916	922	929	936	943	949
645		959	963	969	976	983	990	996	*003	*010	*017
646	81	023	030	037	043	050	057	064	070	077	084
647		090	097	104	111	117	124	131	137	144	151
648		158	164	171	178	184	191	198	204	211	218
649		224	231	238	245	251	258	265	271	278	285
650		291	298	305	311	318	325	331	338	345	351
651		358	365	371	378	385	391	398	405	411	418
652		425	431	438	445	451	458	465	471	478	485
653		491	498	505	511	518	525	531	538	544	551
654		558	564	571	578	584	591	598	604	611	617
655		624	631	637	644	651	657	664	671	677	684
656		690	697	704	710	717	723	730	737	743	750
657		757	763	770	776	783	790	796	803	809	816
658		823	829	836	842	849	856	862	869	875	882
659		889	895	902	908	915	921	928	935	941	948
660		954	961	968	974	981	987	994	*000	*007	*014
661	82	020	027	033	040	046	053	060	066	073	079
662		086	092	099	105	112	119	125	132	138	145
663		151	158	164	171	178	184	191	197	204	210
664		217	223	230	236	243	249	256	263	269	276
665		282	289	295	302	308	315	321	328	334	341
666		347	354	360	367	373	380	387	393	400	406
667		413	419	426	432	439	445	452	458	465	471
668		478	484	491	497	504	510	517	523	530	536
669		543	549	556	562	569	575	582	588	595	601
670		607	614	620	627	633	640	646	653	659	666
671		672	679	685	692	698	705	711	718	724	730
672		737	743	750	756	763	769	776	782	789	795
673		802	808	814	821	827	834	840	847	853	860
674		866	872	879	885	892	898	905	911	918	924
675		930	937	943	950	956	963	969	975	982	988
676		995	*001	*008	*014	*020	*027	*033	*040	*046	*052
677	83	059	065	072	078	085	091	097	104	110	117
678		123	129	136	142	149	155	161	168	174	181
679		187	193	200	206	213	219	225	232	238	245
680		251	257	264	270	276	283	289	296	302	308
N	Log	0	1	2	3	4	5	6	7	8	9

Proportional parts

	7
1	0.7
2	1.4
3	2.1
4	2.8
5	3.5
6	4.2
7	4.9
8	5.6
9	6.3

	6
1	0.6
2	1.2
3	1.8
4	2.4
5	3.0
6	3.6
7	4.2
8	4.8
9	5.4

680 - 735

N	Log 0	1	2	3	4	5	6	7	8	9
680	83 251	257	264	270	276	283	289	296	302	308
681	315	321	327	334	340	347	353	359	366	372
682	378	385	391	398	404	410	417	423	429	436
683	442	448	455	461	467	474	480	487	493	499
684	506	512	518	525	531	537	544	550	556	563
685	569	575	582	588	594	601	607	613	620	626
686	632	639	645	651	658	664	670	677	683	689
687	696	702	708	715	721	727	734	740	746	753
688	759	765	771	778	784	790	797	803	809	816
689	822	828	835	841	847	853	860	866	872	879
690	885	891	897	904	910	916	923	929	935	942
691	948	954	960	967	973	979	985	992	998	*004
692	84 011	017	023	029	036	042	048	055	061	067
693	073	080	086	092	098	105	111	117	123	130
694	136	142	148	155	161	167	173	180	186	192
695	198	205	211	217	223	230	236	242	248	255
696	261	267	273	280	286	292	298	305	311	317
697	323	330	336	342	348	354	361	367	373	379
698	386	392	398	404	410	417	423	429	435	442
699	448	454	460	466	473	479	485	491	497	504
700	510	516	522	528	535	541	547	553	559	566
701	572	578	584	590	597	603	609	615	621	628
702	634	640	646	652	658	665	671	677	683	689
703	696	702	708	714	720	726	733	739	745	751
704	757	763	770	776	782	788	794	800	807	813
705	819	825	831	837	844	850	856	862	868	874
706	880	887	893	899	905	911	917	924	930	936
707	942	948	954	960	967	973	979	985	991	997
708	85 003	009	016	022	028	034	040	046	052	058
709	065	071	077	083	089	095	101	107	114	120
710	126	132	138	144	150	156	163	169	175	181
711	187	193	199	205	211	217	224	230	236	242
712	248	254	260	266	272	278	285	291	297	303
713	309	315	321	327	333	339	345	352	358	364
714	370	376	382	388	394	400	406	412	418	425
715	431	437	443	449	455	461	467	473	479	485
716	491	497	503	509	516	522	528	534	540	546
717	552	558	564	570	576	582	588	594	600	606
718	612	618	625	631	637	643	649	655	661	667
719	673	679	685	691	697	703	709	715	721	727
720	733	739	745	751	757	763	769	775	781	788
721	794	800	806	812	818	824	830	836	842	848
722	854	860	866	872	878	884	890	896	902	908
723	914	920	926	932	938	944	950	956	962	968
724	974	980	986	992	998	*004	*010	*016	*022	*028
725	86 034	040	046	052	058	064	070	076	082	088
726	094	100	106	112	118	124	130	136	141	147
727	153	159	165	171	177	183	189	195	201	207
728	213	219	225	231	237	243	249	255	261	276
729	273	279	285	291	297	303	308	314	320	326
730	332	338	344	350	356	362	368	374	380	386
731	392	398	404	410	415	421	427	433	439	445
732	451	457	463	469	475	481	487	493	499	504
733	510	516	522	528	534	540	546	552	558	564
734	570	576	581	587	593	599	605	611	617	623
735	629	635	641	646	652	658	664	670	676	682
N	Log 0	1	2	3	4	5	6	7	8	9

Proportional parts

	7
1	0.7
2	1.4
3	2.1
4	2.8
5	3.5
6	4.2
7	4.9
8	5.6
9	6.3

	6
1	0.6
2	1.2
3	1.8
4	2.4
5	3.0
6	3.6
7	4.2
8	4.8
9	5.4

735 - 790

N	Log	0	1	2	3	4	5	6	7	8	9
735	86	629	635	641	646	652	658	664	670	676	682
736		688	694	700	705	711	717	723	729	735	741
737		747	753	759	764	770	776	782	788	794	800
738		806	812	817	823	829	835	841	847	853	859
739		864	870	876	882	888	894	900	906	911	917
740		923	929	935	941	947	953	958	964	970	976
741		982	988	994	999	*005	*011	*017	*023	*029	*035
742	87	040	046	052	058	064	070	075	081	087	093
743		099	105	111	116	122	128	134	140	146	151
744		157	163	169	175	181	186	192	198	204	210
745		216	221	227	233	239	245	251	256	262	268
746		274	280	286	291	297	303	309	315	320	326
747		332	338	344	349	355	361	367	373	379	384
748		390	396	402	408	413	419	425	431	437	442
749		448	454	460	466	471	477	483	489	495	500
750		506	512	518	523	529	535	541	547	552	558
751		564	570	576	581	587	593	599	604	610	616
752		622	628	633	639	645	651	656	662	668	674
753		679	685	691	697	703	708	714	720	726	731
754		737	743	749	754	760	766	772	777	783	789
755		795	800	806	812	818	823	829	835	841	846
756		852	858	864	869	875	881	887	892	898	904
757		910	915	921	927	933	938	944	950	955	961
758		967	973	978	984	990	996	*001	*007	*013	*018
759	88	024	030	036	041	047	053	058	064	070	076
760		081	087	093	098	104	110	116	121	127	133
761		138	144	150	156	161	167	173	178	184	190
762		195	201	207	213	218	224	230	235	241	247
763		252	258	264	270	275	281	287	292	298	304
764		309	315	321	326	332	338	343	349	355	360
765		366	372	377	383	389	395	400	406	412	417
766		423	429	434	440	446	451	457	463	468	474
767		480	485	491	497	502	508	513	519	525	530
768		536	542	547	553	559	564	570	576	581	587
769		593	598	604	610	615	621	627	632	638	643
770		649	655	660	666	672	677	683	689	694	700
771		705	711	717	722	728	734	739	745	750	756
772		762	767	773	779	784	790	795	801	807	812
773		818	824	829	835	840	846	852	857	863	868
774		874	880	885	891	897	902	908	913	919	925
775		930	936	941	947	953	958	964	969	975	981
776		986	992	997	*003	*009	*014	*020	*025	*031	*037
777	89	042	048	053	059	064	070	076	081	087	092
778		098	104	109	115	120	126	131	137	143	148
779		154	159	165	170	176	182	187	193	198	204
780		209	215	221	226	232	237	243	248	254	260
781		265	271	276	282	287	293	298	304	310	315
782		321	326	332	337	343	348	354	360	365	371
783		376	382	387	393	398	404	409	415	421	426
784		432	437	443	448	454	459	465	470	476	481
785		487	492	498	504	509	515	520	526	531	537
786		542	548	553	559	564	570	575	581	586	592
787		597	603	609	614	620	625	631	636	642	647
788		653	658	664	669	675	680	686	691	697	702
789		708	713	719	724	730	735	741	746	752	757
790		763	768	774	779	785	790	796	801	807	812
N	Log	0	1	2	3	4	5	6	7	8	9

Proportional parts

	6
1	0.6
2	1.2
3	1.8
4	2.4
5	3.0
6	3.6
7	4.2
8	4.8
9	5.4

	5
1	0.5
2	1.0
3	1.5
4	2.0
5	2.5
6	3.0
7	3.5
8	4.0
9	4.5

790 - 845

N	Log 0	1	2	3	4	5	6	7	8	9
790	89 763	768	774	779	785	790	796	801	807	812
791	818	823	829	834	840	845	851	856	862	867
792	873	878	883	889	894	900	905	911	916	922
793	927	933	938	944	949	955	960	966	971	977
794	982	988	993	998	*004	*009	*015	*020	*026	*031
795	90 037	042	048	053	059	064	069	075	080	086
796	091	097	102	108	113	119	124	129	135	140
797	146	151	157	162	168	173	179	184	189	195
798	200	206	211	217	222	227	233	238	244	249
799	255	260	266	271	276	282	287	293	298	304
800	309	314	320	325	331	336	342	347	352	358
801	363	369	374	380	385	390	396	401	407	412
802	417	423	428	434	439	445	450	455	461	466
803	472	477	482	488	493	499	504	509	515	520
804	526	531	536	542	547	553	558	563	569	574
805	580	585	590	596	601	607	612	617	623	628
806	634	639	644	650	655	660	666	671	677	682
807	687	693	698	703	709	714	720	725	730	736
808	741	747	752	757	763	768	773	779	784	789
809	795	800	806	811	816	822	827	832	838	843
810	849	854	859	865	870	875	881	886	891	897
811	902	907	913	918	924	929	934	940	945	950
812	956	961	966	972	977	982	988	993	998	*004
813	91 009	014	020	025	030	036	041	046	052	057
814	062	068	073	078	084	089	094	100	105	110
815	116	121	126	132	137	142	148	153	158	164
816	169	174	180	185	190	196	201	206	212	217
817	222	228	233	238	243	249	254	259	265	270
818	275	[illegible]	286	291	297	302	307	312	318	323
819	328	334	339	344	350	355	360	365	371	376
820	381	387	392	397	403	408	413	418	424	429
821	434	440	445	450	455	461	466	471	477	482
822	487	492	498	503	508	514	519	524	529	535
823	540	545	551	556	561	566	572	577	582	587
824	593	598	603	609	614	619	624	630	635	640
825	645	651	656	661	666	672	677	682	687	693
826	698	703	709	714	719	724	730	735	740	745
827	751	756	761	766	772	777	782	787	793	798
828	803	808	814	819	824	829	834	840	845	850
829	855	861	866	871	876	882	887	892	897	903
830	908	913	918	924	929	934	939	944	950	955
831	960	965	971	976	981	986	991	997	*002	*007
832	92 012	018	023	028	033	038	044	049	054	059
833	065	070	075	080	085	091	096	101	106	111
834	117	122	127	132	137	143	148	153	158	163
835	169	174	179	184	189	195	200	205	210	215
836	221	226	231	236	241	247	252	257	262	267
837	273	278	283	288	293	298	304	309	314	319
838	324	330	335	340	345	350	355	361	366	371
834	376	381	387	392	397	402	407	412	418	423
840	428	433	438	443	449	454	459	464	469	474
841	480	485	490	495	500	505	511	516	521	526
842	531	536	542	547	552	557	562	567	572	578
843	583	588	593	598	603	609	614	619	624	629
844	634	639	645	650	655	660	665	670	675	681
845	686	691	696	701	706	711	716	722	727	732
N	Log 0	1	2	3	4	5	6	7	8	9

Proportional parts

	6
1	0.6
2	1.2
3	1.8
4	2.4
5	3.0
6	3.6
7	4.2
8	4.8
9	5.4

	5
1	0.5
2	1.0
3	1.5
4	2.0
5	2.5
6	3.0
7	3.5
8	4.0
9	4.5

845 - 900

N	Log 0	1	2	3	4	5	6	7	8	9
845	92 686	691	696	701	706	711	716	722	727	732
846	737	742	747	752	758	763	768	773	778	783
847	788	793	799	804	809	814	819	824	829	834
848	840	845	850	855	860	865	870	875	881	886
849	891	896	901	906	911	916	921	927	932	937
850	942	947	952	957	962	967	973	978	983	988
851	993	998	*003	*008	*013	*018	*024	*029	*034	*039
852	93 044	049	054	059	064	069	075	080	085	090
853	095	100	105	110	115	120	125	131	136	141
854	146	151	156	161	166	171	176	181	186	192
855	197	202	207	212	217	222	227	232	237	242
856	247	252	258	263	268	273	278	283	288	293
857	298	303	308	313	318	323	328	334	339	344
858	349	354	359	364	369	374	379	384	389	394
859	399	404	409	414	420	425	430	435	440	445
860	450	455	460	465	470	475	480	485	490	495
861	500	505	510	515	520	526	531	536	541	546
862	551	556	561	566	571	576	581	586	591	596
863	601	606	611	616	621	626	631	636	641	646
864	651	656	661	666	671	676	682	687	692	697
865	702	707	712	717	722	727	732	737	742	747
866	752	757	762	767	772	777	782	787	792	797
867	802	807	812	817	822	827	832	837	842	847
868	852	857	862	867	872	877	882	887	892	897
869	902	907	912	917	922	927	932	937	942	947
870	952	957	962	967	972	977	982	987	992	997
871	94 002	007	012	017	022	027	032	037	042	047
872	052	057	062	067	072	077	082	086	091	096
873	101	106	111	116	121	126	131	136	141	146
874	151	156	161	166	171	176	181	186	191	196
875	201	206	211	216	221	226	231	236	240	245
876	250	255	260	265	270	275	280	285	290	295
877	300	305	310	315	320	325	330	335	340	345
878	349	354	359	364	369	374	379	384	389	394
879	399	404	409	414	419	424	429	433	438	443
880	448	453	458	463	468	473	478	483	488	493
881	498	503	507	512	517	522	527	532	537	542
882	547	552	557	562	567	571	576	581	586	591
883	596	601	606	611	616	621	626	630	635	640
884	645	650	655	660	665	670	675	680	685	689
885	694	699	704	709	714	719	724	729	734	738
886	743	748	753	758	763	768	773	778	783	787
887	792	797	802	807	812	817	822	827	832	836
888	841	846	851	856	861	866	871	876	880	885
889	890	895	900	905	910	915	919	924	929	934
890	939	944	949	954	959	963	968	973	978	983
891	988	993	998	*002	*007	*012	*017	*022	*027	*032
892	95 036	041	046	051	056	061	066	071	075	080
893	085	090	095	100	105	109	114	119	124	129
894	134	139	143	148	153	158	163	168	173	177
895	182	187	192	197	202	207	211	216	221	226
896	231	236	240	245	250	255	260	265	270	274
897	279	284	289	294	299	303	308	313	318	323
898	328	332	337	342	347	352	357	361	366	371
899	376	381	386	390	395	400	405	410	415	419
900	424	429	434	439	444	448	453	458	463	468
N	Log 0	1	2	3	4	5	6	7	8	9

Proportional parts

	5
1	0.5
2	1.0
3	1.5
4	2.0
5	2.5
6	3.0
7	3.5
8	4.0
9	4.5

	4
1	0.4
2	0.8
3	1.2
4	1.6
5	2.0
6	2.4
7	2.8
8	3.2
9	3.6

900 - 955

N	Log 0	1	2	3	4	5	6	7	8	9
900	95 424	429	434	439	444	448	453	458	463	468
901	472	477	482	487	492	497	501	506	511	516
902	521	525	530	535	540	545	550	554	559	564
903	569	574	578	583	588	593	598	602	607	612
904	617	622	626	631	636	641	646	650	655	660
905	665	670	674	679	684	689	694	698	703	708
906	713	718	722	727	732	737	742	746	751	756
907	761	766	770	775	780	785	789	794	799	804
908	809	813	818	823	828	832	837	842	847	852
909	856	861	866	871	875	880	885	890	895	899
910	904	909	914	918	923	928	933	938	942	947
911	952	957	961	966	971	976	980	985	990	995
912	999	*004	*009	*014	*019	*023	*028	*033	*038	*042
913	96 047	052	057	061	066	071	076	080	085	090
914	095	099	104	109	114	118	123	128	133	137
915	142	147	152	156	161	166	171	175	180	185
916	190	194	199	204	209	213	218	223	227	232
917	237	242	246	251	256	261	265	270	275	280
918	284	289	294	298	303	308	313	317	322	327
919	332	336	341	346	350	355	360	365	369	374
920	379	384	388	393	398	402	407	412	417	421
921	426	431	435	440	445	450	454	459	464	468
922	473	478	483	487	492	497	501	506	511	515
923	520	525	530	534	539	544	548	553	558	562
924	567	572	577	581	586	591	595	600	605	609
925	614	619	624	628	633	638	642	647	652	656
926	661	666	670	675	680	685	689	694	699	703
927	708	713	717	722	727	731	736	741	745	750
928	755	759	764	769	774	778	783	788	792	797
929	802	806	811	816	820	825	830	834	839	844
930	848	853	858	862	867	872	876	881	886	890
931	895	900	904	909	914	918	923	928	932	937
932	942	946	951	956	960	965	970	974	979	984
933	988	993	997	*002	*007	*011	*016	*021	*025	*030
934	97 035	039	044	049	053	058	063	067	072	077
935	081	086	090	095	100	104	109	114	118	123
936	128	132	137	142	146	151	155	160	165	169
937	174	179	183	188	192	197	202	206	211	216
938	220	225	230	234	239	243	248	253	257	262
939	267	271	276	280	285	290	294	299	304	308
940	313	317	322	327	331	336	340	345	350	354
941	359	364	368	373	377	382	387	391	396	400
942	405	410	414	419	424	428	433	437	442	447
943	451	456	460	465	470	474	479	483	488	493
944	497	502	506	511	516	520	525	529	534	539
945	543	548	552	557	562	566	571	575	580	585
946	589	594	598	603	607	612	617	621	626	630
947	635	640	644	649	653	658	663	667	672	676
948	681	685	690	695	699	704	708	713	717	722
949	727	731	736	740	745	749	754	759	763	768
950	772	777	782	786	791	795	800	804	809	813
951	818	823	827	832	836	841	845	850	855	859
952	864	868	873	877	882	886	891	896	900	905
953	909	914	918	923	928	932	937	941	946	950
954	955	959	964	968	973	978	982	987	991	996
955	98 000	005	009	014	019	023	028	032	037	041
N	Log 0	1	2	3	4	5	6	7	8	9

Proportional parts

	5
1	0.5
2	1.0
3	1.5
4	2.0
5	2.5
6	3.0
7	3.5
8	4.0
9	4.5

	4
1	0.4
2	0.8
3	1.2
4	1.6
5	2.0
6	2.4
7	2.8
8	3.2
9	3.6

Proportional parts

955 - 1000

N	Log	0	1	2	3	4	5	6	7	8	9
955	98	000	005	009	014	019	023	028	032	037	041
956		046	050	055	059	064	068	073	078	082	087
957		091	096	100	105	109	114	118	123	127	132
958		137	141	146	150	155	159	164	168	173	177
959		182	186	191	195	200	204	209	214	218	223
960		227	232	236	241	245	250	254	259	263	268
961		272	277	281	286	290	295	299	304	308	313
962		318	322	327	331	336	340	345	349	354	358
963		363	367	372	376	381	385	390	394	399	403
964		408	412	417	421	426	430	435	439	444	448
965		453	457	462	466	471	475	480	484	489	493
966		498	502	507	511	516	520	525	529	534	538
967		543	547	552	556	561	565	570	574	579	583
968		588	592	597	601	605	610	614	619	623	628
969		632	637	641	646	650	655	659	664	668	673
970		677	682	686	691	695	700	704	709	713	717
971		722	726	731	735	740	744	749	753	758	762
972		767	771	776	780	784	789	793	798	802	807
973		811	816	820	825	829	834	838	843	847	851
974		856	860	865	869	874	878	883	887	892	896
975		900	905	909	914	918	923	927	932	936	941
976		945	949	954	958	963	967	972	976	981	985
977		989	994	998	*003	*007	*012	*016	*021	*025	*029
978	99	034	038	043	047	052	056	061	065	069	074
979		078	083	087	092	096	100	105	109	114	118
980		123	127	131	136	140	145	149	154	158	162
981		167	171	176	180	185	189	193	198	202	207
982		211	216	220	224	229	233	238	242	247	251
983		255	260	264	269	273	277	282	286	291	295
984		300	304	308	313	317	322	326	330	335	339
985		344	348	352	357	361	366	370	374	379	383
986		388	392	396	401	405	410	414	419	423	427
987		432	436	441	445	449	454	458	463	467	471
988		476	480	484	489	493	498	502	506	511	515
989		520	524	528	533	537	542	546	550	555	559
990		564	568	572	577	581	585	590	594	599	603
991		607	612	616	621	625	629	634	638	642	647
992		651	656	660	664	669	673	677	682	686	691
993		695	699	704	708	712	717	721	726	730	734
994		739	743	747	752	756	760	765	769	774	778
995		782	787	791	795	800	804	808	813	817	822
996		826	830	835	839	843	848	852	856	861	865
997		870	874	878	883	887	891	896	900	904	909
998		913	917	922	926	930	935	939	944	948	952
999		957	961	965	970	974	978	983	987	991	996
1000	00	000	004	009	013	017	022	026	030	035	039
N	Log	0	1	2	3	4	5	6	7	8	9

Proportional parts

	5
1	0.5
2	1.0
3	1.5
4	2.0
5	2.5
6	3.0
7	3.5
8	4.0
9	4.5

	4
1	0.4
2	0.8
3	1.2
4	1.6
5	2.0
6	2.4
7	2.8
8	3.2
9	3.6

Proportional parts

H

Squares, Square Roots, and Reciprocals

N	N^2	$\sqrt{N}$	$\sqrt{10N}$	$1000/N$
1	1	1.0000	3.1623	1000.0
2	4	1.4142	4.4721	500.00
3	9	1.7321	5.4772	333.33
4	16	2.0000	6.3246	250.00
5	25	2.2361	7.0711	200.00
6	36	2.4495	7.7460	166.67
7	49	2.6458	8.3666	142.86
8	64	2.8284	8.9443	125.00
9	81	3.0000	9.4868	111.11
10	100	3.1623	10.000	100.00
11	121	3.3166	10.488	90.909
12	144	3.4641	10.954	83.333
13	169	3.6056	11.402	76.923
14	196	3.7417	11.832	71.429
15	225	3.8730	12.247	66.667
16	256	4.0000	12.649	62.500
17	289	4.1231	13.038	58.824
18	324	4.2426	13.416	55.556
19	361	4.3589	13.784	52.632
20	400	4.4721	14.142	50.000
21	441	4.5826	14.491	47.619
22	484	4.6904	14.832	45.455
23	529	4.7958	15.166	43.478
24	576	4.8990	15.492	41.667
25	625	5.0000	15.811	40.000
26	676	5.0990	16.125	38.462
27	729	5.1962	16.432	37.037
28	784	5.2915	16.733	35.714
29	841	5.3852	17.029	34.483
30	900	5.4772	17.321	33.333
31	961	5.5678	17.607	32.258
32	1 024	5.6569	17.889	31.250
33	1 089	5.7446	18.166	30.303
34	1 156	5.8310	18.439	29.412
35	1 225	5.9161	18.708	28.571
36	1 296	6.0000	18.974	27.778
37	1 369	6.0828	19.235	27.027
38	1 444	6.1644	19.494	26.316
39	1 521	6.2450	19.748	25.641
40	1 600	6.3246	20.000	25.000
41	1 681	6.4031	20.248	24.390
42	1 764	6.4807	20.494	23.810
43	1 849	6.5574	20.736	23.256
44	1 936	6.6333	20.976	22.727
45	2 025	6.7082	21.213	22.222
46	2 116	6.7823	21.448	21.739
47	2 209	6.8557	21.679	21.277
48	2 304	6.9282	21.909	20.833
49	2 401	7.0000	22.136	20.408
50	2 500	7.0711	22.361	20.000
51	2 601	7.1414	22.583	19.608
52	2 704	7.2111	22.804	19.231
53	2 809	7.2801	23.022	18.868
54	2 916	7.3485	23.238	18.519
55	3 025	7.4162	23.452	18.182
56	3 136	7.4833	23.664	17.857
57	3 249	7.5498	23.875	17.544
58	3 364	7.6158	24.083	17.241
59	3 481	7.6811	24.290	16.949

N	N^2	$\sqrt{N}$	$\sqrt{10N}$	$1000/N$
60	3 600	7.7460	24.495	16.667
61	3 721	7.8103	24.698	16.393
62	3 844	7.8740	24.900	16.129
63	3 969	7.9373	25.100	15.873
64	4 096	8.0000	25.298	15.625
65	4 225	8.0623	25.495	15.385
66	4 356	8.1240	25.690	15.152
67	4 489	8.1854	25.884	14.925
68	4 624	8.2462	26.077	14.706
69	4 761	8.3066	26.268	14.493
70	4 900	8.3666	26.458	14.286
71	5 041	8.4262	26.646	14.085
72	5 184	8.4853	26.833	13.889
73	5 329	8.5440	27.019	13.699
74	5 476	8.6023	27.203	13.514
75	5 625	8.6603	27.386	13.333
76	5 776	8.7178	27.568	13.158
77	5 929	8.7750	27.749	12.987
78	6 084	8.8318	27.928	12.821
79	6 241	8.8882	28.107	12.658
80	6 400	8.9443	28.284	12.500
81	6 561	9.0000	28.461	12.346
82	6 724	9.0554	28.636	12.195
83	6 889	9.1104	28.810	12.048
84	7 056	9.1652	28.983	11.905
85	7 225	9.2195	29.155	11.765
86	7 396	9.2736	29.326	11.628
87	7 569	9.3274	29.496	11.494
88	7 744	9.3808	29.665	11.364
89	7 921	9.4340	29.833	11.236
90	8 100	9.4868	30.000	11.111
91	8 281	9.5394	30.166	10.989
92	8 464	9.5917	30.332	10.870
93	8 649	9.6437	30.496	10.753
94	8 836	9.6954	30.659	10.638
95	9 025	9.7468	30.822	10.526
96	9 216	9.7980	30.984	10.417
97	9 409	9.8489	31.145	10.309
98	9 604	9.8995	31.305	10.204
99	9 801	9.9499	31.464	10.101
100	10 000	10.000	31.623	10.000
101	10 201	10.050	31.781	9.9010
102	10 404	10.100	31.937	9.8039
103	10 609	10.149	32.094	9.7087
104	10 816	10.198	32.249	9.6154
105	11 025	10.247	32.404	9.5238
106	11 236	10.296	32.558	9.4340
107	11 449	10.344	32.711	9.3458
108	11 664	10.392	32.863	9.2593
109	11 881	10.440	33.015	9.1743
110	12 100	10.488	33.166	9.0909
111	12 321	10.536	33.317	9.0090
112	12 544	10.583	33.466	8.9286
113	12 769	10.630	33.615	8.8496
114	12 996	10.677	33.764	8.7719
115	13 225	10.724	33.912	8.6957
116	13 456	10.770	34.059	8.6207
117	13 689	10.817	34.205	8.5470
118	13 924	10.863	34.351	8.4746
119	14 161	10.909	34.496	8.4034
120	14 400	10.954	34.641	8.3333
121	14 641	11.000	34.785	8.2645
122	14 884	11.045	34.929	8.1967
123	15 129	11.091	35.071	8.1301
124	15 376	11.136	35.214	8.0645
125	15 625	11.180	35.355	8.0000
126	15 876	11.225	35.496	7.9365
127	16 129	11.269	35.637	7.8740
128	16 384	11.314	35.777	7.8125
129	16 641	11.358	35.917	7.7519
130	16 900	11.402	36.056	7.6923
131	17 161	11.446	36.194	7.6336
132	17 424	11.489	36.332	7.5758
133	17 689	11.533	36.469	7.5188
134	17 956	11.576	36.606	7.4627
135	18 225	11.619	36.742	7.4074
136	18 496	11.662	36.878	7.3529
137	18 769	11.705	37.014	7.2993
138	19 044	11.747	37.148	7.2464
139	19 321	11.790	37.283	7.1942
140	19 600	11.832	37.417	7.1429
141	19 881	11.874	37.550	7.0922
142	20 164	11.916	37.683	7.0423
143	20 449	11.958	37.815	6.9930
144	20 736	12.000	37.947	6.9444
145	21 025	12.042	38.079	6.8966
146	21 316	12.083	38.210	6.8493
147	21 609	12.124	38.341	6.8027
148	21 904	12.166	38.471	6.7568
149	22 201	12.207	38.601	6.7114
150	22 500	12.247	38.730	6.6667
151	22 801	12.288	38.859	6.6225
152	23 104	12.329	38.987	6.5789
153	23 409	12.369	39.115	6.5359
154	23 716	12.410	39.243	6.4935
155	24 025	12.450	39.370	6.4516
156	24 336	12.490	39.497	6.4103
157	24 649	12.530	39.623	6.3694
158	24 964	12.570	39.749	6.3291
159	25 281	12.610	39.875	6.2893

N	N^2	$\sqrt{N}$	$\sqrt{10N}$	$1000/N$	N	N^2	$\sqrt{N}$	$\sqrt{10N}$	$1000/N$
160	25 600	12.649	40.000	6.2500	210	44 100	14.491	45.826	4.7619
161	25 921	12.689	40.125	6.2112	211	44 521	14.526	45.935	4.7393
162	26 244	12.728	40.249	6.1728	212	44 944	14.560	46.043	4.7170
163	26 569	12.767	40.373	6.1350	213	45 369	14.595	46.152	4.6948
164	26 896	12.806	40.497	6.0976	214	45 796	14.629	46.260	4.6729
165	27 225	12.845	40.620	6.0606	215	46 225	14.663	46.368	4.6512
166	27 556	12.884	40.743	6.0241	216	46 656	14.697	46.476	4.6296
167	27 889	12.923	40.866	5.9880	217	47 089	14.731	46.583	4.6083
168	28 224	12.961	40.988	5.9524	218	47 524	14.765	46.690	4.5872
169	28 561	13.000	41.110	5.9172	219	47 961	14.799	46.797	4.5662
170	28 900	13.038	41.231	5.8824	220	48 400	14.832	46.904	4.5455
171	29 241	13.077	41.352	5.8480	221	48 841	14.866	47.011	4.5249
172	29 584	13.115	41.473	5.8140	222	49 284	14.900	47.117	4.5045
173	29 929	13.153	41.593	5.7803	223	49 729	14.933	47.223	4.4843
174	30 276	13.191	41.713	5.7471	224	50 176	14.967	47.329	4.4643
175	30 625	13.229	41.833	5.7143	225	50 625	15.000	47.434	4.4444
176	30 976	13.267	41.952	5.6818	226	51 076	15.033	47.539	4.4248
177	31 329	13.304	42.071	5.6497	227	51 529	15.067	47.645	4.4053
178	31 684	13.342	42.190	5.6180	228	51 984	15.100	47.749	4.3860
179	32 041	13.379	42.308	5.5866	229	52 441	15.133	47.854	4.3668
180	32 400	13.416	42.426	5.5556	230	52 900	15.166	47.958	4.3478
181	32 761	13.454	42.544	5.5249	231	53 361	15.199	48.062	4.3290
182	33 124	13.491	42.661	5.4945	232	53 824	15.232	48.166	4.3103
183	33 489	13.528	42.779	5.4645	233	54 289	15.264	48.270	4.2918
184	33 856	13.565	42.895	5.4348	234	54 756	15.297	48.374	4.2735
185	34 225	13.601	43.012	5.4054	235	55 225	15.330	48.477	4.2553
186	34 596	13.638	43.128	5.3763	236	55 696	15.362	48.580	4.2373
187	34 969	13.675	43.244	5.3476	237	56 169	15.395	48.683	4.2194
188	35 344	13.711	43.359	5.3191	238	56 644	15.427	48.785	4.2017
189	35 721	13.748	43.474	5.2910	239	57 121	15.460	48.888	4.1841
190	36 100	13.784	43.589	5.2632	240	57 600	15.492	48.990	4.1667
191	36 481	13.820	43.704	5.2356	241	58 081	15.524	49.092	4.1494
192	36 864	13.856	43.818	5.2083	242	58 564	15.556	49.194	4.1322
193	37 249	13.892	43.932	5.1813	243	59 049	15.588	49.295	4.1152
194	37 636	13.928	44.045	5.1546	244	59 536	15.621	49.396	4.0984
195	38 025	13.964	44.159	5.1282	245	60 025	15.652	49.497	4.0816
196	38 416	14.000	44.272	5.1020	246	60 516	15.684	49.598	4.0650
197	38 809	14.036	44.385	5.0761	247	61 009	15.716	49.699	4.0486
198	39 204	14.071	44.497	5.0505	248	61 504	15.748	49.800	4.0323
199	39 601	14.107	44.609	5.0251	249	62 001	15.780	49.900	4.0161
200	40 000	14.142	44.721	5.0000	250	62 500	15.811	50.000	4.0000
201	40 401	14.177	44.833	4.9751	251	63 001	15.843	50.100	3.9841
202	40 804	14.213	44.944	4.9505	252	63 504	15.875	50.200	3.9683
203	41 209	14.248	45.056	4.9261	253	64 009	15.906	50.299	3.9526
204	41 616	14.283	45.166	4.9020	254	64 516	15.937	50.398	3.9370
205	42 025	14.318	45.277	4.8780	255	65 025	15.969	50.498	3.9216
206	42 436	14.353	45.387	4.8544	256	65 536	16.000	50.596	3.9063
207	42 849	14.387	45.497	4.8309	257	66 049	16.031	50.695	3.8911
208	43 264	14.422	45.607	4.8077	258	66 564	16.062	50.794	3.8760
209	43 681	14.457	45.717	4.7847	259	67 081	16.093	50.892	3.8610

N	N^2	$\sqrt{N}$	$\sqrt{10N}$	$1000/N$	N	N^2	$\sqrt{N}$	$\sqrt{10N}$	$1000/N$
260	67 600	16.125	50.990	3.8462	310	96 100	17.607	55.678	3.2258
261	68 121	16.155	51.088	3.8314	311	96 721	17.635	55.767	3.2154
262	68 644	16.186	51.186	3.8168	312	97 344	17.664	55.857	3.2051
263	69 169	16.217	51.284	3.8023	313	97 969	17.692	55.946	3.1949
264	69 696	16.248	51.381	3.7879	314	98 596	17.720	56.036	3.1847
265	70 225	16.279	51.478	3.7736	315	99 225	17.748	56.125	3.1746
266	70 756	16.310	51.575	3.7594	316	99 856	17.776	56.214	3.1646
267	71 289	16.340	51.672	3.7453	317	100 489	17.804	56.303	3.1546
268	71 824	16.371	51.769	3.7313	318	101 124	17.833	56.391	3.1447
269	72 361	16.401	51.865	3.7175	319	101 761	17.861	56.480	3.1348
270	72 900	16.432	51.962	3.7037	320	102 400	17.889	56.569	3.1250
271	73 441	16.462	52.058	3.6900	321	103 041	17.916	56.657	3.1153
272	73 984	16.492	52.154	3.6765	322	103 684	17.944	56.745	3.1056
273	74 529	16.523	52.249	3.6630	323	104 329	17.972	56.833	3.0960
274	75 076	16.553	52.345	3.6496	324	104 976	18.000	56.921	3.0864
275	75 625	16.583	52.440	3.6364	325	105 625	18.028	57.009	3.0769
276	76 176	16.613	52.536	3.6232	326	106 276	18.055	57.096	3.0675
277	76 729	16.643	52.631	3.6101	327	106 929	18.083	57.184	3.0581
278	77 284	16.673	52.726	3.5971	328	107 584	18.111	57.271	3.0488
279	77 841	16.703	52.820	3.5842	329	108 241	18.138	57.359	3.0395
280	78 400	16.733	52.915	3.5714	330	108 900	18.166	57.446	3.0303
281	78 961	16.763	53.009	3.5587	331	109 561	18.193	57.533	3.0211
282	79 524	16.793	53.104	3.5461	332	110 224	18.221	57.619	3.0120
283	80 089	16.823	53.198	3.5336	333	110 889	18.248	57.706	3.0030
284	80 656	16.852	53.292	3.5211	334	111 556	18.276	57.793	2.9940
285	81 225	16.882	53.385	3.5088	335	112 225	18.303	57.879	2.9851
286	81 796	16.912	53.479	3.4965	336	112 896	18.330	57.966	2.9762
287	82 369	16.941	53.572	3.4843	337	113 569	18.358	58.052	2.9674
288	82 944	16.971	53.666	3.4722	338	114 244	18.385	58.138	2.9586
289	83 521	17.000	53.759	3.4602	339	114 921	18.412	58.224	2.9499
290	84 100	17.029	53.852	3.4483	340	115 600	18.439	58.310	2.9412
291	84 681	17.059	53.944	3.4364	341	116 281	18.466	58.395	2.9326
292	85 264	17.088	54.037	3.4247	342	116 964	18.493	58.481	2.9240
293	85 849	17.117	54.129	3.4130	343	117 649	18.520	58.566	2.9155
294	86 436	17.146	54.222	3.4014	344	118 336	18.547	58.652	2.9070
295	87 025	17.176	54.314	3.3898	345	119 025	18.574	58.737	2.8986
296	87 616	17.205	54.406	3.3784	346	119 716	18.601	58.822	2.8902
297	88 209	17.234	54.498	3.3670	347	120 409	18.628	58.907	2.8818
298	88 804	17.263	54.589	3.3557	348	121 104	18.655	58.992	2.8736
299	88 401	17.292	54.681	3.3445	349	121 801	18.682	59.076	2.8653
300	90 000	17.321	54.772	3.3333	350	122 500	18.708	59.161	2.8571
301	90 601	17.349	54.863	3.3223	351	123 201	18.735	59.245	2.8490
302	91 204	17.378	54.955	3.3113	352	123 904	18.762	59.330	2.8409
303	91 809	17.407	55.045	3.3003	353	124 609	18.788	59.414	2.8329
304	92 416	17.436	55.136	3.2895	354	125 316	18.815	59.498	2.8249
305	93 025	17.464	55.227	3.2787	355	126 025	18.841	59.582	2.8169
306	93 636	17.493	55.317	3.2680	356	126 736	18.868	59.666	2.8090
307	94 249	17.521	55.408	3.2573	357	127 449	18.894	59.749	2.8011
308	94 864	17.550	55.498	3.2468	358	128 164	18.921	59.833	2.7933
309	95 481	17.578	55.588	3.2362	359	128 881	18.947	59.917	2.7855

N	N^2	$\sqrt{N}$	$\sqrt{10N}$	$1000/N$	N	N^2	$\sqrt{N}$	$\sqrt{10N}$	$1000/N$
360	129 600	18.974	60.000	2.7778	410	168 100	20.248	64.031	2.4390
361	130 321	19.000	60.083	2.7701	411	168 921	20.273	64.109	2.4331
362	131 044	19.026	60.166	2.7624	412	169 744	20.298	64.187	2.4272
363	131 769	19.053	60.249	2.7548	413	170 569	20.322	64.265	2.4213
364	132 496	19.079	60.332	2.7473	414	171 396	20.347	64.343	2.4155
365	133 225	19.105	60.415	2.7397	415	172 225	20.372	64.420	2.4096
366	133 956	19.131	60.498	2.7322	416	173 056	20.396	64.498	2.4038
367	134 689	19.157	60.581	2.7248	417	173 889	20.421	64.576	2.3981
368	135 424	19.183	60.663	2.7174	418	174 724	20.445	64.653	2.3923
369	136 161	19.209	60.745	2.7100	419	175 561	20.469	64.730	2.3866
370	136 900	19.235	60.828	2.7027	420	176 400	20.494	64.807	2.3810
371	137 641	19.261	60.910	2.6954	421	177 241	20.518	64.885	2.3753
372	138 384	19.287	60.992	2.6882	422	178 084	20.543	64.962	2.3697
373	139 129	19.313	61.074	2.6810	423	178 929	20.567	65.038	2.3641
374	139 876	19.339	61.156	2.6738	424	179 776	20.591	65.115	2.3585
375	140 625	19.365	61.237	2.6667	425	180 625	20.616	65.192	2.3529
376	141 376	19.391	61.319	2.6596	426	181 476	20.640	65.269	2.3474
377	142 129	19.416	61.400	2.6525	427	182 329	20.664	65.345	2.3419
378	142 884	19.442	61.482	2.6455	428	183 184	20.688	65.422	2.3364
379	143 641	19.468	61.563	2.6385	429	184 041	20.712	65.498	2.3310
380	144 400	19.494	61.644	2.6316	430	184 900	20.736	65.574	2.3256
381	145 161	19.519	61.725	2.6247	431	185 761	20.761	65.651	2.3202
382	145 924	19.545	61.806	2.6178	432	186 624	20.785	65.727	2.3148
383	146 689	19.570	61.887	2.6110	433	187 489	20.809	65.803	2.3095
384	147 456	19.596	61.968	2.6042	434	188 356	20.833	65.879	2.3041
385	148 225	19.621	62.048	2.5974	435	189 225	20.857	65.955	2.2989
386	148 996	19.647	62.129	2.5907	436	190 096	20.881	66.030	2.2936
387	149 769	19.672	62.209	2.5840	437	190 969	20.905	66.106	2.2883
388	150 544	19.698	62.290	2.5773	438	191 844	20.928	66.182	2.2831
389	151 321	19.723	62.370	2.5707	439	192 721	20.952	66.257	2.2779
390	152 100	19.748	62.450	2.5641	440	193 600	20.976	66.333	2.2727
391	152 881	19.774	62.530	2.5575	441	194 481	21.000	66.408	2.2676
392	153 664	19.799	62.610	2.5510	442	195 364	21.024	66.483	2.2624
393	154 449	19.824	62.690	2.5445	443	196 249	21.048	66.558	2.2573
394	155 236	19.849	62.769	2.5381	444	197 136	21.071	66.633	2.2523
395	156 025	19.875	62.849	2.5316	445	198 025	21.095	66.708	2.2472
396	156 816	19.900	62.929	2.5253	446	198 916	21.119	66.783	2.2422
397	157 609	19.925	63.008	2.5189	447	199 809	21.142	66.858	2.2371
398	158 404	19.950	63.087	2.5126	448	200 704	21.166	66.933	2.2321
399	159 201	19.975	63.166	2.5063	449	201 601	21.190	67.007	2.2272
400	160 000	20.000	63.246	2.5000	450	202 500	21.213	67.082	2.2222
401	160 801	20.025	63.325	2.4938	451	203 401	21.237	67.157	2.2173
402	161 604	20.050	63.403	2.4876	452	204 304	21.260	67.231	2.2124
403	162 409	20.075	63.482	2.4814	453	205 209	21.284	67.305	2.2075
404	163 216	20.100	63.561	2.4752	454	206 116	21.307	67.380	2.2026
405	164 025	20.125	63.640	2.4691	455	207 025	21.331	67.454	2.1978
406	164 836	20.149	63.718	2.4631	456	207 936	21.354	67.528	2.1930
407	165 649	20.174	63.797	2.4570	457	208 849	21.378	67.602	2.1882
408	166 464	20.199	63.875	2.4510	458	209 764	21.401	67.676	2.1834
409	167 281	20.224	63.953	2.4450	459	210 681	21.424	67.750	2.1786

N	N^2	$\sqrt{N}$	$\sqrt{10N}$	$1000/N$
460	211 600	21.448	67.823	2.1739
461	212 521	21.471	67.897	2.1692
462	213 444	21.494	67.971	2.1645
463	214 369	21.517	68.044	2.1508
464	215 296	21.541	68.118	2.1552
465	216 225	21.564	68.191	2.1505
466	217 156	21.587	68.264	2.1459
467	218 089	21.610	68.337	2.1413
468	219 024	21.633	68.411	2.1368
469	219 961	21.656	68.484	2.1322
470	220 900	21.679	68.557	2.1277
471	221 841	21.703	68.629	2.1231
472	222 784	21.726	68.702	2.1186
473	223 729	21.749	68.775	2.1142
474	224 676	21.772	68.848	2.1097
475	225 625	21.794	68.920	2.1053
476	226 576	21.817	68.993	2.1008
477	227 529	21.840	69.065	2.0964
478	228 484	21.863	69.138	2.0921
479	229 441	21.886	69.210	2.0877
480	230 400	21.909	69.282	2.0833
481	231 361	21.932	69.354	2.0790
482	232 324	21.955	69.426	2.0747
483	233 289	21.977	69.498	2.0704
484	234 256	22.000	69.570	2.0661
485	235 225	22.023	69.642	2.0619
486	236 196	22.045	69.714	2.0576
487	237 169	22.068	69.785	2.0534
488	238 144	22.091	69.857	2.0492
489	239 121	22.113	69.929	2.0450
490	240 100	22.136	70.000	2.0408
491	241 081	22.159	70.071	2.0367
492	242 064	22.181	70.143	2.0325
493	243 049	22.204	70.214	2.0284
494	244 036	22.226	70.285	2.0243
495	245 025	22.249	70.356	2.0202
496	246 016	22.271	70.427	2.0161
497	247 009	22.294	70.498	2.0121
498	248 004	22.316	70.569	2.0080
499	249 001	22.338	70.640	2.0040
500	250 000	22.361	70.711	2.0000
501	251 001	22.383	70.781	1.9960
502	252 004	22.405	70.852	1.9920
503	253 009	22.428	70.922	1.9881
504	254 016	22.450	70.993	1.9841
505	255 025	22.472	71.063	1.9802
506	256 036	22.494	71.134	1.9763
507	257 049	22.517	71.204	1.9724
508	258 064	22.539	71.274	1.9685
509	259 081	22.561	71.344	1.9646

N	N^2	$\sqrt{N}$	$\sqrt{10N}$	$1000/N$
510	260 100	22.583	71.414	1.9608
511	261 121	22.605	71.484	1.9569
512	262 144	22.627	71.554	1.9531
513	263 169	22.650	71.624	1.9493
514	264 196	22.672	71.694	1.9455
515	265 225	22.694	71.764	1.9417
516	266 256	22.716	71.833	1.9380
517	267 289	22.738	71.903	1.9342
518	268 324	22.760	71.972	1.9305
519	269 361	22.782	72.042	1.9268
520	270 400	22.804	72.111	1.9231
521	271 441	22.825	72.180	1.9194
522	272 484	22.847	72.250	1.9157
523	273 529	22.869	72.319	1.9120
524	274 576	22.891	72.388	1.9084
525	275 625	22.913	72.457	1.9048
526	276 676	22.935	72.526	1.9011
527	277 729	22.956	72.595	1.8975
528	278 784	22.978	72.664	1.8939
529	279 841	23.000	72.732	1.8904
530	280 900	23.022	72.801	1.8868
531	281 961	23.043	72.870	1.8832
532	283 024	23.065	72.938	1.8797
533	284 089	23.087	73.007	1.8762
534	285 156	23.108	73.075	1.8727
535	286 225	23.130	73.144	1.8692
536	287 296	23.152	73.212	1.8657
537	288 369	23.173	73.280	1.8622
538	289 444	23.195	73.348	1.8587
539	290 521	23.216	73.417	1.8553
540	291 600	23.238	73.485	1.8519
541	292 681	23.259	73.553	1.8484
542	293 764	23.281	73.621	1.8450
543	294 849	23.302	73.689	1.8416
544	295 936	23.324	73.756	1.8382
545	297 025	23.345	73.824	1.8349
546	298 116	23.367	73.892	1.8315
547	299 209	23.388	73.959	1.8282
548	300 304	23.409	74.027	1.8248
549	301 401	23.431	74.095	1.8215
550	302 500	23.452	74.162	1.8182
551	303 601	23.473	74.229	1.8149
552	304 704	23.495	74.297	1.8116
553	305 809	23.516	74.364	1.8083
554	306 916	23.537	74.431	1.8051
555	308 025	23.558	74.498	1.8018
556	309 136	23.580	74.565	1.7986
557	310 249	23.601	74.632	1.7953
558	311 364	23.622	74.699	1.7921
559	312 481	23.643	74.766	1.7889

N	N^2	$\sqrt{N}$	$\sqrt{10N}$	$1000/N$
560	313 600	23.664	74.833	1.7857
561	314 721	23.685	74.900	1.7825
562	315 844	23.707	74.967	1.7794
563	316 969	23.728	75.033	1.7762
564	318 096	23.749	75.100	1.7731
565	319 225	23.770	75.166	1.7699
566	320 356	23.791	75.233	1.7668
567	321 489	23.812	75.299	1.7637
568	322 624	23.833	75.366	1.7606
569	323 761	23.854	75.432	1.7575
570	324 900	23.875	75.498	1.7544
571	326 041	23.896	75.565	1.7513
572	327 184	23.917	75.631	1.7483
573	328 329	23.937	75.697	1.7452
574	329 476	23.958	75.763	1.7422
575	330 625	23.979	75.829	1.7391
576	331 776	24.000	75.895	1.7361
577	332 929	24.021	75.961	1.7331
578	334 084	24.042	76.026	1.7301
579	335 241	24.062	76.092	1.7271
580	336 400	24.083	76.158	1.7241
581	337 561	24.104	76.223	1.7212
582	338 724	24.125	76.289	1.7182
583	339 889	24.145	76.354	1.7153
584	341 056	24.166	76.420	1.7123
585	342 225	24.187	76.485	1.7094
586	343 396	24.207	76.551	1.7065
587	344 569	24.228	76.616	1.7036
588	345 744	24.249	76.681	1.7007
589	346 921	24.269	76.746	1.6978
590	348 100	24.290	76.811	1.6949
591	349 281	24.310	76.877	1.6920
592	350 464	24.331	76.942	1.6892
593	351 649	24.352	77.006	1.6863
594	352 836	24.372	77.071	1.6835
595	354 025	24.393	77.136	1.6807
596	355 216	24.413	77.201	1.6779
597	356 409	24.434	77.266	1.6750
598	357 604	24.454	77.330	1.6722
599	358 801	24.474	77.395	1.6694
600	360 000	24.495	77.460	1.6667
601	361 201	24.515	77.524	1.6639
602	362 404	24.536	77.589	1.6611
603	363 609	24.556	77.653	1.6584
604	364 816	24.576	77.717	1.6556
605	366 025	24.597	77.782	1.6529
606	367 236	24.617	77.846	1.6502
607	368 449	24.637	77.910	1.6474
608	369 664	24.658	77.974	1.6447
609	370 881	24.678	78.038	1.6420
610	372 100	24.698	78.103	1.6393
611	373 321	24.718	78.166	1.6367
612	374 544	24.739	78.230	1.6340
613	375 769	24.759	78.294	1.6313
614	376 996	24.779	78.358	1.6287
615	378 225	24.799	78.422	1.6260
616	379 456	24.819	78.486	1.6234
617	380 689	24.839	78.549	1.6207
618	381 924	24.860	78.613	1.6181
619	383 161	24.880	78.677	1.6155
620	384 400	24.900	78.740	1.6129
621	385 641	24.920	78.804	1.6103
622	386 884	24.940	78.867	1.6077
623	388 129	24.960	78.930	1.6051
624	389 376	24.980	78.994	1.6026
625	390 625	25.000	79.057	1.6000
626	391 876	25.020	79.120	1.5974
627	393 129	25.040	79.183	1.5949
628	394 384	25.060	79.246	1.5924
629	395 641	25.080	79.310	1.5898
630	396 900	25.100	79.373	1.5873
631	398 161	25.120	79.436	1.5848
632	399 424	25.140	79.498	1.5823
633	400 689	25.159	79.561	1.5798
634	401 956	25.179	79.624	1.5773
635	403 225	25.199	79.687	1.5748
636	404 496	25.219	79.750	1.5723
637	405 769	25.239	79.812	1.5699
638	407 044	25.259	79.875	1.5674
639	408 321	25.278	79.937	1.5649
640	409 600	25.298	80.000	1.5625
641	410 881	25.318	80.062	1.5601
642	412 164	25.338	80.125	1.5576
643	413 449	25.357	80.187	1.5552
644	414 736	25.377	80.250	1.5528
645	416 025	25.397	80.312	1.5504
646	417 316	25.417	80.374	1.5480
647	418 609	25.436	80.436	1.5456
648	419 904	25.456	80.498	1.5432
649	421 201	25.475	80.561	1.5408
650	422 500	25.495	80.623	1.5385
651	423 801	25.515	80.685	1.5361
652	425 104	25.534	80.747	1.5337
653	426 409	25.554	80.808	1.5314
654	427 716	25.573	80.870	1.5291
655	429 025	25.593	80.932	1.5267
656	430 336	25.613	80.994	1.5244
657	431 649	25.632	81.056	1.5221
658	432 964	25.652	81.117	1.5198
659	434 281	25.671	81.179	1.5175

N	N^2	$\sqrt{N}$	$\sqrt{10N}$	$1000/N$
660	435 600	25.690	81.240	1.5152
661	436 921	25.710	81.302	1.5129
662	438 244	25.729	81.363	1.5106
663	439 569	25.749	81.425	1.5083
664	440 896	25.768	81.486	1.5060
665	442 225	25.788	81.548	1.5038
666	443 556	25.807	81.609	1.5015
667	444 889	25.826	81.670	1.4993
668	446 224	25.846	81.731	1.4970
669	447 561	25.865	81.792	1.4948
670	448 900	25.884	81.854	1.4925
671	450 241	25.904	81.915	1.4903
672	451 584	25.923	81.976	1.4881
673	452 929	25.942	82.037	1.4859
674	454 276	25.962	82.098	1.4837
675	455 625	25.981	82.158	1.4815
676	456 976	26.000	82.219	1.4793
677	458 329	26.019	82.280	1.4771
678	459 684	26.038	82.341	1.4749
679	461 041	26.058	82.401	1.4728
680	462 400	26.077	82.462	1.4706
681	463 761	26.096	82.523	1.4684
682	465 124	26.115	82.583	1.4663
683	466 489	26.134	82.644	1.4641
684	467 856	26.153	82.704	1.4620
685	469 225	26.173	82.765	1.4599
686	470 596	26.192	82.825	1.4577
687	471 969	26.211	82.885	1.4556
688	473 344	26.230	82.946	1.4535
689	474 721	26.249	83.006	1.4514
690	476 100	26.268	83.066	1.4493
691	477 481	26.287	83.126	1.4472
692	478 864	26.306	83.187	1.4451
693	480 249	26.325	83.247	1.4430
694	481 636	26.344	83.307	1.4409
695	483 025	26.363	83.367	1.4388
696	484 416	26.382	83.427	1.4368
697	485 809	26.401	83.487	1.4347
698	487 204	26.420	83.546	1.4327
699	488 601	26.439	83.606	1.4306
700	490 000	26.458	83.666	1.4286
701	491 401	26.476	83.726	1.4265
702	492 804	26.495	83.785	1.4245
703	494 209	26.514	83.845	1.4225
704	495 616	26.533	83.905	1.4205
705	497 025	26.552	83.964	1.4184
706	498 436	26.571	84.024	1.4164
707	499 849	26.589	84.083	1.4144
708	501 264	26.608	84.143	1.4124
709	502 681	26.627	84.202	1.4104
710	504 100	26.646	84.262	1.4085
711	505 521	26.665	84.321	1.4065
712	506 944	26.683	84.380	1.4045
713	508 369	26.702	84.439	1.4025
714	509 796	26.721	84.499	1.4006
715	511 225	26.739	84.558	1.3986
716	512 656	26.758	84.617	1.3966
717	514 089	26.777	84.676	1.3947
718	515 524	26.796	84.735	1.3928
719	516 961	26.814	84.794	1.3908
720	518 400	26.833	84.853	1.3889
721	519 841	26.851	84.912	1.3870
722	521 284	26.870	84.971	1.3850
723	522 729	26.889	85.029	1.3831
724	524 176	26.907	85.088	1.3812
725	525 625	26.926	85.147	1.3793
726	527 076	26.944	85.206	1.3774
727	528 529	26.963	85.264	1.3755
728	529 984	26.981	85.323	1.3736
729	531 441	27.000	85.382	1.3717
730	532 900	27.019	85.440	1.3699
731	534 361	27.037	85.499	1.3680
732	535 824	27.056	85.557	1.3661
733	537 289	27.074	85.615	1.3643
734	538 756	27.092	85.674	1.3624
735	540 225	27.111	85.732	1.3605
736	541 696	27.129	85.790	1.3587
737	543 169	27.148	85.849	1.3569
738	544 644	27.166	85.907	1.3550
739	546 121	27.185	85.965	1.3532
740	547 600	27.203	86.023	1.3514
741	549 081	27.221	86.081	1.3495
742	550 564	27.240	86.139	1.3477
743	552 049	27.258	86.197	1.3459
744	553 536	27.276	86.255	1.3441
745	555 025	27.295	86.313	1.3423
746	556 516	27.313	86.371	1.3405
747	558 009	27.331	86.429	1.3387
748	559 504	27.350	86.487	1.3359
749	561 001	27.368	86.545	1.3351
750	562 500	27.386	86.603	1.3333
751	564 001	27.404	86.660	1.3316
752	565 504	27.423	86.718	1.3298
753	567 009	27.441	86.776	1.3280
754	568 516	27.459	86.833	1.3263
755	570 025	27.477	86.891	1.3245
756	571 536	27.495	86.948	1.3228
757	573 049	27.514	87.006	1.3210
758	574 564	27.532	87.063	1.3193
759	576 081	27.550	87.121	1.3175

N	N^2	$\sqrt{N}$	$\sqrt{10N}$	$1000/N$	N	N^2	$\sqrt{N}$	$\sqrt{10N}$	$1000/N$
760	577 600	27.568	87.178	1.3158	810	656 100	28.461	90.000	1.2346
761	579 121	27.586	87.235	1.3141	811	657 721	28.478	90.056	1.2330
762	580 644	27.604	87.293	1.3123	812	659 344	28.496	90.111	1.2315
763	582 169	27.622	87.350	1.3106	813	660 969	28.513	90.167	1.2300
764	583 696	27.641	87.407	1.3089	814	662 596	28.531	90.222	1.2285
765	585 225	27.659	87.464	1.3072	815	664 225	28.548	90.277	1.2270
766	586 756	27.677	87.521	1.3055	816	665 856	28.566	90.333	1.2255
767	588 289	27.695	87.579	1.3038	817	667 489	28.583	90.388	1.2240
768	589 824	27.713	87.636	1.3021	818	669 124	28.601	90.443	1.2225
769	591 361	27.731	87.693	1.3004	819	670 761	28.618	90.499	1.2210
770	592 900	27.749	87.750	1.2987	820	672 400	28.636	90.554	1.2195
771	594 441	27.767	87.807	1.2970	821	674 041	28.653	90.609	1.2180
772	595 984	27.785	87.864	1.2953	822	675 684	28.671	90.664	1.2165
773	597 529	27.803	87.920	1.2937	823	677 329	28.688	90.719	1.2151
774	599 076	27.821	87.977	1.2920	824	678 976	28.705	90.774	1.2136
775	600 625	27.839	88.034	1.2903	825	680 625	28.723	90.830	1.2121
776	602 176	27.857	88.091	1.2887	826	682 276	28.740	90.885	1.2107
777	603 729	27.875	88.148	1.2870	827	683 929	28.758	90.940	1.2092
778	605 284	27.893	88.204	1.2853	828	685 584	28.775	90.995	1.2077
779	606 841	27.911	88.261	1.2837	829	687 241	28.792	91.049	1.2063
780	608 400	27.928	88.318	1.2821	830	688 900	28.810	91.104	1.2048
781	609 961	27.946	88.374	1.2804	831	690 561	28.827	91.159	1.2034
782	611 524	27.964	88.431	1.2788	832	692 224	28.844	91.214	1.2019
783	613 089	27.982	88.487	1.2771	833	693 889	28.862	91.269	1.2005
784	614 656	28.000	88.544	1.2755	834	695 556	28.879	91.324	1.1990
785	616 225	28.018	88.600	1.2739	835	697 225	28.896	91.378	1.1976
786	617 796	28.036	88.657	1.2723	836	698 896	28.914	91.433	1.1962
787	619 369	28.054	88.713	1.2706	837	700 569	28.931	91.488	1.1947
788	620 944	28.071	88.769	1.2690	838	702 244	28.948	91.542	1.1933
789	622 521	28.089	88.826	1.2674	839	703 921	28.966	91.597	1.1919
790	624 100	28.107	88.882	1.2658	840	705 600	28.983	91.652	1.1905
791	625 681	28.125	88.938	1.2642	841	707 281	29.000	91.706	1.1891
792	627 264	28.142	88.994	1.2626	842	708 964	29.017	91.761	1.1876
793	628 849	28.160	89.051	1.2610	843	710 649	29.034	91.815	1.1862
794	630 436	28.178	89.107	1.2594	844	712 336	29.052	91.869	1.1848
795	632 025	28.196	89.163	1.2579	845	714 025	29.069	91.924	1.1834
796	633 616	28.213	89.219	1.2563	846	715 716	29.086	91.978	1.1820
797	635 209	28.231	89.275	1.2547	847	717 409	29.103	92.033	1.1806
798	636 804	28.249	89.331	1.2531	848	719 104	29.120	92.087	1.1792
799	638 401	28.267	89.387	1.2516	849	720 801	29.138	92.141	1.1779
800	640 000	28.284	89.443	1.2500	850	722 500	29.155	92.195	1.1765
801	641 601	28.302	89.499	1.2484	851	724 201	29.172	92.250	1.1751
802	643 204	28.320	89.554	1.2469	852	725 904	29.189	92.304	1.1737
803	644 809	28.337	89.610	1.2453	853	727 609	29.206	92.358	1.1723
804	646 416	28.355	89.666	1.2438	854	729 316	29.223	92.412	1.1710
805	648 025	28.373	89.722	1.2422	855	731 025	29.240	92.466	1.1696
806	649 636	28.390	89.778	1.2407	856	732 736	29.257	92.520	1.1682
807	651 249	28.408	89.833	1.2392	857	734 449	29.275	92.574	1.1669
808	652 864	28.425	89.889	1.2376	858	736 164	29.292	92.628	1.1655
809	654 481	28.443	89.944	1.2361	859	737 881	29.309	92.682	1.1641

N	N^2	$\sqrt{N}$	$\sqrt{10N}$	$1000/N$
860	739 600	29.326	92.736	1.1628
861	741 321	29.343	92.790	1.1614
862	743 044	29.360	92.844	1.1601
863	744 769	29.377	92.898	1.1587
864	746 496	29.394	92.952	1.1574
865	748 225	29.411	93.005	1.1561
866	749 956	29.428	93.059	1.1547
867	751 689	29.445	93.113	1.1534
868	753 424	29.462	93.167	1.1521
869	755 161	29.479	93.220	1.1507
870	756 900	29.496	93.274	1.1494
871	758 641	29.513	93.327	1.1481
872	760 384	29.530	93.381	1.1468
873	762 129	29.547	93.434	1.1455
874	763 876	29.563	93.488	1.1442
875	765 625	29.580	93.541	1.1429
876	767 376	29.597	93.595	1.1416
877	769 129	29.614	93.648	1.1403
878	770 884	29.631	93.702	1.1390
879	772 641	29.648	93.755	1.1377
880	774 400	29.665	93.808	1.1364
881	776 161	29.682	93.862	1.1351
882	777 924	29.698	93.915	1.1338
883	779 689	29.715	93.968	1.1325
884	781 456	29.732	94.021	1.1312
885	783 225	29.749	94.074	1.1299
886	784 996	29.766	94.128	1.1287
887	786 769	29.783	94.181	1.1274
888	788 544	29.799	94.234	1.1261
889	790 321	29.816	94.287	1.1249
890	792 100	29.833	94.340	1.1236
891	793 881	29.850	94.393	1.1223
892	795 664	29.866	94.446	1.1211
893	797 449	29.883	94.499	1.1198
894	799 236	29.900	94.552	1.1186
895	801 025	29.917	94.604	1.1173
896	802 816	29.933	94.657	1.1161
897	804 609	29.950	94.710	1.1148
898	806 404	29.967	94.763	1.1136
899	808 201	29.983	94.816	1.1123
900	810 000	30.000	94.868	1.1111
901	811 801	30.017	94.921	1.1099
902	813 604	30.033	94.974	1.1086
903	815 409	30.050	94.026	1.1074
904	817 216	30.067	95.079	1.1062
905	819 025	30.083	95.131	1.1050
906	820 836	30.100	95.184	1.1038
907	822 649	30.116	95.237	1.1025
908	824 464	30.133	95.289	1.1013
909	826 281	30.150	95.341	1.1001
910	828 100	30.166	95.394	1.0989
911	829 921	30.183	95.446	1.0977
912	831 744	30.199	95.499	1.0965
913	833 569	30.216	95.551	1.0953
914	835 396	30.232	95.603	1.0941
915	837 225	30.249	95.656	1.0929
916	839 056	30.265	95.708	1.0917
917	840 889	30.282	95.760	1.0905
918	842 724	30.299	95.812	1.0893
919	844 561	30.315	95.864	1.0881
920	846 400	30.332	95.917	1.0870
921	848 241	30.348	95.969	1.0858
922	850 084	30.364	96.021	1.0846
923	851 929	30.381	96.073	1.0834
924	853 776	30.397	96.125	1.0823
925	855 625	30.414	96.177	1.0811
926	857 476	30.430	96.229	1.0799
927	859 329	30.447	96.281	1.0787
928	861 184	30.463	96.333	1.0776
929	863 041	30.480	96.385	1.0764
930	864 900	30.496	96.437	1.0753
931	866 761	30.512	96.488	1.0741
932	868 624	30.529	96.540	1.0730
933	870 489	30.545	96.592	1.0718
934	872 356	30.561	96.644	1.0707
935	874 225	30.578	96.695	1.0695
936	876 096	30.594	96.747	1.0684
937	877 969	30.610	96.799	1.0672
938	879 844	30.627	96.850	1.0661
939	881 721	30.643	96.902	1.0650
940	883 600	30.659	96.954	1.0638
941	885 481	30.676	96.005	1.0627
942	887 364	30.692	97.057	1.0616
943	889 249	30.708	97.108	1.0604
944	891 136	30.725	97.160	1.0593
945	893 025	30.741	97.211	1.0582
946	894 916	30.757	97.263	1.0571
947	896 809	30.773	97.314	1.0560
948	898 704	30.790	97.365	1.0549
949	900 601	30.806	97.417	1.0537
950	902 500	30.822	97.468	1.0526
951	904 401	30.838	97.519	1.0515
952	906 304	30.855	97.570	1.0504
953	908 209	30.871	97.622	1.0493
954	910 116	30.887	97.673	1.0482
955	912 025	30.903	97.724	1.0471
956	913 936	30.919	97.775	1.0460
957	915 849	30.935	97.826	1.0449
958	917 764	30.952	97.877	1.0438
959	919 681	30.968	97.929	1.0428

N	N^2	$\sqrt{N}$	$\sqrt{10N}$	$1000/N$	N	N^2	$\sqrt{N}$	$\sqrt{10N}$	$1000/N$
960	921 600	30.984	97.980	1.0417	980	960 400	31.305	98.995	1.0204
961	923 521	31.000	98.031	1.0406	981	962 361	31.321	99.045	1.0194
962	925 444	31.016	98.082	1.0395	982	964 324	31.337	99.096	1.0183
963	927 369	31.032	98.133	1.0384	983	966 289	31.353	99.146	1.0173
964	929 296	31.048	98.184	1.0373	984	968 256	31.369	99.197	1.0163
965	931 225	31.064	98.234	1.0363	985	970 225	31.385	99.247	1.0152
966	933 156	31.081	98.285	1.0352	986	972 196	31.401	99.298	1.0142
967	935 089	31.097	98.336	1.0341	987	974 169	31.417	99.348	1.0132
968	937 024	31.113	98.387	1.0331	988	976 144	31.432	99.398	1.0121
969	938 961	31.129	98.438	1.0320	989	978 121	31.448	99.448	1.0111
970	940 900	31.145	98.489	1.0309	990	980 100	31.464	99.499	1.0101
971	942 841	31.161	98.539	1.0299	991	982 081	31.480	99.549	1.0091
972	944 784	31.177	98.590	1.0288	992	984 064	31.496	99.599	1.0081
973	946 729	31.193	98.641	1.0277	993	986 049	31.512	99.649	1.0070
974	948 676	31.209	98.691	1.0267	994	988 036	31.528	99.700	1.0060
975	950 625	31.225	98.742	1.0256	995	990 025	31.544	99.750	1.0050
976	952 576	31.241	98.793	1.0246	996	992 016	31.559	99.800	1.0040
977	954 529	31.257	98.843	1.0235	997	994 009	31.575	99.850	1.0030
978	956 484	31.273	98.894	1.0225	998	996 004	31.591	99.900	1.0020
979	958 441	31.289	98.944	1.0215	999	998 001	31.607	99.950	1.0010

I

Greek Alphabet

Alpha	Α	α	Iota	Ι	ι	Rho	Ρ	ρ
Beta	Β	β	Kappa	Κ	κ	Sigma	Σ	σ
Gamma	Γ	γ	Lambda	Λ	λ	Tau	Τ	τ
Delta	Δ	δ	Mu	Μ	μ	Upsilon	Υ	υ
Epsilon	Ε	ϵ	Nu	Ν	ν	Phi	Φ	ϕ
Zeta	Ζ	ζ	Xi	Ξ	ξ	Chi	Χ	χ
Eta	Η	η	Omicron	Ο	o	Psi	Ψ	ψ
Theta	Θ	θ	Pi	Π	π	Omega	Ω	ω

Index

MANPOWER DEVELOPMENT

MANPOWER DEVELOPMENT

THE SYSTEM TRAINING CONCEPT

ELIAS H. PORTER

System Development Corporation, Santa Monica, California

HARPER & ROW, PUBLISHERS, *New York, Evanston, and London*

FIRST EDITION

LIBRARY OF CONGRESS CATALOG CARD NUMBER: *64–12709*

CONTENTS

PREFACE

To relate in detail the historical, step-by-step development of the system training concept and its eventual application to the learning needs of large-scale military systems would indeed be an undertaking for an historian. I am not an historian and I shall not attempt an historian's task.

My training and experience have been in the broad field of psychology. My contact with the manpower development capacities of the system training concept over the past eight years has been tremendously exciting to me and equally rewarding. My horizons have broadened markedly. It is the evolution of the system training concept, with its related "system thinking," that intrigues me; and it is this about which I write. The reader may expect to meet here with some simplifying of history. This is done in the interest of highlighting the points I wish to make. My aim is to make ideas clear, rather than to chronicle events in a precise way.

If the reader can see applications of the concepts presented in the following chapters, the mission of this volume will have been fulfilled.

The sources of help in the preparation of this book are many too numerous to mention. My thanks are due to the one-time staff of RAND's Systems Research Laboratory and to all my friends and co-workers at System Development Corporation.

ELIAS H. PORTER

System Development Corporation
Santa Monica, California
January 1964

INTRODUCTION:

The Climate for Breakthrough

In times past, change has often been unwanted: Today, it is as often actively sought. This book is about a manpower development technology, system training, and its use by managers who seek to make their organizations more effective.

The tremendous technological advances during World War II brought with them their share of changes. One of these changes was a change in a way of thinking, a change in the criteria for judging the difference between a good answer and a poor answer. At first, the demand for this new way of thinking was limited. As time has gone on, the demand for this new way of thinking has become imperative in the design and development of our enormously complex military systems.

Let us consider for a moment one avenue of technological change that demanded a first step in the evolution of this new way of thinking: system thinking.

At the outset of World War II, an aeronautical engineer could design a total airplane. He could take a given engine, design the nacelle, pick a suitable wing and empennage structure, and build an airplane. As motors became more powerful and the aircraft became larger and heavier, the engineer ran into trouble. The pilot could no longer handle the stick because the weight of the air against the ailerons was just too great. The only way to handle it was to draw some of the power from the engines to run motors that were strong enough to manipulate the ailerons. But this idea did not work out so well. Pilots missed the "feel" of pressure on the joy stick and would "overcontrol" the aircraft. The solution was to develop another motor to inject a resistance that put the feeling of pressure back into the stick. The time had come when the design of an aircraft was no longer a "thing unto itself," a strictly mechanical process. Design now had to take into account the interaction between the man and the machine.

Engineers were asked to develop aircraft capable of flying different kinds of missions: long flights, short flights; high altitude, low altitude; daytime, nighttime; clear weather, all weather; subsonic, supersonic, and so on. As diversity of aircraft increased, so did the problem of having the right parts and the right service equipment at the right place at the right time. The increasing interdependence of men, machines, missions, and maintenance forced the engineer to bear all these variables in mind. He was no longer designing an aircraft; he was now designing a total weapon system.

The tremendous growth of special-purpose electronic components created another avenue leading to a system frame of reference in thought. To put it most simply, electronic components interact with each other and alter the behavior of individual components. The problem of just how to put the components together became central. The time had passed when one could think of one component as independent of another. Knowledge of how one part would work by itself was no longer any guarantee of how the part would work when it was placed in a system with other parts.

As World War II drew to a close, two things were clear to the Air Force. On the one hand, it was clear that the Air Force faced a future in which very complex weapon systems would become common. On the other hand, it was also clear that the engineers and scientists who had contributed so much to wartime advances were turning to peaceful pursuits.

Here was a problem to be solved. The Air Force wanted advice on the directions it might most profitably take in the development of systems to handle future military necessities. Should rockets be developed? What about satellites? How far should the development of supersonic aircraft be taken? How vulnerable are air bases to missile attack?

To minimize, the chance of undue influence by doctrinaire groups within the military organization, the decision was made to contract for the planning services with a nonmilitary organization. In 1946 the Air Force contracted with Douglas Aircraft Company to provide this long-range thinking under some very special arrangements. Douglas was to hire some top scientific talent to cope with the assignment. The Air Force took the position that it would in no way dictate to the group the problems on which they should work. The areas studied would be determined by the group itself. Should the group want to inquire as to problems faced by the Air Force, the problems would be described, but this was not to be construed as an assignment. This "thinking ahead" effort was called Project RAND (Project Research ANd Development).

Within a relatively short time, Project RAND had established its usefulness and value to the Air Force. At the same time, a decision was reached to detach the effort from a profit-making company. In 1948 Project RAND separated from Douglas, and with the aid of the Ford Foundation, the RAND Corporation was established as a private, nonprofit organization to perform work solely in the interests of national defense and the public welfare.

One of the problems that RAND undertook in those early days was an effort to determine what type of bomber the Air Force would need in 1960. This was a very complex problem, since one could not think about the bomber without thinking of the logistic problems involved, the location of landing fields throughout the world, the problems of escape from the force of nuclear detonations, the problems of cost, and other similar aspects of defense. One crucial problem that arose was concerned with the matter of time. Because any reasonably intelligent enemy would strike first at our power to retaliate, it became essential to determine just how much warning time there would be in which the bombers might take off.

When electronic engineers went out to the radar stations along our coast lines to learn how much warning time could be provided, they discovered a discrepancy between the theoretical capacity of the radar to detect an incoming aircraft and the actual detection capacity of the equipment when operated by human beings. Moreover, there was the question of just how many incoming, hostile aircraft a given station could detect and track and how many interceptors it could control effectively. Special missions were flown by aircraft to aid in getting empirical information about detection capacity. Flights were made both outbound and inbound. The outbound flights were seen at greater distances than were the inbound flights. Which figures should be taken, the outbound or the inbound? Or should the engineers take an average? It occurred to them that perceptual thresholds have been studied by psychologists for many years and that possibly they could get some help from a psychologist. A canvass of RAND employees showed no psychologist to be among its members.

Not long afterward a group of psychologists was invited to RAND to hear about the corporation's activities and to consider whether psychologists could make a contribution to RAND's work. The group reported that there appeared to be a number of problems for which psychologists could contribute solutions. Subsequently, RAND hired three psychologists.

This was the climate into which these psychologists came. Everywhere there was "system talk": inputs, outputs, cross-puts; signal, noise; overload, feedback; open, closed series, and parallel systems. Here was the freedom to think, to investigate the press of real life and real-time problems, and to do this thinking within a new frame of reference. As the thinking progressed, a new concept developed—that it was possible to view an organization such as an air-defense, man-machine system as a single organism and that it was possible to study the behavior of such an organism. It was the climate for a breakthrough.

MANPOWER DEVELOPMENT

CHAPTER 1

SYSTEMS, COMPONENTS, AND ORGANIZATIONAL BEHAVIOR

It is the express purpose of this book to state the concepts of system training and to make them sufficiently clear for the reader to develop his own applications of the system training concept. Experience has indicated that efforts to communicate successfully to others the principles of system training is all too often a difficult task because of the interaction of two facts. One of these facts is that system training was developed in the air defense environment and is usually explained or described in the context of air defense terminology. The second fact is that "system thinking" is a relatively recent development and there are not available many, simple, easily comprehended, concrete models around which people can organize their thinking about systems. In the absence of such a model (a mental hat-rack on which to hang ideas), and in the presence of the unfamiliar terminology of air defense operations, people often come away from an explanation of system training with a fascination for the processes of air defense, but with only the vaguest ideas about system training.

It has been the experience of the writer that the concepts associated with system training are often better illustrated by referring to systems with which almost everyone is familiar. Much of what follows will be of this order.

Let us start off by clarifying what we mean by a "system." *Webster's New Collegiate Dictionary* gives us the first definition of system: "An assemblage of objects united by some form of regular interaction or interdependence; an organic or organized whole; as, the solar *system;* a new telegraph *system.*" A fifth meaning of system is: "regular method or order; as, to have *system* in one's business." It is clearly the first definition rather than the fifth that we intend to connote when we use the term "system." That is, we intend to convey the notion of an assemblage of objects acting in concert rather than the notion of a method or regularized work procedure.

The kinds of systems that industrial and military managers are concerned with on a daily basis are contrived systems. In other words, men create systems or organizations to achieve certain goals. We may not know the purposes or goals of a solar system, but it is easy to see the purposes or goals of a telegraph system. The telegraph system "wants" to transform written messages with sufficient accuracy, sufficient speed, and sufficient reliability so that people will pay more money to use the system than it costs to operate it. Men, machines, and management work together to accomplish a valued service. When thinking of man-contrived systems, then, the term *system* is better defined as a contrived organization of men and machines united under principles of management to accomplish certain valued goals.

The notion of an assemblage of objects doing something together is an immediately meaningful concept to us. Similarly meaningful and less abstract is the notion of "a contrived organization of men and machines united under principles of management to accomplish certain valued goals." In fact, we are all accustomed to thinking in terms of organized assemblages of men, machines, and management. What so often escapes us, however, is the dynamic interaction between the parts of the system as they seek to carry out the purposes of the system; yet it is the control of these dynamic interactions that constitutes a major managerial activity.

Let us consider an illustration of dynamic interaction between men, machines, and management, an illustration that will serve as a model for "system thinking" in this book.

One of the major management problems in the short-order restaurant industry* is the management of the human relations problems. Personnel turnover has been notoriously high. The temperamental disposition of cooks is legendary. Customers can get mighty touchy on occasions.

William Foote Whyte,† social anthropologist, was once called upon to consult with the restaurant industry about their human relations problems. After a period of study, he reported on one fact that was so obvious that no one had ever seen it before. The fact he observed was that the human relations problems occur principally during the rush hours. It is then that waitresses are most apt to break out into tears. It is then that cooks are most apt to walk off the job. It is then that managers are most apt to dismiss employees summarily. It is then that customers are most apt to lose their tempers.

Dr. Whyte conceptualized the stress pattern much as follows: There is stress between the customer and waitress, between waitress and cook, between management and waitress, between management and cook, and one-way stress between customer and management.

* We chose to draw on a restaurant illustration for the simple reason that everyone is familiar with all the components, the work procedures, and the system purpose. There are no giant computers, luminescent displays, or strange work procedures to distract one from seeing the system dynamics. One can see either forest or trees at will.

† Dr. Whyte reports on his work in the restaurant industry in *Human Relations in the Restaurant Industry,* McGraw-Hill Book Co., Inc., 1948. I have had the pleasure of going over my interpretation of the significance of the spindle with Dr. Whyte personally. For the purposes of the exposition I intend, he does not object to my dramatization and simplification of his work.

The problem he faced was that of finding some way to reduce the tensions, to reduce the stress between the components of the system.

In addition to his observation that the human relations

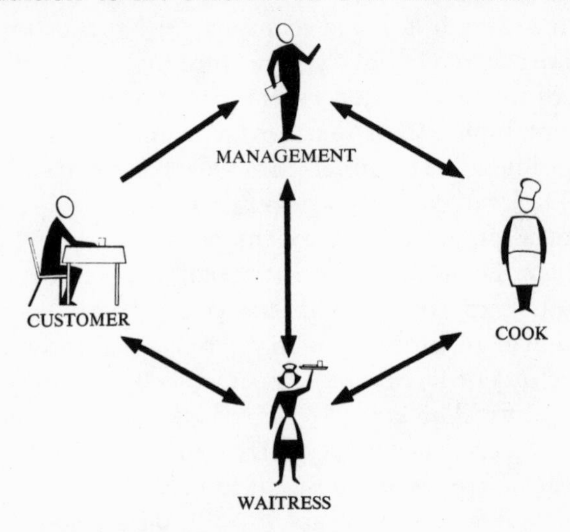

FIGURE 1. *Diagramatic sketch of rush hour stress pattern between customer, waitress, cook, and manager.*

problems occur mostly during the rush hours, Dr. Whyte observed that the in-house status hierarchy gave management highest status, the cook next highest status, and the waitress (always a "local hire") least status. Dr. Whyte conjectured that part of the tension between waitress and cook might be due to the fact that a lower-status person, the waitress, was giving orders to a higher-status person, the cook. It occurred to him that if somehow or another the face-to-face contact between waitress and cook could be broken, tension might be eased.

During the course of his observations, he had noticed one waitress who, rather than call out her order, would write out her order on a slip and hang it on a nail at the edge of the service counter. This was the clue to the development of the "spindle," the round, metal wheel on which the waitress may fasten her orders and from which the cook may take the orders with no need for face-to-face contact.

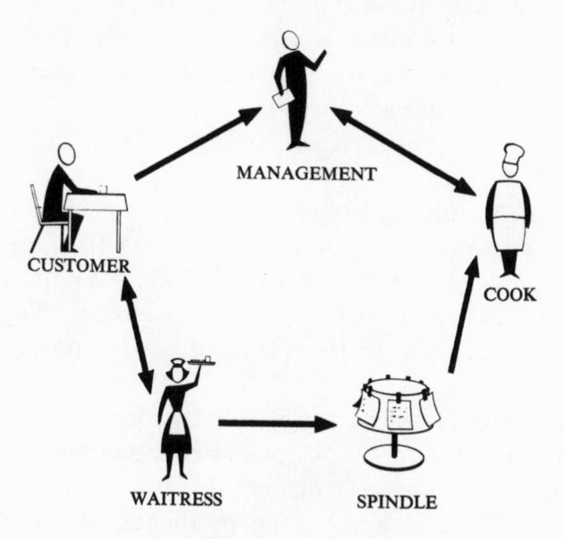

FIGURE 2. *The introduction of the spindle breaks up the face-to-face relation between the waitress and the cook.*

Reputedly, what Dr. Whyte refers to as "the lowly spindle" apparently has done more to reduce the human relations problems in the restaurant industry than any other single development. To those who travel much, it is clear that the spindle has spread from coast to coast and border to border within a decade.

The function that the spindle plays in the system can be understood from a different viewpoint as something other than the solution to a status conflict problem. Let us understand it now from a "systems" frame of reference.

First of all it is obvious that the spindle functions as a "memory." It does all the remembering for the cook. He does not have to remember orders called out by waitresses; the spindle does it for him.

Secondly, the spindle acts as a "buffer." A buffer is any device that can accept inputs at one rate and deliver outputs at another rate. In the instance of the spindle, ten waitresses may arrive almost simultaneously and put their orders on the spindle. The cook, however, may take the orders off the spindle at a rate suited to his work capabilities. The spindle thus buffers the cook against input rates that might overload him.

Thirdly, the spindle functions in two ways as a queuing device. It forms a queue, or waiting line, of the orders and holds each order in its proper place in line. Also, the spindle does all the "standing in line" for the waitresses. No longer need they go through the frustration of having to wait to put in orders.

Fourthly, the spindle accepts events (orders) that have occurred in serial order (that is, one after the other) and pulls them together to create a display. In other words, the arrangement of the orders on the perimeter of the spindle permits the cook to see at a glance all the orders. By reason of this display, the cook has what we call "random access" to all the "information" that is in the system at that point. The advantage to the cook is obvious. He can see that there are, for example, four different orders for hamburgers. It is almost as simple for the cook to prepare four hamburgers at the same time as it is to prepare one. The random access to the information permits the cook to organize his work against the total work load of the moment rather than against each order separately.

Before going on to the fifth system function served by the spindle, we must go back to the restaurant before the advent of the spindle and consider the restaurant as an information processing system.

To begin with, information on the menu existed in the physical form of the printed word. The customer would transform this information into the physical form of some spoken words. The waitress would first transform the information into the physical form of written notes, go to the kitchen, and transform the information once again into the physical form of spoken words. The cook would transform the information into the physical form of prepared food. This would be picked up by the waitress and delivered to the customer.

Now, every so often, an error was made and something was delivered to the customer that he had not ordered.

Who made the mistake, the waitress or the cook?

In the waitress's recall of events, she "knows" in her own mind that she called in the correct order; so, the cook must have made the error. The cook, on the other hand, "knows" that he prepared exactly what the waitress told him to prepare; so, if an error was made, it must have been the waitress who did it.

What kind of learning is promoted under these circumstances? The people involved learn to hate each other, to distrust each other, and to look after their own interests. The learning is emotional, costly, and irrelevant to the system's goals.

The fifth and final system function served by the spindle is that the order-tickets serve as documentary evidence to which both waitress and cook can refer in the event of an error. Either the waitress made a recording error or the cook misread the ticket. In either case, the one who made the error has unequivocal feedback for the first time.

What kind of learning is promoted under these modified circumstances? It is quite different. By having an objective source for checking errors, it is possible for both waitress and cook to discover and correct habitual errors. Possibly they can begin to discover that some errors are due to ambiguities in the "signals." For example, maybe orders for hamburgers (HB) and beefburgers (BB) get mixed up randomly and frequently; therefore a decision is reached to change the name "beefburger" (BB) to Caravan Special (CS) so that the symbology will transmit itself through the system with less ambiguity. The waitress and cook may discover that errors arise because of the printed format on the order ticket. They may approach management with suggestions for a better format. The use of the spindle tends to promote learning to solve some of the system's problems.

The essential point to be made by this restaurant illustration of a system is that we add a new dimension to our capacity to view complex organizations when we perceive them as "information processing" systems and trace the "information" through the system, asking at each interface (point of transfer from one component to the next) how the information is being transferred. Consider that until recently most efforts to solve such problems as the human relations problems in the restaurant industry would have been largely limited to actions such as the institution of incentive schemes, time and motion studies, special skill training, or human relations training. Each of these approaches would be an effort to improve the performance of the components *regardless of how poorly the system might be designed.* The development of "system thinking" adds a very important tool to our kit. It helps us to perceive much of the dynamics of interaction between men, machines, and management, and suggests ways of solving information flow problems.

In later chapters reference will be made to the notion that organizations, as do individuals, behave; and that organizations, as do individuals, adjust to their environment. We are aware that organizations do adjust over time; otherwise, they die. The manufacturer of buggy whips found it necessary to adjust.

In addition to those types of changes and adjustments that take place over time and in response to the changing environment, there are a number of "adjustment dynamics," as it were, which organizations make to variations in the input rate or work load. As we understand how systems respond to input overloads (rush hours or seasons), we see organizations as being living, dynamically adjusting organisms.

The most common adjustment systems make to increasing levels of input is to increase the number of channels to handle the information. Restaurants put on more waitresses and cooks. Schools hire more teachers. Stores hire more clerks to handle the Christmas rush.

Many readers can remember going to a restaurant during the rush hour and simply standing in line until one's turn came. This is a second common adjustment in the dynamics of systems. It permits queues or waiting lines to form. The post office forms queues, too. At Christmas time, bags of mail have to be stacked in piles until they can be handled. The stock market may queue when it is overloaded. Quotations accumulate until they can be sent. This stacking up, or holding, of "information" in a waiting line is a dynamic adjustment known as *queuing*.

An interesting example of man-machine relations is evident in the modern short-order restaurant's handling of queuing. As one enters, the hostess takes one's name and the size of one's party and enters it on a slip of paper. One need no longer hold his position in the queue by his elbows. His position in the queue is held by that simple machine, the slip of paper.

As restaurants become more modern, seating arrangements

become more diversified. Rather than all tables being uniform in size, now there are small booths, small tables, big booths, big tables, small units that can be put together to make large units, and so on. This type of development created a new avenue of adjustment for restaurants. With diversity of seating capacity, it became possible to seat parties of two at the small tables or booths, parties of four at the larger tables or booths, and even larger parties at combinations of tables. With this degree of flexibility in seating, it now became possible to practice *filtering,* another dynamic adjustment by which parties are held in the queue until a table of appropriate size is ready. One party may wait much longer than a party of a different size, depending upon the availability of the appropriately sized table. Because the hostess has a visual display of the sizes of parties in the queue, she may draw from the queue selectively, thus permitting a greater efficiency in seating. Where the seating diversification is suited to the seating needs of the clientele, and when the hostess knows what she is doing, very few seats need be empty long.

We can easily recognize filtering in a number of other systems with which we are all familiar. The post office handles special delivery mail before first class mail and first class mail before parcel post items. In emergencies, long distance operators will accept only emergency calls. Radar scope readers will give minute-by-minute reports on unknown aircraft and much less frequent reports on known, friendly aircraft. Police make emergency calls before routine investigations. Filtering is the act of paying differential attention to inputs in terms of the criticality of the inputs to the system's goals or the system's organization, or both. Filtering is a way in which systems can adjust to the input load.

Systems can adjust to overload situations by just not dealing with all the inputs. This adjustment is called *omission.* The telephone system, when overloaded, simply fails to accept your call. All you get is a busy signal. The post office will not accept packages over a certain size. The short-order restaurant puts on the menu the words, "No substitutions." The restaurant *could* simply turn people away. This would be an act of omission. But it seems to be a better system design to omit the acceptance of nonstandard, time-consuming orders than to omit the opportunity to take the customer's money; hence the words on the menu, "No substitutions."

Let us consider one more of these adjustment dynamics, the making of errors. From time to time, some manufacturing organizations, when pressed with work, will forego quality control measures. They find it cheaper to replace an item than to control for quality. During rush seasons, the post office accepts the fact that temporary help will make more errors than experienced help. Librarians find the filing error rate is higher when the staff is overloaded. Waitresses make more errors during rush hours than when the load is low, but they also serve more people.

There are other dynamic adjustments that systems can make, but we have considered enough to establish the point that when we think of system training, we are conceptualizing a highly dynamic assemblage of interdependent components woven into a system by principles of organization and of management. The system interacts with its environment in such a way that we can truly say the organization behaves. When we think of training a system, we think of how we can bring the organization to the highest possible state of flexibility in its behavioral response to its environment.

CHAPTER 2

WHY STUDY ORGANIZATIONS?

Now let us consider some of the things we may expect to result from the study of an organization, such as an air defense organization, and some of the values to be obtained.

One of the most remarkable phenomena of the twentieth century is the degree of specialization and consequent lack of communication that has arisen among scientists who study the behavior of organisms. In addition to the appearance of a high degree of specialization in subject matter, rather rigid lines have been drawn in defining the appropriate object or organism for study. Thus, psychologists study the individual organism, be it rat or human; sociologists study the group; anthropologists study the culture of the human group; and political scientists study the power behavior of individual and group. The individual-group dichotomy is particularly evident in traditional experimental psychology, the goal of which is rather obviously to discover general laws for describing and predicting behavior of individual organisms. Clinical psychology deals with the adjustment of individual human beings. Social psychology studies the effect of membership in groups upon individual behavior.

The individual organism is a convenient entity. We run into few definitional problems in describing and bounding the individual organism because we have a convenient biological interface, the skin, as a reference. But the very act of accepting the skin as a boundary creates some real problems to the psychologist. If he invades the skin to see what is going on, he may alter important functions, severely restrict the behavior that the organism is free to display, or severely restrict the environment to which it could react. It would be nice to be able to be on the inside of an intact skin and be free to observe what happens.

When one looks for the definition of "organization," one finds "organism" as one meaning of the word. A science of behavior should concern itself with all kinds of organisms, including human organizations. In fact, there are some interesting advantages to be gained from considering a human organization as an organism in the same sense that a rat is an organism. The great advantage in using the human organization as the object of study seemed to the RAND experimenters to be that one could obtain access to the inner workings of this organism in ways most difficult to achieve with the rat or any other individual organism. That is, it is possible, by rather expensive means, to contain human organizations within the walls of a laboratory and to observe and study the variables that intervene between input and output directly. This method of gathering variables seems more productive than to infer them, as the psychologist does, or to ignore them, as some psychologists seem to recommend. It is possible to get under the skin of the human organization and to tap into its nervous system rather directly because the communication network of the human organization operates with messages already encoded into meaningful symbols. The rat's nervous system is apparently operated by messages in the codes of the nerve impulse, which we have not yet been able to break. Nevertheless, the fact that members of human organizations communicate with one another by means of meaningful symbols, although a very useful property, is not an unmitigated joy. The sheer volume of verbal communication required to operate a human organization is always awe-inspiring and creates special problems of recording and analysis for which modern, high-speed, data processing equipment is essential.

But the real conceptual advance should not be obscured by the technical difficulties referred to above. By moving out of the skin of the individual and into the skin of an organization, one gains the ability to manipulate the organization of behavior, to manipulate the interaction between components of the organizations, to manipulate the hierarchy of structure, and to manipulate the environment in which the organization lives. We have our rat in a box, with the environment under manipulative control; but the box is a large laboratory, and the organism is spread out before our eyes and ears and special measuring devices.

In the best of all possible worlds, it might have been desirable to have conducted the investigations to be discussed here within a well-established, completely theoretical framework or system. Although much of what was known about individual psychology was transferred to the studies of the extended organism, it is fair to say that the problem of human organizational behavior was approached in much the same way as the naturalist would prepare to study a phenomenon. The only framework was that supplied by the decision to try to contain the phenomenon of organizational development within a laboratory, and to observe it carefully under as much control as could be exercised without losing the phenomenon entirely. Thus, for example, the naturalist, interested in studying the sexual behavior of lions, first finds a spot in nature where the phenomenon is likely to occur, builds special observation facilities such as a platform in a tree, and removes himself from influencing the behavior he hopes to observe, so that he will not lose his access to the phenomenon. After careful and complete observation, replicated as many times as feasible, the naturalist then begins the job of classification and generalization and produces a theoretical framework.

The RAND experimenters entered this phase of scientific work by attempting to distill observational and measurement data to produce a more abstract and general description of organizational development. With this framework, it was possible to design a large number of traditional "research" problems, since RAND psychologists now had a much better idea of what relevant questions should be asked. But the report here consists primarily of certain insights and hypotheses about organizational development, put together into a framework rather than in a series of traditional research studies. It had been the intention of the experimenters to observe first in the naturalistic manner and later to alter and control single variables in the time-honored way of science. It turned out, however, that as they controlled the inputs to the organization, and measured the outputs and fed back information to the organization, some rather remarkable behavior came into being which became the center of interest. The observations were neither as naturalistic as the would be lion observer nor as controlled as the usual psychological experimentation. Indeed, it was impossible to control competely the inputs to the organization because the organization, by its own actions, created problems for itself —just as real life organizations do.

The human organizations studied were really man-machine systems. Some functions were performed by machines and some were performed by men. In such a mixture of men and machines, how were the experimenters to look upon the men? It seemed reasonable, at least as a first cut, to try to describe the men as generalized components of the system and thus to avoid or postpone attempts to deal with the men as individuals.

In the design of an electronic circuit, the engineer first deals with the components, such as resistors and condensers, in terms of their general, abstract characteristics, tolerances, and interactions. When he comes to the actual building of a circuit, he is faced with the problems of accepting, rejecting, or adjusting components on the basis of their intimate, personal characteristics; that is, he is forced to deal with the "personalities" of the components. Since we attempt to build machine components to be as much alike or as uniform as possible, the principal tool available to the builder is that of selection. If he could adjust the values of fixed components, he would not need to indulge in selection.

In the design of a man-machine organization, the designer tries to find the optimal mixture of men and machines to carry out a given task. The manager or builder now finds that he has an adaptable set of components (men) and a relatively fixed set of components (machines) to accomplish the task. If the builder of the electronic circuit cannot make it accomplish the designed task, a new design is created. Similarly, if the manager of a man-machine organization cannot make it accomplish the designed task, a new design is created.

But the manager of a man-machine organization has available to him a unique resource: the general capacity for flexibility and the learning ability of the men. This resource may be maximized by the utilization of appropriate management techniques, or it may be frittered away through mismanagement in a variety of ways, requiring more rapid redesign than would otherwise be necessary. Rapid redesign of man-machine systems may not be the only solution to rapid changes in the system task. It is possible that managerial improvements, utilizing the resource of human learning, may effectively cut down on the necessity for expensive retooling. It is possible that a too rapid rate of redesign never permits either the manager or the designer to discover the limits to which the system can perform.

These questions of optimal rate of redesign serve here to illuminate the broad issue of how to treat "individuality" of both machine components and human components of a system. Machine components tend to have fixed "personalities"; they are either within tolerance limits for the system or outside tolerance limits. The human components do not come in uniform packages, and within wide limits, they do not have fixed personalities. They are capable of adjustment, modification, adaptation, and learning, and they are capable of operating the system in a range extending from the miserable to the heroic.

To argue that system performance is dependent solely upon the individual personality of the manager or of any other individual man in the system would be equivalent to arguing that the functioning of the body is directly related to the behavior of a single cortical neuron. Such a statement may very well be true, but the demonstration of the relationship is well beyond the current state-of-the-art in physiology. Similarly, the current state-of-the-art in system design does not yet permit us to include in an abstract model the detail involved in describing individual personalities and their effect on system performance. System designers are forced to deal with the uniformities of human behavior, and they leave to the manager the problem of adjusting personalities, values, individual wants and desires, and preferences to make the system work.

The complexity of individual personality has often discouraged the man-machine system designer in the past, and he has tried two general solutions. The first was to confine his designing to the machine components only, in which case he obtained such exaggerated predictions of system performance that no one believed him. The second was to "degrade" his predictions of system performance by assuming some amount of disruption of machine operation at various points in the system in which men were present. Although system designers are now aware of the need to introduce the "human factor" into system design, as yet there is little methodology to accomplish the introduction, other than costly experience. One solution to this problem is to try to distill from managerial investigation and experience those uniformities in human behavior that can be treated abstractly in terms equivalent to machine design.

In the most general sense, we desperately need to know how to exercise control over human behavior. Mankind's rapidly increasing ability to control and manipulate the physical forces of Nature has freed us from many of the coercions and constraints imposed by the inherent "cussedness" of things. It has been pointed out that so-called scientific management as a method of control over human behavior is inadequate, possibly because it does not account sufficiently for the noneconomic aspects of motivation. People are not inherently "cussed," but we still do not know how to design and manage the system of controls, checks, and balances that make organizations viable, healthy, and productive. In particular, we do not know how to sit right down and design organizations guaranteed to adapt successfully to a world that is continually changing.

As a matter of fact, we do not even know how to measure organizational effectiveness. Organizational effectiveness, as we view it, is much like the accepted concept of human intelligence. Intelligence is estimated from performance, but the performances cover a wide range of activities and indicate the individual's potential for growth, viability, or adaptability. The idiot savant who is a wizard with numbers performs well in one task, but he is not intelligent. A given organization may be highly productive, but not have the capacity to change "intelligently." Estimation of these characteristics of an organization will undoubtedly prove as difficult as was the measurement of intelligence of an individual. But the important point to be noted here is that no single measure of performance will be satisfactory. The practical problem of assessing or measuring organizational effectiveness should receive the same amount of attention from scientists that the problem of intelligence measurement has received.

The phenomenon of "scientific management" has been the answer to complexity in the business organization. All the machinery of work simplification, time and motion study, incentive pay, scientific planning, operations analysis, job shred-out, and the emergence of a special class of professional managers are techniques and tools of the scientific management movement. Man has been treated in the oversimplified image of economic theory. The old notion that people are purchased by offering them employment is being challenged on all sides. The old barriers to free choice of employers are breaking down as a result of a fundamental change in both culture and the ease of transportation. The sign of change is the large amount of turnover in the business world, particularly among skilled and junior managerial personnel; they change jobs and find it easy to do so. The new mobility of workers creates serious problems of design and management of business organizations. If the same or better pay can be achieved by moving to a different firm, the economic incentive is effectively removed from scientific management. What will substitute for the financial motive? It seems clear that methods will have to be found that are competitive with purely economic coercions to create the kind of stability necessary for organizational growth. And these methods appear to lie in the field of managerial technique.

The concept of control in the military services is encrusted with hoary tradition. A superior in the hierarchical structure makes decisions and issues an order, and an inferior carries it out, without question. This concept of control now finds itself at the mercy of the expanding technology of warfare and the realization that specialized knowledge is required for informed decision-making and that the inferior with specialized knowledge in many cases is the appropriate decision-maker. This conflict between the old tradition of unquestioning obedience and new technology is being only partially resolved, as testified by the high turnover in the specialized branches of the armed forces.

The question of control is becoming urgent with reference to the modern military weapon system. Here, large numbers of men and machines are designed to work together in gigantic, interacting teams. Often, these teams are spread out over continents, requiring great efforts in communication to coordinate or control the team. Efforts to exercise control are responsible for the emergence of design solutions, such as combat information centers, communications centers, the air defense direction centers, and command and control centers. Experience with these designs of man-machine systems has already indicated that it is necessary to pay particular attention to the managerial problems created by such control centers.

We conclude from the foregoing discussion that the study of human organizations is important from both a theoretical-psychological point of view and an eminently practical standpoint. In particular, the problem of rapid change and its effects on organizational stability deserves continuous attention. Although many economists, political scientists, sociologists, and practical men-of-affairs have made observations of human organizations and a "lore" has grown up from the solution of organizational problems, the application of experimental method and psychological theory to human organizational problems has not been encouraged. Part of the reason is doubtless to be found in the technological problems encountered in such studies. But the major reason seems to be that psychology has concentrated on the individual organism or the small group. The succeeding chapters will demonstrate that the human organization is a proper organism for psychological study.

One note of caution seems called for, however, on the part of both psychologists and managers. It is highly characteristic of human beings to describe their work in terms of the work procedures they use and not in terms of the functions they fulfill. This holds true for most psychologists and for managers' views of what psychology is. Most psychologists and managers view psychology as the giving of tests, doing laboratory researches, practicing psychotherapy, consulting, and so on. Despite the variety of work settings, the psychologist's scientific function is to make individual behavior more predictable. The studies reported here are clearly aimed at this goal. The methodology is unique. Many will not perceive it as "psychology" for that very reason. But the reader will discover, be he psychologist or manager, that by understanding more of organizational behavior, individual behavior becomes much more predictable.

CHAPTER 3

REAL-TIME PROBLEMS AND SCIENTIFIC METHOD

In any military, industrial, educational, or similar culture, there are complex organizations striving after some goal or goals and are guided by structures of rules and regulations for achieving these goals. But to anyone who has lived in such cultures, it is clear that the organizations do not always operate in the way the book says they should. Errors are made, opportunities are missed, inefficiencies exist.

Good students may somehow be lost to the educational system while poor students are retained. Penetrating hostile aircraft may go undiscovered or unapprehended. A company may lose contract after contract. Mail gets lost for no apparent reason or is materially delayed in delivery. And yet, if one were to study closely the rules and regulations of an organization, it would most certainly appear that if every man did as he was supposed to do, things should go well.

Certainly, a contribution to the understanding of the Air Force as to how man-machine systems operate and how errors can be reduced or avoided would be a contribution of unquestioned value. It might not seem to be any great contribution if an understanding of how our educational system works were to result in the saving of three or four bright students out of the many thousands attending school, but a different set of values holds when one thinks of saving three or four cities from being vaporized by enemy nuclear weapons.

When your mail is not delivered, when a bright student drops from school, when a fire rages out of control in valuable watershed country, when bombers penetrate a defense system, these are "real-time" problems. They exist in the here and now. In contrast with real-time problems are "non" real-time problems, problems that exist in reality but for which time is not the important factor. For example, the tobacco grower whose tobacco is attacked by tobacco rust faces a real-time problem, but the biochemists who study the molecular structure and characteristics of the tobacco rust are working in "non" real-time. The teacher before a class works in real-time; the psychologist studying the nature of the learning process works in "non" real-time.

The problem that had to be solved first by RAND psychologists was the problem of electing a method of studying man-machine systems operating in real-time. It may seem odd that this should have been a problem, but it was, although its existence as a problem was not apparent until after it had been solved.

The situation at the RAND Corporation in 1950 should be described in more detail because it illuminates the choice of problem and the mode of attack. The operation of RAND Corporation has been described as a technique in synthesis whereby scientific knowledge and talents are brought to bear on military problems to aid the Air Force in the formulation of plans and policies. The technique is multidisciplinary: Diverse skills and professions are organized to function as a team, and this team is of general applicability and can be employed in the analysis and solution of almost any type of complex problem requiring a scientific approach.

RAND consisted originally of a small group of engineers, mathematicians, and operations analysts. By 1950, a Social

Science Division was well established to carry out studies of political and historical considerations that would influence the choice of weapon systems by the Air Force. Communication between the "hardware" and the "software" divisions was difficult, and for a variety of reasons. The "hardware" scientists, accustomed to dealing with measured numerical quantities, amenable to mathematical manipulations in abstract models of reality, found the "software" scientists unaccountably vague when they were asked to specify the political climate ten years hence, when the weapon system now on the drawing boards would be in the inventory of the Air Force. The "software" scientists, on the other hand, found the operations analyst cheerfully willing to accept almost any estimate from an "expert" as long as it was quantitative and fitted into his abstract mode. The "hardware" scientists were impatient with the "software" world of conditional prediction because they were used to the world of physical nature, in which the boundaries of natural law could be extrapolated over a ten-year period with some confidence.

In 1950, someone at RAND heard of the new field of human engineering, possibly as a result of the publication of a human engineering handbook.* The executive secretary of the American Psychological Association was asked to name possible consultants, and as a result a number of psychologists were invited to attend a summer conference at RAND.

The first problem this group confronted was the communication problem. They were asked, singly and together, to puzzle out the numerical values of "degradation factors" to be applied to weapon-system performance because people were to be introduced into the system at many points. The psychologists' response was one of polite public interest but private

* J. L. Kennedy (ed.), *Handbook of human engineering data for design engineers.* Port Washington, N.Y.: Special Devices Center, Office of Naval Research. Report SDC 199–1, 1949.

horror. No framework of constructive approaches was available. Some said that human performance was a function of the kind of selection and training of the personnel. Others thought that the only way to begin to answer questions of how much humans degraded system performance would be to conduct detailed historical studies on weapon systems already in

FIGURE 3. *The System Research Laboratory research team.* From left to right: *William C. Biel, Allen Newell, John L. Kennedy, Robert L. Chapman. The setting is the observation deck of the laboratory.*

the inventory and then extrapolate. A few concluded that the problem was not formulated or delineated properly; they suggested that RAND had misconstrued the objective. The psychologists were all saying, in one way or another, "This is a problem of managing, not of planning. What kind of management will the Air Force have ten years from now and what tools from the manager's kit will they be using? Selection and training are tools from the kit. Are there others that the Air Force is not using? Are they using the ones they know now to the fullest extent?"*

Two avenues were open and were rather thoroughly ex-

* Six months later, in early 1951, one of this original group of consultants, John L. Kennedy, joined RAND's Social Science Division to "institute research on the optimal man-machine relationship in weapon systems."

Dr. Kennedy had obtained his doctorate in psychology at Brown University under Leonard Carmichael. He had been active in the formulation of human engineering as technical aide to the Applied Psychology Panel of Office of Scientific Research and Development during World War II, and had edited the *Handbook of Human Engineering Data* at Tufts University. He was also head of the Department of Psychology at Tufts University and Director of the Institute of Applied Experimental Psychology, a research center for human engineering.

The second member of the research team was Robert L. Chapman, a systems researcher and Director of Project Cadillac, a Navy Special Devices Center project, under contract with New York University, to design an Airborne Combat Information Center. Dr. Chapman's doctorate was taken in psychometrics under L. L. Thurstone at the University of Chicago, and he had additional experience in human engineering with Dunlap and Associates. In the course of Project Cadillac, he had been struck with the interaction between equipment design and management and was eager to develop experimental methods to investigate the managerial function in a systems context.

William C. Biel, from the Psychology Branch of the Aero-Medical Laboratory at Wright Field, was a third member of the research team. Dr. Biel had long experience with the problem of management of research and had become aware of the systems problem in his Wright Field work on human engineering. He had taken his doctorate in psychology under C. P. Stone at Stanford and had taught psychology in various universities, had directed a National Defense Research Council Applied Psychology Panel research project on antiaircraft personnel and training during World War II. He was aware of the frustrations of attempting to influence equipment design and the interactions of design with the managerial problem.

A fourth person who joined the research team was Allen Newell, who had been in the Mathematics Division at RAND for approximately a year. With an undergraduate major in physics at Stanford and several years of graduate work in mathematics at Princeton, he had been hired to work with Merril M. Flood on the development of abstract models of the Air Force Logistics System. He had spent some time at Wright Air Development Center in becoming familiar with the Air Force logistic problems. Although Newell's approach to the system problem was much influenced by the abstract mathematical model tradition, he was struck by the importance of managerial and people problems in the operating Air Force and the effect of these on assumptions required for the abstract model.

plored. One was to accept the *Zeitgeist* and become immersed in some component human-engineering problems *ad hoc* to a given system and to become an "expert" or wise consultant to designers and analysts. The other was to embark on a long-term exploration of the managerial role in the Air Force, to try to develop new tools for the managerial kit, and to organize the new and old tools into a framework or model that would permit the analyst to estimate with some confidence the contribution of the human factor to system effectiveness. The research to be reported is the result of choosing the second road.

The framework of human engineering proposed that worker effectiveness, military or civilian, could be increased by the process of improving design of equipment for human use. That is, the problem of effectiveness was seen in an engineering context, and the hope was that early attention to design details would so lighten the burden on the operator that his effectiveness would improve. There was much talk about "matching the man to the machine and the machine to the man," rather like the impedance matching in an electronic circuit. Certain rather glaring oversights on the part of the designers (such as underestimating the space required to seat a man, or locating controls out of reach of the operator, or poor choice of scales for displays) were played up as examples of the great practical improvements to be gained from the conduct of comparative studies on several kinds of dials, four configurations of control handles, and seven levels of background noise on the displays.

It had become rather evident a few years earlier that the major design problems were rather easily fixed by early consultation with persons who were familiar with and emphasized the characteristics of the human operator. The comparative experimentation on alternative design configurations of displays and controls, although sometimes yielding statistically significant differences, did not yield the dramatic differences in system effectiveness that had been forecast. Something was missing in the framework, but what? At the time, it seemed to the investigators that the reason small design changes did not produce dramatic effects on man-machine performance was that people exhibit a tremendous range of adaptation.

One study on the effects of variation in physical parameters on tracking performance with handwheels revealed that, over a rather large range, the value of the parameters had little effect on performance. It was certainly possible to find combinations of variables, in their most unfavorable values, that would seriously affect the performance. But the general finding was that the subjects quickly learned to adjust their performance to less-than-optimal design parameters. This finding, by itself, is rather unremarkable because everyone knows that people can learn. But, when the capacity for adaptation and learning is added to the human engineering framework, a rather remarkable twist is given to it. The design problem shifts from the designer of "hardware" to the design of weapon systems, for example, in which people can utilize this capacity for learning and adaptation to the fullest extent. The problem shifts from engineering to psychology, particularly to the psychology of learning.

The research team became interested in organization theory and managerial practices, in physical and cultural constraints on learning and maturation, and in ways of removing these constraints. The goal of the proposed research became the understanding of human learning in organizations or systems. The kind of learning in which the research team became interested was not rote learning or individual skill learning but procedural learning. Put in computer language, their interest was in the "reprograming" of the people and the rules they followed in carrying out a complex, cooperative enterprise.

The research team was struck with the observation that *the rules a man applies to what he does are in many cases more important than how well or how skillfully he performs.* What a man attends to, the timing of what he does, whom he informs about what he does, are all criteria of performance as important as speed and accuracy of performance. And these criteria, as are speed and accuracy, are all subject to learning and adaptation. These additional criteria of performance make up the procedural side of human organizations, an area often neglected by human engineering and experimental psychology.

In experimental psychology, we try to fix the procedural variables by giving "instructions" to the subject. In most operating organizations, the procedural variables are fixed through the enforcement of "standard operating procedures." The question finally formulated was this: "What happens in a human organization when it is faced with the problem of devising its own operating procedures, of programing itself?" Obviously, habit, tradition, and assumptions will be the boundary conditions initially. Can means be found for overcoming these powerful constraints in order to initiate self-organizing, self-reprograming behavior in the face of a continually changing environment?

Physical constraints on learning and maturing were mentioned in a previous paragraph. Every organization exists in an environment in which physical laws limit performance. The "task" of the organization usually involves manipulations in the physical environment, mediated by machines. In the weapon-system case, this relationship of the task to the physical environment is obvious. But even social or political organizations exist in a time-space environment in which the activities of the members are shaped by such factors as where they live and how often they can meet. To a considerable extent, the kinds of machines or aids designed to assist the organization in its task will limit what it can accomplish.

The time-honored method of scientific investigation in the field of psychology is the controlled observation of the single variable. An experiment is set up, and observations are made on two groups or under two conditions. In the experimental group, the experimental variable is present; in the control group, the experimental variable is absent or different. One variable at a time is studied. This method just had to be rejected as not suitable. The real-time problems of Air Force groups involve so many variables that any effort to study these variables singly would be so time consuming as to result in no help to the Air Force. Consider that in an air defense sector, there may be five crews of forty men each. Personnel turnover goes on continuously and unevenly among the crews. The site may be in an isolated spot or near a large city. The task facing the crews may be fairly heavy should the site be near San Francisco with its heavy air traffic, or the task may be one of keeping awake should the site be one in northern Montana. No two crews are likely to duplicate ages of the men, length of experience, educational level, and so on. To study the many variables independently would be so time consuming that, before any clear and helpful answers could be achieved, air defense would be automated. A whole new series of experiments would be necessary; and before they could be completed, defense against air-breathing aircraft would be no longer needed.

Possibly the most significant influence on the experimenters' thinking in 1951 was the concept of the man-machine system itself. They had come from an academic tradition in which it was customary to factor a complex problem into convenient components for purposes of experimental investigation and control. The standard and acceptable title of the research paper was, "The Effect of X on Y." They were plunged into an environment in which it was insisted that X and Y interact with A, B, C, and D, and that the object of investigation was to understand these interactions. Faced with the frustrations of the human engineering framework, it was only natural that they would eagerly accept and attempt to exploit the system concept. But the system concept represents a different level of aspiration for the scientist. He is required not only to describe components, but also to fit component knowledge together into meaningful wholes, to provide practical decision-makers with credible advice based upon his understanding of system interactions. He can no longer hide behind the veil of "knowledge for the sake of knowledge." He must deal with the system as a whole.

The new criteria for study of an organism were emerging. The researcher must be inside its skin, but not involved in its functioning. A traditional approach of manipulating single variables was out; means would have to be devised to sense the significant effects of multiple interactions. The environment in which the organism lived would have to be accessible to controlled manipulation.

As stated earlier, when given a task to do, an organization will establish rules, habits, and traditions. It seemed to the investigators that the best way to overcome the powerful effects of habit and tradition would be to face the organization with an ever-increasing task load so that it would either adapt by changing its procedures or face the prospect of collapse. The machines available would be kept fixed, but the events to be dealt with would be greatly complicated, so that the organization would be forced to live dangerously. The complete and final design of such an experiment would require continual adjustment of the load to maintain a level slightly below the full capacity of the organization at the time. But this was impractical because of time and computer resources. In the second and subsequent experiments, the experimenters were able to achieve a series of steps in adjusting this load.

But where does one find a task and a physical environment

that can be manipulated in the manner described above? One early attempt was a rather typical war game, called DORIS. The players, five in number (five is a magic number for such enterprises), were required to exchange information and supplies in the conduct of an abstract strategic war. The environment and the task were so rarefied and abstract that the only freedom the subjects found was to play against the experimenter rather than against the task or the other players. The players formed coalitions against the experimenters, and the outcome was determined by how clever the experimenters could be in avoiding the traps set by the players. It was soon evident that DORIS did not provide such an environment and task and that the subjects would fight the task rather than the experimenters. In this situation, the experimenters became a part of the task environment of the subjects.

Therefore a search was made for a complex task in a physical environment, subject to physical laws, that the human organization would recognize as compelling enough to make them want to fight the environment rather than the experimenters. The latter searched for an environment that could be simulated and manipulated to bring pressure on the organization to adapt and learn. The "good" solution to all these requirements turned out to be the Air Defense environment and the formal structure of an air defense radar station. The solution was good in that ways were found of utilizing modern, high-speed computing techniques for producing the task environment synthetically. The solution was good in that enough detail could be injected into this synthetic environment so that the people in the organization could find ways of adapting to an increasing task difficulty. Finally, it was possible to remove the experimenters as elements of the task and direct the attention of the organization to its physical and cultural constraints as the proper areas of problem solution.

FIGURE 4. *View of the simulated radar site as seen from the observation deck in the laboratory.*

The empirical investigations that resulted from the framework sketched above were four in number: CASEY, COWBOY, COBRA, and COGWHEEL. Each of these laboratory periods of observation involved keeping an organization of 30 to 40 people under continuous observation and measurement during a regular work shift of six weeks to four months while their work load was manipulated to force procedural learning.

Although the load was manipulated in accordance with a standard statistical design, these were not experiments in the traditional sense of empirical testing of an hypothesis. They were concentrated periods of observation and manipulation, under controlled conditions, with techniques chosen to force organizational learning. From these periods of concentrated observation, during which many raw data were collected and stored for future analysis, the experimenters hoped to be able to gain enough insight into organizational processes so that an abstract and general model of organizational learning could be developed.

Many managerial techniques were put together to form the initial conditions under which the crews worked. More were improvised during the course of the investigations. After such investigation, an attempt was made to write down the managerial principles utilized and to record their apparent effectiveness. The data collected in the four investigations were massive. They have been summarized, coded, and tabulated in part only. Because there were so many of these data, a strategy for selection of relevant parts had to be worked out. Analysis of the data was guided by the developing theory.

Finally, the organization and operation of the research team itself should be described. In terms of formal organization, Dr. Kennedy was the project leader; Dr. Chapman was the laboratory planner-manager; Dr. Biel was the personnel planner and manager; and Allen Newell was the planner and manager of design and production of the synthetic environment. In actual practice, these roles were played at various times by various combinations of people. The staging of a laboratory investigation required a staff of up to 25 people, and more than once the ensuing activities taxed the capacity of RAND's Numerical Analysis Department's computing machines and staff. The laboratory was operated by a senior staff, consisting of the project leader and the managers, a technical staff, and a clerical staff. During actual laboratory occupancy by a crew, temporary additions to the group of experimenters were made on loan from other RAND divisions.

The planning was carried out jointly by the senior staff, utilizing the face-to-face conference technique. Each problem of design and management was given a thorough study (within compelling time limits) in its own right, and particular attention was devoted to the integration of plans and procedures. The face-to-face conference method, as a technique for problem solution and integration, worked rather well in this case, for reasons that were not at all clear to the team members. It may have been that the work was done under such a high level of stress that the usual problems of status, reward for individual effectiveness, comfort, and personal animosities that hamper a research team effort were postponable because "the problem was the boss."

In summary, the problem was to discover how to inject human factor considerations into estimates of effectiveness of future weapon systems. The application of criteria, such as have been described previously, made it desirable to put a lifelike model of an air defense radar station into a large laboratory, the Systems Research Laboratory, for detailed study and data collection. Four investigations were conducted, each holding machine characteristics constant and utilizing managerial techniques designed to force the man-machine system to indulge in procedural learning.

CHAPTER 4

SEARCH AND SERENDIPITY

Before proceeding to describe the Systems Research Laboratory and its duplication of an air defense site, let us first take a look at how air defense was conducted by a typical, manual (done "by hand" rather than by automation), air defense sector in the early 1950s.

In Figure 5, are shown four air defense divisions (AD DIVs). Each division is divided into four sectors. Each sector has a direction center (represented by the operations building with a radome, or radar dome, on the top). Note that in the northwest sector of AD DIV 1, there are three smaller operations buildings with radomes on their tops. These are early warning stations. They report by telephone into the direction center because the direction center is tied into an airfield where interceptors may be scrambled and directed over radio by the direction center to intercept an unknown aircraft.

When a flight of enemy aircraft was spotted by radar during World War II, the interceptor pilots could be told the location, speed, and direction of the enemy flight. By proceeding to an intercept point, the pilots could generally see the enemy aircraft. In fighter parlance, they "eyeballed" the enemy. With the advent of high-speed aircraft, "eyeballing" became impossible. Closing speeds of aircraft were too great. By the time a pilot saw the "enemy," if he ever did, he was too close to position himself for either an identification "pass" or a firing "pass." It became necessary to put radar in the interceptors and to have someone at a radar station on the ground directing the interceptor to a point where the pilot could "paint" the unknown aircraft on his airborne radar and take over the closing phases of the intercept.

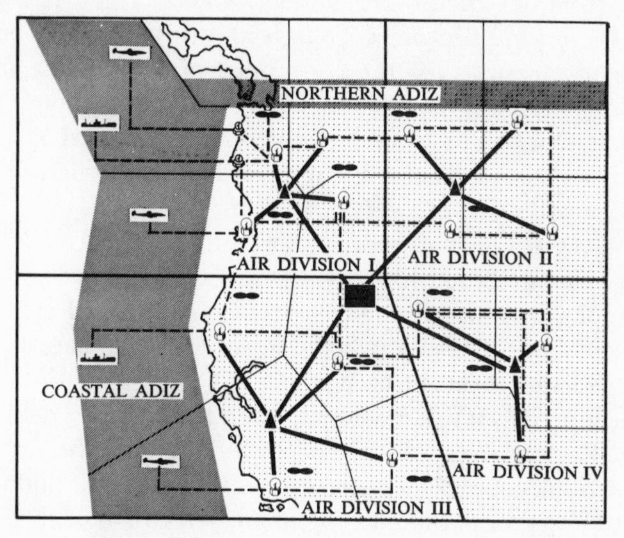

FIGURE 5. *Schematic diagram of an air defense force with four divisions. Airborne early warning aircraft and picket ships radio messages to early warning sites (small radar domes) or to direction centers (larger radar domes). Messages flow from direction centers to division headquarters (triangles) and on to force headquarters (oblong). Note division and sector boundaries. Propellers represent air fields from which direction centers scramble interceptors. ADIZ stands for Air Defense Identification Zone. The mission of the air defense system was to identify or intercept aircraft before they emerged from the ADIZ.*

One could not depend only on a ring of radars around the periphery of the United States because an enemy bomber that penetrated the ring would be in the clear. Consequently, it became necessary to have a network of stations so that extensive coverage would permit defense in depth. To coordinate the efforts of the several radar stations in a given area, all of which might be making demands on the same airfields, it was necessary to establish a division headquarters to act as a coordinator. To coordinate the utilization and transfer of air forces from one division to another, a Force Combat Operations Center was necessary. To have an overview of the entire battle and to supervise the regrouping of forces after an attack, the NORAD (North American Air Defense Command) Combat Operations Center was necessary. In brief, a radar station was only a small part of a continent-wide network. It had to work as part of a very large team.

That a great deal of team work was necessary becomes clear when certain relationships between adjacent stations are seen. Figure 6 shows how the radar coverage overlapped considerably and how airborne radar patrols and radar patrol ships extended the coverage to seaward. The dot-dash lines that divide up AD DIV 1 are sector boundaries. They delineate areas of prime responsibility for each direction center.

The object of air defense was to locate an aircraft and identify it between the time it entered an ADIZ (two of these Air Defense Identification Zones are shown) and the time it reached the inner border of the ADIZ. If it was an hostile aircraft, the objective was to shoot it down before it penetrated the inner border. If there were too many to shoot down, or if one got through anyway, then the objective was to pass the word inland so that interceptors from inland fields could be brought into action.

As enemy aircraft approached supersonic speeds, the need for the earliest possible warning became crucial. A matter of a short delay in information processing could result in a missed intercept and a devastated city. The pressure in air defense was high. There was not a great deal of opportunity to correct errors, and the consequences of errors were potentially great.

Aircraft penetrating an ADIZ could be identified by two major means. One means was by flight plan. Before an aircraft left Hawaii, for example, it filed a flight plan with the Civil

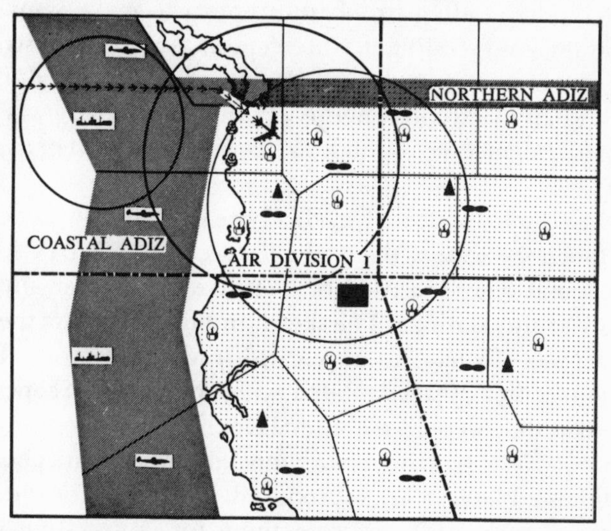

FIGURE 6. *Schematic diagram illustrating the flight path (line of arrowheads) of a bomber. It is first seen by a picket ship, then by successive direction centers. The rings suggest the overlapping radar coverages of adjacent sites. When messages are passed to adjacent sites in the line of flight but who do not yet "see" the aircraft, they receive "early warning."*

Aeronautics Authority. The CAA Air Movements Information Section (AMIS) forwarded the flight plan to the direction center whose sector would be penetrated. By inspection of Figure 6, it can be seen that a penetrating aircraft (line of little arrows) might first be seen by a picket ship and then by an early warning site before it would be seen by the direction center that had the forwarded flight plan. If those earlier sightings were not "told" to the direction center, the direction center was left with very little time to make an identification from the flight plan before the aircraft crossed the inner boundary of the ADIZ. If there was no flight plan that "fit" an aircraft, the second means of identification was used; namely, the sending up of interceptors to make visual identification. And sending up interceptors was an expensive business, expensive in two ways. It cost thousands of dollars to send up an interceptor, and every interceptor that was in the air and exhausting its fuel was degrading our defense capability.

The sector duplicated in the Systems Research Laboratory was much the same as the northwest sector of AD DIV 1 in Figures 5 and 6. It consisted of one direction center and three early warning stations. The sketch in Figure 7 shows the essential aspects of what was duplicated in the laboratory. The direction center was simulated in some detail. Scopes were placed as they were in real life. Telephone lines connected the operators. The plotting board, tote board, and status board (to be discussed later) were reproduced. Provisions for the Senior Director were made, as were those for cross-telling (to adjacent stations) and forward-telling (to higher headquarters). The Air Movements Identification Section received flight plans from a simulated Air Movements Information Section office (in an adjacent room). Controllers talked over simulated radio channels to simulated interceptor pilots who sat in adjacent rooms. The early warning stations were provided with simulated radar inputs. They called in information over simulated long-distance lines. When scrambles were called, a simulator in an adjacent room acted as an interceptor operations clerk at a fighter base. Simulators in adjacent rooms played the lifelike roles of men at adjacent sites and higher headquarters.

It is interesting to note that the experimenters originally intended to study only the direction center itself. At the outset, during shakedown runs before the CASEY experiments,

FIGURE 7. *A view from the back of a typical direction center in the old manual system of air defense.*

members of the staff read in early-warning information from prepared scripts. It soon became apparent that the interaction between direction-center procedures and early-warning procedures was extensive. This plunged the experimenters once again into the system they were studying. It was fun and was exciting, but not very good science. Immediately, three simulated early-warning sites were instituted and manned by the subjects. Later, a division headquarters was also simulated.

It became quite clear that an important principle was being discovered. The more abstract and remote from reality the experiment was (such as the game DORIS, described in Chapter 3), the more the subjects turned to playing against the experimenters. Conversely, the more concrete and proximal to reality the experiment became, the more the subjects turned to a bona fide grappling with the task.

To illustrate the matter of "involvement," contrast the behavior of the players in DORIS, who tried to outwit the experimenters, with the officer in one of the later laboratory experiments who stepped off a dais and broke his leg. The involvement of the crew in the "defense" of the sector was so great that it was ten minutes before the accident was brought to the attention of the staff. The next day the officer appeared, cast and all, "because they can't get along without me." While this was probably the most dramatic evidence of the reality that gripped the players in the simulated defense center, there were many other instances, each of which demonstrated that the players were *not* playing.

The most important aspect of the simulation seemed to be not so much that the physical resemblance to a stimulus should be precisely simulated, but that the behavior of the stimulus should be realistic and the consequences of handling or mishandling the stimulus should be highly credible. As we shall see in a moment, to get crew involvement in the task, a simulated radar blip need not look like a radar blip; but it is essential that it move from one location to another in a realistic manner (it should not fly through mountains, land in lakes, change altitude, or speed unrealistically)* and that its mishandling should have realistic consequences (a pilot excitedly calls in that he sees a mushroom cloud over Seattle).

The fact is that the radar blips were little printed figures on a sheet of paper. IBM had just come out with a new tabulator. Whereas the old tabulator would print ten characters per inch, the new tabulator would print twenty characters per inch. This meant that, on a standard 18 by 18 inch sheet, instead of being confined to 80 rows and 80 columns, it was possible to print a figure in any intersection of 160 rows and 160 columns. By using a high speed digital computer, it was possible to compute just where an aircraft in flight would be "seen" on each sweep of a radar antenna. Each "position" could be described in terms of the columns and rows, punched into an IBM card and printed out on that sheet of multifold paper that represented a given sweep of the radar antenna. By using multifold paper (one sheet attached to and folding onto the preceding one), it was possible to simulate a 100-minute radar input on 200 sheets, each sheet representing one sweep of a radar antenna revolving twice per minute.

It was the custom in the manual air defense system to have displayed on the PPI (Plan Position Indicator) scopes the compass rose (strobes of light every 10 degrees of azimuth

* In one instance, through a computer error that was not caught in time, one flight came through well above supersonic speed. When later the crew grumbled about the unreality of such performance, the experimenters "pointed out" that it was a submarine launched missile, thus restoring "reality" for the crew. This was not the only time that ingenuity was demanded of the experimenters. The experimenters evolved the motto, "Lie when necessary," and it was often necessary to lie to keep "reality" intact.

from magnetic north) with range markers for every 10 miles of distance from the station. Accordingly, a compass rose was etched onto a plate glass cover under which the multifold sheets were displayed. Each sheet remained stationary for 28 seconds before the next sheet moved into view.

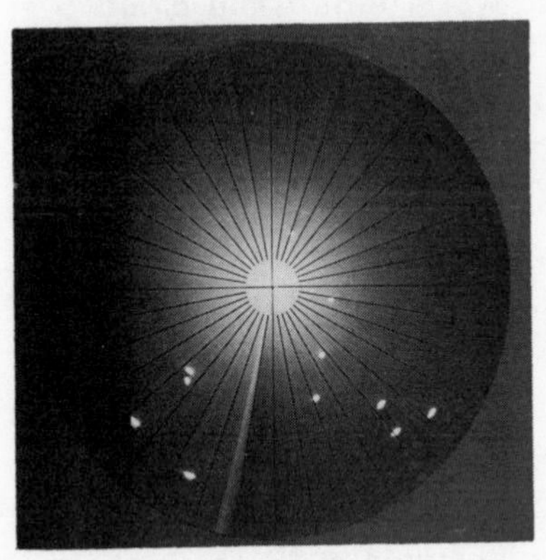

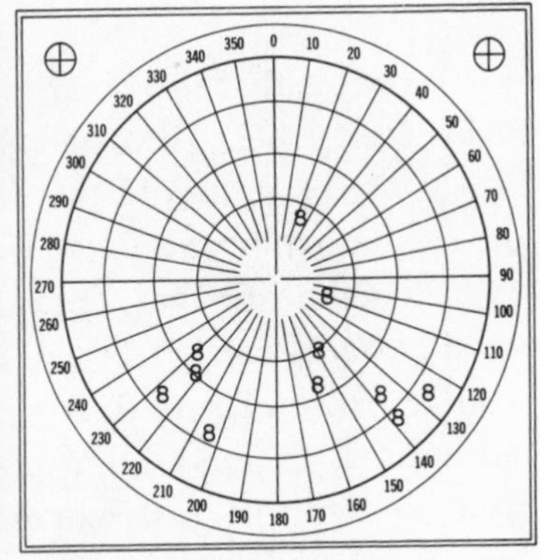

FIGURE 8. *Artist's drawing of the display of a real radar scope on the left and the simulated display used in the laboratory on the right. The Figure 8's did not look like real blips—but they acted like them.*

Figure 8 shows a real-life PPI scope display on the left and the simulated PPI scope display on the right. It is easy to see that the simulated blip could never be mistaken for a real blip.

Figure 9 shows how the multifold paper was fed through the simulated scope to give a 100-minute serial presentation. There were eight scopes of three different types (PPI scopes, height scopes, and early warning scopes) for which inputs had to be simulated. Each 100-minute period required 1600 sheets and about 80 teletype messages. Thus, information came into the system at the rate of about 300 symbols per minute and was complex enough to keep the crews busy.

The scope readers and early warning scope readers would

call in over telephone lines to plotters the locations of blips. The plotters, standing behind the plotting board (where they

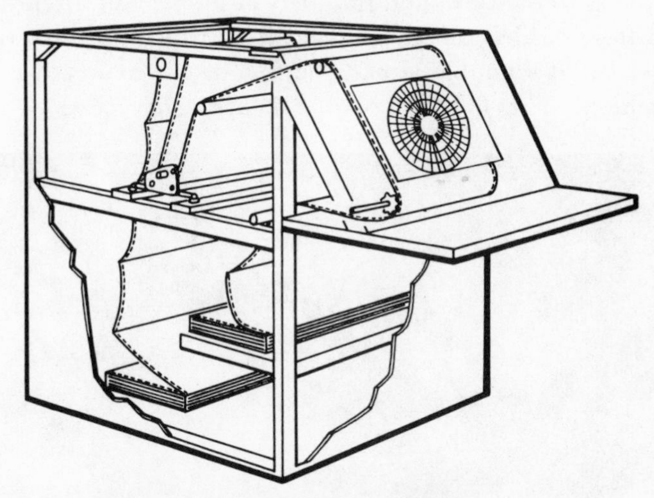

FIGURE 9. *A cutaway sketch of the laboratory version of a radar scope showing how the multifold paper on which the blips were printed was presented to an operator one sheet at a time.*

would not block anyone's view) would write on the clear, plastic board in grease pencil. Figure 10 shows how this was done. Note that the plotting board had "geo-ref" markers on it. Geo-ref (geographical reference) markers were literally the intersections of minutes of latitude and longitude. Their function was simple. They permitted two stations to use a common reference system when talking with each other. To illustrate, let us consider two adjacent stations with an aircraft flying midway between them. To one station the aircraft would be at 270 degrees (due West) and to the other station the aircraft would be at 90 degrees (due East). Obviously, they could not talk to each other in these relative azimuth terms, but had to resort to labeled latitude-longitude locations.

To the left of the plotting board were the status and fighter boards. The status board displayed up-to-the-minute information as to the types and numbers of interceptor aircraft at each stage of alert at each airfield from which the direction center could scramble aircraft, and it displayed weather information. The fighter board displayed the location and

FIGURE 10. *A closeup of the plotting board showing the "geo-ref" markers.*

movement of fighters in the process of making intercepts. To the right was a "tote" board. On this board, the plotters filled in information relevant to tracks under surveillance and the status of any intercept mission.

We have one last item before discussing the experiments themselves. Psychological research over the years has made clear what everyone "knows" by common sense: If you are trying to learn something, but you never find out how well you are doing, you don't learn much. You must have "knowledge of results" to learn.

This is understandable enough and easy to do something about when the task is to supply knowledge of results to an individual operator. After all, there are rules for reading a scope. The operator learns to call out, "I have an initial plot at zero three zero, range two-hundred and twenty miles," or "I have a move on Bravo Metro: two niner five, range eighty-eight." If the operator does not follow prescribed R-T (radiotelephone) procedures, he can be corrected. The same holds true for all operators. There are defined procedures, and deviations from the procedures can be identified and corrected —up to a point.

Imagine a scope reader under conditions of a sudden increase in load. The number of blips jumps from three to fifteen, with two blips unknown and two of the tracks apparently about to cross each other. Where should he put his greatest energy? On the crossing tracks? On the unknowns? On areas where new tracks might appear? On the known tracks about to enter another sector? There aren't any rules that apply to complex situations because the answers are so dependent upon so many other things. What is the state of alert? Is enemy action expected? Are the unknowns in formation? Are the unknowns probably commercial aircraft that are off flight plan? Are the unknowns flying toward a target area? Are there interceptors up on CAP (Combat Air Patrol)? Are the unknowns in a flight lane or threatening to penetrate an ADIZ? Who is the plotter? Who is the MI (Movements Identification) man?

As the task situation becomes more complex, there is a demand for something beyond operator skills. There is a demand for wisdom in the application of skills and in team play.

When a direction center crew and early warning crew totaling some forty men is in full swing with a heavy load, it is the team play, the interactions, that count most heavily in achieving success. The scope reader may now be giving greatest attention to tracks designated by the senior director as necessitating minute-by-minute reports. The MI man may be calling back to the CAA to find out whether there are any relevant delayed flight plans. The plotter may be calling MI's attention to a new track, which has appeared close to shore, flying low and fast.

Just as surely as one's eyes, arms, torso, and legs act in a coordinated fashion in walking, so do the components act in a coordinated fashion in an air defense center. And when a team of forty men is acting in this highly integrated, coordinated manner, they are as much a single organism as are the eyes, arms, torso, and legs of a human being.

But what kind of knowledge of results do you give such an organism?

Certainly, any knowledge of results ought to be relevant to the task the organism is attempting to accomplish. If the information given is not relevant, it could be misleading and lead to the adoption of irrelevant behavior.

Most of us, when we think about training, oversimplify things tremendously. We do this by restricting our view of training to training in skills which are sufficiently well defined so that we as trainers can state when the trainee is doing things correctly or incorrectly. Ask yourself this question, "What does General Motors Corporation need to learn in order to stay in business, and how can it be provided with appropriate training?"

It seems certain that everyone would hasten to agree that if General Motors Corporation failed from this day forward to learn anything new, it would soon be defunct. Knowing this, however, does not tell us much about *what* General Motors needs to learn or how it can be trained; that is, how it can be brought to learn what it needs to learn to survive.

This was a major problem facing the laboratory experimenters. What information about its performance could be given the direction center crew and the early warning crews so that, as an organism, it could learn? Obviously, the information given would not be in the nature of "correction" of individual crew members. What General Motors needs to learn is not achieved simply by "correcting" the errors of assemblers on the assembly line, important as that might be.

What the experimenters settled upon was to give the crew information on *how*—not how well, but *how*—the crew handled each critical track. Because each aircraft track had been computed as to where the aircraft would be "seen" at each sweep of the antenna, and this information had been punched into IBM cards, it was possible to prepare maps of the entire track history of each critical* flight, showing the time of initial appearance of the track on the radar scope, where it appeared, where it went, its altitude, its speed, its identification, any changes in speed or altitude, and any places where it faded from view. By the use of this map, it was possible to observe the crew and record their estimates of speed, altitude, time of initial appearance, time of initial plot, dead-reckoning accuracy during period of fade, and so on.

Additionally, it was possible to prepare listings of all critical tracks in a problem in the order of their appearance, and with all relevant information as to speed, altitude, type of aircraft, time of appearance, and so on.

Equipped with these aids, the experimenters could observe the crew and record data such as the time of initial appearance of a track, when it was first plotted, when it was identified, the estimated speed, the estimated altitude, when it was "scrambled" on, the results of the scramble, any loss of continuity in maintaining the track, and "bomb damage." As the information was gathered, it was recorded on prepared

* A critical flight was a flight that was unknown, one that required action to be taken. In this sense, it was critical to the system's mission.

forms, which were gathered every few minutes so that the information on them could be punched into IBM cards. Within five to ten minutes after a problem had been run, it was possible to sort the IBM cards and print out the history of actions taken on each track. This information, annotated with the actions taken, constituted the knowledge of results that were given.

Figure 11 is a replica of one of the early, experimental report forms. The information was entered on a Vu-graph film in black grease pencil, to be displayed to the crew following a problem run. It reads as follows:

> This is Problem No. 423 run on 22 June. The flight in question was given the track number "Charley 49." Its number on the experimenters records was 0261. The facts were as follows: It was a friendly aircraft without a flight plan. It first appeared on Gadfly's (an early-warning station) scope at 1:06. It was headed for Portland from Helena. It was by itself at an altitude of 20,000 feet at a speed of 300 knots. The crew initially plotted the track at 1:25 (some 19 minutes after it had appeared on the scope). They numbered it Charley 49. They identified it as a single aircraft at 18,000 feet and flying at 320 knots. They declared it unknown at 1:26 (only 1 minute after it was plotted). They scrambled Bravo Whiskey interceptors at 1:32. When airborne, the interceptors were ordered to 20,000 feet altitude. The aircraft was sighted by the interceptor at 1:48 and its identity as a Friendly aircraft established at 1:56. It was duly noted that this was a California Pacific Airways aircraft numbered B377, experiment serial number 0261 and that no flight plan had been forthcoming from CAA Air Movement Information Section.

Was it negligence that the flight was not plotted for 19 minutes after it appeared on the Gadfly scope? Or was the crew so busy with known hostiles or several aircraft appearing simultaneously that this was remarkably good work? The regulations say it should be plotted within 3 minutes. The experimenters passed no judgments; they simply provided facts.

Was it real "expertise" that led the Movements Identifica-

TRAINING OPERATIONS REPORT

PROBLEM 423 DATE 22 June

THIS REPORT REFERS TO TRACK C 49 (FLIGHT NUMBER 0261)

THE FACTS

IDENTIFICATION: .... F W/o FP
APPEARED IN EW: .... GADFLY
FIRST APPEARANCE TIME: 1:06
DESTINATION: .... PDX from HLN
NUMBER OF AIRBORNE OBJECTS: 1
ALTITUDE: 20
SPEED: 300

CREW ACTION

(1) INITIAL SURVEILLANCE REPORT:
TIME APPEARED ON PLOTTING BOARD: 1:25
TRACK DESIGNATOR: C49
NUMBER OF AIRBORNE OBJECTS: 1
ALTITUDE: 18
SPEED: 320
IDENTIFICATION: .... V 1:26

(2) TACTICAL PROCEDURES:
SCRAMBLED FLIGHTS: .... B/W
SCRAMBLED TIME: 1:32
AIRBORNE TIME: 1:36
ALTITUDE ORDER: 20
OTHERS: ....

(3) RESULTS OF SCRAMBLE
TALLY-HO: 1:48
TARGET IDENTIFIED: .... F 1:56
POUNCE ORDER: ....
SPLASH: ....
MISSED INTERCEPTION: ....

COMMENTS:

CPA B 377, SERIAL #0261 —
NO FLIGHT PLAN FURNISHED.

FIGURE 11. *Replica of early, experimental report form for giving knowledge of results to crew.*

tion man to identify the aircraft as unknown in only 1 minute? The information he had was off by 2000 feet and 20 knots of speed. Bearing in mind that (in real life) this was a $2000 decision, should he have been so hasty? Could he have done anything to increase his certainty? The experimenters passed no judgments; they simply provided facts.

It is most important that the reader recognize this unique handling of feedback of information to the crew. The experimenters were trying to study an organization as an organism in the hope of uncovering some generalizable principles of organization management. If the experimenters were to feed back to the crew any evaluation of the crew's performance, they would obviously influence the crew's behavior and thereby become part of the organization they were studying. By keeping all feedback in strictly objective form and by avoiding any moralization, any didactic teaching, or any evaluation, the experimenters were able to keep any changes in crew behavior a function of the crew alone.

In order not to be misleading as to the technique by which the observers fed back information to the crew, it should be pointed out that the observers presented summaries of their observations to the senior director of the crews and did not remain in the debriefing room. The senior director conducted the problem-solving discussions; the observers did not. As we shall see later, this turned out to be an extremely profitable procedure.

So much then for the air defense task, the simulation of the direction center, and the means of providing knowledge of results. Let us now consider the experimental runs and their findings.

The first "crew," dubbed the CASEY crew, was made up of college students from the University of California at Los Angeles and Santa Monica City College. Because they were unfamiliar with the component tasks such as scope reading and plotting, the students were given an initial period of indoctrination. As their component skills began to develop, the experimental problems were begun.

FIGURE 12. *Sketch depicting post exercise discussion being conducted by senior director* (center left). *Observers absented themselves after giving summaries to the senior director.*

The experimenters predicted that if the crew were given a task load equivalent to a heavy, real-life load for a professional crew, they would learn gradually, and their efficiency would finally taper off near the upper level, as shown in Figure 13.

In the words of the experimenters:

This prediction proved to be woefully inaccurate. The range of task-difficulty was indeed stressful—for the first few problems. After this, however, the problems were not difficult at all. In fact, the organization learned its way right out of the experiment. Within a couple of days, the college students were maintaining highly effective defense of their area while playing word games and doing homework on the side.*

The experimenters, as soon as they were fully aware of the level of performance achieved by the CASEY crew, did about the only thing they could. They prepared some new problems with still heavier loads. But problems took time to prepare and it was possible to have new problems on only the last two experimental runs. The problems for the next-to-last session were double the "heavy" load. The problems for the last session were triple the "heavy" load.

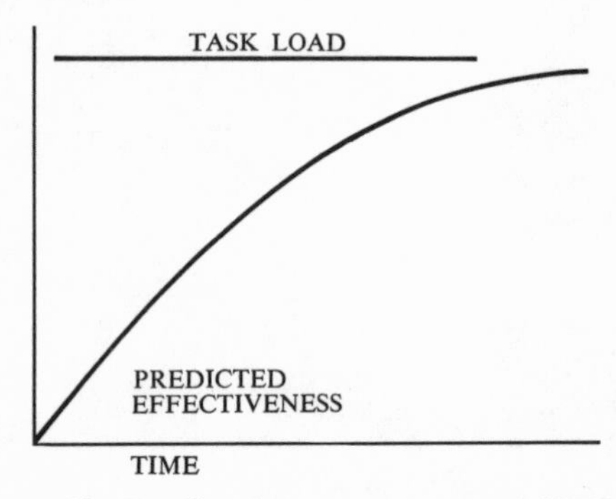

FIGURE 13. *Predicted performance for CASEY crew.*

One might expect that the crew would drop in efficiency when suddenly confronted with twice the load to handle. The surprising fact was that there was no significant drop in efficiency. The CASEY crew—sweating to be sure, and at one point on the verge of breakdown and saved only by a short leveling of the load—maintained almost the same level of efficiency they had reached on the "heavy" load problems.

* R. L. Chapman,, John L. Kennedy, A. Newell, and W. C. Biel, "The Systems Research Laboratory's Air Defense Experiments," *Management Science,* Vol. 5, No. 3 (April, 1959) 260.

On the last night, however, the triple load was too much for the crew. (As it turned out later, it was really not too much—only too soon.) As the load became too much, efficiency dropped off. The individual members were doing their jobs, but organization was gone. The scope readers read their scopes all right, but there was so much to read they began to lose integrity of continuity. They would read in an increasingly random manner. Other members of the crew behaved similarly. They did whatever seemed to thrust itself upon them. The first component to break was the Movements Identification man. With both hands full of flight plan slips, he stared up at the plotting board (which looked like a snowstorm), stared at his movements identification map table, stared at his hands full of flight plans, and then threw them all into the air. What he said at that point was duly recorded by the phonographic recorder but is not available for publication here. Soon he was joined by others and the problem was finally halted.

In the days that followed, the experimenters verified the records of the high performance of the CASEY crew on the double-load problem. When the results were shown to top management of The RAND Corporation, the Air Defense Command was contacted and invited to send someone to Santa Monica to see the results; for here was something of interest: a crew that had been somehow trained to carry with efficiency twice a heavy air defense load.

The reader will have to bear with the fact that just how many aircraft the simulated direction center could handle, how many "hostile" aircraft it was able to intercept, the "damage" to cities that was suffered, all would begin to reveal to the interested, potential enemy our capacity to defend ourselves against a manned bomber attck. Of course persons with proper security clearances and a need to know can obtain the appropriate technical reports from The RAND Corporation. It must suffice in this publication to speak in general terms.

The results were undeniable—the CASEY crew had handled an exceptionally heavy load. But possibly, the thinking went, it was because they were a bunch of bright young college kids. "What would happen," the question was asked, "if we were to put general run Air Force personnel into the laboratory?"

The next two experiments were performed using military crews and a new experimental design. This time, as shown in Figure 14, the experimenters predicted that the efficiency

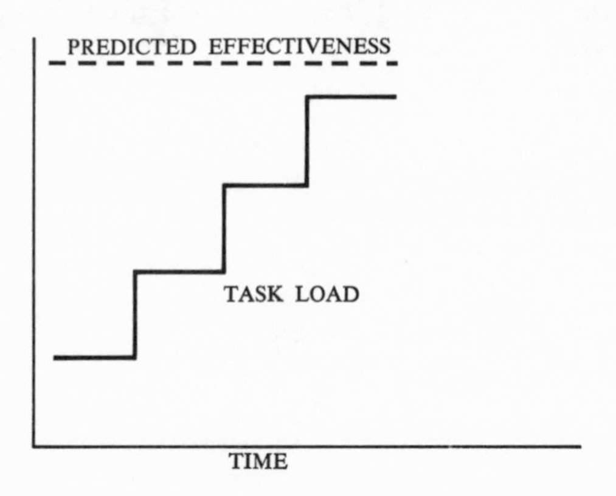

FIGURE 14. *The revised prediction of performance for COWBOY and COBRA crews. This prediction of performance was more accurate.*

level would remain the same while the load was increased.

Four levels of task load were devised, starting from a load level judged to be sufficiently heavy as to cause some stress for the average professional crew. Each increase in load level was roughly equivalent to the original load level; thus the second level was twice as great; the third, three times as great; and the fourth, four times as great.

As predicted, the COWBOY and COBRA crews, professional Air Force Air Defense Command personnel, were able to maintain their effectiveness even in the face of a load four times as great as one that they had found originally stressful. It was not always smooth sailing as the loads were increased and both crews were apparently reaching their maximum performances. Nevertheless, their performances were far superior to what had theretofore been considered as excellent.

So much for the laboratory studies now. They shall be referred to in a later chapter, which attempts an explanation of how this learning occurred. For now, it is sufficient to point out that a series of experiments, undertaken to explore for general principles of organization-management, resulted in the discovery of the tremendous capacity of men to learn and to develop ways of coping with a task with no change in the tools given them to do the job. Just as television's "Sergeant Bilko" was a monument to man's capacity to "get around" a system, the Systems Research Laboratory experiments were a monument to man's capacity to make a system *really* work.

The experimenters had not expected to discover such a tremendously powerful management tool, but they did. They discovered how to train a system; how to train many men, all doing different jobs, to work with their equipment, their procedures, and with each other to achieve increasingly more effective system operation.

From the search . . . serendipity.

CHAPTER 5

FIELD TEST AND EXPANSION

From the early RAND experiments, it was clear that college students could improve organizational effectiveness. It was equally clear, if not clearer, that military personnel could improve organizational effectiveness *in the laboratory.*

In the laboratory studies, the experimenters used every psychological persuasion to provide incentive. The crews were given lectures on the vital role of air defense. They were told that it was extremely important that the studies be undertaken. Their motivations were aroused by various appeals to their responsibilities. Throughout the application of all these stimuli, the experimenters kept themselves distant and mysterious, scientists in search of the significant.

What would happen, though, if one tried to train a crew stationed in some remote northern site? Crew motivation might be understandably different. Instead of hearing impressive speeches on the vital role each member of the crew was playing in defending our nation, they would be more likely to be hearing a KP roll call. There would be no mysterious scientists in the background creating an aura of importance for every action taken and every word spoken. It would be more likely that the routine of daily living would have to be broken up to make room for "some exercise that nobody needed." Would a crew, under these circumstances, show the same desire for organizational adaptation?

The Air Defense Command decided it was well worth finding out what would happen. But who should do it? This type of development work was not in the RAND Corporation tradition. But RAND had the computer facilities that were necessary to produce the problems. RAND had the "know how" for producing the problems. RAND had the knowledge of air defense operations. RAND had the "know how" of getting a system to learn. In short, RAND was obliged to go ahead or, otherwise, cause a prolonged delay while some other organization was being formed and trained.

When the decision was made to develop the laboratory procedures into an active training program, it was clear that much work lay ahead. Engineering developments would be needed. Standard forms would have to replace the informal, changing forms and aids used in the laboratory for recording crew performance. An indoctrination program had to be developed to introduce Air Force personnel effectively to this totally new and far from uncomplicated training vehicle. To these three efforts, which were undertaken consecutively, the remainder of this chapter is devoted.

The first step was the activation of the "60 Day Study Group." This group, made up of Air Force representatives and RAND personnel, specified the problems that had to be solved in order to adapt the training vehicle to the conditions that existed in the nearly 160 radar sites arranged across the continental United States. Crews were to be trained at the very scopes they used for air defense, and therefore equipment was needed to "package" the computations made by the computer as to where each aircraft was at each sweep of the radar antenna, and then to display realistic blips on the scopes at the radar sites. M. O. Kappler, a member of RAND's Engineering Division who had been interested in and strongly encouraged the Systems Research Laboratory's work from its inception, undertook this engineering task.

Through the use of computers, a cathode ray tube, and a 70-mm camera, it was possible economically to "package" an air defense problem on a roll of 70-mm film. A "problem reproducer" was developed. As the film was fed slowly to the reproducer, it would "read" the blips stored on the film and display them on the scope faces at the proper azimuths and ranges.

The problem reproducer was really more complicated than as described here. It was recognized at the outset that training eventually would require scope displays of permanent echoes, electronic jamming, and chaff. Provisions for including these displays were a very real part of the engineering effort.

While the engineering developments were going on, an effort was undertaken to develop standardized training aids suitable for use in the field. Each of these aids and the purpose each served, is described under the various headings below.

Problem Description. The problem description aid was essentially a short verbal description of the problem, how it developed, and what operational functions it was intended to stress. For example, one problem might contain a few single sneak attacks intended to stress surveillance functions. Another might contain massive raids intended to stress the function of allocation of intercepters. A third might contain unknown aircraft flying straight along the division line between two sectors intended to stress intersite cooperation.

The problem descriptions permitted the division commander to select a problem most closely suited to the training needs in his division.

Threat Summary Map. The summary map was intended to be used by the division commander in the selection of a

FIGURE 15. *This is the machine that "packaged" the problems. Blips are projected onto the face of an upright cathode ray tube (being pointed to by operator) and photographed, frame by frame, by a 70-mm camera mounted above the tube. Each frame contained all the blips that would be "seen" at each sweep of a radar antenna.*

problem. On a map of the division area, arrows plotted the paths of critical (stressful) flights for each 15 minutes of problem time. Thus, eight maps represented the full problem and permitted the commander to visualize how the threat developed.

FIGURE 16. *"Problem Reproducer." These machines were located at each radar site and were connected to the radar scopes by cables. As the film moved through the machine, the blips were "read" and transmitted to the scopes in the operations room.*

Flight Reference List. This aid was developed for use by the TOR (Training Operations Report) team, the team trained to observe and record crew activities. The flight reference list contained a listing of each and every flight which would appear in the problem and when and where it would appear. For each flight, the list specified the type of aircraft, its serial number, its altitude at point of entry, its operator, its speed, its origin and destination, time of arrival at destination, the time of initial appearance in the system, site at which it would be first seen, and the site or sites to which it would be critical. The flight reference list alerted TOR team members as to what was coming next that needed to be observed.

The flight reference list was "reality." It was the unimpeachable source of what the true facts really were. If the crew had erred by intercepting and identifying the wrong aircraft, by failing to even spot an aircraft, by misjudging altitudes or speeds, it was the flight reference list that established that they had been in error. It was extremely important that the flight reference list not contain errors, that it be always unimpeachable, and that it be consistent with other aids yet to be described.*

Flight Plan Information. Flight information was intended for the airman at the station who would simulate the Air Movement Information Service (AMIS). The aid consisted of a listing of flight plans for the aircraft in the problem. The first several of these were "called in" to the Movements Identification (MI) operator in the operations room before the

* The writer recalls very vividly his first experience with the "unimpeachable source" in the laboratory. I had the position of controller, the operator who gives directions to pilots in making an intercept. I made the intercept very nicely. Later, in the debriefing, it was pointed out that I had intercepted the wrong aircraft. I couldn't believe it. I actually had to leave the debriefing room, go to the operations room, and sit at the controller's scope before I could see what I had done. Fortunately, the plotting board had not been erased nor had I erased my grease pencil marks from the controller's scope face. There it was: The bogey I was supposed to be after was 100 miles South and West of the station, the aircraft I intercepted was 150 miles South and West of the station. In shifting my gaze from the plotting board to the scope face I had skipped from the 100-mile range marker to the 150-mile range marker, not once, but repeatedly. The emotional impact was profound. Where I had, at one moment, totally rejected the possibility of being wrong, now at the next moment, I accepted the TOR team report as infallible. From that point on an "error" became a signal to learn.

problem began. Thus, when the problem started, the MI operator would have the information that he would have had in real life prior to the point in time corresponding to the starting time of the problem.

The AMIS simulator would then call in other flight plans according to a time code in the flight plan information script. The script also instructed the AMIS simulator not to call in certain designated flight plans at all, but to wait until the MI operator called him to verify whether there was a flight plan for a given aircraft. If the MI operator did call in, the AMIS simulator would then give him the desired information, plus some excuse such as, "It just came in," or "Didn't I call that one into you?" If the MI operator failed to call the AMIS simulator, he learned about it in the debriefing.

TOR Maps. The TOR (Training Operations Report) maps were intended as aids to the TOR team. These maps consisted of the entire track history of each critical flight. On a single page, a series of arrows showed the exact path of the critical flight. Each arrowhead located the aircraft at every 3-minute interval. On the right margin of the page was listed such information as the time the aircraft first appeared, in which sector it first appeared, what subsequent sectors it would pass through and when, the time it would fade from view, and when it reappeared in view.

These TOR maps enabled the TOR team to follow with a great deal of precision the discrepancies between the crew's estimates of altitudes, speeds, and identifications of aircraft and the "true" altitudes, speeds, and identifications.

TOR Work Sheets. The TOR work sheets were simply standardized forms on which the TOR teams were to record their observations. As each problem was produced, part of the task was to print out on the TOR work sheet the information on each critical flight (in the order in which each appeared), which was needed by the TOR team to identify each flight and its characteristics properly so as to make positive observation possible.

Intelligence Information. This script consisted of information to be given to the crew before a problem. It contained typical intelligence briefings about the state of world tensions and the probabilities of hostile action. Every effort was made to introduce realism so as to heighten crew anticipations of projected developments in the problem.

Battle Damage Script. Obviously, in the event of a real attack, should a hostile bomber manage to penetrate our defense structure and drop bombs, there would be damage that would be reported back to the defense team in the due course of time. Accordingly, each simulated hostile aircraft was assigned a target, and in the event the crews did not intercept and destroy the simulated hostile aircraft, "damage" ensued. The battle damage script contained instructions to simulation personnel at Division Headquarters as to whom they should call, when they should call, and what they should say. There were times when this script was the first clue that the enemy was attacking.

Correlation Maps. The correlation maps were a second set of maps for aiding the TOR team. The TOR maps, described earlier, showed the history of single critical aircraft. The correlation maps were different in that they showed the location of all flights, friendly and hostile, that were in the air at a given moment of time. One correlation map showed all aircraft that were "visible" to the radar, and another map showed the location of all aircraft not "visible" to the radar because they were at a low altitude, taking off or landing, entering a fade area, or were otherwise not visible. Separate maps were prepared for every 3 minutes of time; these enabled the TOR team to monitor crew actions with a great deal of precision. And, of course, separate sets of maps had to be produced for each radar site.

Pilot Cards and OPS Logs. Cards and logs were developed for the use of the personnel who were simulating interceptor pilots. Each "pilot" sat before a PPI scope. A piece of electronic gear with knobs and dials permitted him to project a blip onto the scopes in the Operations Room and to "fly" the blip in directions and speeds "radioed" to him by the Controller in the Operations Room. Since the "pilot" might be "flying" three or four "intercepts" at the same time, he needed a pilot card on which he could record each aircraft he was flying so as not to misidentify the aircraft to which a new order referred. At the same time, he needed to keep an operations log, detailing the orders he received and the actions he took, to be used later in the debriefings. And, of course, each pilot had a correlation map so that he could report the correct identification of any aircraft he intercepted.

TOR Summary Forms. Standardized forms were used by TOR team members to summarize the history of the crew's actions when handling critical tracks, for presentation in the debriefing period.

Lateral-tell Maps. Tell maps were much like the correlation maps. They showed the locations of aircraft at 3-minute intervals. In real-life operations, an aircraft is cross-told or lateral-told as it moves across division and sector boundaries. The lateral-tell maps were sent to direction centers adjacent to the division being exercised so that the lateral-tell function could be carried out by simulators at those adjacent direction centers.

The foregoing descriptions suggest only vaguely the effort required to develop aids that could make training possible in the field. Some idea of the size of the effort required to produce these problems and their associated aids is suggested by the fact that in a typical problem, some ten radar stations were involved, their antennae were rotated five times per minute, the problem lasted for 120 minutes, an average of 100 aircraft would be in the air at all times, and computations were necessary for latitude, longitude, altitude, and time. To produce one problem required some 2,400,000 computer calculations. Problems were produced at the rate of one every week for sixteen air divisions and one every four months for the three air forces, Eastern Air Force, Central Air Force, and Western Air Force. In addition, there was the requirement for an annual continent-wide problem. The production effort required some 250 people and saturated the capacity of an IBM 704 computer on a round-the-clock basis.

In addition to the engineering effort and the development of the training aids, it was necessary to devise a training vehicle to train Air Force personnel in how to conduct this new and complex system-training methodology. This was achieved by building an Indoctrination Direction Center. This direction center essentially duplicated a real-life direction center (radar station). Real radar scopes were used. The plotting board and tote boards were simulations of standard boards. The degree of realism was very high indeed.

Prior to the initiation of the training program in a given air division, officers and airmen from that air division were brought to Santa Monica for a six-week period. A carefully prepared program of indoctrination and training in the use of the aids was presented. This proved to have been a necessary activity inasmuch as the concept of training as *controlled discovery* was effectively grasped only through experiencing it.

When all was in readiness, the crews to be trained in the field were given shakedown runs on simple problems and then given problems of increasing difficulty. The problems were ordinarily 2 hours in length, and each crew was usually exercised twice a week. Figure 17 displays the complexity of a division-wide exercise.

One might ask why the training was not given in a more

nearly "massed" way (two problems per day for four days a week), as it was in the laboratory. There were several reasons, and these were just the type of reason that so often faces efforts to apply laboratory findings to a field situation. First of all, most stations were organized on a five-crew schedule: four 6-hour shift crews and a standby crew. To give five crews training of 3 hours or more per day for four days each week would

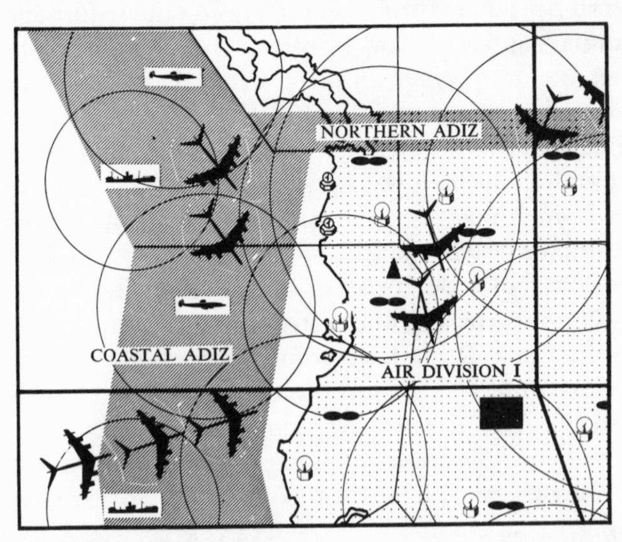

FIGURE 17. *A division-wide problem was complex. Airborne Early Warning aircraft, Picket Ships, Early Warning ground sites, Direction centers, and Division Headquarters had to act as a unified team while each could "see" only part of the whole picture.*

have been an impossibility for the simulation and TOR team. Secondly, there were other training needs that demanded time, such as live exercises. Thirdly, there were scheduled shutdowns of each site for preventive maintenance. Fourthly, there were accidental shutdowns. Fifthly, there were emergency situations that took priority. Last, but not least, there was the need to *do* air defense as well as to train for it.

During a system training exercise, it was the practice to get a top scope man and a top MI (Movements Identification) man to sit to one side and conduct "hip pocket" air defense. In the event of an unknown aircraft entering the area, the remainder of the crew could be alerted and be on full air defense within seconds by throwing a special switch on the side of the scopes, which would cut out the simulated air picture and put on the live air picture.

As the initial problem reproducers came off the manufacturing line, they were installed one by one at the direction centers in the 27th Air Division (Defense). Site-centered problems were used for shakedown purposes. When all the direction centers had their gear operating properly, the envisaged division-wide problems were begun. The operational gains achieved through this system training moved the Air Defense Command to adopt a plan to extend the System Training Program to all continental United States air defense divisions. At the same time, efforts were begun to develop the problem production technology that would permit Force-wide and eventually continent-wide problems.

Clearly, the System Training Program had fulfilled its major promise. It provided an expandable technology for the training and evaluation of a highly complex man-machine system at a fractional cost of live exercises.

To provide the problem material and the proper aids for each site was no small task, as is indicated in Figure 18. Yet the gains achieved by training the division as a team were deemed sufficiently more valuable than those achieved by training individual crews. To all intents and purposes, individual crew training was not engaged in, and the division-wide exercise became the smallest unit of training.

To undertake the installation of equipment, the initiation of training, and the continued production of problem materials needed for a nation-wide training program required more manpower and resources than then available. The "System Training Project" became the "System Training Department" within the Social Science Division of RAND. The search for behavioral scientists began in earnest, for the field

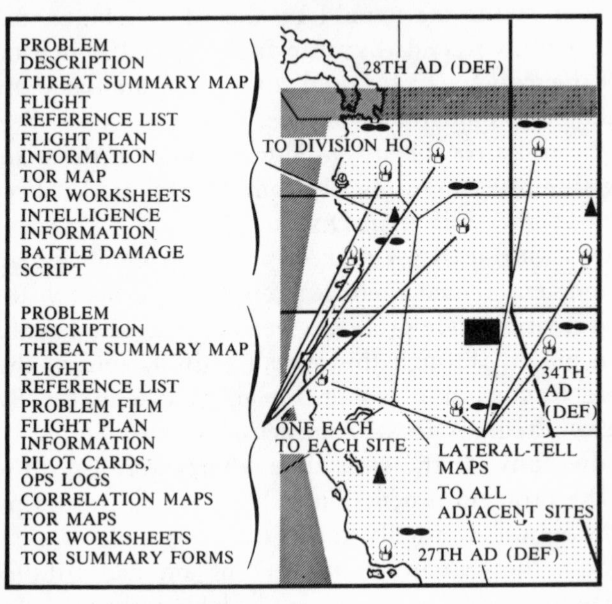

FIGURE 18. *Listings of the aids that had to be sent to different locales in order to conduct an exercise.*

test had demonstrated, with some force, that the culturally shared concepts of training individuals rather than systems are not so easily discarded by people in training. Without frequent guidance, interpretations, and moral support by professional behavioral scientists, the training exercises tend to degrade into exercises comparable to parade ground drills rather than realistic battle experiences.

It was not long after the System Training Department was formed in 1955 that The RAND Corporation was approached once again by the Air Defense Command. The new semi-automated SAGE (Semi-Automatic Ground Environment) system of air defense was off the drawing boards and in production. The system was based on the giant AN-FSQ/7 military computer. The Lincoln Laboratory, developer of the system, needed assistance in writing the initial computer programs and someone was needed to write the program adaptations for specific sectors, install and check out the programs, and then to write the revisions to the programs as new weapon systems (such as advanced design interceptors and missiles) were to come into the system. (At the peak of this effort, over 1100 programers were involved in this effort.) Once again RAND agreed to help out.

The system training effort and the programing effort, both being activities associated with the development of large-scale systems, made a good meld, even suggesting their own name, and the System Development Division of The RAND Corporation came into being. Two years later, the division "spun off" to form the independent System Development Corporation. The RAND Corporation continues to look into the long range, "ten-years-ahead" type of problem, and the System Development Corporation concerns itself with current system design and development activities, a more immediate time orientation.

Coincident with the development of the System Training Program for the manual system of air defense, there began the development of another training program for the SAGE system of air defense. This effort began in late 1955, when a few behavioral scientists were detached from the Santa Monica office and assigned to work at the Lincoln Laboratory facilities near Lexington, Massachusetts. The complexity of the SAGE system required a sizeable training development effort. A group of some forty behavioral scientists spent approximately two years in the preparation of suitable training aids and programs.

All the foregoing applications of the system training developments reflect at least one bond of continuity—the progress of system training through theory, laboratory simulation, and practical application to organization and group learning capabilities. The technology for system training was successfully transferred from the laboratory setting, developed into very large-scale training efforts, and adapted to two new and different large-scale military systems.

The experience gained during a decade of dealing with large-scale organizational problems has not yielded a true science of organizational management with precise measurements and established facts. But it has yielded an art that has developed to such a state as to be explainable, widely applicable, and extremely useful. In the remaining chapters, there will be efforts to explain the concept of organizational "training needs," the principles involved in the development of a program to train organizations, and some illustrations of how these concepts and principles can be adapted to different types of organizations with quite different training needs.

CHAPTER 6

A FIELD EVALUATION OF SYSTEM TRAINING

Two types of events are constant plagues to those who must manage manpower in systems both large and small. One of these is the performance of employees or operators when "things go wrong," that is, when something new or something out of the ordinary is encountered by the operators. To many managers, it must seem that no operator ever uses his head. When an employee demonstrates a capacity to adjust to the new and unusual and gets the job done somehow, he is a highly valued man. One of the major goals of system training is the training of team members to be flexible and to get the job done in the face of the unusual. As the principles of system training are discussed and illustrated, it will become clear how it is possible to train teams to adapt to evolving, changing conditions.

A second type of event that plagues managers is the attitude of many employees or operators toward other parts of the organization, an attitude characterized by the expression, "After me, you come first." A salesman expects the manufacturing department to meet his needs immediately. The manufacturing department wants to maintain its schedule regardless of the salesman's needs for quick action in a special case. A personnel department needs personnel requisitions to plan its work. An operating department does not want to submit a requisition until it knows whom it is going to get. One group of men on an assembly line will "foul up" another group by speeding up and overloading the latter group. All too often there is a marked disregard for the needs of other members of the team. All too often there is a self-interest, which is disruptive to the team effort.

These two types of events demand a great deal of managers' time and effort. As new situations are encountered, managers must devise new work procedures, devise new policy statements, and sometimes shift personnel. When disruptive self-interest is evident, managers must cajole, make arbitrary decisions, devise new regulations, take disciplinary action, or in some other way manage to accomplish the organization's goals.

The ability to adjust rapidly and the ability to be a cooperative team member are abilities that can be trained to a large extent, at least an extent undreamed of before the Systems Research Laboratory's studies. The method of training, however, is based on principles different from those customarily applied when training personnel for doing jobs that can be well specified. These different principles are discussed in this chapter.

In any sizeable organization there is a broad range of job demands. On the one extreme are the jobs that demand highly repetitive and routine behavior. Sorting mail, cleaning house, making change, typing and filing, and filling orders from stock-room supplies are examples of such jobs. On the other extreme are the jobs that require a different set of skills, far from routine or repetitive. Assessing market trends, determining operating policy, devising advertising strategy, and directing sales efforts are jobs that require the *adaptation* of skills to an ever-changing situation as well as the routine *application* of skills.

On the one hand, the typist must *apply* with routine consistency the skills of spelling. On the other hand, the executive must *adapt* with routine consistency a host of skills. The rules of spelling are well fixed, but there are often no fixed rules for the action an executive may have to take. He may take any one of several different actions with equal success or with minor variations in success, or he may take the action that wrecks the company as the effects of the action accumulate over time.

We are accustomed to training procedures for the routine application of skills. Essentially, these procedures (1) set forth the task to be accomplished, (2) provide an opportunity for practice, (3) provide "reward" for correct responses and "punishments" for incorrect responses, and (4) provide an opportunity for continued practice until the desired level of competence has been reached.

System training, on the other hand, is being directed more toward the *adaptation* of already learned skills and differs from the customary training procedures. Instead of a class of forty *men* being trained to do the same thing, think of forty *team members* being trained, each to do something different yet to perform the total task well. Here the training process has different procedures:

1. It first sets up a simulated, meaningful task to be dealt with by the team as a whole.
2. The task is presented in a real-life setting (or a realistic facsimile).
3. The system provides objective knowledge of results at the end of the exercise, and this permits team members to reconstruct the situation with which they were faced, the actions they took, and the consequences of their actions upon the system task.
4. Team members have opportunity to discuss the situation-response-consequence data in the absence of outside (in

the sense of outside the crew) evaluation of goodness or badness and in the absence of outside didactics (in the sense of "teaching" what the right actions "should have been").

Unlike customary procedures for training in fixed skills where the same situation is presented over and over for practice, system training procedures are most effective when the problems are varied and repeated only when it is certain that the crew does not recognize the problem as it develops. The untimely repetition of an air defense problem, for example, has resulted in such things as a Weapons Director saying, "That first 'Invader' won't be here for half an hour, yet. I'm going out for a coffee." Experience with system training exercises has indicated (especially in the SAGE system of air defense, with its totally new, button-pushing skills being demanded of operators) that where component skills are lacking among operators, the repetition of the same exercise, combined with direct, didactic teaching, is highly effective in helping operators to acquire mastery over complex tasks. Put in the simplest words, if an operator-position requires five different sets of skills and the task requires a flexible interleaving of the application of these skills, repetitive practice on the same complex problem helps operators to achieve the second-order, interleaving skills. Once these second-order skills have been achieved, however, it seems best not to repeat recognizable problems. To do so invites the operators to conclude that they have "arrived," that their present procedures are the "correct" procedures. The Systems Research Laboratory experiments indicated, to the contrary, that it is largely after operator skills are well learned that the operators are really ready to tap the human capacity for evolving new procedures that serve the system's goals.

To get a close picture of how system training can affect crew performance, let us consider in some detail the outcomes of a study conducted at the radar site known as M-130 ("M" for mobile, "130" for 130th site.) This site, located near Winston-Salem, North Carolina, had just been completed as a permanent (P) site except for telephone lines connecting it with other adjacent sites and with the 85th Air Division (Defense) headquarters. The site was fully manned with crews drawn from other parts of the radar defense system.

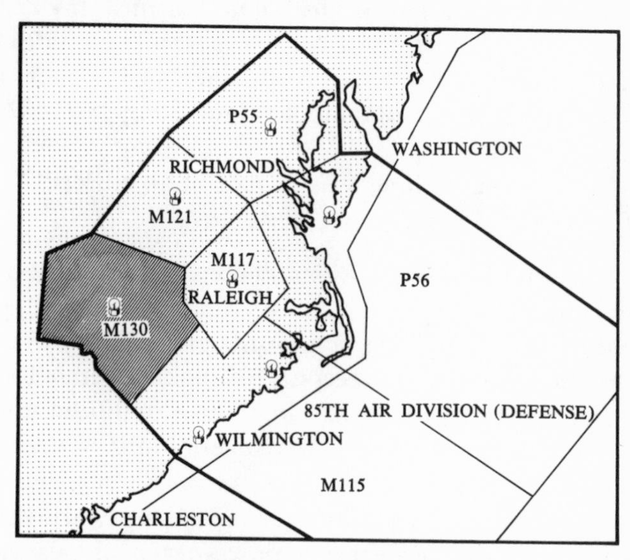

FIGURE 19. *Sketch of the 85th Air Division (Defense) showing the inland location of the M-130 sector.*

As is seen in Figure 19, M-130 was an "inland" site. Its defense missions consisted of the following:

1. Cross-telling to the appropriate site or sites the "friendly" identification of any flights originating within the M-130 sector and passing into any adjacent sector or sectors in the 85th Division or into any adjacent sector or sectors in adjacent divisions.

2. Maintaining track continuity on any flights passing over the M-130 area.

3. Taking over control of interceptors scrambled by an adjacent site and passing into the M-130 area. (For example, M-115 might have scrambled after an inbound flight, but might not have completed the intercept before the aircraft penetrated the M-130 sector.)

4. Taking appropriate tactical action against any critical flight (such as unknown flight, hostile aircraft or aircraft needing navigational assistance) entering the M-130 sector. (For example, an unknown, inbound flight missed by M-115 would be a critical flight.)

5. Taking over all functions in part of an adjacent sector that for some reason had to "go off the air."

To accomplish these missions, the crews depended upon certain skills: scope reading, height finding, plotting, dead reckoning, radio-telephone procedures, cross-telling, weapons direction (directing an interceptor to a point where an intercept can be made), and so on. The men had all been trained for their jobs. They had the "component" skills—some more, some less.

It was impossible to form four crews completely identical in all aspects, but a great deal of care was taken to balance inequities among crew capabilities, as is shown in Table 1. X_1 and X_2 refer to the experimental crews and C_1 and C_2 refer to the control crews. The X_1 and X_2 crews received system training, whereas the control crews were exercised and trained in the conventional manner. These differences will be made explicit later. At this point, we are concerned with the capabilities brought to the air defense task by the crews.

Although the crews were well matched with regard to military rank, job classification, and operational knowledge, the experimental crews had slightly fewer months of experience in doing aircraft control and warning work, and for the most part, they did not do so well as the control crews at the outset of the study.

TABLE 1. THE BALANCE OF INITIAL CREW CAPABILITY

	Crews			
	X_1	X_2	C_1	C_2
Operations Experience				
Mean months of experience[a]	13.4	11.8	11.8	13.3
Number of men with over a year of experience	4	6	6	6
Number of men with three or fewer months of experience	4	4	3	3
Military Rank				
Staff Sergeants	1	0	1	0
Airmen 1st Class	2	3	2	3
Airmen 2nd Class	7	6	6	7
Airmen 3rd Class	2	3	3	2
85th Air Division "Operational Proficiency Test" Scores	36.9	38.2	39.3	36.2

[a] Each crew was composed of twelve men plus the senior director (an officer). The senior director is not included in these figures.

Simulation personnel (not members of any of the crews) were trained to simulate adjacent stations, division headquarters, pilots, and the operator at the Air Movements Information Section of the Air Route Traffic Control Center. Two military men were trained extensively in what to observe, how to observe, and how to record specific crew actions.

Each of the four crews were given the same air defense problems. These problems, 2 hours each in length, were presented by the problem reproducer and the simulation personnel. The first problem was used for shakedown purposes. After all members of the operating crews, the simulation teams, and the observation teams were familiarized with the operation, two successive, heavy load problems were run as an initial test. These same two problems were run again at the end of the training period as a post-test. In between these testings, six other problems were each run twice. In order to minimize influencing the results of the study by off-hour barracks talk between members of different crews, precautions were taken to vary the order in which crews received the training problems. With the exception of the shakedown problems and one unique test problem, no problem was run twice on the same day. Little things, such as the track numbers of tracks "told in" from the simulated adjacent stations, were altered in order to eliminate features of a problem that might be remembered by crew members. From all indications, the crew members were unaware of ever receiving the same problem twice. To provide heightened motivation and to eliminate further inter-crew barracks talk, a "Crew of the Month" award was established. The crew members were aware that their first month's award would be based upon the training problems; and they were told that if they wanted to win, they should not talk with members of other crews about the handling or nature of problems.

At the conclusion of each problem exercise, the control crews went their individual ways. No formal post-exercise discussions were held for these crews. The experimental crews, however, were presented with the systematic observations gathered by the trained observers, and were given an opportunity to discuss and evaluate the data and to seek solutions to operational problems. The experimenters observed the senior directors as they conducted the discussion sessions and afterward "critiqued" the senior director on his leadership of the crew as a problem-solving group. This critique centered principally around the extent to which the senior director concentrated on problem areas and used the observers' data to throw light on the problems.

Because of the precautions taken, the experimenters felt sure that the crews were largely, if not completely, unaware that two of them (the experimental crews) were being treated differently with regard to information about their performance.

Specifically, what was the nature of this information?

The experimental crews were told how many aircraft had initially appeared in the area for which plotting was required, how many were actually detected, the average time-delay between the initial appearance on the radar scope, and the plotting of the aircraft on the plotting board, the number of aircraft that were lost and replotted as new tracks, and the number of times track numbers were switched. With respect to aircraft that had been cross-told into M-130, the experimental crews were told the number of such flights for which plotting had been required, the average time-delay from initial cross-tell to initial plot, the number of flights on which tracking continuity had been maintained, the number that had been lost because they faded from the scopes, the number that had not been detected, the number that had been detected but carried as new tracks, the number that had been detected but had been mixed up with other tracks, and the number of tracks that should have been cross-told but had not been.

The experimental crews were also told the number of friendly aircraft without flight plans or off flight plans (and therefore requiring identification by interception) that had been intercepted and those that had not been intercepted. As to "invading" aircraft, the experimental crews were told the number of mass raids involved, the number of aircraft in the raids, the number "splashed," the number that completed their bomb runs, the number of bombs dropped, and the location of the targets hit. The same information was given for all single raids.

With respect to the cross-telling to other sites, the experimental crews were told the number of critical and noncritical flights that should have been cross-told, how many had been cross-told, and the average time-delay between the plotting of the track and the moment of cross-telling.

With regard to interceptions, the experimental crews were told the number of unknowns or "invaders" against which scramble action had been taken (or control of the intercept received from adjacent sites), and how many intercepts had been completed or missed because of lack of fuel, incorrect altitude, wrong track, ammunition expended, track fading prior to intercept, or ending the intercept in a tail chase.

The information given to the experimental crews did not tell them *why* they were having trouble, but it did help them learn *where* they were having trouble. As they endeavored to discover *why* they were having trouble, they could also call on the observers for specific information about any flight. Because these were simulated flights, it was possible to tell the crews exactly when the flight first appeared on the scopes, what type of aircraft it was, its point of origin, its destination, its speed, its altitude, and whether or not it was friendly, off flight plan, or hostile. Because the observers had recorded crew actions, it was possible to tell the crews when they had made an initial plotting of the track, the speed they had estimated, the altitude they had estimated, the identification given the flight, when and where it had faded (if it did), and any changes in the crew's estimates of speed and altitude or confusions in track continuity and identification.

How was performance affected? The findings are presented below.

First, let us ask what influence the two training conditions had on the crews' ability to detect any and all tracks that appeared in the M-130 area. The bars in Figure 20 show the percentages of flights detected in the pretests and post-tests. While all crews showed some improvement, the two experimental crews, X_1 and X_2, were 85 percent and 90 percent better in the post-test than in the pretest, whereas the two control crews, C_1

and C_2, improved their performance by 4 percent and 23 percent, respectively.

Let us now consider only those flights that originated in the M-130 area. These flights, if continuing on into an adjacent

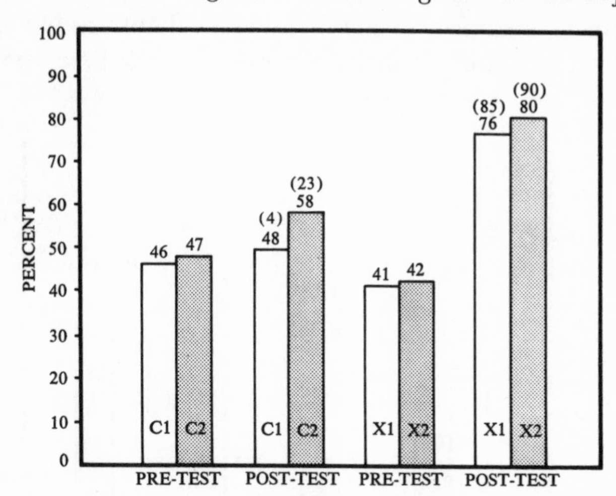

FIGURE 20. *Percentage of all flights appearing in the M-130 area that were detected by control and experimental crews during pretest and post-test. Figures in parentheses show percent improvement of post-test performance over pretest performance.*

sector, would have had to be cross-told or they would have been declared "unknown" by the adjacent site and scrambled on. In Figure 21 we see that both experimental crews improved by 117 percent and 30 percent. One of the control crews dropped by 10 percent in performance and the other improved by 70 percent.

A flight may be cross-told into a site, but that is no guarantee that it will be detected by the site. In Figure 22, the performance of the crews in detecting cross-told tracks is shown. The control crews improved by 9 percent and 8 percent, and the experimental crews improved by 52 percent and 115 percent.

Another measure of performance taken in the study relates to the speed with which tracks were detected. This measure was taken by observing the lapsed time between the initial appearance of a flight on the scope (or the time of initial "tell" from an adjacent sector) and the time the flight was plotted on the plotting board. In Figure 23, the results of these measures are presented.

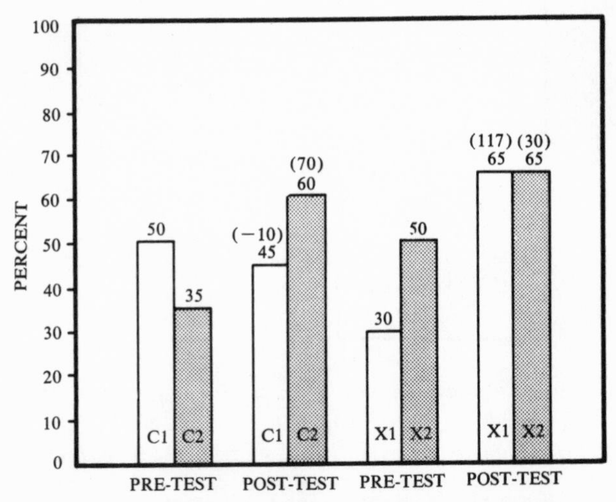

FIGURE 21. *Percentage of flights originating in M-130 area that were detected by control and experimental crews. Figures in parentheses show percent improvement of post-test performance over pretest performance.*

When tracks are cross-told into a sector, the crew is told that a track exists and where it is located. Tracks appearing initially within a sector are a different problem. The blips must be noticed and observed over a period of time to make certain that there is movement of the blip, that is, that the blip is an actual echo from a moving object and not "noise." To make matters more difficult, there is the matter of "blip-scan ratio." When aircraft are just beginning to penetrate into the area covered by the radar beam, the echo return will not always be strong enough to show on the scope. Several scans (rotations of the antenna) may go by before an echo is strong enough to register a second time. The closer the aircraft comes, of course, the stronger the echoes become until the ratio of blip-to-scan becomes 1. Early in its approach, then, a blip may appear; but if on the next few scans nothing more can be seen, the blip may be disregarded.

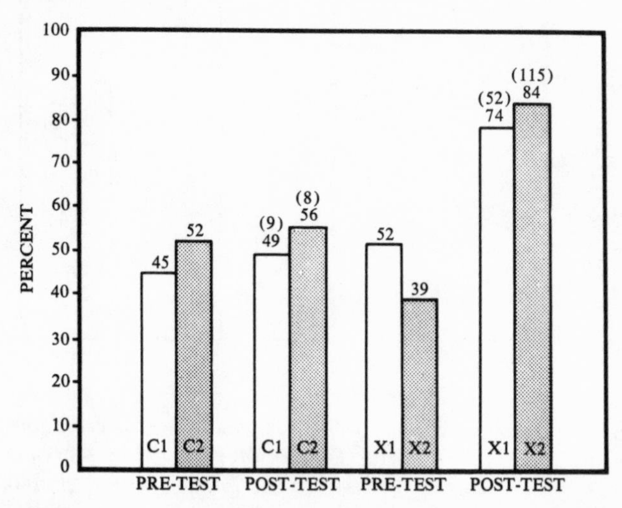

FIGURE 22. *Percentage of cross-told tracks detected by control and experimental crews. Figures in parentheses show improvement of post-test performance over pretest performance.*

An additional difficulty in detecting initial appearances can arise from "ground clutter" or "permanent echo." Just as a searchlight lights up the ground in front of it at the same time it is sending a beam into the sky, so does a radar reflect onto the ground around it, causing echoes to bounce back to the receiver. These echoes "paint" a "permanent" blotchy area around the center of the scope all the time. If an airfield is located in the area from which ground clutter is being received, aircraft originating there cannot be seen until they emerge from the ground clutter area. Green Five was an airway extending from Atlanta, Georgia, to Richmond, Virginia. It crossed the M-130 area. Many initial appearances of aircraft

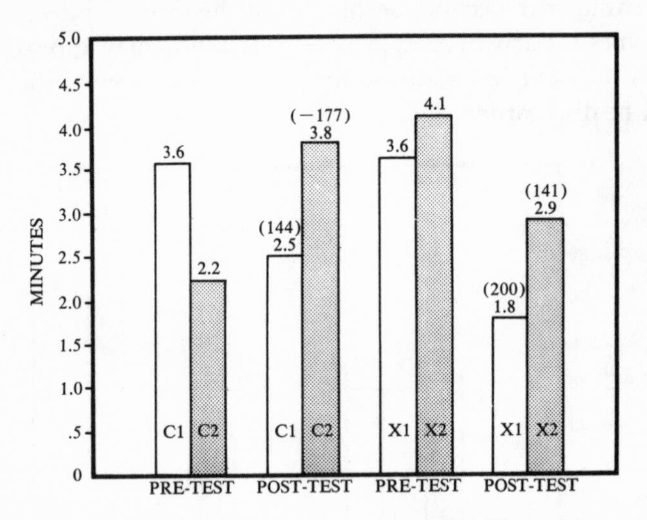

FIGURE 23. *Minutes of lapsed time between initial appearance of a flight on the scope or initial "tell" from an adjacent sector and time of plotting on plotting board. Figures in parentheses represent percentage of improvement of post-test performance over pretest performance.*

occurred as aircraft emerged from the ground clutter. In their discussion of time-lags in detecting aircraft, both experimental crews achieved insight into this fact. What is more, both experimental crews developed insight into the blip-scan ratio problem and adapted their procedures so as to maximize early detection of aircraft penetrating the radar coverage periphery and of aircraft emerging from ground clutter. How these insights improved crew performance is shown in Figure 24.

When a flight has been detected and an initial plot has been made, the first step in "establishing" the track has been accomplished. Subsequent observations of blip movement must be plotted to determine the direction of the track movement. Estimates of speed must be made and altitude must be determined. Additionally, the track must be assigned a number.

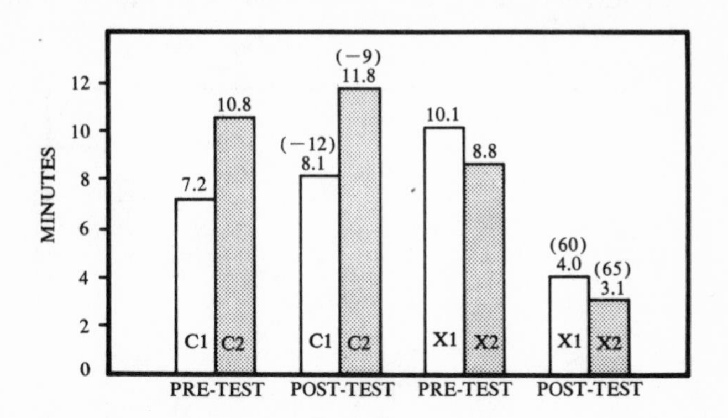

FIGURE 24. *Lapsed time between initial appearance on the scope of flights originating in M-130 area and time of plotting on plotting board. Figures in parentheses show percentage of improvement of post-test performance over pretest performance.*

When all these things have been done, the track is "established." Figure 25 shows the ability of control and experimental crews to detect aircraft and actually to get tracks established. (It may occur to the reader that the performance of the crews, even after training, does not augur well for air defense. Bear in mind that the problems used as the pretest and post-test were heavy-load problems and filled with flights that appeared and faded within a span of 2 or 3 minutes. The problems were deliberately stressful, and it is probable that no crew could have achieved 100 percent performance.)

By averaging the gains or losses for the control groups and for the experimental crews (*cf.* Figures 24 and 25), we can see that the control crews detected and established 8 percent more tracks at the time of the post-test, but required 10 percent more time. At the time of the pretest, the control crews established 67 percent more tracks than did the experimental crews and were a little faster; but, by the time of the post-test, the experimental crews were handling 81 percent more tracks than the control crews, with approximately one-third as much delay.

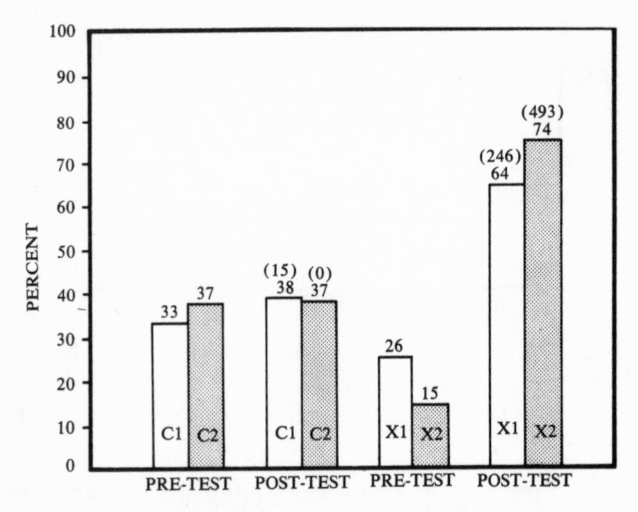

FIGURE 25. *Percentage of tracks "established" by control and experimental crews. Figures in parentheses show percentage of improvement of post-test performance over pretest performance.*

The reader will recall that one of the major missions of the M-130 site was that of cross-telling information about tracks headed for adjacent sectors. Figure 26 shows how well the crews did at cross-telling information on "critical" tracks, tracks such as "unknowns" and "invaders."

The purpose of "cross-telling" is to provide warning time to adjacent sites, most especially warning time of the approach of hostile aircraft and aircraft of unknown identity. Figure 27 presents the average amounts of warning time provided to adjacent sites by the crews.

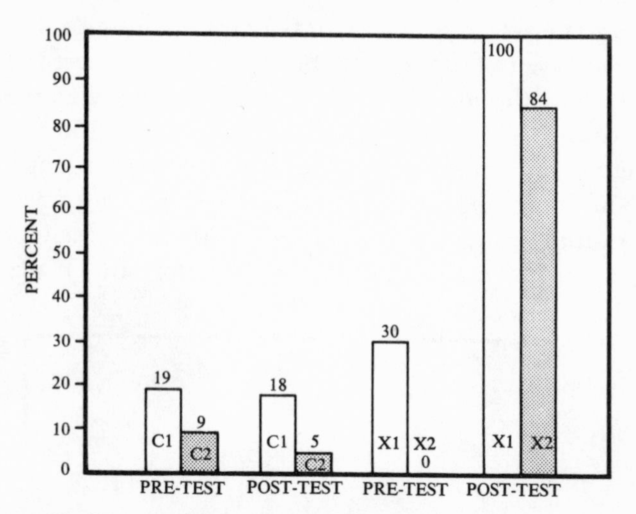

Figure 26. *Percentage of critical tracks that were cross-told to adjacent sectors.*

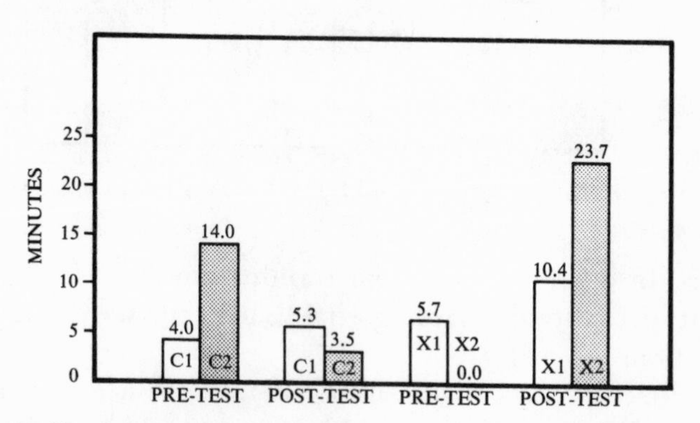

Figure 27. *Average number of minutes of early warning time provided adjacent sectors by cross-telling.*

The final pay-off in air defense is, of course, the taking of appropriate action against critical aircraft. Figure 28 shows all crews to have improved, with the experimental crews showing nearly twice the amount of improvement achieved by the control crews.

Let us consider one final set of data before going on to discuss the "hows and whys" of superior performance under system training conditions. As has been stressed in earlier chapters, system training aims at the development of adaptive

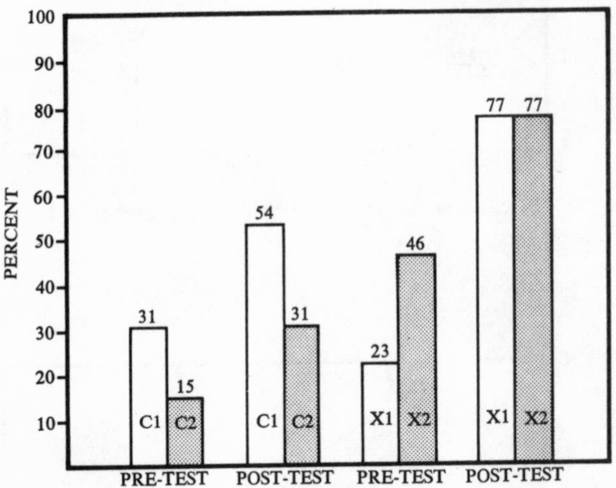

FIGURE 28. *Percentage of critical flights against which appropriate tactical action was taken.*

skills. In other words, system training aims at the development of facility in adapting established skills to unexpected situations.

A difficult "peace-to-war" problem was modified to place an extremely heavy, unexpected load on to the M-130 site. The M-115 site, on which M-130 normally depended for much of its identification information, early warning, and authority to scramble interceptors, was "bombed out" early in the problem. All the M-115 responsibilities were delegated to M-130.

Thus the surveillance load was increased, the identification load was increased, and the interception load was increased. As it would have happened in real life, the M-130 crews found themselves scrambling interceptors out of an airfield with which M-130 had no direct communication line, making it necessary to relay scramble orders through an adjacent station. As will be seen in the figures that follow, the experimental crews were superior in their performance.

Figure 29 shows the performance of the crews in detecting flights and establishing tracks for those flights.

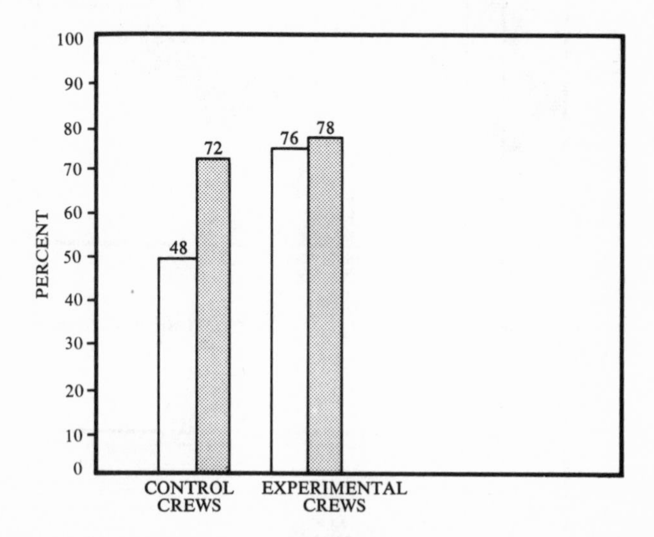

FIGURE 29. *Percentage of flights detected and established under emergency conditions.*

When a crew is overloaded, it cannot do everything. The mark of a well-trained crew is its ability to handle the more important events at the expense of the less important. The superior training of the experimental crews is evidenced in their cross-telling of critical tracks. Figure 30 shows the percentage of flights that should have been cross-told and which were cross-told. (Once again, the purpose of "cross-telling" is to provide warning time to adjacent sites, most especially on hostile aircraft and aircraft of unknown identity.) Figure 31 indicates the continued higher performance of the experimental crews.

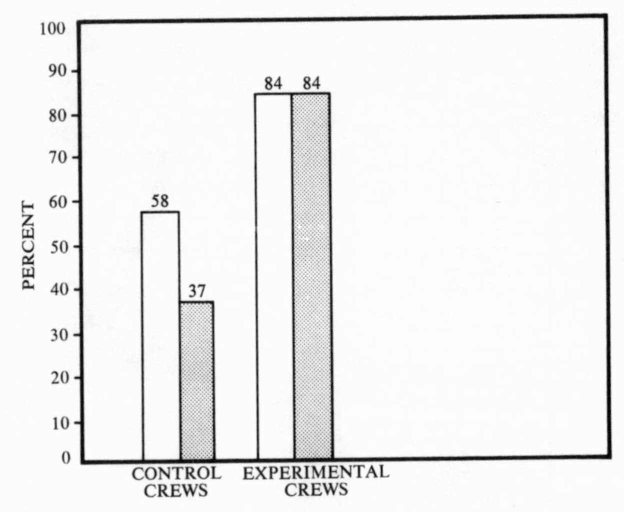

FIGURE 30. *Percentage of critical tracks cross-told under emergency conditions.*

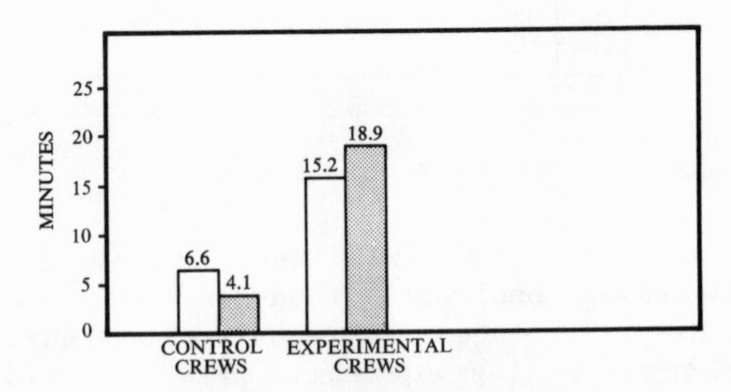

FIGURE 31. *Average number of minutes of early warning time on critical tracks provided under emergency conditions.*

And, once again, the payoff in air defense is the taking of appropriate tactical action against unknown and hostile aircraft and giving aid to aircraft in distress. In Figure 32 the performance of the crews in taking tactical action is shown. The experimental crews did roughly four times better than did the control crews.

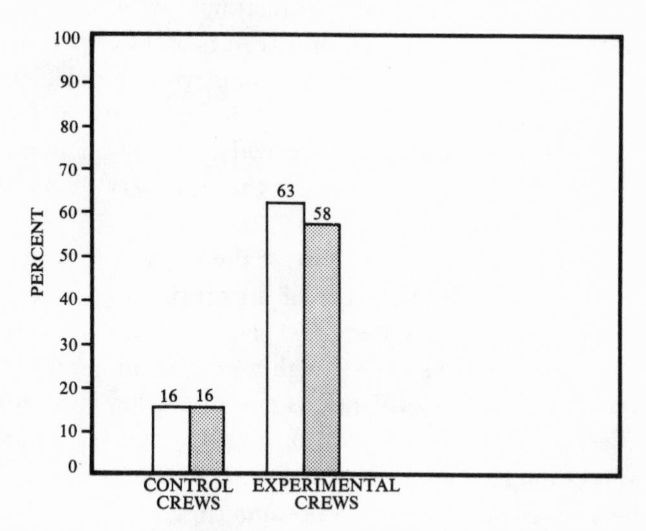

FIGURE 32. *Percentage of critical aircraft against which appropriate tactical action was taken under emergency condition.*

So much, then, for the types of information given to the experimental groups (but not the control groups) and so much for the evidences of superior performance by the experimental crews. Let us now look into the matter of the post-exercise discussion and problem-solving sessions, or "debriefings."

The debriefings ordinarily took place about 10 to 15 minutes after the conclusion of a problem run. This small delay was necessary to permit the observers to prepare summaries of their observations. The senior director, the senior officer of the crew, led the discussion. The observers remained for the discussion, but confined their activity to presenting summary information and to answering questions from their detailed information. If any evaluation of goodness of performance was made, it was made by some member of the crew-in-training. No outsider was permitted to make any evaluations or to offer "instruction."

As mentioned earlier, the investigators* observed the leadership performance of the senior directors of the experimental groups and discussed their observations with the officers following the crew debriefings. The principal concern during these discussions was the extent to which the officers used the information available to them for the discovery of problem areas and problem causes.

Some readers may wonder why, if the object was to train a crew most effectively, the help of an outside expert was rejected. Obviously, the members of the observation team, knowing the problems as thoroughly as they did, and having observed a crew's performance as closely as they did, should have been in an excellent position to point out areas of difficulty and to suggest answers to problems.

The answer is, at one and the same time, both simple and complex. In the first place, one major training goal is the development of problem-solving skills *among crew members,* not among experts. To have the problem-solving activity centered in experts robs crew members of the opportunity to *exercise* all the poor judgment that it takes to learn to have good judgment. In the second (and more complex) place, one must consider the nature of the air defense job. As Chapman, Kennedy, Newell, and Biel (1959)† point out, ". . . a de-

* Benjamin B. Tregoe, a social anthropologist, and Charles H. Kepner, a social psychologist, were the principal investigators and were supported by the members of the research staff.

† R. L. Chapman, J. L. Kennedy, A. Newell, and W. C. Biel, "The Systems Research Laboratory's Air Defense Experiments," *Management Science,* Vol. 5, No. 3 (April, 1959) 226.

scription of a crew's rules of operation, *with all contingencies and qualifications expressed,* would occupy volumes." Rules of operations to cover contingencies depend upon a myriad of events such as: who is actually on the crew, who is on leave, who is sick, what is the nature of the particular.air emergency, how many are there of them, what is the load of background traffic, what is developing in adjacent sites, how many interceptors are available, what is the weather, what demands are being made by Division Headquarters, what effects follow from earlier actions, plus all the individual and group events that influence humans from day to day. While logically it would be possible to say that in a given, single instance a certain pattern of response would be best, it is extremely unlikely that the totality of those circumstances would ever repeat themselves. In such a complex of events, however, crews can come to recognize changes in these patterns. When the opportunity is presented to explore many processing procedures, crews become aware of alternate ways of acting. These two skills, sensitivity to changing patterns in information and awareness of alternative ways of handling the information, combine to contribute a greater potential for adapting responses to the particular nature of the environment at the moment.

How do these sensitivities and awareness become developed? The evidence, such as is seen in the M-130 study, suggests that they are not developed so rapidly through experience alone as they are when available information permits the isolation of problem areas and the development of insight into what kinds of consequences are peculiar to what kinds of events and actions.

It seems appropriate at this point to illustrate the distinction between the kinds of "knowledge of results" available to the experimental and to the control crews. For our illustration, let us use the knowledge of results available to a crossteller under the control and experimental conditions.

Figure 33 presents the information flow from the plotting board at the first site (PB_1) to the cross-teller (CT). The cross-teller "tells" by telephone (solid arrow) over distance to a plotter (P) who plots the data on the plotting board at the second site (PB_2). The plotted information is then available

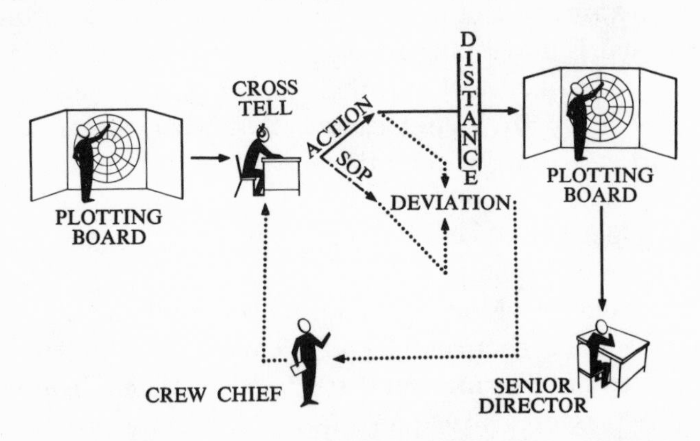

FIGURE 33. *Information appearing on the plotting board at one sector is cross-told over a distance to a plotter at an adjacent sector and becomes available to the senior director at that sector. Meanwhile, the only way of correcting the cross-teller's errors is through the crew chief's sensing deviations from SOP's (Standard Operating Procedures) and feeding back information to the cross-teller.*

to the senior director at the second site. To guide his behavior, the cross-teller has certain standard operating procedures, or SOPs (dotted arrow). The crew chief at the first site has only certain things he can observe. By monitoring the cross-teller's behavior for a period of time, the crew chief is able to observe deviations from SOPs (dot-dash arrows) and to give the cross-teller "feedback" (dotted arrow).

Figure 33 stresses that even though the function of the cross-teller is to provide early warning time to the second site, the design of the system is such that he cannot learn how effective he is. The only "knowledge of results" he can get is about his performance relative to SOPs and that is obtainable only from the crew chief. And the type of "knowledge of results" he gets from the crew chief may vary from being relatively "noise free" to very "noisy"; that is, it may contain a lot or little information relative to the fulfillment of the cross-telling function and a little or a lot of information on the crew-chief's state of mind.

The cross-teller has two sets of expectations as he performs. On one hand, he has expectations of what his behavior will result in at the second site. In other words, he expects to provide some warning time. On the other hand, he expects that certain of his acts will result in certain behavior by the crew chief. We can expect that the cross-teller will so behave as to maximize the approval-giving behavior of the crew chief and to minimize retaliatory behavior by the crew chief. Figure 34

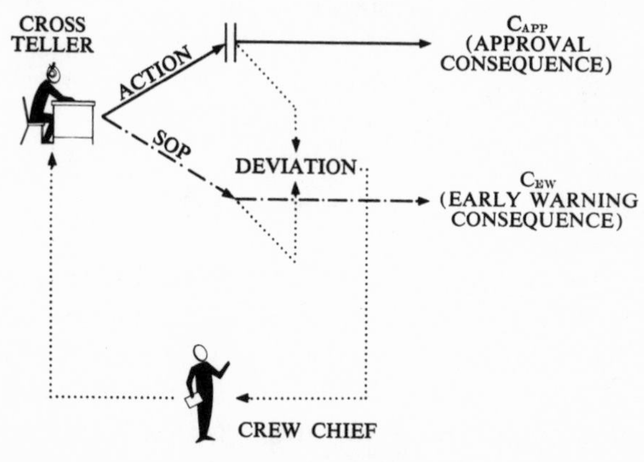

FIGURE 34. *When the cross-teller is dependent upon the crew chief for correction, we can expect him to seek approval as well as to provide early warning.*

represents the relationship between the cross-teller and the crew chief. The heavy lines represent the fact that the cross-teller has two sets of expectations, the consequences of providing early warning (C_{EW}) and the consequences of approval or disapproval (C_{APP}) by the crew chief.

The crew chief can respond in at least three basically different ways. First, he could, in an objective manner, restrict his behavior simply to describing to the cross-teller the extent of his deviation from an established SOP, just as an artillery spotter might simply report on deviation of a hit from the target. This type of feedback is the most noise-free. It leaves the judgment of what to do to correct the action in the hands of the cross-teller. It maximizes attention to the consequences relative to providing early warning, and minimizes the approval-disapproval expectations. Secondly, the crew chief could *give directions* to the cross-teller, which would tell him what to do. This would shift the locus of judgment making from the cross-teller to the crew chief and begins to shift the cross-teller's attention primarily to the crew chief's behavior. Thirdly, the crew chief could provide evaluation solely; that is, he could restrict his behavior to giving approval or disapproval, without specifying why. This kind of behavior gives the cross-teller a lot of information about the crew chief's state of mind, but very little information about the warning time provided to the adjacent site.

The situation for the cross-tellers in the experimental groups is quite different, as is represented in Figure 35. As the cross-teller "tells," he expects certain consequences. The trained observers record the actual consequences in a Training Operations Report (TOR). Also recorded in the TOR are the wealth of facts described earlier relative to flight characteristics and to what else was going on in the system at the time of the "tell." The availability of the Training Operations Report to the cross-teller directly, as well as through the senior director, permits the teller to compare actual consequences with expected consequences and with SOPs. It literally eliminates the crew chief as the sole source of "knowledge of results."

Probably the most significant outcome of the M-130 study was not a discovery but rather a recognition in a new context of the long known and universally accepted principle that knowledge of results really does aid learning. It is easy to

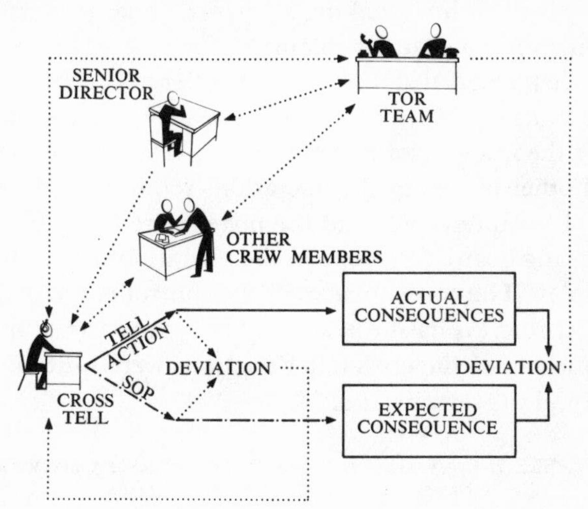

FIGURE 35. *Under conditions of system training the cross-teller gets feedback from the TOR team of the actual consequences of his behavior at adjacent sectors as well as feedback from the senior director and other crew members. He is now in a position to learn how his behavior affects others.*

recognize that throwing darts over a barrier at a target the thrower cannot see will result in poorer performance than when the target is visible and the success of each throw is visible to the thrower. It was not easy to recognize that the various air defense functions differed markedly in the visibility of the consequences of operator actions taken.

We are totally unaccustomed to looking at jobs in this way. Were we to walk into a bank and see many people at work or were we to take a tour of a mail order house, we would observe people engaged in a variety of activities. If we wanted to know more about their jobs, we might get a detailed explanation from a supervisor or we might read a job description. In either case, we should get information solely on what the operator is supposed to do. Were we to ask, "How can the employee tell when he is making an error?" it seems certain that we should draw a complete blank.

It so happened that when a controller was controlling an intercept, he could see on the radar scope the merging of the blips of the interceptor and the bogey. What's more, so could several other people in the operations room. In addition, the tracks of the interceptor and the bogey were being plotted on the plotting board. Everyone in the operations room could see the display. The consequences of the controller's actions were highly visible. As has been stressed in earlier paragraphs, the consequences of the cross-teller's actions were quite invisible to him and to everyone else.

TABLE 2. Comparison of Average Performance Gain with Visibility of Five Air Defense Functions[a]

		Average Performance Gain (Pretest to Post-test), Percent	
Degree of Visibility[b]	Function	Experimental Crews	Control Crews
High	Tactical action	14.0	11.5
	Track establishment	46.5	1.5
Medium	Input processing	35.5	5.5
	Track maintenance	49.0	-6.5
Low	Lateral tell-out	62.0	-9.5

[a] Adapted from L. T. Alexander, C. H. Kepner, and B. B. Tregoe, "The Effectiveness of Knowledge of Results in the Military System Training Program," *J. Appl. Psychology,* Vol. 46, 3 (June 1962), 202–212.

[b] Subjectively ordered.

When the different operational functions were grouped (subjectively, it is to be admitted) from high visibility of consequences to low visibility of consequences, it was clear that the experimental group made its greatest gains in those functions where on-the-job visibility of consequences was lowest.

A comparison of the relationships between sources of knowledge of results and cross-tellers, as sketched in Figures 34 and 35, leaves little doubt as to why the experimental crews were in a much more favorable position to learn what they needed to learn to perform more effectively. They not only had "knowledge of results," but also knowledge of those results or consequences that gave them insight as to what behavior led to what consequences.

The diagrams suggest—and one might well presume—that with all the situation-information and all the consequence-information available to a crew, and with an officer to lead the discussion, the problem-solving process during a debriefing would be a highly ordered and clearly intellectual discussion period in which problems would be isolated, alternate solutions weighed, and modifications of procedures determined. That this is not always (or even often) the case is strongly suggested by the Systems Research Laboratory studies cited in earlier chapters. In their report of these studies, Chapman, Kennedy, Newell, and Biel (1949) state:

> We believe that the debriefings following each session, where the operating results were reviewed, were crucial to the learning that led to improved performance. But we have been unable to relate the content of these discussions directly to crew development. Procedures were frequently changed without any sign that the operating problem had been recognized or a solution proposed. As a matter of fact, procedural changes sometimes moved in one direction while discussions went in another.
>
> On the first day of the second set—a very nervy day for us—the Cowboy

crew floundered and threatened to break under more stress than we had predicted the load increase would cause. During the debriefing the crew sat dull, resigned, and discussionless while the results were read. But the next day many procedural changes were in evidence and performance improved. (Post-experimental interviews indicate very little discussion outside the laboratory took place.) The Cobra crew took the load increase of the second set in stride (we had braced ourselves) only to falter at the beginning of the third set (we had not).

One crew had surveillance difficulties that were discussed at length both in debriefings and during operations. Much blame was focused on the air surveillance officer; many suggestions were made—profane and otherwise. No resolution was found at the time. Somewhat later the man in question went on sick call for the first few hours of a day. Another officer filled in for him and this temporary arrangement became permanent. All of this happened very casually and with little apparent reference to the previous discussions.

As the crews were confronted by increasingly difficult tasks, they questioned the organization's goal ("the best defense is a good offense"), the adequacy of their equipment ("the grease pencils are no damn good") and registered many signs of bad morale. But these seemed to be symptoms of stress—tension release—that were followed by procedural changes. Bad morale may not always be an omen of impending failure inasmuch as even these four "good" crews exhibited such symptoms in the course of their development.*

The primary reason for the quotation above is to emphasize one of the important characteristics of self-directed learning, that is, its frequent, apparent lack of direction. The uninformed observer, who expects problem solving to proceed in a coherent, logical, step-by-step manner, will all too often see only chaos. Why is this? What of a constructive nature is going on that promotes learning in one direction while discussion goes in another? I believe there are two sets of events at work. One relates to how our culture leads us to look at the nature of learning, and the second relates to im-

* R. L. Chapman, J. L. Kennedy, A. Newell, and W. C. Biel, "The Systems Research Laboratory's Air Defense Experiments," *Management Science,* Vol. 5, 3 (April 1959), 264.

portant emotional factors in the self-directed learning process. Let us consider these two sets of events in this order.

As parents and just plain people, we tend to be interested in "learning," as such, primarily when we are interested in "teaching." We want to housebreak the cat and toilet-train the child. We want our children to have polite manners. We want the children to mind their mother. We apply rewards and punishments to make some ways of behaving pleasurable and profitable, and other ways of behaving risky and uncomfortable. We learn that the way to control behavior in others is to manipulate rewards and punishments.

It is generally true that if one makes a certain way of behaving sufficiently pleasurable and profitable, people will learn to behave in the desired way. There is much to say for the notion that rewards and punishments are not what control the learning process so much as they are things that get "learned about" in the course of learning. Consider, for example, a young child who turns on the gas stove for the first time and so has his hand soundly slapped by his mother. The child "learns" some things, that is for sure. He learns such things as: Mother is a punishing person, exploring new things may lead to punishment, turning on the handle makes the flame go on, and if you really want to turn on the stove, wait until mother is not there. If the consequences or anticipated consequences of turning on the stove are sufficiently fearsome, the child may not express what he has learned about turning the knob. But to say that the child has learned not to turn on the stove does not seem realistic.

As is suggested above, learning of this order seems more properly viewed as the development of concepts of "what-leads-to-what." The concepts may be "fuzzy" and "lightly" held. Then we call them notions. They may be extremely clear and firmly held. We call these convictions. Much of what occurs in debriefings is a matter of ordering and reordering perceptions and concepts, notions, and convictions. Since most of the time that we are interested in someone else's learning we are carefully controlling the content of what is to be learned, we tend to focus on the learner's manipulation of content as evidence of what he is learning. Thus, when we are watching self-directed learning, we often fail to perceive the processes of learning that are taking place.

Self-directed learning in groups (such as crews in debriefings) appears to follow a sometimes clear and sometimes obscure developmental pattern. The first phase of this development seems to be *blame fixing on others.* This is understandable in this way: Ordinarily, crew members (even as you and I) in the course of their work are trying to do things properly. Each action they take is taken because, at that moment in time, it seems the proper thing to do. Occasionally they are aware that they have "slipped up" on some action and do their best to correct it. At times, they find difficulty in handling their jobs because of the actions or inactions of others and because of equipment limitations. More frequently, however, their experiences are of having done all the right things. (We have all had the experience of observing someone happily, industriously, and unconsciously doing completely the wrong thing, yet believing himself to be doing completely the right thing. Some of us have even been the object of observation at such a time.) To be presented with evidence that one has been in error when in one's experience all the right things have been done is an incongruity. The individual's resolution of such incongruities is a necessary step in learning. Unless the conception of one's infallibility is altered, one simply cannot utilize information that would help one to avoid similar errors in the future.

How are such conflicting conceptions altered? We find a clue in the field of psychotherapy. One of the basic precepts of most schools of psychotherapy is that the patient, in the final analysis, must "cure" himself. In other words, here, too, we are presented with self-directed learning rather than other-directed learning. Characteristically, patients go through a process of denying any evidence that they are in error. When this process of denying evidence is not halted but permitted to express itself fully, a point is reached where the patient is able to begin to accept the evidence. It does not seem strange to the therapeutically trained person that the self-directed learning in a crew should be characterized by a denial of evidence of error, and that the greater the denial, the greater its acceptability becomes. As with therapeutic movement, the movement toward acceptance of incorrectness in group learning is very often characterized by initially blaming someone or something *distant from the self*. One of the attributes of a good leader in a task-oriented, problem-solving group is his ability to induce group members to express and explore completely their feelings that they are blameless and that others are the source of error.

A second phase often found in self-directed learning, both in psychotherapy and in task-oriented groups, is *blame fixing on oneself*. It is very much as though going successfully through the first phase results in a new skill, the skill of accepting evidence of error. In psychotherapy, this phenomenon is most often described as a dropping of defenses. In the task-oriented, problem-solving group, it appears more as though group members learn that rewarding consequences, rather than fearsome consequences, follow the acceptance of evidence of error; and they no longer experience themselves as error-free. It seems to become easier for people to say, "I goofed."

The third phase of development is characterized by a growing disregard for blame fixing and a growing attention to learning how errors have occurred and how they can be avoided in the future. Throughout the first two phases, and still remaining in the third phase, is an underlying attitude or conviction that there is a single, best way to do the job and that the task is to learn this single, best way.

It is as though continued experience with searching for the single, best answer leads to the fourth stage of development, the emergence of the concept of acceptable and contingent alternative actions. As this concept grows, standard operating procedures become viewed more as best-working hypotheses than as rigid rules. In this stage of development, alternative actions are tried out to determine what consequences follow what actions. The motivation is to take the action so as to learn about what happens, rather than to take the action because it is perceived as the best thing to do. This is the stage of hypothesis testing, of active exploration of the consequences of different answers to problems. Individuals who have developed this far in the problem solving skills show a high degree of adaptability to slight variations and changes in information patterns.

The activity of solving problems such as are found in mathematics and engineering seems qualitatively different from the activity of solving human-system performance problems. In the latter case, the biggest "problem" seems to arise from the the individual's conviction that he has performed correctly. It appears that much of what is important to learn is a matter of attitudes toward one's self and toward information that can prove one to have been in error. Much of the lack of logical correlation between the topics discussed in debriefings and the actions taken by crew members probably reflects the struggles of attitude formation and change. The four phases of development are certainly not always seen in clear-cut steps, but occasionally they are. Nor, once achieved, is the highest phase necessarily a permanent state of affairs. The studies conducted in the Systems Research Laboratory and subsequent experience with crews in field locations suggest that heavy, sudden increases in stress that are not handled well by the crews may present crew members with the incongruous experiences of having done everything correctly apparently but actually of having done things incorrectly, with the consequent symptomatic blame-fixing behavior in evidence.

Although there are no definitive analyses yet made, it has been suggested that there is probably an orderliness in the types of changes made under conditions of system training. Observation suggests that earliest learning and change takes place around what may be called "Own Operating Procedures." As an individual begins to learn the consequences of his own actions, he becomes more aware of what he is doing and how it may help and hinder other team members. As he comes to see his role in the crew more and more clearly, he begins to see how his section influences other sections of the crew. He becomes more aware of the existence of what may be called "Crew Operating Procedures." As his ability to perceive the crew as an entity (and as a flexible, adaptable unit) increases, he comes more clearly to see how the crew fits into the larger system. There is reason to believe that proficiency and flexibility increase as individuals develop a broader and more accurate picture of (1) the situations with which they must deal, (2) the limitations of procedures and equipments, and (3) the consequences of alternative actions.

CHAPTER 7

ADAPTATIONS OF SYSTEM TRAINING CONCEPTS

In this chapter the aim is to help those who originate or direct training programs and to explore ways in which they can adapt the central concepts of system training to their own organizational needs.

Since training needs vary so widely in kind, four very diverse adaptations will be presented in the hope that the reader will find something in common between one or more of the adaptations and his own organization and its training needs. The first adaptation to be presented is the development of a safety program to train school children to cope with such emergencies as fire. The second adaptation considers a program to help train an assembly line operation, such as that found in a mail-order house. The third adaptation comprises a "command and control system" situation such as that used by fire-fighting forces. The fourth adaptation of system training concepts is to the training of business managers.

Most readers have taken part in fire drills in public schools. At the appointed time, unannounced to the pupils, the alarm is sounded. The principal starts his stop watch. The children assemble in their rooms in columns of twos and march through the corridors to predesignated exits and to assigned locations outside the building. The principal stops his stop watch. Shortly thereafter the pupils march back to their classrooms.

Numerous school tragedies testify that this training is inadequate for many disaster situations. All too often some exits are blocked. Smoke fills the air, visibility is poor, and panic reigns. Open exits are often not found soon enough to permit escape. Sometimes exits are not even looked for. Moreover, formation of columns of twos and marching to predesignated exits does not allow for alternatives to cope with changing conditions of a progressive fire. And yet, learning the methods of dealing with such emergencies is the central reason for giving training. The first step, then, in adapting system training concepts to disaster drills in elementary schools would consist in determining the types of disasters for which training is likely to be needed. Studies of the types of disasters that have struck schools of different constructions in different areas should yield a variety of events around which exercises could be developed. It seems probable that not all possible types of disasters could be simulated well. At the same time, it seems equally probable that simulation of all possible types is not necessary in order to obtain a high degree of the training effect desired; namely, the ability to cope with fire emergencies. Experience with system training suggests that flexibility in skill application is itself a skill and is highly transferable under changing conditions and different situations. Were a serious effort made to develop a training program, it is likely that a relatively few simulated variations of a few basic situations would suffice to show how basic procedures could be applied in several different ways.

Our first step would be to enlist the aid of someone knowledgeable about how and where fires start, and how they would spread as time went on. Presumably, such help would be available from a fire department. A second step would be to study a given school building to determine a number of locations where, if fire did break out, it could endanger the children.

Let us suppose it has been determined, in a particular three-story school under study, that a storage bin in the basement under the east entrance stair well (Fig. 36) could be a likely starting point for a dangerous fire. If a fire were to occur there, the sequence of events listed below might take place.

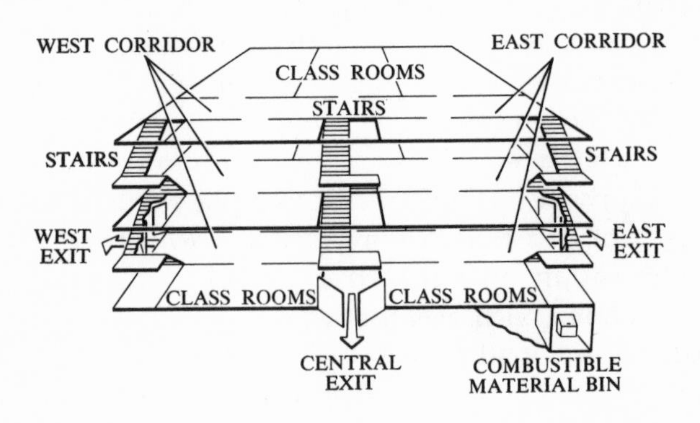

FIGURE 36. *Schematic diagram of three-story school building showing corridors, stairs, and exits.*

These events are based upon those obtained from test fires conducted by the Los Angeles Fire Department in 1959 and reported in *Operation School Burning,* National Fire Protection Association, International, 60 Batterymarch Street, Boston 10, Massachusetts, 1959. The reader is invited not to be critical of the events as they are listed here. There is departure from true realism, principally because the purpose is to simulate possible emergencies for training, not to simulate the true-blue course of a red-hot fire. Accordingly, to emphasize the need for calling the Fire Department immediately, we let the telephone service be disrupted and the fire alarm system become inoperative. We further assume that no overhead sprinklers are installed, and so on.

0900 Fire breaks out in storage bin under stair well at East exit.
Conditions in corridors:
1st Floor East–clear
1st Floor West–clear
2nd Floor East–clear
2nd Floor West–clear
3rd Floor East–clear
3rd Floor West–clear

0902 Conditions in corridors:
1st Floor East–smoke appears
1st Floor West–clear
2nd Floor East–clear
2nd Floor West–clear
3rd Floor East–clear
3rd Floor West–clear

0903 Conditions in corridors:
1st Floor East–smoke untenable, East exit impassable
1st Floor West–smoke appears
2nd Floor East–smoke appears
2nd Floor West–clear
3rd Floor East–clear
3rd Floor West–clear
Telephone junction box in basement becomes inoperative

0904 Conditions in corridors:
1st Floor East–smoke clearing, erect passage possible, heat at 125° F
1st Floor West–smoke untenable, central exit impassable
2nd Floor East–smoke medium density
2nd Floor West–smoke appearing
3rd Floor East–smoke appearing
3rd Floor West–clear

0905 Conditions in corridors:
1st Floor East–just tenable, erect passage still possible, heat at 140° F
1st Floor West–smoke untenable, central exit just passable
2nd Floor East–smoke untenable
2nd Floor West–smoke medium density

3rd Floor East—light smoke
3rd Floor West—clear
Fire damages electric equipment in basement; power gone; use of fire alarm no longer possible

0906 Conditions in corridors:
1st Floor East—smoke clearing; temperature no longer tenable; East exit impassable
1st Floor West—smoke untenable; heat at 100° F
2nd Floor East—smoke untenable
2nd Floor West—smoke untenable
3rd Floor East—smoke untenable
3rd Floor West—clear

0907 Conditions in corridors:
1st Floor East—untenable smoke, lethal heat
1st Floor West—untenable smoke, heat at 125° F
2nd Floor East—untenable smoke
2nd Floor West—untenable smoke
3rd Floor East—untenable smoke
3rd Floor West—light smoke

0908 Conditions in corridors:
1st Floor East—untenable smoke, lethal heat
1st Floor West—untenable smoke, lethal heat; West exit impassable
2nd Floor East—untenable smoke, heat at 125° F
2nd Floor West—untenable smoke, heat at 120° F
3rd Floor East—untenable smoke
3rd Floor West—untenable smoke

0909 All corridors reach untenable smoke and heat conditions; cellulose-fiber acoustical tile (unpainted) ignites, and flame front sweeps both West and East corridors rendering all exits completely impassable; exit from windows is all that remains possible.

These events are the events to be simulated. How would one do it? There are several constraints to consider in answering this question. Highly realistic simulation of a fire might be both prohibitively expensive and dangerous. Moreover, to expose children to high realism *at the outset* of their training might be traumatic and disruptive to the learning of the desired skills. The U.S. Navy has its apprentice seaman fight actual fires in simulated ship compartments. Experience, to date, with system training suggests that the degree of realism in simulation need be only *enough to bring the trainees to take actions they would take in reality.* Cost of simulation, age of the trainees, and extent of prior experience would be the major constraints* and would undoubtedly vary from situation to situation.

At the outset of training, and for younger children, it might be best to start off with large cards that say, "It is smoky here," and "It is hot here." These cards could be displayed at the proper places and times by the personnel conducting the training. As the children gain in age and experience, simulated, nontoxic smoke might be used at the appropriate places and time. At the high school level, it may be possible to arrange more realistic experiences with real fire under controlled conditions with the help of a local fire department.

Just how far one would want to go in simulating reality is an open question. It seems reasonable to expect that one would, in the long run, want to go far enough so that the trainees can learn to perceive developing danger, to perceive alternative escape routes, and to take sensible actions in accordance with the danger and the alternatives. At some schools, fire drills are conducted in which signs erected say "EXIT BLOCKED." Although this brings the pupils to seek an alternative exit, the sign does not help them realize why

* Constraints of other types would undoubtedly arise in any given community. The fire department and the police department would probably be unable to supply the men necessary to assist in such training. The school board would be unable to fund any additional costs over present training methods. Parents would be fearful that their children would be hurt. Such constraints to the undertaking of system training exercises would be encountered. It is presumed here that gains in children's knowing what to do when disaster strikes are sufficiently valued in this hypothetical community that ways have been found to meet these barriers to undertaking the training. Thus the discussion will be confined to the technical aspects of developing the training vehicle.

the exit is blocked. If it were the last exit really passable, even though smoky and hot, one would not want a child to hesitate in getting on his hands and knees and crawling out. Conventional fire drills do not train children to deal with the emergencies that arise when things do not go right.

In any event, let us presume that we have settled on a kind of simulation suited to the age and experience level of the pupils. The day for the exercise has come. The teachers review with the pupils the rules and alternatives to be followed in the event of fire. The training personnel (probably firemen) have all been briefed on the course of the fire and exactly where and when they are to simulate each given condition. Those trainers who are taking the role of observers have their stop watches and observation forms so that they can record pupils' actions and the times of the actions. The children have all turned in their slips giving written parental permission to engage in the drill. All the children are dressed in play clothes. A few minutes before the time for the drill, the trainers arrive and take their stations. At the same time, stand-by equipment arrives—just in case a real fire should break out during the drill.

At the appointed moment, the outbreak of the fire is simulated. Observers have noted the movements in the corridors and the location of key personnel. Sooner or later someone—pupil or staff member—notices the smoke (or sign) and takes an action such as taking a closer look to verify that a fire does in fact exist. The observer records the action and the time. The discoverer of the fire may call out "Fire!" He may run to get the principal, he may run to his home room to tell his teacher, or he may run to the nearest fire hose and drag it out. The observers make no effort to tell him what he should do; they record only what action is taken and the time involved. Should a trainee take a "lethal" action, such as opening a door and being blasted by "flame," the observer would then tell the trainee to simulate death (after which, of course, he cannot spread the alarm).

Supposing that the pupil has run to the principal's office; an observer will record the actions that take place there. Possibly the principal runs to verify the fact of the fire. Possibly he is in the midst of an important conference, and the clerk is afraid to disturb him—so, she runs to verify the fact of the fire. The observer would limit his activities to recording actions taken and the times involved.

In our example, the East corridor exit is impassable by the end of 3 minutes. If as much as 2 minutes were lost in sounding the fire alarm, it is probable that classes on the second and third floors that ordinarily would use the East exit would now be forced to find a different exit. Observers would record just how they went about this and how long it took. Observers would be particularly interested in noting the source of any confusion. They would also be careful to note the actions of stragglers.

As classes left the building and assembled outside, observers would note whether or not the positions taken would interfere with fire fighting and reserve equipment when it arrived.

When the exercise had been completed, post-exercise discussions would then be held. Observers would reconstruct for the pupils and staff the occurrence of the fire, describe its nature, explain how it had developed over time, and recount the actions taken and the "consequences" of these actions. The observers would not act as critics but as resource people. Since the goal would be to promote pupil and staff inquiry and thought, criticisms would serve only to defeat the goal. On the other hand, if observers serve simply to be available for questions of fact, pupils and staff will be encouraged to think for themselves.

Whether the post-exercise discussions would be held with

classes individually, with all personnel in the assembly hall, or with staff alone might well vary from one exercise to the next. Had the most critical incident been the failure of office personnel to call the fire department promptly, it might well be that the training director would feel it most profitable to meet with the office personnel separately. Had the most critical incident been excessive noise by pupils, the training director might wish to have home-room discussion sessions. Experience would soon indicate the more profitable procedures.

Let us turn now to a second area of application, the assembly line operation of a mail-order house. Generally speaking, the sequence of events in filling orders is as follows: Sacks of mail are delivered to the organization. They are distributed among a number of people assigned to open the mail. Each letter is opened, the order form unfolded, and the payment (check, money order, or cash) is pinned to the order form. The form is checked to make sure that the return address is on it before the envelope is discarded. The stacks of orders and payments are distributed among a number of clerks who check item costs and verify the correctness of the payment. The payment is then detached and sent to the accounting office.

Since a mail-order house carries large numbers of different items, a great deal of space is required. One item may be found on the first floor, another item on the fourth floor, and still another item may be found in an adjacent warehouse. The clerks break down the customer's order by preparing the needed number of "pick slips" to go to the different locations in the building. The pick slips are then routed to "pickers," who go directly to the bins and draw the items, which are sent by conveyor belt or chute to the assembly room. Here the items are assembled and checked against the

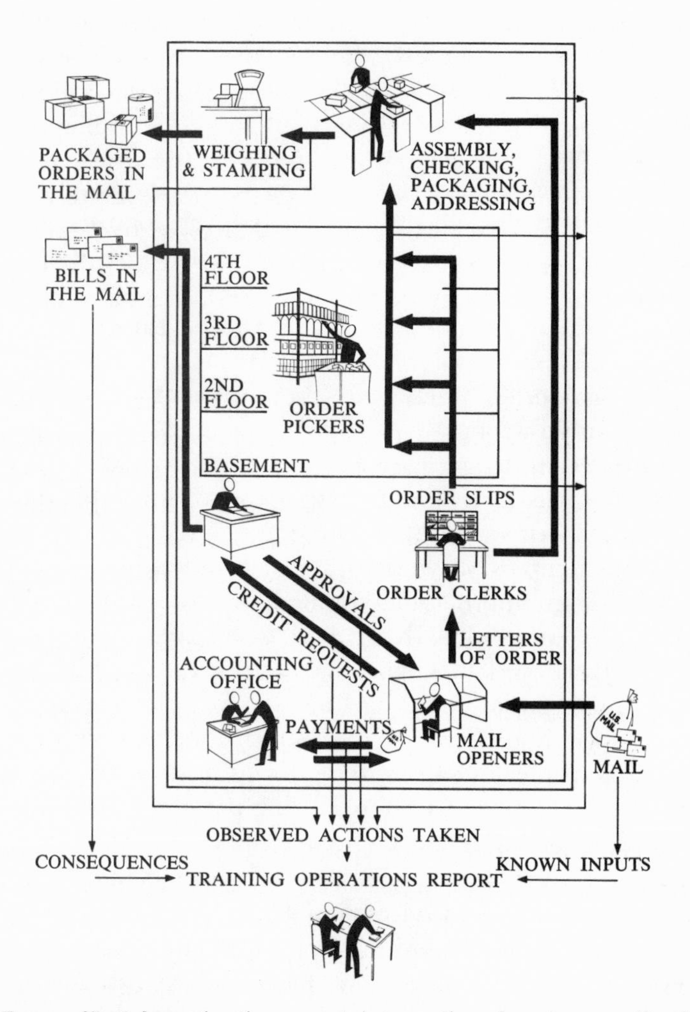

FIGURE 37. *Schematic diagram of information flow in a mail-order house and the observation of actions taken for the preparation of a Training Operations Report.*

original order. Incorrectly picked items, if noted, are returned to stock, and the pick slip goes through the mill again. When the order is all assembled, it is packaged, weighed, stamped, and sent on its way to the post office.

There are many people in the mail-order house system. There are many chances for error. When the employee is introduced to the job, instruction is given in just what to do. The supervisor watches closely until the employee "catches on."

Even when everyone tries his best to do things correctly, errors will occur. Somewhere between the arrival of a letter at the mail-order house and the shipment of a package things can go wrong.

Were we to design a training program for such a system, we should need first of all to design a set of simulated inputs. We should first study thoroughly the different ways in which the system inputs vary: legibility of handwriting, completeness of order information, conflicting information, seasonal variations, times of delivery, and so on. We should try to isolate those variables most likely to create trouble some place along the order-filling line.

Next we should need to devise forms for observers to use during the course of an exercise, forms on which they could record actions taken by the operating personnel. When these were devised, we should then have the capability of pulling together information about input characteristics, actions taken, and subsystem outputs and the final system outputs.

Let us ask at this point what types of "problems" we wish to conduct. Experience may have indicated that errors among the mail openers increase considerably when the load is heavy. We may wish to devise a heavy load problem to stress this portion of the system. Experience may have indicated that when some bins run out of stock but the items are available in the warehouse, order pickers fail to notify the warehouse, mark the order slip "out of stock," or even choose an item close to that ordered when, with a little thought and intelligent action, the order could have been filled properly. We may wish, then, to devise a problem that will ensure runs on certain items so as to stress this type of system functioning. And again, experience may have indicated that errors occur more frequently in the assembly area when the orders are many-item orders. We may wish to devise problems that will stress this part of the system.

Whatever the function is that we wish to stress, we draw from a "library" of inputs those inputs (and the required quantity of them) that will stress the function to the degree desired. As the problem is prepared, each input is given a number or identifying symbol so that each action taken in its handling can be duly noted by the observers.

The day for the exercise arrives, and the start of the exercise is announced. The inputs are introduced into the system. Operating personnel process them as they would any other orders. The observers make their recordings of actions taken. The system output is duly noted. The exercise comes to an end, and a training output report is prepared. The time has arrived for the post-exercise discussion period.

Before analyzing the post-exercise discussion, let us examine for a moment some of the problems faced by the training team in such an organization as a mail-order house.

If operations were shut down and only simulated inputs handled for a couple of hours, and handled all the way through the system, there would be a mighty large pile of items to be returned to the bins. This would run up the cost of the exercise considerably. Once in a while this might be deemed worth while. It is also possible, however, that slips of paper or tokens marked to represent each item could be used in place of the item. Since there would be nothing for the packaging, weighing, and stamping functions to do, it is possible that these people could be utilized as observers. Also, the use of slips of paper or tokens representative of items makes it possible to control the number of items in the bin and in the warehouse at the outset of a problem. This could be very useful when it was desired to stress the handling of stock shortages.

Still another variation in the exercise procedure might be to mix the problem inputs with the real orders. One would want to make certain that the problem inputs were distinctive (color coded, perhaps) so that operating personnel would recognize them. (The object is not to fool the people in training but to heighten their awareness of their actions and to lead them into problem-solving attitudes.)

Yet another variation in training procedure is that of subsystem training. Let us presume, for the moment, that it is desired to stress only the letter-opening functions. Monitors could be assigned to stop the simulated inputs after they had been processed by the letter openers and not permit them to continue on in the system. Of course this would mean that, should one want to stress the order-picking subsystem, one also would need to devise simulated order slips tailored to produce the stress desired.

We return now to the post-exercise discussion. There will be a great temptation among management personnel to want to use the observation data to pinpoint less efficient personnel. Do *not* try it! The consequences of *any* such effort will soon be sensed, and the value of the exercises will be negated. With a rapidity that will astonish management, operating personnel will learn how to treat the exercises as a contest with management. They will learn how to cover errors and to cover for each other. Meanwhile, the causes of common errors will continue to remain hidden to all. As a matter of fact, it might often be anticipated that operating personnel will be suspicious of the exercises until the post-exercise discussion periods have shown that management does not intend to use the data punitively.

Once the data have been gathered, it can be organized for presentation in two different ways. One way is to trace the complete history of actions taken on individual orders. The second way is to present an analysis of the actions taken at one of the functional subsystems on all items of a certain critical nature. For example, we could trace simulated Order No. J-23 all through the system. Or we could point out to the mail openers that out of 20 inputs in which return addresses were on the envelopes but not on the order letter, 15 were treated as if no return address were available at all.*

Experience has indicated that both methods may, but not necessarily will, be effective. Where the operating team is not too large and where team members are able to learn to sense someone else's error and take compensatory action for it, the tracing of the history of individual events may reveal to team members what someone else's error looks like and how compensatory action can be taken. This certainly seemed to be true in the case of crews in the manual system of air defense. On the other hand, where the total team is quite large, and there is little or no chance to understand how one could compensate for someone else's error or even sense that an error has been made, presentation of the history of individual items seems to yield little training. This seemed to be true in the training of the large-scale, computer-based SAGE system of air defense.

The present state-of-the-art, however, suggests that aggregating information across the actions taken with regard to

* Any reader who knows the mail-order business might be quick to point out that order *forms* are used and that therefore this could not happen. To them I would say that it did happen years ago, but that the system learned to adjust so as to eliminate such a source of error. After an error cause is discovered, the answer is usually easy to achieve. System training helps to disclose causes of errors.

a class of similar situations encountered by a functional subsystem is almost universally helpful.

So much, then, for training in an assembly-line type of operation. Let us now proceed to a different type of training need, that of controlling resources, as in the management of fire fighting equipment, personnel, and facilities.

In the example of the training of school children to cope with the emergencies of a developing fire, and in the example of training mail-order house personnel in their processing of orders, the consequences of actions are direct results of actions. In the case of resource management, however, the situation is quite different. The consequences of actions taken by a fire boss will be a product of a dynamic interaction of several variables. The fire boss may dispatch equipment to a given spot where the chances of stopping the advance of a fire line are excellent. Then the wind shifts, the threat is on a new front, equipment is out of position, and a totally new set of requirements exists. Flames sweeping up a draw at a rapid rate may cause an inexperienced crew boss to radio excitedly to the fire boss that the fire is completely out of control. Ten minutes later an experienced crew boss calls in that everything is under complete control, that in a few more minutes the front will have reached the crest, and with the wind remaining as it is, the front will burn out.

The problems of the fire boss are increased because of two facts: He must sense what is going on through others, and he must act through others. Whereas an order picker can see the contents of a bin and the bin is clearly labeled, a fire boss cannot see the stimulus situation directly; he receives only reports of other's perceptions. An order picker can pick an item from a bin, but the fire boss must depend upon others to take actions.

The multiple inputs to, and multiple outputs from, the

fire boss are depicted in Figure 38. As reports of a fire and its initial development begin to come in from one or more sources, the fire boss must assess the threat. Temperature, humidity, winds, type of growth, accessibility of equipment, accessibility to fire, location of fire, time of day, visibility—

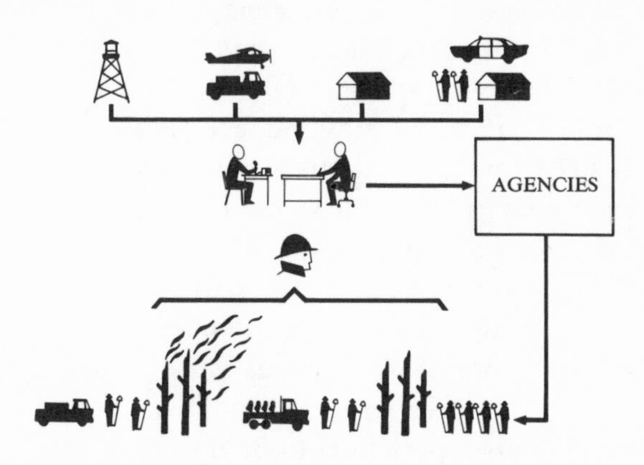

FIGURE 38. *The fire boss receives inputs from lookout towers, spotter planes, fire trucks, maintenance areas, police and fire fighters. He not only controls through communicating to on-line crew chiefs but also through communicating with other agencies such as law enforcement, Red Cross, and health agencies who act to support the on-line crews.*

all these factors will influence his assessment of how threatening the fire is. He may re-evaluate this threat many times during the course of a large fire. Problems could be designed to give extensive experience with the assessment of a wide variety of threatening situations.

Depending upon his analysis of the threat, the fire boss evolves a strategy for combating the fire. As his analysis of the threat undergoes re-evaluation, his strategy must be constrained by finances, available equipment, and time required to position crews. Crews cannot keep fighting forever. They must have food and rest. Problems could well be designed that would stress the need for rapid alteration of strategy.

A strategy is basically a conceptual "road map." It says, in effect, "If you can't get there by this route, here is an alternate route." The execution of strategy consists of a series of decisions, decisions that the most direct route is closed and which alternative route is to be taken. The wisdom to evolve strategy and to assess its impact comes primarily from experience. System training exercises (it may be more accurate to label them subsystem training exercises) could be designed to help younger men to acquire wisdom and older hands to test new strategies. It would be possible to fight the same "fire" over and over, to test not only alternative strategies but to try out entirely untried strategies that no one would dare try in an actual fire condition.

We can envision a physical layout much as that suggested in Figure 39. In an exercise room would be located display, dispatch, and control personnel to be trained. In the simulation room would be located those personnel who would simulate the interactions that would occur in real life. Before

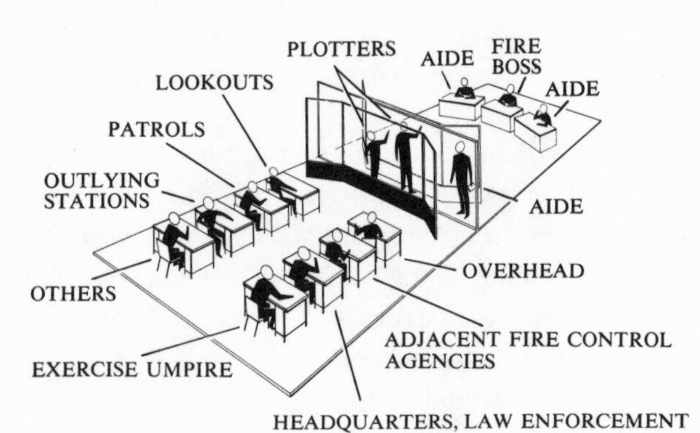

FIGURE 39. *Schematic diagram suggestive of training laboratory. The fire boss and his aides are located in one room* (right) *while simulation personnel and the exercise umpire are located in an adjoining room* (left).

the start of a problem, the fire boss would be briefed on such items as the weather, crew and equipment status, tourist movement, and fire conditions in the area.

At the appointed time, working from prepared scripts, lookouts and patrols would begin to call in reports. The fire boss would begin to control the forces at his disposal. He would interact with the overhead personnel, adjacent fire control agencies, superior headquarters, and law enforcement agencies, as needed. According to the "rules" set up for the effect of any action taken by the fire boss, the exercise umpire would direct plotters at the display board to alter the display so as to show the effect, and arrange with overhead or other simulators as to when they would realistically note the change and "report" the effect back to the fire boss.

Because a large fire might require hours and even days to bring under control, it would undoubtedly be necessary to compress time, letting 1 hour represent several. The extent of time-compression might vary widely, depending upon the training problem. One could imagine that for inexperienced personnel who need to learn who and when to notify of a fire outbreak, the problem could be run in real time inasmuch as only the initial time period would be of consequence.

And, of course, after the exercise, the post-exercise discussion is held. The problem is retraced. The events that happened and did not get reported to the fire boss would be examined. The impact of limited communication channels, equipment breakdowns, misunderstood orders, and so on, would be examined. Discussions with the exercise umpires (presumably experienced) would help to develop insights into the workings of the system and its limitations. Procedural changes could be evolved and tested in subsequent exercises. And the fire-boss-in-training could go home content in the knowledge that that was one error he'd never make again. But, best of all, a problem-solving attitude would be engendered among operational personnel, an attitude from which any organization can profit.

So much, then, for some suggestions for training in the control of forces. Let us now proceed to the last illustration: system training for business operations.

There are a number of business games for the training of management personnel. Experience with these games indicates that they have much to offer. Not only do participants in these games come away with reports of new and significant insights into business management, but new and more sophisticated games are thereby being developed. Several universities are adopting management games as regular parts of the curriculum. We note that in those games the central learning is in how to compete.

There is absent in these games, however, a major learning opportunity that a system training approach would supply. This opportunity is for the members of a real-life organization to learn to work cooperatively, rather than competitively, with one another. Typically, participation in management games is among peers. One week it is for company presidents; another week, for vice-presidents; and so on. It is easy for a company president to announce to his staff, "One never grows too old to learn, and there's a lot about management I don't know. So next week I'm going to Lake Mugwump where the university is conducting a training workshop for management." Rare is the president who would announce to his staff, "One never grows too old to learn, and there's a lot about running this company I don't know. I think you and I are the best means of learning from and teaching one another." Wise is the man who knows he can use more training. Brave is the man who faces the possibility of learning from his subordinates.

To the man both wise and brave, then, the following paragraphs are dedicated.

Kepner and Tregoe* describe in the *Harvard Business Review* a game that can be used to obtain much intraorganizational learning. Prepared "problems" are brought to a company late in the afternoon. The normal activities of the management team are stopped, and they undertake the "problem" inputs. At the end of a 2-hour period, the executives gather and are told the issues involved. The actions taken are discussed, lack or losses of information are disclosed, and procedural problems are revealed. Each executive learns much of how his job affects others, and of how their needs affect his actions. This game is also used for cross-training. Executives can switch positions and learn that the other men's jobs are not the "snap" they thought them to be.

It seems quite reasonable to presume that business organizations can develop their own in-house training programs, although many managers may frankly question what it is they can learn from such exercises. It is in answer to such a question that I address the following remarks.

From childhood to adulthood there are many factors that tend to develop and strengthen in us a "component" view of much of our activity. There are "right" and "accepted" ways to do things. If we follow the rules, we are "right." If we depart from the established rules and make an error, we are "wrong" and are punished in some way. We tend to look at others in the same way: If they do their jobs as they are supposed to do them, all will go well.

This type of thinking leads us to look at the human components in a business organization rather than at the flow of information between components. We know that all errors

* C. H. Kepner and B. B. Tregoe, "Developing Decision Makers," *Harvard Business Review,* Vol. 38, 5 (September-October 1960).

in business operations are not due to people; often they are due to procedural failures. And yet we act as though all errors are human errors.

Consider what would happen if we were to take the following position: People *never* make errors, only systems do. If the system had been really designed right, all errors would be caught before getting out of the system. One of the things that would happen is that it would lead us to take an entirely different attitude toward "errors." The occurrence of an error would be a signal that something was wrong with procedures. We would then want to analyze the functions involved and institute corrective action.

Let us take a simple example in illustration. Almost all readers have had the experience of going to the bank to deposit a check and to keep part in cash. The receiving clerk inspects the check for endorsement, inspects the deposit slip, makes and initials the entry in the deposit book, counts out the cash, makes a notation on a pad of paper, the top sheet of which has carbon on the bottom side, pulls out the carbon copy of the cash disbursed and places it with the check and deposit slip.

I asked one bank teller if he ever forgot to make a notation on the little pad. He chuckled and acknowledged that indeed he did forget every so often. Then I asked what happened when he did. He told me that his cash drawer would not balance at the end of the day. I asked what would happen then. He said that he would have to go over all his transactions for the day to find where he'd made his error. He went on to assure me that it did not really make much difference because all transactions were double-checked by the girls at the tabulating machines.

If we should look at this example with the view that people never make mistakes, but only systems do, we view this situation quite differently. It is immediately clear that the pad of notations of cash disbursed is a memory device, but it is a memory device to which an entry does not necessarily have to be made *before* the cash is disbursed. Suppose that a system training exercise adapted to the bank's operation had shown up such an error. During the debriefing, the question would be raised, "How could we change things so that such an error could not occur?" It is quite possible that someone might come up with the idea of a modified adding machine that would keep track of disbursements and receipts but which would have to be operated before the cash drawer would open.

It seems to me that games or training exercises, tailor-made to a particular organization and dedicated to the concept that system designs and procedures rather than people are the major source of repetitive error, would hold much promise for improvement in operations and much promise of developing constructive problem-solving attitudes. To the skeptical people who cannot visualize what they would learn from a system training program in their own organizations, I say, "I don't know exactly what you would learn about your operations, but I predict you will learn a great deal, including how to learn."

Finally, in closing, let me make some personal observations about what I think have been two significant developments over the past decade and a half and which are of special interest to behavioral scientists.

There is no question in my mind that the system training technology is a real breakthrough in the technology of manpower development. A technology that can markedly increase system performance without change in hardware or in personnel, and only in procedures, has much to recommend it. My humanistically oriented colleagues will appreciate what I mean when I say that just as television's Sergeant Bilko is a monument to man's capacity to circumvent a system's purpose, system training is a monument to man's capacity to identify with and accomplish a system's purpose. The very existence of the suggestion box testifies to management's awareness of the capacity of men to come up with good ideas. The very existence of standard operating procedures and procedure and policy guides testifies to management's need to know (for purposes of control) just what goes on on the job. The very existence of personnel rating procedures testifies to management's need to evaluate performance.

Where the suggestion box is passive and simply awaits ideas, the system training technology is active in its search for ideas. Where standard operating procedures carry a strong connotation of the "final, unalterable answer," the system training technology invites invention, flexibility, and understanding of the consequences of actions. Where personnel rating procedures disregard the setting in which the person is embedded, the system training technology highlights the dynamic relationship of the person to his work environment. Just how widely the technology can be applied is as yet uncertain, but there is every reason to think that it can be adapted to a very wide range of systems.

The second development I consider worthy of note has been the evolution of a new professional role for behavioral scientists, the role as member of the large-scale system design team. This role has evolved in a number of settings, mostly in settings associated with military systems of one sort or another. Most of my colleagues will agree, I believe, that learning to deal with big systems has been a rewarding educational experience and one that has more often than not severely strained the ties with Academia. We came into the world of systems armed with a set of skills that all too often prepared us only to tinker with components. We all too often had to learn to see the forest.

As we rubbed elbows with operations people, with engineers, and with computer programers in tackling live problems in live systems, we began more and more to see how the design of systems influenced their behavior as organisms. And as we developed skill in communicating with engineers, programers, and operations personnel (we had to learn their languages—the languages of the behavioral scientists are often unclear, imprecise, and hard to learn), we began to participate in system design and redesign. This new role for the behavioral scientist is fully as complex as the role, for example, of the clinical psychologist, but as yet it is not as clearly defined.

The major impact of this new technology and of this new breed of (behavioral scientist) researcher is yet to be felt in business and industry.

INDEX

INDEX

Set in Linotype Baskerville
Composed by American Book–Stratford Press, Inc.
Printed by The Murray Printing Company
Bound by American Book–Stratford Press, Inc.
HARPER & ROW, PUBLISHERS, INCORPORATED